Morphogenesis in Plants

Morphogenesis in Plants

A Contemporary Study

C. W. WARDLAW
University of Manchester

METHUEN & CO LTD
11 NEW FETTER LANE   LONDON EC4

First published 1968
© C. W. Wardlaw 1968
Printed in Great Britain
by Richard Clay (The Chaucer Press), Ltd.,
Bungay, Suffolk

Distributed in the U.S.A.
by Barnes and Noble Inc.

To my many friends in Morphogenesis and, in particular, to those who did me honour by contributing to that gracious Festschrift, *Trends in Plant Morphogenesis* (1966).

Contents

7

Preface

When the writer, after much cogitation and effort, and towards the end of his (official) academic career, published his book, *Organization and Evolution in Plants* (1965), and when, during the same year, his not inconsiderable contributions to Volume 15 of the *Handbuch der Pflanzenphysiologie – Differenzierung und Entwicklung* belatedly saw the light of day, he felt, perhaps not without some justification that, if he had not produced a *chef d'œuvre*, he had probably uttered his swansong! But not so. The Fates, in the form of one of his publishers, Messrs Methuen and Co Ltd, almost immediately called his attention to the fact that the stock of a little volume, *Morphogenesis in Plants*, published in 1952, was running out, and query: was a revised or, indeed, an entirely new edition, desirable? In the circumstances this inquiry seemed to be rather all-of-a-sudden. But, on reflection, it appeared to the writer that he was somewhat in the position of a certain learned professor who had contrived a violin of quite unique and unusual design. On being asked how he had managed to produce such a remarkable instrument, he replied modestly (it is alleged) that he had made the whole thing out of his own head and had enough wood left to make another. Indeed, it has been a great pleasure to write this book. The writer's chief regret is that he has been unable to do justice to the most recent publications.

To willing helpers he now returns grateful thanks. In particular, he wishes to express thanks to Miss J. Shore, Mrs O. Davidson and Miss J. Davis for unstinted secretarial assistance; to Miss A. Walton for help with some of the illustrations; to various authors and publishers for the use of illustrations, all of which are fully acknowledged in the text; and, not least, to his Publishers, Messrs Methuen & Company Limited, for their invariable courtesy and help in all matters relating to the production of this book. Finally, he has to thank his wife for all her good nature and patience during the progress of these literary adventures.

C. W. WARDLAW

June 1st, 1967

Introduction

RETROSPECT

In 1952 the author published two volumes on the subject of *morphogenesis* in plants. One of these, *Phylogeny and Morphogenesis*, dealt in some detail with the criteria, aims and achievements of both comparative and general (or causal) morphology, and with some essentially reciprocal relationships which exist between the two studies. In the other volume, *Morphogenesis in Plants*, the writer attempted to indicate briefly, and as simply and directly as possible for students and research workers, some of the fascinating interest and importance of the phenomena of the inception and development of form and structure in plants; and, by selected examples, he illustrated the scope of the information that was then available and was rapidly beginning to accrue from different investigations, i.e. those of experimental morphologists, physiologists and geneticists. Over the years, this little book has enjoyed a wide and general distribution and a kind reception. However, since its publication the subject of plant morphogenesis has made very considerable progress and, directly or indirectly, has attracted many new adherents. As a consequence, an entirely new volume, and not merely a revised edition, now seems to be justified. Hence the title, *Morphogenesis in Plants – A Contemporary Study*.

To attempt such a monograph, still bearing in mind the need for broad, representative treatment, simplicity and brevity, is evidently no mean task. Fortunately, because of the number of distinguished and dedicated botanists who now work in this field, the author has been able to draw freely not only on many original papers of great interest and importance but also on excellent reviews and symposium reports of recent date. And, not least, there are the vast resources of information, of the highest relevance, now available in the recently published volume on *Differentiation and Development* in the *Encyclopedia of Plant Physiology*[1] (Editor, W. Ruhland; Sub-editor, Anton Lang. Volume 15, Parts 1 and 2, 1965). (*See* also reading list at end of Chapter II.)

[1] *Handbuch der Pflanzenphysiologie*, Bd 15, *Differenzierung und Entwicklung*; Part 1, pp. 1647; Part 2, pp. 1362 (Publ. Springer-Verlag, Berlin, Heidelberg, New York, 1965).

MORPHOGENESIS: DEFINITION AND SCOPE

The term *morphogenesis*, from Greek words meaning the origin of form and, by implication, the differentiation of the associated internal structural features, is used by biologists to connote the inception and development of morphological characters. Even in these days of devotion to 'molecular biology' and to other specialized branches, no botanist who has confidence in the importance of his science and who understands that, after all, Botany is the *Science of Plants*, of *whole organisms*, essentially recognizable because of their *specific and distinctive configuration*, need hesitate to argue and urge the importance of the *comprehensive* study of morphogenesis. All plants, whether of microscopic or of large dimensions, are dynamic, three-dimensional geometric entities. This is the *physical reality* that first and always confronts the eye of the observer, the reality that results from the nature of the specific genetical constitution and from *all* the *physical, chemical* and other processes that are involved in metabolism, growth and development in a particular environment.

The morphology of an organism, or of one of its constituent organs, may be regarded as a resultant effect of all the physiological processes involved in growth and development. These are sometimes regarded as being 'antecedent'. Nevertheless, we should not – indeed, we must not – lose sight of the fact that the actual physical configuration, i.e. the size, shape, disposition and structure of organs and tissues, affects in different ways, and at different stages in ontogenesis, the nature and effectiveness of functional activities. Accordingly, in the interests of a progressive botanical science, the claims of biophysics should be urged just as strongly as those of biochemistry (or biological chemistry); but as we know, it is the latter branch of science that is in the ascendant at the present time. Both approaches are necessary and, indeed, in the end, they are inseparable. If our interest is truly in organisms, and not simply in some of their constituent processes, studies of morphogenesis are quite essential. A long time ago, Hofmeister (1868) asked the question: how do the observed forms come to be as they are? And he had in mind interpretations in terms of physics, chemistry and mathematics. However, as we shall see in the course of this book, adequate answers cannot be given solely in terms of these disciplines, but we must make the fullest use of them. In the writer's submission, the acceptable interpretations will be essentially biological ones; for the organization of even the simplest organism, with its specific genetical constitution, exists at levels which comprise, but transcend, the scope of the physical sciences as presently pursued.

All morphogenesis, whether in lower or higher plants, begins with an *organized* entity, be it a spore, a zygote, a generative cell, a gemma or a bud; and the term *morphogenesis* connotes *all* the activities that are involved, stage by stage throughout ontogenesis (essentially a *continuum*), from the spore, zygote, etc., to the specific and distinctive form and structure, believed to be functionally effective and adaptive, which are characteristic of the adult state. It thus takes cognizance of the genetic factors, present in the generative cell from the outset and evoked, often in a characteristic sequence, at different stages in ontogenesis; and it includes the early or embryonic development, the inception, development and final conformation of the several organs, the differentiation of tissues, and the harmonious development and the integrated wholeness, or unity, of the individual. Regulation of physiological activities, from the inception of growth in the generative cell onwards, leads to the differentiation of characteristic organs and tissues, usually with distinctive functions, and often described as being essential to the 'economy of the organism' in the adult state. However, since the main organogenic patterns have their inception in embryonic regions, i.e. long before any adult functioning is involved, perhaps the old idea of division of labour should be replaced by one in which we think in terms of chemical equilibria during morphogenesis and of complementarity of utilization of metabolic materials by different regions, all in a unitary reaction system.

The student of morphogenesis recognizes the importance of Galileo's Principle of Similitude, i.e. that changes in the size of a living organism have unavoidable, mathematical, physical and physiological aspects, e.g. in the relation of surface to volume. In brief, in morphogenesis we are interested in, and concerned with, *all* the factors which are involved in bringing the eventual specific form into being. Of course, *morphology* – we owe the term to Goethe – is also concerned with *form*; and, according to Arber (1950), form, in its wider, original meaning, comprised not only the external manifestation of organization in an individual organism throughout its life but the whole of its intrinsic nature. If the term *morphology* were generally accepted and used in this connotation there would be little to choose between it and *morphogenesis*. However, over the years the term *morphology* has lost much of its wider connotation as a result of restriction, e.g. as in the post-Darwinian period of *comparative morphology*. Moreover, one can scarcely avoid the impression that some distinguished contemporary physiologists think so poorly of morphology as a branch of botanical science that they almost lean over backwards to avoid being contaminated by it in any way! Indeed, without any adequate reference to form or structure, some botanists contribute physiological and biochemical information, admittedly of great value, about developmental processes under the heading of *morphogenesis*; others maintain their respectability by using the term 'physiology of development'. But surely, unless the writer is sadly mistaken, the use of the term *morphogenesis* is only appropriate in those studies where the investigator demonstrates, or attempts to demonstrate, *how a particular physiological process, or a system of biochemical reactions, can be closely and directly related to the ultimate visible reality, i.e. the manifestation of form.* This is, admittedly, a very rigorous requirement. But we should be clear, at least ideally, about our scientific aims. Accordingly, in this book, and especially as we move into the era of biochemistry and biophysics, the writer reiterates the importance of a knowledge of morphogenesis. The development of specific form, it is averred, in company with observers from Aristotle to Needham and Sinnott, is the manifestation of life that is of paramount importance to biologists of liberal outlook.

However, since the author is reiterating the claims of morphology so strongly, let us be frank. All too often, the morphologist stops just at the point where the more searching study of the underlying physiological–genetical factors really begins; nevertheless, he performs a vital service: he indicates what is there to be investigated. But one can also think of excellently conceived physiological studies that have obviously been undertaken without an adequate knowledge of the *observable* morphogenetic developments. Somewhere between these extremes we ought to do better! In fact, it is exceedingly difficult to take the next investigational steps, i.e. after the morphological facts have been ascertained. In morphogenesis, as work progresses, we shall become more and more deeply involved in the physics and physical chemistry of organic and other molecules of all shapes and sizes. So, in general, we shall be searching for underlying physical and chemical 'explanations', or interpretations, of morphogenetic phenomena, these to be incorporated in a more comprehensive biological system of ideas and interpretations.

MORPHOGENESIS IN BOTANICAL SCIENCE

It is not difficult to understand why some insight into morphogenesis is so important, not only to the general botanist (if that sub-species still survives in these days of unavoidable specialization!) but to the specialist worker, wherever his interests may lie. Our first scientific knowledge of a plant is based on observation of its growth and form. We recognize any particular species at a glance, as it were 'by head'. In fact, we observe its specific and distinctive *characters*, i.e. its particular morphological and structural features, such as the shape(s) of the leaf, the extent of branching, the cross-sectional tissue pattern in the shoot or rhizome, and so on. Our elementary knowledge of plants, in short, is based on morphological observation, usually but sometimes erroneously regarded as a simple study well within the competence of most people. Associated with morphology we have all the rich diversity of anatomy and histology. Because, in the past, these branches were often taught as static, descriptive subjects, the element of wonder which, one would suppose, microscopic observations would surely evoke in any lively and perceptive student, has all too often been deadened. Yet anatomical and histological features, properly observed, are essential to any well-founded study of plants. However, there is a wide gap between the morphological and anatomical *observation* and *description* of organs and tissues and their interpretation, or explanation, in terms of the causal factors which may have been involved in their inception and development. In fact, when we set aside the facile assumptions or 'explanations' which have been advanced to account for some particular organismal form or structure we usually find that our knowledge is sketchy and inadequate.

The morphologist is not alone in shortcomings of this kind. When a physiologist tells us that a particular combination of growth substances in a culture medium promotes bud formation and that a different combination of the substances promotes root formation, he is, of course, contributing new and very valuable information. But he is in no close sense explaining why, under one set of conditions, buds are formed and, under another set, roots. So it emerges that the more we reflect on the phenomena of morphogenesis, the more evident it becomes that no single branch of botanical science – be it morphology, physiology, genetics or ecology – can provide a full and satisfying account: we must draw upon the whole corpus of botanical knowledge and of the physical sciences; and, notwithstanding the difficulties, which are admittedly great, we must attempt to unify and to integrate our information. For only by so doing can we hope to interpret the most salient features of living organisms, i.e. their cellular organization and their distinctive and orderly development at all stages (in particular, *see* Wardlaw, 1965a, for a discussion of organization in plants). The study of morphogenesis in plants, leading on to a consideration of the very general phenomenon of specific organization, is thus seen to occupy a central position and to have an integrative function in botanical science – an important consideration in these days of specialization and partition.

Briefly Historical

A realization of the importance of morphogenesis is not new. A century ago Schleiden gave new life to botany by teaching that the high road to discovery lay in the study of development. About the same time Naegeli elaborated the cell theory of plant construction, and upheld the view that the history of development was not merely to be regarded as one of the various ways of investigating plant form, but as being identical with the investigation of organic nature. In particular, he showed that in many plants the inception of organs and their subsequent development could be referred to cell formation at apical growing points. Then followed the notable work of Hofmeister, who not only investigated the reproduction and embryology of bryophytes, pteridophytes and seed plants but also tried to explore the factors which determine the regular succession of changes in form and structure during development. The work of Sachs (and the publication of the English edition of his *Text-book* (1875), which coincided approximately with the revival of botanical studies in British universities) also ranks as one of the major contributions to our knowledge of morphogenesis. His theory of chemical correlation and morphogenesis may be mentioned as being of particular interest; but, indeed, his whole outlook on the subject was of a searching and comprehensive character.

Although Goebel had published his important work on experimental morphology, *Einleitung in die experimentelle Morphologie der Pflanzen*, in 1908, and W. H. Lang had given his well-known and distinguished address on 'Phyletic and Causal Morphology' in 1915, a considerable amount of time elapsed before studies of experimental embryology and morphogenesis in plants could be regarded as being well on their way, supported by increasing numbers of adherents. Descriptive morphological and anatomical studies still remained in the ascendant for several decades. In plant embryology, for example, the stages in development from the fertilized ovum onwards had been ascertained and illustrated in quite considerable detail for all the major phyla; and in some countries this work still continues with unabated energy. But inquiries into the factors which determine or regulate the very characteristic developments, e.g. the establishment of polarity, the cellular pattern in the growing embryo, the establishment of metabolic and other gradients, the effects of general nutrients and of more specific growth factors, and so on, were still but few in number even in 1950 (*see* Wardlaw, 1955, for an initial review of experimental investigations; and Maheshwari, 1950, 1962, 1963, for an account of more recent work). Similarly, with regard to shoot, root and flower morphogenesis, descriptive morphological and anatomical studies of the respective apical meristems prepared the way for the new analytical and experimental investigations which have gained greatly in momentum from about 1940 onwards. Some of these investigations have been reviewed by the author (Wardlaw, 1952a, b; 1965a, b); by Sinnott (1960); by Clowes (1961); and by many distinguished workers in the *Encyclopedia of Plant Physiology*, Vol. 15, 1965, already mentioned.

From this brief survey, it will be apparent that the study of morphogenesis in plants is in a phase of rapid expansion at the hands of many adherents. Accordingly, a brief contemporary survey, comprising both general and special aspects, may perhaps be regarded as timely.

PROSPECT

The *materials* for the study of morphogenesis include growing generative cells, e.g. zygotes, spores or single cells; gemmae, buds and similar reproductive structures; the apical growing points of shoots, leaves, roots, inflorescences and flowers; cells, organs and tissues growing *in vitro*; teratologies; the galls induced by pathogenic agents, etc. In other words, wherever embryonic cells, tissues, regions or organs are induced to grow, differentiate and develop, with the formation of characteristic organs and tissue systems, we have a morphogenetic situation. It need hardly be said that some materials are much more suitable for investigation than others; indeed, as W. H. Lang (1915) pointed out, the search for favourable materials for investigation may well prove a not inconsiderable part of the task. Young embryos are not only very small and delicate but, in all plants above the organizational level of the algae, are encased in surrounding tissues and difficult to excise undamaged. On the evidence, moreover, the early development of the zygote appears to depend on special metabolic substances of maternal origin (but *see* p. 63). And similarly for the apices of vascular plants; although there is indeed a vast array of pteridophyte, gymnosperm and angiosperm shoot apices, not all are equally good as material for experimental investigation, e.g. for surgical treatments, excision for growth in culture media, etc. In fact, experience has shown that, because of their small size, delicacy, presence of mucilaginous hairs, special metabolic requirements, etc., many angiosperm apices are difficult to handle experimentally. Of course, only a very small number of plant species have so far been subjected to any considerable amount of experimentation as far as their shoot and floral apices are concerned. Comparable remarks could be made in respect of roots. However, it should also be said that, although an apex may appear to be rather intractable at first sight, it is surprising – and here the writer speaks with conviction from personal experience – how, on further observation and dissection, it begins to seem quite a 'reasonable' subject for further investigation.

So much for the materials. What of the methods? The answer is simple: they are the methods of Botany; for the student of morphogenesis is interested in all the processes and factors, genetical, physico-chemical, environmental and organismal, which contribute to the distinctive organizational features of the species. Needless to say, in a specialized monograph such as this a considerable knowledge of plant anatomy, physiology and genetics on the part of the reader must be taken for granted; otherwise the volume would become unduly lengthy and complex. If one were to state the ideal procedure in the comprehensive morphogenetic investigation of a particular species it would perhaps take the following form: (i) we should know as much as possible about the genetic constitution of the species; (ii) we should attempt to relate the presence of particular genes to the substance or substances which they evoke or determine in the nucleus and cytoplasm; (iii) we should follow the metabolic reactions, or sequence of reactions, in which these substances participate; (iv) we should observe the growth, chemical differentiation and eventual physical conformation to which these metabolic events contribute; (v) we should further consider how these nascent and later morphogenetic developments affect, or perhaps regulate, other contemporary or subsequent morphogenetic developments; (vi) as no gene, or other factor, works in isolation, but always in a system, we should try to understand how the workings of organismal reaction systems, viewed in their physico-chemical and mathematical aspects, yield the orderly, harmonious and specific morphological development which we observe.

This ideal will be difficult to realize: in morphogenesis we are not only concerned with the isolation of single factors, or situations, for special investigation, as in the physical sciences: we are concerned with resultant and reciprocal effects of complex systems and sequences of reactions; and, at every stage, from the zygote or generative cell onwards through ontogenesis, an antecedent specific organization, which must be taken 'as given' but which can also be investigated, is ever-present. Any morphogenetic development is undoubtedly very complex. But the vision is splendid and the challenge to botanists, wherever their special interest may lie, is exciting. As every reader of this book will know, many botanical investigators have become ardent adherents of the new Molecular Biology – the realm of the recent and new 'break-throughs'. This is as it should be: the deep probing into the fundamental nature of hereditary substances, into cellular processes involving genes and their products, into the cytoplasmic organization and the action of exogenous and endogenous metabolic materials, is quite essential if botanical science is to advance. There is indeed a most wonderful organization to be explored at the molecular and cellular levels; and in due course, in this volume, we shall consider how contemporary knowledge of this aspect is contributing to our major theme. But let us never forget the wider visions in biology. Organization in plants and animals, as Needham (1942) pointed out, exists at several different levels, from the molecule and organelle, through the cellular to the multicellular organ and tissue, to the harmoniously developed and integrated whole organism, with its distinctive features and all its functional activities during growth, reproduction and survival. Not least, let us constantly bear in mind that the processes of evolution, sustained over vast spans of time, and comprising all the phenomena of molecular biology and of morphogenesis, as well as of other branches such as ecology and population genetics, have yielded a truly astonishing number of different species, each a unique physical entity – species which, for the greater part, we recognize by their morphological characters.

Finally, there are enigmatic themes with a deep philosophic content. Every student of biology knows that, during the reproductive process, like gives rise to like. Yet, in the individual development from the single-celled zygote how varied are the organs and tissues which are differentiated during growth; but, no less, how orderly and distinctive are the patterns.

CHAPTER II

New Developments in Morphogenesis:
General Considerations

THE INITIAL APPROACH

Any investigation that is *truly morphogenetic* necessarily begins with observation of the form and structure of the species selected for study; for without such observation there can be no adequate basis for the further, physiological study of the phenomena of development. The visible formal and structural features throughout the individual development are the raw materials of morphogenetic investigations. Here it may be duly emphasized that these observations, for example of the precise place and mode of inception and development of new primordia at the shoot apex, must be of the highest order of precision; for it is from contemplation of these *basic facts* that we proceed to the formulation of explanatory or interpretive hypotheses. The next stage may usefully include extending observations to other species, in particular to establish the generality or otherwise of particular phenomena. Work of this kind brings its own rewards: it is satisfying to know that, because of the prevalence of *homology of organization* in the Plant Kingdom (*see* Wardlaw, 1965a), a particular investigation may help in the elucidation of an important common phenomenon and contribute towards the formulation of a general principle. However, for the species selected for close investigation, the next step is to test, by experimental means if possible, the validity of the hypothesis that has been proposed to 'explain' some particular morphogenetic development. In any biological phenomenon various factors may be held to be causally involved. Usually, our aim is to demonstrate the effect of some particular factor considered to be of major importance.

A first requirement, if progress is to be made, is that hypotheses relating to supposed morphogenetic factors must be of a kind, and in a form, that lend themselves to experimental tests, preferably of a simple and direct character. Moreover, following the great and effective procedure in physics and chemistry, an experiment based on a well-founded hypothesis should have a predictable result; and when the predicted result is obtained the investigator may well feel that his thinking is along the right lines.

Even so, the cautious and critical investigator is also aware that every morphogenetic phenomenon is full of inner complexities, and that to know the whole truth in biology can seldom, if ever, be possible. That experiments with predictable results can be, and have been, devised in studies of morphogenesis will be seen in later chapters.

In the present state of knowledge certain morphological theories do not readily lend themselves to validation by crucial experiments. Nevertheless, other observational and certain analytical and interpretative procedures may be feasible; and, sooner or later, new clues are obtained and the experimental testing of some critical part of the theory may become possible. The constant search for experimental validation of ideas is not only highly satisfying to the investigator: it is virtually the life-blood of contemporary investigations of plant morphogenesis. However, having recognized its merits, one may also note that the experimental approach is only one among others to the problems of specific form. Since the phenomena of morphogenesis are essentially multi-aspect in character, the data of morphology, anatomy, histology, ultra-microscopy, physiology, genetics and ecology must all be drawn upon; and reference must be made to physics, physical chemistry and mathematics in the interpretation of certain developments. As already noted, no factor ever acts in isolation, but inevitably and invariably as one of a whole nexus, or system, of factors. Indeed, when one reflects on the essential 'wholeness', holism or unity of any organism, however large and complex it may be, it seems reasonable, as a working hypothesis, to regard any particular factor in a morphogenetic development as *a component* of a *complex unitary reaction system*, in which factors of different kinds react and interact, all working in conformity with *physico-chemical principles*, or laws. Admittedly, some of the physico-chemical principles, which might be of great use, have not yet been stated explicitly for the benefit of biologists.

In morphogenesis we are ultimately concerned with the analysis of genetically determined metabolism, growth and bio-physical states of organic materials. Some knowledge of general physiology is accordingly assumed; in particular, of metabolism in cells and tissues; the utilization and morphogenetic effects of general and special metabolic substances; respiration and energy relationships; the establishment of growth centres and gradients; the translocation of materials to loci of utilization; the formation of more or less permanent skeletal materials; and so on. Processes such as the localized inception and growth of particular organs and differential growth must evidently be given close attention; while the *inception of primary patterns*, whether of organs or tissues, in embryonic regions may well be regarded as the very essence of morphogenesis.

PROGRESS IN MORPHOGENESIS

Since it is virtually impossible to think seriously about plants or animals without considering some aspect of their form and structure, it is not surprising that morphology is a very ancient and pervasive subject. So, too, since botanists have been acutely interested in problems of development and causality for more than a hundred years, it would be difficult to indicate conceptual approaches to morphogenesis that are new in any absolute sense. Thus, we may recall that Schleiden (1842) emphasized that the highroad to new discovery lay in the study of development; Naegeli addressed himself to problems of cell formation at the apical growing point; and Hofmeister (1862) revealed the life histories of cryptogams, illustrating in detail the embryogenesis of many species. Later, Hofmeister (1868), in his *Allgemeine Morphologie der Gewächse* – the general morphology of plants (growth, or growing things) – posed what we still regard as some of the leading questions in causal morphology, or morphogenesis. From 1880 onwards, Sachs elaborated in broad outline his theory of chemical morphogenesis and correlation, i.e. that differences between organs are due to differences in their chemical composition and that substances with special formative activities or properties move in different directions through the plant. As botanists know, this theory is still generally acceptable. By the end of the nineteenth century causal morphology had virtually become a branch of physiology, and, indeed, whoever studies any process of development with thoroughness will find that the distinction between morphology and physiology cannot be maintained. The later decades of the nineteenth century also witnessed the publication of other illuminating ideas, e.g. Errera's (1886) physico-chemical concept of cell division by walls of minimal area, various theories of phyllotaxis and so on. Ideas of a mathematical, physical and physico-chemical kind, bearing on phenomena of growth and form, were brought together and expounded with compelling lucidity by D'Arcy Thompson in 1917. Goebel's great books on the *Organography of Plants* must also be mentioned as virtual treasure-houses of information on formative processes in plants.

With the reservations indicated above it is, however, a fact that, during the past thirty years, there has been a considerable development of new ideas and extensions and reappraisals of old ones. Accordingly, in this book a special effort will be made to introduce readers to: (i) new thinking on morphogenesis, and (ii) new factual evidence, often based on new techniques.

There is no one way in which a book on morphogenesis should be written. Each author to his own plan. Accordingly, in this book the author's intention is to deal, conceptually and factually, with recent and new developments in several major aspects of morphogenesis namely: (i) embryogenesis; (ii) comparative studies of apices, etc.; (iii) experimental morphogenesis; (iv) genetical investigations; (v) physiological and bio-chemical investigations, including tissue and organ culture; biophysical and mathematical investigations. Wherever possible, an integration of the data of the several aspects will be attempted.

RECENT AND NEW LITERATURE

Although the aim in this book is to bring recent and new work on morpho-genesis to the attention of students and others, reference will also be made to some earlier works, since these contain the germ of what was later to grow into more extensive investigations. For the writer holds, with con-viction, that lack of continuity in botanical scholarship, which is not un-common today, does the science little credit or service.

Reference has already been made to some of the outstanding books that had already been published by 1920. Readers will find information, and sometimes inspiration, relevant to morphogenesis in the following books. This list makes no claim to completeness: rather it includes those works, in chronological sequence, which the writer has himself found particularly enlightening.

D'Arcy W. Thompson, 1917, *On Growth and Form*, 2nd Edn., 1942, abridged edition by J. T. Bonner, 1961; J. Smuts, 1922, *Holism and Evolution*; O. Schüepp, 1926, *Meristeme*, 2nd Edn., 1966; J. H. Woodger, 1929, *Biological Principles*; F. O. Bower, 1930, *Size and Form in Plants*; J. S. Huxley, 1932, *Problems of Relative Growth*; A. I. Oparin, 1938, *The Origin of Life*, also later editions and versions; P. Weiss, 1939, *Principles of Development*; C. D. Darlington, 1939, *Evolution of Genetic Systems*, revised edn. 1958; C. H. Waddington, 1939, *An Introduction to Modern Genetics*; C. H. Waddington, 1940, *Organizers and Genes*; A. S. Foster, 1942, *Practical Plant Anatomy*; J. Needham, 1942, *Biochemistry and Morpho-genesis*; W. E. Agar, 1943, *A Contribution to the Theory of the Living Organism*, 2nd Edn., 1951; P. R. White, 1943, *A Handbook of Plant Tissue Culture*; E. Schrödinger, 1944; *What is Life?*; R. S. Lillie, 1945, *General Biology and Philosophy of Organism*; W. E. Le Gros Clark and P. B. Medawar, 1945, *Essays on Growth and Form*, presented to D'Arcy Went-worth Thompson; S. J. Holmes, 1948, *Organic Form and Related Biological Problems*; J. F. Danielli and R. Brown, 1948, *Growth*, A Symposium; E. Bünning, 1948, *Entwicklungs- und Bewegungsphysiologie der Pflanze*, and later editions; L. G. Barth, 1949, *Embryology*, revised edn. 1953; C. D. Darlington & K. Mather, 1949, *The Elements of Genetics*; A. Arber, 1950, *The Natural Philosophy of Plant Form*; J. Brachet, 1950, *Chemical*

Embryology; R. G. Gautheret, 1950, *La Culture des Tissues Végétaux et les Phénomènes de l'Histogénèse*; D. A. Johansen, 1950, *Plant Embryology*; P. Maheshwari, 1950, *An Introduction to the Embryology of Angiosperms*; G. R. de Beer, 1951, *Embryos and Ancestors*; L. C. Dunn, 1951, *Genetics in the 20th Century*; F. Skoog, 1951, *Plant Growth Substances*, A Symposium; J. T. Bonner, 1952, *Morphogenesis: An Essay on Development*; L. J. Audus, 1953, *Plant Growth Substances*, 2nd Edn., 1959; K. Esau, 1953, *Plant Anatomy*, 2nd Edn., 1965; I. W. Bailey, 1954, *Contributions to Plant Anatomy*; A. H. Sparrow *et al.*, 1954, *Abnormal and Pathological Plant Growth*, A Symposium; T. Dobzhansky, 1955, *Evolution, Genetics and Man*; F. L. Milthorpe, 1956, *The Growth of Leaves*, A Symposium; R. L. Wain and F. Wightman, 1956, *The Chemistry and Mode of Action of Plant Growth Substances*, A Symposium; P. R. White, 1956, *Decennial Review Conference on Tissue Culture*, A Symposium; H. K. Porter, 1957, *The Biological Action of Growth Substances*, A Symposium; C. H. Waddington, 1957, *The Strategy of the Genes*; J. T. Bonner, 1958, *The Evolution of Development*; R. J. Gautheret, 1959, *La Culture des Tissues Végétaux: Techniques et Réalisations*; C. H. Waddington, 1959, *Biological Organization*, A Symposium; L. Picken, 1960, *The Organization of Cells*; E. W. Sinnott, 1960, *Plant Morphogenesis*; A. M. MacLeod and L. S. Cobley, 1961, *Contemporary Botanical Thought*, A Symposium; F. A. L. Clowes, 1961, *Apical Meristems*; C. H. Waddington, 1961, *The Nature of Life*; M. X. Zarrow, 1961, *Growth in Living Systems*, A Symposium; C. H. Waddington, 1962, *New Patterns in Genetics and Development*; P. Maheshwari, 1962, *Plant Embryology*, A Symposium; J. A. Romberger, 1963, *Meristems, Growth and Development in Woody Plants*; E. W. Sinnott, 1963, *The Problem of Organic Form*; P. Maheshwari, 1963, *Recent Advances in the Embryology of Angiosperms*; P. Maheshwari and N. S. Ranga Swamy, 1963, *Plant Tissue and Organ Culture*; J. A. Ramsay, 1965, *The Experimental Basis of Modern Biology*; W. Ruhland and A. Lang, 1965, *Handbuch der Pflanzenphysiologie*, Vol. 15 – *Differenzierung und Entwicklung*; W. Zimmermann and P. G. Ozenda, 2nd Edn. continuing, *Handbuch der Pflanzenanatomie*; K. Esau, 1965, *Vascular Differentiation in Plants*; Cold Spring Harbor Symposia on Quantitative Biology; Symposia of the Society for Experimental Biology; Symposia of the Growth Society; Symposia of the Linnean Society; Advances in Morphogenesis, continuing.

CHAPTER III

Embryogenesis: General Account

INTRODUCTION

In morphogenesis, as in other studies, we should try to begin at the beginning, i.e. with a zygote, spore or other, single generative cell. The embryology of species from different taxonomic groups has long been studied by the traditional methods of the anatomist and histologist, the results, typically illustrated by as many 'stages' in embryogenesis as possible, being regarded as a necessary contribution to knowledge, but especially to comparative morphology. During more recent years, however, new ideas and new techniques, e.g. embryo culture, have been increasingly applied to the problems of growth and form in embryos, and much new information, some of it of a fascinating and unexpected kind, is beginning to accrue. In cognate investigations by Steward (1958 *et seq.*), Steward *et al.* (1952 *et seq.*), Reinert (1959) and by others, it has been shown that *pseudo-embryos* or *embryoids* can be obtained from small cellular clusters or aggregates which have been grown in shaken culture media. Quite recently Konar and Nataraja (1965) have shown that embryo-like structures can be obtained at will from the stem epidermis of *Ranunculus sceleratus* (*see* p. 81). So, in one way and another, while classical anatomical investigations of embryos are still being actively carried out by workers in various parts of the world, it is becoming increasingly appreciated by botanists, who have lagged far behind the zoologists in this aspect of the study of development, that plant embryogenesis affords wide scope and varied opportunities for experimental work.

The writer's book *Embryogenesis in Plants* (1955) was the first broad survey in which embryological developments in all classes of plants, from algae to angiosperms, were considered in their dynamic aspects, i.e. in terms of physico-chemical information (or conjecture) and of the results of experimental investigations. Although the facts available were scanty, an attempt was made to offer some explanation of the visible developments in terms of the genetical, physical, physiological and other factors and relationships which may be involved; and to show that such an approach enabled us to understand some of the remarkable parallelisms of development, or homologies of organization, found in all the major taxonomic groups.

The terms *embryo* and *germ* connote the initial developmental phase in all classes of plants and are so used in this volume. Also, the zygote, spore or other *generative cell* is held to be endowed with all the genetical potentialities of the species, these being ultimately referable to a specific physico-chemical organization.

EMBRYOGENESIS IN GENERAL

A comprehensive survey of early embryogenesis in plants, i.e. of the mode of growth and development of a single cell, whether it be enclosed in an archegonium or embryo-sac, or free-floating as in the brown algae, has shown that *all* plant embryos have important features in common. This finding suggests that the same, or closely comparable, internal and external factors may be at work in all embryos. The zygote and developing embryo may be envisaged as a reaction system (*see* pp. 31, 49). These reaction systems, in different taxonomic groups, though they include many factors of a rather specific kind, may also have many factors which are common to all. But a possibility which should be mentioned here is that differently constituted reaction systems, functioning in conformity with the laws of physical chemistry, may nevertheless yield closely comparable primary morphogenetic patterns.

In the development of the spherical or ellipsoidal zygote of a brown alga such as *Fucus* sp., or equally of a moss, a liverwort, a lycopod or a seed plant, the following typical features are of general occurrence:

1. From the outset, the zygote affords evidence of the early establishment of *polarity*, leading to a filamentous or axial development, with a distinction of *apex* and *base* (or of *distal* and *proximal* regions), the first partition wall being at right-angles to the nascent axis (Fig. 3.1).

2. The apical or distal pole of the embryo filament typically becomes the locus of active protein synthesis, growth and morphogenesis; i.e. it becomes the principal embryonic region in which, roots excepted, the major organogenic developments will take place. The basal or proximal pole is usually characterized by the accumulation of osmotically active substances, the cells in many species becoming vacuolated and enlarged (Fig. 3.2).

3. As the germ enlarges its cells divide (Figs. 3.1, 3.2), the partition walls being laid down in general conformity with Errera's Law of Cell Division by Walls of Minimal Area. As a result, young and enlarging embryos typically have a characteristic tissue pattern. These patterns may be similar in species of quite different taxonomic affinity.

4. In relation to the establishment of polar gradients, an acropetal gradient of decreasing cell size is characteristic of developing embryos (Fig. 3.3). The distal, perennially embryonic region of the axis, which

typically consists of small densely protoplasmic cells with small vacuoles, becomes histologically organized as an apical meristem.

5. In a zygote or young embryo it seems probable that nutrients may be taken in over the entire surface. Sooner or later, however, it may reasonably be inferred from the visual evidence that nutrients are mainly taken up by the tissues in the basal region and translocated to the apex. The latter phenomenon involves the inception of a nascent pathway of translocation between source and locus of utilization, and later the differentiation of more or less specialized conducting tissues.

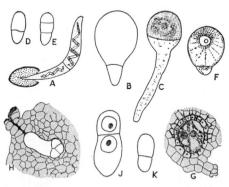

FIG. 3.1. The first division of the zygote or spore in different groups. A, *Spirogyra velata*, germinating zygospore (after West and Fritsch). B, *Fucus* sp. (after Rostafinski). C, *Polysiphonia atrorubescens*, germinating tetraspore (after Chemin). D, *Targionia hypophylla* (after Campbell). E, *Radula* sp. (after Leitgeb). F, *Osmunda claytoniana*, germinating spore (after Campbell). G, *Adiantum concinnum*, divided zygote (after Atkinson). H, *Lycopodium phlegmaria* (after Treub). J, *Chenopodium bonus-henricus*. K, *Luzula forsteri* (after Souèges). (From C. W. Wardlaw, *Embryogenesis in Plants*, 1955.)

6. The organs and tissues, formed in the delicate apical meristem, become firm and rigid as maturation takes place. The formation of the plant axis with its lateral organs is thus essentially a continuing accretionary process.

7. As ontogenesis proceeds, the effects of genetical, organismal and environmental factors on the embryonic development become increasingly conspicuous and the embryo becomes an object of distinctive form and characteristic histological constitution.

8. Pervading all the aspects of development briefly indicated above, in which the participation of physical factors is evident, there is evidence of the elaboration of specific organization. The *inception of a primary pattern* can be observed in the *initial* differentiation of organs and tissues.

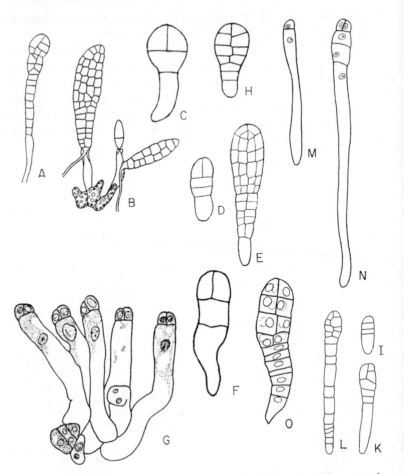

FIG. 3.2. Early stages in the development of embryos in different major groups illustrating: (i) the filamentous or polarized development of the young plant, and (ii) Errera's principle of cell division by walls of minimal area. A, *Fritschiella tuberosa* (a green alga; after M.O.P. Iyengar). B, *Laminaria digitata* (a brown alga, young sporophytes still attached to oogonia; after F. Oltmanns). C, *Fucus vesiculosus* (a brown alga; after G. Thuret and F. Oltmanns). D, E, *Radula complanata* (Hepaticae: Junger-manniales; after H. Leitgeb). F, *Selaginella spinulosa* (Lycopodiales; after H. Bruchmann). G, *Sequoia sempervirens* (a gymnosperm; after J. T. Buchholz): several embryos. H, *Poa annua* (a monocotyledon; after R. Souèges). I, K, *Goodyera discolor*. L, *Orchis latifolia* (Orchidaceae; after M. Treub). M, N, *Cardamine pratensis* (a dicotyledon; after A. Lebègue). O, *Daucus carota* (a dicotyledon; after H. A. Borthwick). (From C. W. Ward-law, *Embryogenesis in Plants*, 1955.)

According to the species, these primary patterns are *elaborated and modified* as a result of (*a*) *differential growth* and (*b*) the *serial evocation and action of genes* (*see also* p. 110) (Wardlaw, 1955).

Occasional exceptions to these general statements could, of course, be indicated. Nevertheless, the early embryogenesis in all classes of plants affords remarkable evidence of homology of organization (for a fuller

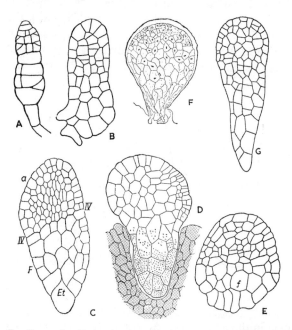

FIG. 3.3. Gradient of cell size in the embryonic development. A, *Delesseria ruscifolia*, red alga, germling (after Nienburg). B, *Notothylas* sp., Anthocerotales, young sporophyte (after Lang). C, *Lycopodium selago; et,* suspensor, *f,* foot, *a,* apex (after Bruchmann). D, *Lycopodium cernuum,* the enlarged cells of the foot in contact with the prothallus contain starch grains (after Treub). E, *Osmunda cinnamomea,* showing the large cells of the foot, *f,* and the smaller cells of the embryonic distal region (after Cross). F, *Ginkgo biloba,* young embryo (after Lyon). G, *Zea mays,* young embryo (after Randolph). (From C. W. Wardlaw, *Embryogenesis in Plants*, 1955.)

exposition of this point, *see* Wardlaw, 1965a). This information encourages the view that, in the search for causal explanations of the very diverse morphology of plants, the task may, in some ways at least, be less complex than is often supposed. In other words, it appears that a relatively small number of basic processes are common to the primary developments in all classes of plants, however different the adult forms may be.

With these findings before us as a general guide, consideration may now be given to such 'explanations', or interpretations, as are available of some of the phenomena of embryogenesis.

THE OVUM AND ZYGOTE

Botanists know all too little about the organization of the ovum and the zygote: in this respect, they lag very far behind the zoologists. In the animal embryo the early differentiation can be interpreted in relation to the organization of the zygote (or of the ovum) and to the characteristic heterogeneous distribution of substances in it. By contrast, botanical

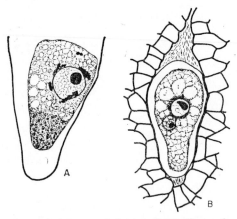

FIG. 3.4. *Fegatella conica* (*Conocephalum conicum*). Examples of ova showing differentiation in the protoplasm. A, an unfertilized ovum. B, a fertilized ovum; the male and female nuclei have not yet fused. (After K. L. Meyer, *Planta*, 1929.)

literature is surprisingly poor in detailed accounts and illustrations of ova and zygotes. Yet, in every ontogenesis, with all its general and specific developments, the organization and metabolism of the zygote are the essential starting-points.

Studies of the ova and zygotes of animals are providing increasing evidence of regional metabolism and differentiation in the protoplast. In favourable plant materials, e.g. *Fegatella conica* (Hepaticae, Fig. 3.4), it can be seen that there are differences in the physical constitution of the protoplasm at the distal and proximal poles of the unfertilized ova. There is an aggregation of the denser protoplasmic materials at the apical pole and vacuolation at the basal pole. Bunning (1948, 1952) suggested that, when polarity is induced in a developing zygote or spore, chemical gradients, or gradients of electrical potential, may be directly involved and may, indeed, be demonstrable.

That chemical gradients, involving a heterogeneous distribution (or segregation) of metabolic or structural substances, are already present in the unfertilized enclosed ova of archegoniate and seed plants, or that protoplasts with initially homogeneously distributed metabolites readily become heterogeneous after the stimulus of fertilization, may reasonably be inferred or, at least, conjectured from direct histological observations, e.g. as in the fertilized ova of algae such as *Fucus*.

On the basis of experimental and other evidence, the protoplast of an ovum or zygote may tentatively be envisaged as an organized, heterogeneous *system* of organic and other substances. It may, perhaps, be regarded as a *unitary reaction system*, in which many components, or factors, react and interact; i.e. it is the locus both of the chemical reactions of metabolism, e.g. enzyme activities, and of the action of external factors such as light, temperature, gravity, etc. In this system cytoplasmic and nuclear proteins and their precursors are main components; but the system is evidently a multifarious and very complex one. For example, when the eggs of certain algae were centrifuged, stratification of some of the protoplasmic ingredients was observed; but although the framework of viscid cytoplasm was distorted, it was usually able to recover after some time. In some eggs the cytoplasm may move in the cell like a liquid (Needham, 1942); but it may nevertheless return to its original position after derangement; i.e. the paracrystalline state exists in living cells. Evidently, there are many intimate structural properties of protoplasm, eventually to be interpreted in terms of a neo-physical chemistry, of which we still know very little (*see* Wardlaw, 1955, 1965a).

To summarize the contemporary position, it may be accepted that the cytoplasm of most ova and zygotes is heterogeneous in nature, or readily becomes so from an antecedent homogeneous state; that potential metabolic processes are quickly activated; that various centres of special metabolism are present in the cytoplasm; and that there are probably specific molecular orientations in relation to surfaces and interfaces that determine cellular polarity. (*See* Additional Note, p. 61.)

The Fern Ovum. The importance of some knowledge of the organization of generative cells is evident if one considers the very different courses of development in the fern gametophyte and sporophyte. Each has its origin in a single cell – the spore and zygote respectively; and, ploidy apart, both have the same genetic constitution. Bell (1959) suggested that the very considerable differences between the two alternating generations may be ascribed to the action of factors in the cytoplasms of the spore and the zygote. In the view of DeMaggio and Wetmore (1961, 1963) this idea is too indefinite to afford an adequate approach to the relevant problems of causality. However, from further investigations of *Pteridium aquilinum*, Bell (1963) concluded that the ovum is a rather special and, indeed, peculiar cell, and that it is cytochemically and cytologically very different from the spore; the latter is regarded as having the usual cytological organization found in unspecialized, potentially meristematic cells. By using staining techniques and autoradiography Bell also demonstrated that the ovum is quite different from the adjacent somatic cells. Deoxyribonucleic acid (DNA) was found to be present in a stable state in both the nucleus and the cytoplasm of the mature ovum, a high concentration being noted round the nucleus. The egg cytoplasm also contains considerably larger amounts of ribonucleic acid (RNA) than the adjacent somatic gametophyte cells, this being especially evident in the outer peripheral regions; and large amounts of basic proteins are also present in it. Several very curious ultrastructural peculiarities have been revealed by electron microscopy in the maturing ovum. For example, as maturation progresses, the periphery of the nucleus protrudes into the cytoplasm as 'blebs', this apparently coinciding with the outward movement of nuclear DNA.

All the details and arguments cannot be given here, but Bell suggested: (i) that the cytoplasm of the mature ovum undergoes transformation under nuclear influence, and (ii) that the presence of new organelles in the ovum cytoplasm, largely mediated by the nucleus, may account for the organizational differences which subsequently become manifest as the spore and zygote develop into the gametophyte and sporophyte respectively. The main point to be made here is that this study of the fern ovum shows how much still remains to be discovered about the organization of generative cells. Comparable studies of the ova of the larger brown algae, of bryophytes, other pteridophytes, gymnosperms and flowering plants, are required. Indeed, they afford an unusually varied, important and virtually untouched field for investigation.

The Angiosperm Ovum. Although information on the organization of the ovum in seed plants is scanty, some recent investigations are of interest both for their factual content and as an indication of what can be achieved.

Studies of the angiosperm ovum, especially at the time of fertilization and after, have been reviewed by Steffen (1963). Richter-Landmann (1959) observed the male plasm, with its inclusions, inside the ovum of *Impatiens glandulifera*. The sperm contributed some 20 plastids and 50 mitochondria to the ovum, in which 150–450 plastids and 1,000–2,500 mitochondria were estimated. In studies of living materials from orchids, Poddubnaya-Arnoldi (1958–60) also made observations on the behaviour of organelles during fertilization and early embryogenesis. Several investigators have reported significant changes in the egg nucleus prior to its fusion with the sperm nucleus (Steffan, 1963). These include an increase in its size, and changes in its DNA content – usually a decrease in the species so far studied. However, this important karyological phenomenon requires fuller investigation. A point mentioned by several workers is that the DNA introduced into the ovum nucleus, with its low DNA content, by the sperm nucleus, has a stimulatory effect; this suggestion, however, is still controversial (Steffan, 1963). Rowlands (1954), for example, found that apomictic egg nuclei have a high DNA content. It appears that, where the DNA content of the ovum nucleus is low, an increase in DNA is an essential condition for nuclear division, this leading to the first stage of regulated zygotic development. It has been observed that the increase in DNA takes place more quickly in the endosperm nucleus than in the ovum nucleus; and hence, perhaps, the earlier division of the former.

POLARITY

In Bünning's view, differentiation has its inception in the establishment of polarity in a cell or embryonic region. For this and other reasons, polarity is rightly regarded as a fundamental phenomenon in the development of plants. In a different vein, Sinnott (1960) referred to polarity as one of the basic principles in morphogenesis that has to be accepted 'as given'. This outlook is probably referable to the fact that the cause of polarity, and its usually irreversible character, have proved exceedingly difficult to understand or define. That genetical factors are involved is clearly indicated by the fact that, in some pteridophytes, the development of the embryo is invariably exoscopic (i.e. with the embryo apex directed towards the neck of the archegonium); whereas, in others, as also in virtually all seed plants, the embryogeny is invariably endoscopic (i.e. with the embryo apex directed away from the neck of the archegonium, or towards the centre of the embryo-sac). Here, too, it may be noted that, once established, polarity is usually irreversible.

Polarity in the Zygotes of Fucus *spp.* Since the most extensive experimental investigations of the inception of polarity in plant zygotes have been based on the free-floating eggs of brown algae – mostly species of Fucales – the main facts may now be reviewed (Whitaker and Whitaker *et al.*, 1931–40). Although it is now known that the spherical ovum of *Fucus* consists of concentric layers of different chemical constitution, there is no reason to suppose that its cytoplasm comprises different regions of special metabolism, as in many animal eggs. However, after fertilization the

B

initially 'homogeneous' cytoplasm in the *Fucus* egg soon becomes meta-bolically differentiated and heterogeneous, and polarity is established. The visual evidence is that a rhizoid begins to grow out at the basal pole, nuclear division takes place and a wall is formed at right-angles to the direction of the rhizoidal outgrowth. Whitaker and his co-workers, and Olson and Du Buy (1937), were able to demonstrate, by means of experiments of considerable ingenuity and delicacy, that various physical and chemical factors can be specified which contribute to the polarized development (Fig. 3.5).

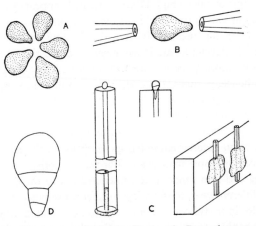

FIG. 3.5. Experiments on polarity in *Fucus*. A, In a cluster of zygotes, the rhizoidal development is typically centripetal. B, When a fertilized egg is placed in a gradient of pH, i.e. between two pipettes of solution, the rhizoid grows out on the more acid side (A and B, after Whitaker). C, Apparatus for determining the effect of various solutions on the segmentation of *Fucus*; (*see* text) (after Olson and DuBuy). D, Segmentation in *Fucus* (after Rosta-finski). (From C. W. Wardlaw, *Embryogenesis in Plants*, 1955.)

In the developing zygote of *Fucus*, growth and differentiation, i.e. both quantitative and qualitative changes, take place simultaneously. If a single zygote is kept in the dark and as free as possible from gradients or asym-metry of environmental factors a single rhizoid grows out and develops normally. Whitaker suggested that a labile and readily alterable polarity is already established, perhaps due to conditions during oogenesis, or that it is determined by chance, environmental factors, e.g. that the rhizoid may emerge at the point of entry of the spermatozoid, as suggested by Knapp (1931) for *Cystoseira*. Experimental observations on the establishment of polarity in *Fucus* include the following: (1) unilateral illumination of zygotes by white light leads to the development of rhizoids on the least illuminated side; only the shorter wavelengths of the visible spectrum are effective; (2) when a zygote is exposed to a direct electric current the rhizoid develops on the side towards the positive pole, at which negative ions, including those of auxin, probably accumulate; (3) if zygotes are developing in a considerable group or cluster, rhizoidal formation is towards the centre, i.e. towards the locus of high concentration of some non-specific, exuded substance, or of increased CO_2 concentration, i.e. of higher pH (Fig. 3.5); (4) when a single zygote is placed between acid and alkaline pipettes of sea-water (pH 6·0–8·0), the rhizoid develops on the acid side; gradient rather than actual pH appears to be the effective factor (Fig. 3.5); (5) zygotes also respond to a small temperature gradient, the rhizoids being formed on the warmer side.

Whatever the explanation of the inception of polarity in the ova of *Fucus* and related genera may be, the movement of auxin to the basal pole seems to be a consistently associated development. In fact, DuBuy and Olson (1937) succeeded in extracting an unspecified auxin. They also demonstrated that rhizoids are formed on the side supplied with the greatest concentration of IAA (Fig. 3.5). Van Overbeek (1940) showed that auxin is present in the ova of *Macrocystis*. From these observations, it can be seen that several factors, all affecting metabolic processes, result in a polarized distribution of materials within the zygote. However, the phenomenon is not simply one of aggregation of materials by diffusion. In experiments on centrifuging zygotes the polarity remained unchanged, although some of the contents became stratified. It thus appears that the irreversible polarity is based on some more permanent material, i.e. on a structural basis (review in Wardlaw, 1955). Yet, as we have seen, under the impact of external factors protoplasmic changes do take place which lead to the polarized state. (*N.B. See also* Wettstein, 1965, for recent literature and Additional Note, p. 61.)

In animal ova Needham (1942) regarded the phenomenon as essentially one of protoplasmic organization, the many and varied constituent molecules being so disposed as to constitute a definite structure which, on further development, is manifested as polarity.

The work pioneered by Whitaker and his co-workers has been continued and extended by Japanese investigators (Figs. 3.6–3.9). However, already in 1927 Tahara had made experiments on the eggs of *Sargassum*. Nakazawa (1950), using zygotes of *Sargassum confusum*, found that polarity was not affected by the stratification in the protoplasm induced by centrifuging at 3,000 cycles per minute for one hour. In further studies of the same kind, Nakazawa (1951) used unfertilized and newly fertilized ova of *Coccophora Langsdorfii* and of *Sargassum tortile*. These were centrifuged at 50,000 cycles per minute for 5 minutes. In *Coccophora* a marked stratification into an oily layer, a chromatophore and nuclear layer, and a clear cytoplasmic layer resulted in both unfertilized and fertilized eggs. However, when the rhizoids duly developed, their positions relative to the plane of stratification were quite random (Fig. 3.7). *Sargassum* yielded comparable results as regards the stratification of the ova or zygote contents. However, when the zygote began to divide the cleavages were seen to be irregular, the locus of

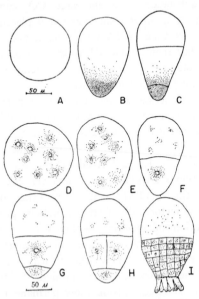

FIG. 3.6. *Coccophora Langsdorfii.* Ova and young embryos showing differential, vital staining. A, Unfertilized egg. B, Recently fertilized egg. C, Developing embryo, the rhizoidal, basal region being deeply stained (after S. Nakazawa, *Sci. Rept. Tohoku Univ.*, 1953). D–I, Abnormal eggs, with eight nuclei, which result in the formation of half-embryos; *see* text. (After S. Nakazawa, *Bot. Mag. Tokyo*, 1955.)

outgrowth of the rhizoid being unrelated either to the stratification or to the cellular pattern (Fig. 3.7). These somewhat irregularly developed zygotes recovered and grew into normal embryos. Tahara (1927) had obtained somewhat comparable results in materials which had been subjected to hypertonic treatments. Nakazawa reported that, as a result of centrifugation, unfertilized nuclei were activated and participated in the irregular cleavage pattern of the ovum. This investigator's conclusion was that polarity in the species investigated is probably a property, e.g. the viscosity, of the cortical cytoplasm of the ovum. In species of *Fucus* this region may be more easily modified. In further experiments Nakazawa (1956) concluded that the polarity in *Coccophora* was already established before fertilization.

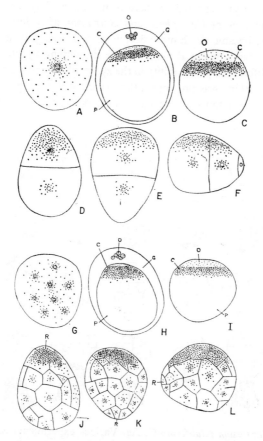

FIG. 3.7. Eggs of *Coccophora Langsdorfii*. A, Before centrifuging. B, Centrifuged before fertilization; oil drops (O) are seen in the gelatinous coat (G) on the centripetal side. C, Centrifuged after fertilization. D, A two-cell-stage with the rhizoid pole peaked on the centripetal side. E, The same, peaked on the centrifugal side. F, A three-cell-stage with the primordial cell of the rhizoids forming on the side lateral to the centrifuging axis. C, Chromatophores. G, Gelatinous coat. O, Oil drops. R, Rhizoid pole. P, Plasmic zone.

Eggs of *Sargassum tortile*. G, Uncentrifuged. H, Centrifuged before fertilization; oil drops are seen in the gelatinous coat on the centripetal side. I, Centrifuged after fertilization. J–L, Irregular cleavages resulting from centrifuging. J, The rhizoid pole is formed on the centripetal side. K, It is formed on the centrifugal side; and L, the rhizoid is lateral. (After S. Nakazawa, *Sci. Rept. Tohoku Univ.*, 1951.)

Nakazawa (1953) reported an increase in permeability and vital stainability in the eggs of *Coccophora* and *Sargassum* after fertilization: the rhizoidal pole became much more deeply stained (Fig. 3.6), and there was an evident polar gradient throughout the developing zygote. In further studies on differential permeability in the zygote, Nakazawa (1957a, b, c, d) found that lecithine was present on the *surface* of the egg protoplasm and was at its densest towards the basal pole, possibly increasing the per-

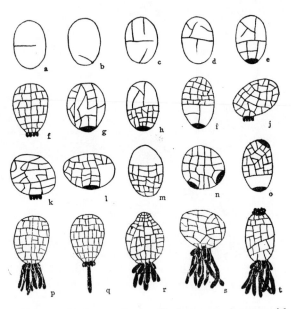

FIG. 3.8. *Sargassum piluliferum* C. Ag. Various experiments with fertilized eggs.
    a–o. 10 hours after preparation. p–t. 1 day after preparation. Black regions indicate the rhizoid-cells or the rhizoids. f,p,r. Normal embryos. a–e, g–o, s, t. Various abnormal embryos. (After M. Hiroe and S. Inoh, *Biol. Jour.*, Okayama Univ., 1955.)

meability in this region; and hence, perhaps, affecting the outgrowth of the rhizoid.

In *Coccophora Langsdorfii* Nakazawa (1955) observed the fertilization of occasional anomalous ova in which eight nuclei were present. (These ova very closely resembled the normal ova of *Sargassum*, in which eight nuclei are present.) Seven of the eight nuclei gradually degenerated and the fertilized ovum underwent cleavage. This, however, was not accompanied by nuclear division. The one large nucleus entered the basal cell of the young embryo, and all the subsequent divisions, with cell-wall formation, were restricted to the basal portion of what was virtually a half embryo with a large 'vacant' (?) apical cell (Fig. 3.6 D–I).

Hiroe and Inoh (1955) reported observations and experiments on the eggs of *Sargassum piluliferum*. On being discharged the ova contain eight nuclei. Unfertilized eggs underwent various anomalous changes, but no

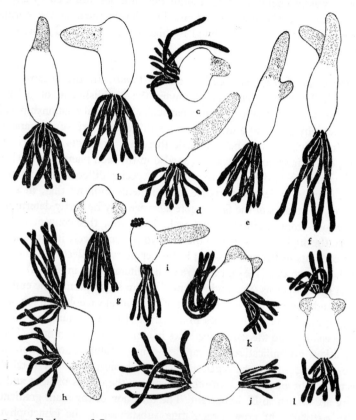

FIG. 3.9. Embryos of *Sargassum piluliferum* C. Ag. (8 days after preparation: stippling indicates the excrescent meristems and black the rhizoids). a. Normal embryo. b–l. Various abnormalities in embryo-polarity. (After M. Hiroe and S. Inoh, *Biol. Jour.* Okayama Univ., 1955.)

real or sustained development ensued. However, some of them formed a rhizoid-like outgrowth. In fertilized eggs, on the other hand, in relation to the conditions of temperature and light provided, observations of very considerable interest were made on the mode of segmentation, rhizoid development, meristem organization and embryonic growth (Figs. 3.8, 3.9). The illustrations show various anomalous developments, e.g. two rhizoidal regions, two meristematic regions, 'half-embryos' (i.e. partly segmented embryos) and so on. The single embryo, with apical–basal polarity and a regular segmentation pattern, is the normal condition. Rhizoidal formation was increased by exposure to short-term illumination and inhibited under long light exposure. Meristematic development, by contrast, was promoted by long illumination and not inhibited by any of the imposed experimental conditions. The development of the normal segmentation pattern was inhibited by high temperature and short-term illumination.

The Ovum in Archegoniate and Flowering Plants. In the encapsulated embryo in bryophytes and pteridophytes the establishment of polarity brings the developing embryo into a particular positional relationship with the gametophyte, e.g. in a moss, in line with the long axis of the gametophyte in which, it may be assumed, there are gradients of nutrients, auxins, etc. (Fig. 3.10). Here again, as also in the seed plants, the basis of polarity is little understood. In different species different factors may assume greater or less importance. Experiments indicate that, in some instances, the planes of the first zygote cleavage may be partly determined by pressure from the archegonial wall. Evidently, this concept cannot apply in the angiosperms, where the embryo projects freely into the semi-liquid contents of the embryo-sac; but other pressure effects are not precluded. (Ryczkowski (1965a, b, where earlier literature is indicated) stated that, in gymnosperms (the 'endosperm'), and in angiosperms (the embryo sac and endosperm), the osmotic value of the central vacuolar sap in young rapidly growing ovules increases to a characteristic maximum (0·53 M in *Cycas revoluta*), and thereafter decreases in almost fully grown ones. These observations are indicative of a rapid in-flow of solutions of osmotically active substances from the vegetative region. Physical as well as metabolic aspects may be important.) In other instances the effects of light and of gravity are known to be important. The direction of the main gradients, and in particular of growth-regulating substances in the gametophyte, seem likely to be important in determining polarity in the nascent embryo: in many plants, as already noted, an acropetal gradient of decreasing cell size is characteristic of the early stages of the embryogeny. Indeed, much has been made of the concept that gradients of various kinds are effective agents in morphogenesis (Child, 1941; Prat, 1945, 1948, 1954). This idea, however, has not met with general acceptance, e.g. *see* Weiss (1939).

Polarity in General. Polarity is not only of primary importance in early embryogenesis: polar phenomena pervade all development. The relevant problems have been the subjects of extensive reviews (Bloch, 1965;

Bonner, 1952; Bünning, 1957; Wettstein, 1965; Halbsguth, 1965). Justice cannot be done to the topic in the space available in this book (*see* Bloch, 1965, and Wettstein, 1965, for encyclopaedic treatments). As Bloch (1965) has noted, although the bipolar shoot–root relationship is perhaps the most

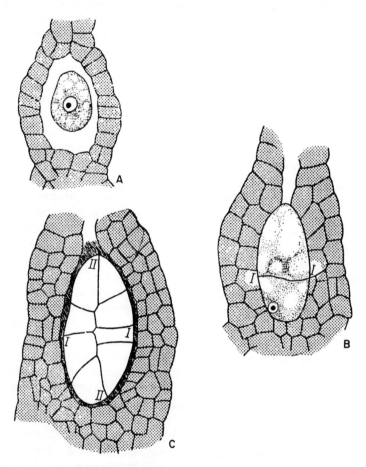

FIG. 3.10. *Targionia hypophylla* (Marchantiales). A, Venter of mature archegonium with ovum; B, the first division of the zygote; C, the regular segmentation pattern in the developing embryo (×500) (after F. Cavers, *New Phytol.*, 1900).

common and best example of polarity, it is a relatively specific instance of a general phenomenon. Complex polarity relationships are also manifested in dorsiventral organs such as leaves, in the gametophytes of liverworts and ferns, and so on. To quote: 'In a broad sense polarity designates any *internal asymmetrical state within a living system* as expressed in differentiation between two ends or two surfaces, and also between the ends or surfaces and the central region.' However, even in this recent review, Bloch is unable to accept any of the proposed explanations of polarity as being adequate: information of a fundamental kind relating to the physicochemical constitution and properties of protoplasm is still lacking. Wettstein (1965) has cited various examples of the loss, or modification, of the normal polarity in germinating moss and fern spores as a result of various chemical treatments, e.g. IAA, colchicine, vitamin B_1, chloralhydrate, etc.

THE DEVELOPMENT OF THE HISTOLOGICAL PATTERN

Closely associated with the establishment of polarity and growth in the elongating embryo is the development of a characteristic histological pattern. As already noted, the first division of the zygote, with few exceptions, is by a wall laid down at right-angles to the direction of elongation, i.e. to the polar axis. Thereafter, on further growth, a segmentation pattern of considerable regularity, typical of the species, and in conformity with the shape of the embryo, develops (Fig. 3.11). Now, in a growing embryo, as in all physical systems, it may be accepted that there will be a tendency towards equilibrium, or steady state, also described as dynamic equilibrium. As D'Arcy Thompson (1917, 1942) cogently pointed out: 'no organic forms exist, save such as are in conformity with physical and mathematical laws'. Accordingly, during a morphogenetic process, as the mature and relatively permanent form is reached, it will tend towards a state of equilibrium, i.e. of minimal free energy or maximal entropy. Among the physical forces which may affect morphogenesis are gravity, the intermolecular forces of cohesion, friction, surface tension, mechanical pressure, molecular diffusion and chemical, electrical and thermal force. There may also be forces of a kind that have not yet been investigated by physicists or physical chemists.

During embryogenesis the germ undergoes an increase in size, and because of the incidence of physical factors, and for inescapable mathematical reasons, momentous changes in form and structure usually ensue. According to Galileo's Principle of Similitude, whereas in an enlarging object, or in an organism, surface varies as the square of the linear dimension, volume varies as the cube; and the proportion of surface to bulk is constantly changing if the shape remains unaltered. In embryos it is not surprising that changes in external form and internal structure take place as a result of the impact of different incident forces. Indeed, it is the commonplace of experience that ontogenesis is characterized by remarkable changes in form and structure. At every stage we may perceive, or discover, if we have the mind for it, evidence of the classical physical relationships of energy and matter in the determination of the eventual form and structure.

D'Arcy Thompson (1917) dealt in considerable detail with surface tension as a factor determining the shape of isolated single cells and of the segmentation pattern in a tissue mass, e.g. a young embryo. A living cell (he said) is a complex field of energy, the energy being distributed internally through the cytoplasm and externally over the outer surface; and any change in the ratio of these two energy components will disturb the equilibrium of the system. Cell division, by keeping constant the ratio of surface to mass, will thus tend to maintain equilibrium. If these premises are valid it is understandable why small unicellular organisms are spherical or assume simple forms; i.e. physical factors are closely involved in determining the forms of cells. A change in tension at any point, for example due to some metabolic change, may lead to asymmetry, i.e. to a change in form; and one asymmetry is liable to beget another. Because of the importance of surface and/or other forces in moulding cell shape, structural features to which functional adaptation has been ascribed may, in this view, be of purely secondary biological importance. However, not all observers share D'Arcy Thompson's views on the importance of surface tension in determining the form of unicellular organisms (*see* Danielli 1945). Indeed, very little critical experimental investigation has so far been attempted.

In the development of the regular and distinctive segmentation patterns in bryophyte and other embryos, D'Arcy Thompson considered that surface tension was a major factor. In an enlarging organism (he said) a reduction in surface energy is essential for the maintenance of equilibrium, i.e. stability. Accordingly, there will be a tendency towards the maximum reduction in the extent of the surfaces created by cell division: cells will tend to divide by walls of minimal area. This principle has a wide application in plants. It applies to the division of the spores of liverworts, the formation of pollen tetrads, the segmentation of young embryos and the division of apical cells. The conception of cell division by partition walls of minimal area goes far towards an explanation of phenomena which have been much discussed by biologists. Hofmeister observed that when a cell divides, the new wall is always perpendicular to what was previously the principal direction of growth; e.g. as in the vertical files of pith cells in the subapical region of the shoot. Such cells are thus typically divided by walls of minimal area. In 1877 Sachs formulated his rule of rectangular section – that in all tissues new cell walls are laid down at right-angles to those already present. Actually, this was an extension of Schwendener's hypothesis of 1860, that the final result of cell division in a tissue, as at the apex of a flowering plant, consists in the cell walls being aligned in a system of

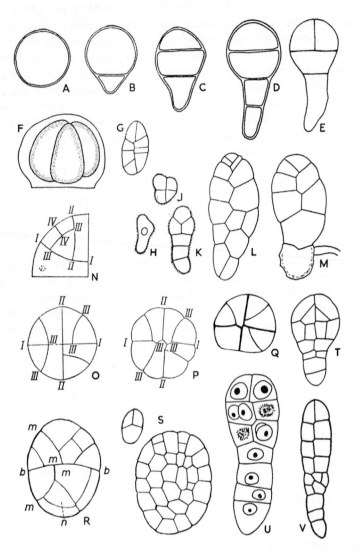

FIG. 3.11. The development of the segmentation pattern in the embryogeny in different groups. A–D, *Antithamnion plumula*, germinating spores (after Kylin). E, *Fucus vesiculosus*, young embryo (after Thuret and Oltmanns). F, *Cystoclonium purpurascens*, the subspherical spore has divided into two and then into four equal quadrants (after Kylin). G, *Targionia hypophylla*, early segmentation pattern (after Campbell). H–L, *Lejeunia serphyllifolia* (Jungermanniales), spore germination leading to organization of an apical cell (after Goebel). M, *Blechnum spicant* (leptosporangiate fern), spore germination, leading to organization of an apical cell. N, O, P, Diagrams illustrating the ideal segmentation pattern in a dividing sphere (or circle)

orthogonal trajectories. Hofmeister and Sachs were mainly concerned with the positions of new walls from the biological point of view and rather less with their dependence on physical factors. Berthold (1886), however, adopted the principle of minimal areas, comparing the forms of cells and the disposition of their partition walls with those which would be assumed by a system of weightless films under the influence of surface tension. Independently, in the same year, Errera definitely ascribed to the embryonic cell wall the properties of a semi-liquid film and deduced that it must be subject to ordinary physical laws and must accordingly assume a form in conformity with the principle of minimal areas. In other words, at the time of its formation a cell wall tends to assume the form which would be assumed under the same conditions by a weightless liquid film. Another fundamental rule which we also owe to Errera is that 'the incipient partition wall of a dividing cell tends to be such that its area is the least possible by which the given space-content can be enclosed'.

These conceptions are of great value to the student of morphogenesis, especially in relation to the segmentation patterns in the embryos of a wide range of plants (Fig. 3.11). It could, perhaps, be argued that, since the morphogenetic effect is seemingly a physical one, it is extrinsic to the genetical system. But it is inescapable that inherent, i.e. genetical, factors are also involved. Since they control cell metabolism and the production of the material utilized in wall formation, they are also directly involved in generating the physical forces, e.g. surface tensions, which may be the proximal morphogenetic agents. If this argument is valid – the author regards it as unavoidable – it enables us to comprehend how a morpho-genetic process may at one and the same time take place in conformity with physical laws and yet have its own characteristic specificity: it unifies, or links, both homology of organization and genetic specificity.

The ideas and observations set out here as being appropriate to embryo-genic patterns are also applicable to other meristematic regions, e.g. the apices of shoots, leaves, roots and other regions of active cell division.

---

and its quadrants; each cell is equally divided by a wall of minimal area; I–I, II–II, III–III, IV–IV, the successive partition walls. P, Shows the characteristic readjustment at points of wall conjunction (after D'Arcy Thompson). Q, *Marsilea vestita*, showing a segmentation pattern in the developing embryo that approximates to the ideal pattern illustrated in P (after Campbell). R, *Equisetum arvense*, young embryo; b–b, basal wall; m–m, first vertical wall; n, root initial (after Sadebeck). S, *Epipactis palustris* (Orchidaceae), young and fully formed embryos (after Treub). T, *Drosera rotundifolia* (after Souèges). U, *Chenopodium bonus-henricus* (after Souèges). V, *Scapania nemorosa* (Jungermanniales), young sporophyte (after Leitgeb). (From C. W. Wardlaw, *Embryogenesis in Plants*, 1955.)

Unequal Cell Division and Related Phenomena. In an ideal physical situation a growing spherical zygote, with a homogeneous distribution of its protoplasmic ingredients, and with the same conditions on all sides, would eventually divide into two equal hemispheres; and similarly an ellipsoidal zygote would yield two equal parts. But it is a simple fact of observation that, in a great many zygotes, as also in other dividing embryonic or meristematic cells, the partition wall does not divide the parent cell into two equivalent daughter cells. In many embryos the distal cell is small and the proximal cell large. However, as a movement of certain metabolic substances to one pole and of different substances to the other has already taken place, and different reactions evoked, the energy relationships at the two poles may be expected to be different. If the position of the partition wall restores the developing system as a whole to a steady state it is in no way surprising that the two daughter cells, in which rather different chemical reactions are undoubtedly taking place, are of different sizes.

For some considerable time Errera's views on cell division were more or less vigorously opposed by a number of biologists, and a reserved attitude persisted even into the later editions of Strasburger's well-known *Textbook of Botany*. Errera's views, however, have steadily gained ground and, with the passage of time, have received strong support. Indeed, some embryologists have affirmed that the segmentations during early embryogenesis are purely physical in nature, i.e. that the histological patterns in plants and animals are essentially referable to molecular physics – a view very different from that of comparative embryologists, who regarded the position of each new wall as having phylogenetic significance. (As the author has indicated above, they can have both.) Errera himself pointed out that his principle could have great importance in that it enables us to understand something of the inception of many organic forms and to relate 'cellular architecture' to molecular physics. One may perhaps note, as a curious fact, that Errera's Law, which sheds so much light on the phenomena of cell shape, division and pattern, and which implies the polarized movement of metabolic materials, hormones, etc., and the establishment and effects of physiological, bioelectrical and other gradients, has received so little attention in standard textbooks (Wardlaw, 1960).

Illustrations of Errera's Law are to be encountered everywhere in embryonic and meristematic tissues. In particular, the early embryogenesis in all classes of plants bears witness to the generality and value of his concept. The development of the nearly spherical leptosporangiate fern embryo up to, and beyond, the octant stage, approximates closely to the idealized division of a sphere into cells of equal volume by walls of minimal area (Fig. 3.11). Critics of Errera's Law, e.g. those who point out that cambial cells evidently do not divide by walls of minimal area, view the matter from too narrow a basis. In essence, Errera was calling attention to a basic physiological and physical relationship, the relationship so aptly described in the title of his classical paper – a fundamental condition of equilibrium in living cells. In this general approach we are reminded of the writings of Plateau, from which Errera's idea was derived; for Plateau stated quite clearly that a surface of minimal area was to be understood as a relative minimum, determined as it would be by *all the material exigencies*. If, therefore, we accept Errera's Law in its general aspect (as he himself clearly intended), recognizing that in different biological circumstances other factors will inevitably become incident and may affect the pattern of wall formation to a greater or less extent, then the value of the Law, far from being diminished by seeming exceptions, is enhanced by them. This certainly has been the writer's experience in studies of embryogenesis; for plant embryos not only afford beautiful examples of the application of the Law in its simplest form but also many seeming exceptions which serve to intensify our attempt to understand developmental processes. Thus, in the simplest case some plant embryos illustrate the equal division of a spherical or ellipsoidal zygote by a wall of minimal area; and the further divisions, up to a point, are also in close conformity with Errera's Law. On the other hand, unequal division of the zygote by a transverse wall is also of very general occurrence. If, however, we accept the Law as being applicable we are led to consider other factors that may be involved in the developmental processes, e.g. the polarized segregation of different metabolites, as already indicated. The distal pole becomes densely protoplasmic and the main seat of protein synthesis, whereas the basal pole is often characterized by an accumulation of osmotically active substances and by enlargement (Fig. 3.12). Accordingly, the forces generated during the very different metabolism at the two poles will affect the position in which the first partition wall will be laid down. This, in fact, is usually such that a small embryonic cell is separated from a larger basal cell, i.e. the first partition wall is not one of minimal area. But, having regard to all the circumstances, Errera's Law, in the precise form stated by him, will still apply, the unequal cell division calling attention to the fact that certain factors, which have become incident in development, have modified the working of the Law as envisaged in an idealized situation. The developing embryo as a whole is in a state of dynamic equilibrium, and it was with the maintenance of this state that Errera was so profoundly concerned. In the encapsulated embryos of archegoniate and seed plants the pre-fertilization ovum has already been exposed to various factors, e.g. physiological gradients in the maternal environment, and if its polarity has not already been determined this takes place at a very early stage in the zygotic development. In these embryos the inception of polarity is sometimes demonstrably, and

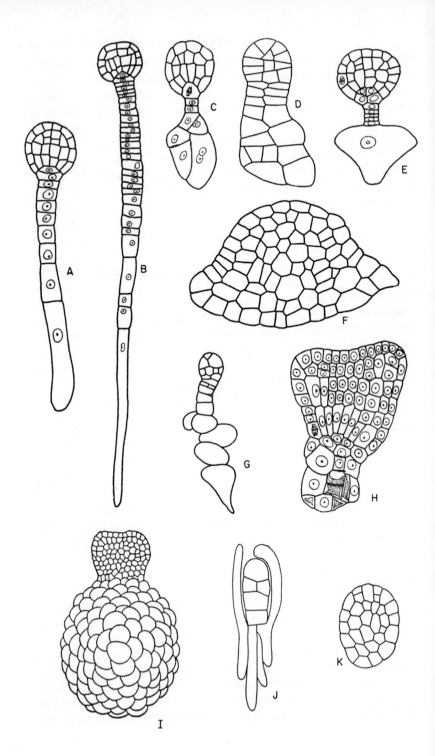

presumably almost always, attended by metabolic differences at the poles; and hence the first transverse wall is unlikely to be one of minimal area. The first longitudinal division of the distal embryonic cell, on the other hand, usually exemplifies Errera's Law. Because the Law deals with a fundamental relationship during the growth and development of organisms, it thus retains its place in contemporary studies of morphogenesis and physiological genetics.

Comparable unequal cell divisions, often associated with the polarized movement of metabolic substances, and with growth, are common in other aspects of development (see Bünning, 1957).

Tissue Pattern. The course of embryogenesis in all classes of plants is characterized by orderly development, i.e. by the amplification and manifestation of the organization which is held to be present in the zygote or in the ovum. In particular, the inception and elaboration of the tissue pattern during ontogenesis is a composite effect. In an elongating organ, such as a shoot or a root, the characteristic tissue pattern can be related to the axial development that follows the establishment of polarity, to factors determining a concentric mode of differentiation in which we can distinguish epidermis, cortex and stele, and to the same or other factors determining a radiate mode of differentiation, as in the distribution of the vascular tissues. These evident components of the tissue pattern are still quite insufficiently understood. Genic action is undoubtedly involved in the underlying metabolic processes. The characteristic differential or allometric growth of the embryo, i.e. the distribution of growth in different directions which results in the production of a characteristic shape, is held to be under genic control. But, as we know, factors in the environment may effect similar developments. Thus, although we accept that genes are fundamental biochemical agents in the differentiation of tissues, other factors and relationships of an essentially extrinsic character are also involved. In short, the phenomenon of organization in the embryo, including tissue patterns, is essentially a multi-aspect and integrative one (see also Chapter XI).

THE ORGANISM AS A REACTION SYSTEM

Certain assumptions have been made as a basis for interpreting features of embryogenesis and morphogenesis (Wardlaw, 1965a). It will be appreciated

---

FIG. 3.12. Embryos of flowering plants, illustrating the range in size of the suspensor. A, *Cardamine pratensis.* B, *Barbarea vulgaris.* C, *Saxifraga caespitosa.* D, *Malus communis.* E, *Penthorum sedoides.* F, *Eriocaulon septangulare.* G, *Sherardia arvensis.* H, *Oxyspora panicum.* I, *Cytisus laburnum.* J, *Phalaenopsis grandiflora.* K, *Epipactis palustris.* (From various authors, acknowledged in C. W. Wardlaw, *Embryogenesis in Plants*, 1955.)

that these assumptions involve a great over-simplification of what we know must be very complex situations. But they afford a starting-point.

1. A developing zygote is held to be a complex, specific, diffusion reaction system, which functions in conformity with the laws of physical chemistry and physics. In considering how complex and unique the reaction system of a particular species must be, it is salutary to remember that the constitution of its protoplasm is the result of a long evolutionary process.

2. A biochemical pattern, i.e. a patternized distribution of metabolites, always underlies and precedes the visible morphological or histological pattern.

3. The inception of a patternized distribution of metabolites – which may be described as one of the most important, enigmatic and challenging problems in biology – is held to be a phenomenon of physical chemistry, i.e. the physical chemistry of metabolic systems present in embryonic regions and tissues.

4. A contemporary diffusion reaction theory of morphogenesis (Turing, 1952; Wardlaw, 1953, 1965a) postulates that in a zygote or embryonic tissue, in which the metabolic substances may initially be distributed in a homogeneous manner, a regular, patternized distribution of specific metabolites may eventually result, affording the basis for the inception of a morphological or histological pattern.

Support for the concept that a patternized distribution of metabolites precedes the visible morphogenetic developments has been given by Rondet (1962). In a histochemical study of RNA distribution in the embryology of *Alyssum maritimum*, he demonstrated that the young spherical embryo has a considerable and uniform distribution of RNA, whereas the suspensor shows only small amounts, i.e. feeble colour reactions to Brachet's test. The developing endosperm is also rich in ribonucleic acids. As the embryo develops, evidence of a heterogeneous distribution of RNA becomes apparent, the amounts present in the nascent, still unorganized distal apical meristem and also in the region of the root meristem being feeble, i.e. by comparison with the actively developing cotyledons and hypocotyl region. In fact, Rondet described the region of the root initials as remaining passive throughout embryogenesis. The hitherto inert shoot apical region, on the other hand, undergoes activation, becomes rich in RNA, and develops its characteristic histological organization, i.e. a two-layered tunica overlying the corpus. There is greater biochemical activity on the flanks of the meristem than at the centre, periclinal divisions in the former resulting in the formation of the *anneau initial* (or formative ring). There is also active accumulation of RNA in the corpus cells of the subapical region, these constituting the medullary meristem. Thus organized, the embryo enters into the phase of epicotyledonary ontogenesis.

THE EARLY HISTOLOGICAL PATTERN IN LEPTOSPORANGIATE FERNS

A compelling example of the establishment of a regulated, patternized distribution of metabolic materials in early embryogenesis is afforded by leptosporangiate ferns. In species of *Dryopteris*, *Adiantum*, *Onoclea*,

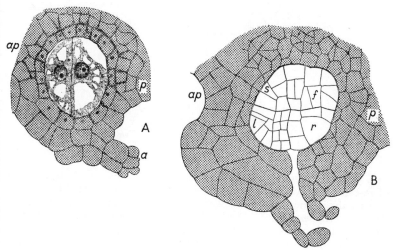

FIG. 3.13. Early embryogeny in ferns. A, *Pteris serratula*. First division of zygote, as seen in l.s. of the archegonium (*a*); the smaller segment is towards the prothallus apex (*ap*); p, prothallus. B, *Adiantum concinnum*. Post-octant stage, as seen in a longitudinal median section of the prothallus and archegonium; *ap*, direction of apex of prothallus; *s*, shoot apex; *l*, first leaf; *f*, foot; *r*, first root. (After G. F. Atkinson, *The Biology of Ferns*, 1894.)

Gymnogramme, etc., the archegonia are typically formed on the lower side of the heart-shaped prothallus and have their necks directed downwards, or obliquely downwards. The fertilized ovum is approximately spherical in shape, and the first partition wall, known as the *basal wall*, lies in the axis of the archegonium and at right-angles to the axis of the prothallus (Figs. 3.13, 3.14). The polarity of the embryo is now irreversibly determined: from the anterior or *epibasal* segment, which lies towards the apex of the prothallus, the shoot apex and the first leaf will be formed; from the posterior or *hypobasal* segment the first root and the foot will originate. The second partition wall is at right-angles to the first and lies in the axis

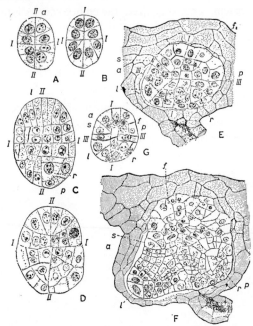

FIG. 3.14. *Gymnogramme sulphurea*, a leptosporangiate fern. A, B, Sections of 16-celled embryo, cut at right-angles to the archegonial axis; the sections traverse the inferior octants in A and the superior octants in B; the anterior octants are uppermost. C. D, E, Older embryos; in C and D the inferior and superior octants respectively have been cut parallel to the transverse wall; in E, the section is a longitudinal median one; i.e. it is cut parallel to the axes of the archegonium and the prothallus; C shows that the first leaf is derived from both octants; the root initial can be seen in one of the posterior octants; in E the first leaf, the shoot apex, the first root and the foot are distinguishable. F, A still older embryo in longitudinal median section. G, *Scolopendrium vulgare*, longitudinal median section of embryo, showing the obliquity of the first partition walls in the anterior octants, no 'epibasal disc' being formed; I–I, first or basal wall; II–II, second or median wall; III–III, third or transverse wall; *l*, leaf; *s*, shoot apex, *r*, root; *f*, foot. (After M. A. Vladesco, *Rev. Gén. Bot.*, 1935.)

of the archegonium and of the prothallus; it is described as the *median wall*. The embryo now consists of *quadrants*; these can be seen in plan by looking down on the under surface of the prothallus. The third wall is a transverse one, i.e. it is perpendicular to the archegonial axis and to the first two walls. The embryo now consists of *octants*. These initial divisions, and those which follow, usually take place in a very regular manner; indeed, they are in close agreement with the ideal segmentation pattern that would be obtained in a sphere dividing by walls of minimal area (Fig. 3.11) (*see*

D'Arcy Thompson, 1917, 1942; Thomson and Hall, 1933). The positions of the walls are not determined by external factors such as light or gravity but by factors within the zygote or adjacent prothallial tissue. Vladesco (1935) held that, with occasional exceptions, the sequence in wall formation described above is general in leptosporangiate ferns.

Leptosporangiate fern embryos have no suspensor. At the first division of the zygote, however, as in *Pteris serratula* (Fig. 3.13), the epibasal segment may be slightly smaller than the other; but in *Marsilea*, the hypobasal segment is the smaller. Vladesco (1935) stated that the epibasal segment is usually the smaller. If we regard the approximately spherical zygote as a reaction system this unequal division would be indicative of cytoplasmic or metabolic differences, probably both, at the anterior and posterior poles. Longitudinal sections of the embryo of *Gymnogramme* at the octant stage, in the plane of the transverse walls, show that it is ovoid and elongated along its polar axis, Fig. 3.14 (Vladesco, 1935).

Now, in the small sphere of meristematic cells illustrated in Fig. 3.14, it is apparent that a considerable amount of biochemical or physiological differentiation must already have taken place; for the several quadrant regions – which can be indicated as the anterior-superior, the anterior-inferior, the posterior-superior, and the posterior-inferior quadrants – soon develop into (1) the shoot apex, (2) the first leaf, (3) the root and (4) the foot, respectively. In short, the main organographic regions are determined at an early stage.

The earlier investigators of cryptogams tried to relate the formation of the several organs to the individual quadrants in a more or less precise manner. A more critical scrutiny of the facts of the embryonic development, however, showed that such views are untenable (Vladesco, 1935). That individual quadrants do give rise to particular organs is not in question, but there is no close and obligatory relationship between the segmentation pattern and organ formation. Although the orientation of the walls during the division of the octants is such as to define what appear to be 'three-sided' apical cells, these do not, in fact, function as the apical cells of the leaf and shoot. Indeed, the delineation of the so-called epibasal and hypobasal discs is by no means constant: it is not found in *Scolopendrium vulgare*. The first leaf, as in *Gymnogramme sulphurea* (Vladesco, 1935), and many other ferns, originates equally from both of the anterior-inferior octants: it does not begin from the three-sided cell in one of the octants, with a concomitant suppression of the other. However, the root apex, which is formed early in embryogenesis, originates from a single octant in relation to the normal pattern of segmentation. The shoot apex, like the leaf, is not formed by the growth of the three-sided cell in one of the anterior-superior octants, as had been generally thought: the apical

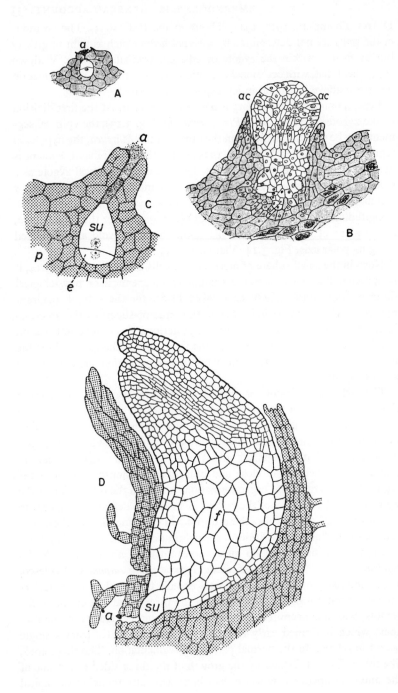

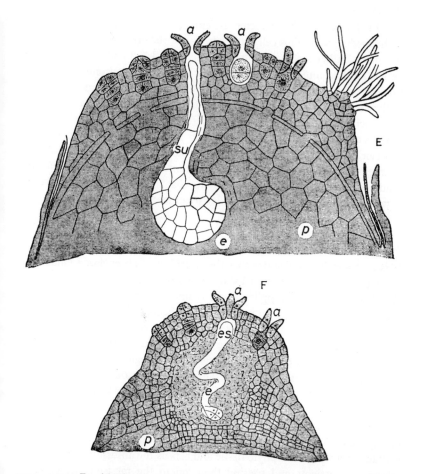

FIG. 3.15. Pteridophyte embryos. A, B, *Tmesipteris tannensis* (×50).
A, transverse section of prothallus, showing archegonium (*a*) and the newly
divided zygote in l.s. The embryology is exoscopic, the epibasal (outer)
segment developing into the shoot and the hypobasal segment into the foot.
B, an older, leafless, rootless embryo which is about to dichotomize; two
apical cells (*ac*) can be distinguished. C, *Lycopodium clavatum* (×150). The
embryology is endoscopic, with the large suspensor cell (*su*) towards the neck
of the archegonium (*a*); epibasal segment (*e*); prothallus (*p*). D, *Lycopodium
selago* (×96). The enlarged endoscopic embryo, with its considerable foot
(*f*) has burst out of the prothallial tissue. E, *Selaginella poulteri* (×225).
The endoscopic embryo, with its long suspensor (*su*) is deeply embedded in
the prothallial tissue (*p*). F, *Selaginella galeottii* (×150). The embryo (*e*) in
this species develops deeply within the digested prothallial tissue (*p*) at the
base of an elongated embryo-tube (*es*). (A, B, after J. E. Hollway, *Trans.
New Zealand Inst.*, 1921. C, D, after H. Bruchmann, *Flora*, 1910. E, F, after
H. Bruchmann, *Flora* 1909–13.)

initial is formed by the characteristic enlargement of one of the cells close to the median wall. This cell may be in one or the other of the two octants. It remains rather inconspicuous until the second leaf and the second root initials are becoming differentiated. The initial of the second leaf, which Vladesco considered to be independent of the shoot apex, and to pertain to the embryonic tissue mass, may occur in the same octant as the shoot apical cell, or in the other anterior-superior octant. The foot, which soon consists of enlarged vacuolated cells, does not only include the posterior-superior quadrant but may also comprise some of the tissue derived from segments of the anterior-superior quadrant, as in *Pteridium aquilinum*. Vladesco summarized the facts by saying that the octants as such have no organogenic significance. (For a fuller treatment *see* Wardlaw, 1955.)

POSITION AND NUTRITION

It is a reasonable conjecture that the nutrition of an enclosed embryo is more or less closely affected by its position in the gametophyte tissue. Gradients of nutrient supplies to the ovum or zygote may be among the factors which determine its polarity. In archegoniate and seed plants the visual evidence supports the view that, from an early stage, nutrients are not absorbed over the entire surface of the embryo but are taken up by the basal region and passed on to the distal growing region, i.e. as in the adult shoot. Even in filamentous algae there are indications of the acropetal translocation of the materials used in the distal region of active growth and morphogenesis.

In bryophytes and in *Psilotum*, *Tmesipteris* and *Equisetum*, where the embryogeny is exoscopic (Fig. 3.15), the hypobasal region remains in contact with the gametophyte tissue and acts as the absorptive foot region, taking up nutrients and passing them on to the meristematic epibasal region. Indeed, we should not expect the epibasal cell, which lies in contiguity with the archegonium neck and will soon emerge from the gametophyte tissue, to be a major absorptive region. These concepts seem to be in conformity with our knowledge of axial growth. Nevertheless, it is doubtful if such reasoning, based on a consideration of the anatomical data, goes to the root of the matter. In species with endoscopic embryos, e.g. *Lycopodium*, *Selaginella*, etc., the suspensor and the nutrient-absorbing foot are in contiguity with the archegonium neck and the embryo grows inwards and becomes deeply embedded in the fleshy tissue of the prothallus (Fig. 3.15). So we may ask: do these embedded embryos absorb nutrients over their entire surface, or is the uptake mainly confined to the foot? While the embryo is still very small, it may be that nutrients are absorbed over the whole of its surface; but, as it enlarges, the indications

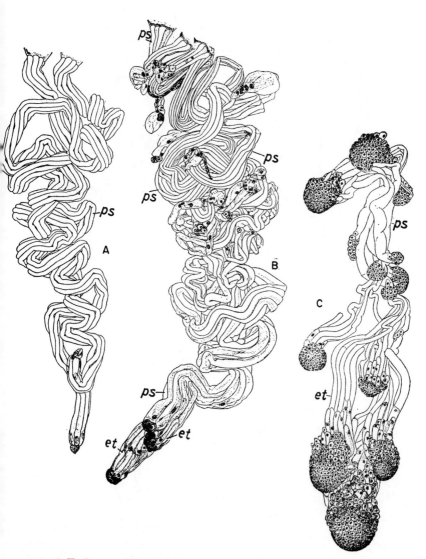

FIG. 3.16. Embryos of Podocarpaceae. A, B, *Podocarpus urbanii*. A, Two
embryo systems with prosuspensors (*ps*) bearing two and three binucleate
cells. B, Three embryo systems, the longest with three embryos developing
massive secondary suspensors from embryonal tubes (*et*); many small
embryos are present at the ends of prosuspensor cells (×45). C, *Torreya
californica*. Complex embryo system dissected from a fully enlarged ovule;
ps, prosuspensor cells; *et*, embryonal tubes, giving rise to suspensors (×37).
(A, B, after J. T. Buchholz, *Bot. Gaz.*, 1941; C, after J. T. Buchholz,
Bull. Torrey Bot. Club, 1940.)

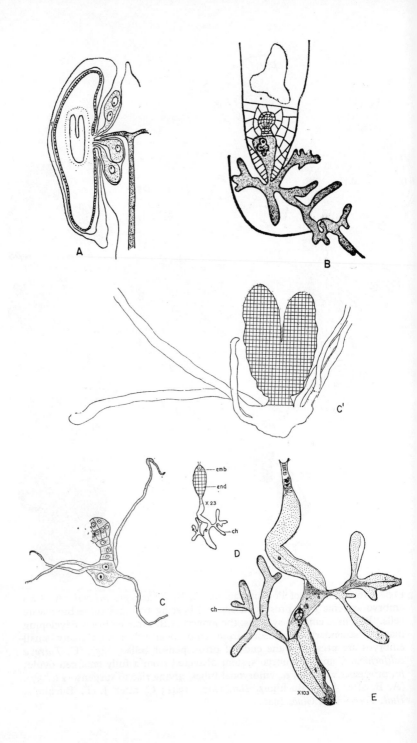

emb
end
X 23
ch
D
ch
X 103
E

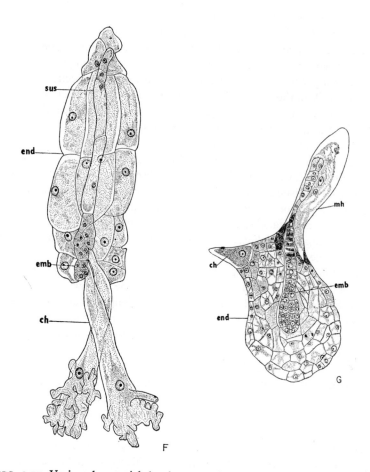

FIG. 3.17. Various haustorial developments in the embryology of flowering plants. A, *Plantago lanceolata* (×180). L.s. of seed, showing embryo and conspicuous endosperm haustoria (after G. O. Cooper, *Amer. Jour. Bot.*, 1942). B, *Sedum acre*. Apical region of the ovule, showing the embryo with its suspensor which has developed as a long, branched haustorial organ (after J. Mauritzon, Diss. Lund, 1933). C, C', *Dicraea stylosa*. Globular and older embryos with long haustorial outgrowths of the suspensor (after A. J. Muk-kada, *Plant Embryology*, 1962). D, E, *Cajophora sylvestris*. Dissected whole mounts. D, the embryo (*emb*), the endosperm (*end*) and highly developed chalazal haustorium (*ch*). E, the chalazal haustorium magnified (after V. Garcia, *Plant Embryology*, 1962). F, *Exocarpus sparteus*. An elongated em-bryo (*emb*), with its suspensor (*sus*) and associated endosperm (*end*). Large chalazal haustoria (*ch*) have been formed (after M. Ram, *Phytomorph.*, 1959). G, *Barleria cristata*. Endosperm with micropylar (*mh*) and chalazal (*ch*) haustoria; *emb*, embryo; *end*, endosperm. The central chamber has been completely transformed into cellular endosperm (after Mohan Ram, *Jour. Ind. Bot. Soc.*, 1962).

are that the foot is the main absorptive region. In the embryos of some species, e.g. *Selaginella* spp. (Fig. 3.15), the distal or apical region appears to secrete enzymes which digest the tissue of the gametophyte. Certainly, from an early stage, there is a marked difference in the respective developments of cells in the basal and apical regions. The cells of the foot become considerably, sometimes greatly, distended and vacuolated; they may extend what appear to be suctorial processes into the tissue of the prothallus; they may contain deposits of starch grains. In such embryos a gradient of cell-size from the proximal to the distal region is a characteristic feature. Collectively, the foregoing observations indicate that the relation of the distal to the basal region of the axis, which we perceive in a normal adult shoot, is established very early in ontogenesis. A growing body of experimental evidence supports the view that the shoot apex is a self-determining, morphogenetic region: this relationship is established at an early stage in the embryogeny. (*See also* Fig. 3.3, p. 29.)

On the further growth of an endoscopic embryo, the apex emerges from the prothallus, but the foot continues for some time to draw upon the prothallus for nutrients. At this stage there can no longer be any question of the nutrients being absorbed over the whole embryonic surface. In this development we probably see what is no more than the continuation of a system established at a much earlier stage.

The position of the embryo relative to the nutritional resources of the contiguous maternal tissues is a very wide, varied and important topic. As we have seen, the characteristic development of the embryo in leptosporangiate ferns appears to be closely related to the disposition of the archegonium and the physical gradients present in the gametophyte. An extensive list, based on quite different phyletic lines, of curious and unexpected developments in embryos that are evidently related to nutritional factors, could readily be prepared. Thus, in different species of *Lycopodium* more or less considerable parenchymatous developments are present in different regions of the embryo. In *L. clavatum* the foot is greatly enlarged, whereas in *L. cernuum* the shoot region becomes greatly distended into a bulbous, starch-filled tissue, sometimes described as a protocorm. In different *Selaginella* species, also, the foot region may show more or less considerable enlargements. However, in this genus, with its *endoscopic* embryogeny, the most remarkable developments are to be seen in the suspensor. In *S. poulteri*, for example, a rapidly elongating suspensor thrusts the embryo proper well down into the nutrient-providing tissue of the gametophyte (Fig. 3.15). In *S. galeottii* the archegonial cavity elongates into a long tube (*Embryoschlauch*) which penetrates deeply into the prothallus. The embryo, which is slow to develop, can be seen at the inner end of this tube as a small gemma-like body, with only a few segmentations.

Meanwhile, rapid digestion has been induced in the cells of the gameto-phyte adjacent to the embryonic tube (Fig. 3.15). The gymnosperms are remarkable not only for the polyembryony which characterizes the group as a whole but also for the quite extraordinary extent of the suspensor development in some species (Fig. 3.16). Here, quite evidently, the special morphogenetic developments are in some way related to the very con-siderable nutritional resources in both the gametophytic and sporophytic tissues in which the elongating filamentous embryos are growing. The flowering plants afford many examples of embryos of almost 'standardized' configuration, in which the embryo obtains its nutrition from an endo-sperm that is progressively digested. This 'normal' embryonic develop-ment is in itself a sufficiently complex and intriguing process. However, a wider survey reveals some truly extraordinary embryonic developments, these being again closely related to the problems of nutrition. For example, the embryo in some species develops a more or less extensive, and some-times complex, haustorium, or haustorial appendage, which may range deeply into the nucellar tissue. In the embryogeny of other species there are also more or less complex haustorial developments; but, in them, it is the embryo sac, or the endosperm, from which the proliferating organ is formed (Fig. 3.17) (*see* Maheshwari 1950, 1962, 1963).

Additional Note on Polarity. In two valuable studies of polarity, S. Nakazawa (*Protoplasma*, 52, 274–294, 1960; *Sci. Repts. Univ. Tôhoku*, Biol., 27, 57–92, 1961) substantially supports Bünning's (1957) view that polarity is due to an orderly arrangement of polar molecules, all orientated statistically in the same direction, and spirally disposed in the outer cytoplasm (or cortex) – a region not readily moveable by centrifugation, etc. The inception and functional properties of morphogenetic fields, e.g. associated with organ sites, are attributed to such polarity. However, these ideas of a regular molecular structure in the cortical cytoplasm have yet to be validated.

CHAPTER IV

Experimental Embryology

The experimental approach to the phenomena of embryogenesis in plants and to cognate problems of regeneration from single, or small groups of, cells is now rapidly gaining momentum. In fact, recent years have seen a very brisk outturn of new work, suggesting fascinating opportunities for further research.

EMBRYO CULTURE

Consideration of the development of embryos *in situ* leads on naturally to cognate studies of the behaviour of excised embryos in culture. From modest beginnings, and greatly helped by progress in the aseptic culture of tissues in media of known composition, the literature of embryo culture is now growing rapidly (for reviews, *see* Wardlaw, 1955, 1965a, b; Maheshwari, 1950a, b; 1952, 1962a, b; 1963; Maheshwari and Ranga Swami, 1963). Justice cannot be done to this important topic in the limited space available here. Accordingly, the writer has had to select a few aspects of special importance in morphogenesis. Maheshwari (1950a, b) summarized the literature on embryo culture from its inception at the hands of Hannig in 1904. In the following statements an attempt has been made to indicate some of the principal results to date.

1. Fairly-well-developed embryos, e.g. of species of Cruciferae, etc., if excised from the embryo-sac at the 'heart-shaped stage' and older, can be readily grown in aseptic culture to fully developed normal embryos, in media containing sugars, mineral salts, amino acids, plant extracts and gelatin or agar. Instances are known in which some of the 'stages' in the normal embryonic development may be eliminated; in other instances there may be modifications of the normal ontogenesis, indicating that nutritional factors have a direct effect on the normal course of embryogenesis. In Tukey's (1937) experiments on excised embryos of deciduous fruits he observed that the younger embryos were taken into culture, the more abnormal were their morphogenetic developments.

2. Partly developed embryos, excised from the shrunken seeds obtained from certain interspecific crosses, and often regarded as being abortive or

non-viable, can be successfully cultured to maturity and eventually grown into large adult plants, e.g. early aborting *Prunus* hybrids. This result is of considerable practical importance in genetics and horticulture, in that this procedure enables potentially valuable and specially interesting hybrids to be reared.

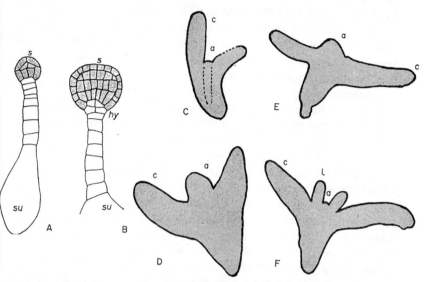

FIG. 4.I. *Capsella, in vitro* culture of young embryos. A, B, indication of stage of development at which embryos were dissected out and cultured. C–F, longitudinal sections of early heart-shaped embryos after having been grown for different periods in culture. C, An embryo after 3 weeks in culture in the dark: *a* shoot apex. The root apex is not visible in the plane of sectioning. *c*, cotyledon. D, A light-grown culture of comparable age. The shoot meristem (*a*) is prominent. E, Section of embryo after 5 weeks in the dark. Sections showed a lack of cytohistological zonation pattern in the apical meristem. F, A light-grown embryo 5 weeks old showing the formation of the first pair of leaves. (A, B, after Souèges; C–F, redrawn diagrammatically from photographic illustrations of V. Raghavan and J. C. Torrey, *Amer. Journ. Bot.*, 1963.)

3. In aborting hybrid embryos, but also in embryos in general, a critical operation is to ensure the growth *in vitro* of very young embryos, i.e. pro-embryos, in which the embryo proper is still at the relatively small spherical or globular stage. For many years this cultural operation defeated plant embryologists. Recently, however, Raghavan and Torrey (1964) have shown that young globular embryos of *Capsella bursa-pastoris* can be induced to continue their normal growth and differentiation *in vitro*, in media containing a combination of IAA, kinetin and adenine sulphate

(Fig. 4.1). In this medium early heart-shaped embryos showed root inhibition when grown in a 12 hours light/12 hours dark cycle, whereas, in dark-grown embryos, roots were actively developed. With globular embryos the effects of the added growth factors on growth and morphogenesis could be partly replaced by using high concentrations of sucrose, i.e. 12–18 per cent, in the medium. (These observations may also have relevance to older shoot apices, in that there may be variations or fluctuations, either short-term during active growth or long-term in relation to seasonal factors, in the supplies of IAA, kinetin, adenine, sugars, etc., to the organogenic region (*see* p. 203).)

4. Impetus was given to the study of embryo culture by van Overbeek, Conklin and Blakeslee (1941, 1942), and by van Overbeek (1942), when they showed that whereas mature embryos of *Datura stramonium* are self-sufficient in respect of growth factors and can readily be grown on simple media into seedlings, very small excised embryos require growth factors, those present in coconut milk being very effective. Excised embryos, only slightly beyond the proembryo stage, remained embryonic in the presence of coconut milk in the dark for at least 10 days; and root growth was suppressed. When the 'embryo factor' extracted from coconut milk was added to a somewhat complex medium (containing agar, minerals, dextrose, vitamins B_1, B_6, C_1, pantothenic, nicotinic and succinic acids, adenine and glycine), very small embryos increased in volume up to 500 times and even to 3,500 times in the course of a week. In the control cultures embryos were placed in the same medium but lacking the 'embryo factor'. They did not grow, though some developed into undifferentiated callus-like bodies. In general, hormonal and other regulating or 'morphogenetic' substances, such as those present in coconut milk, have now been shown to be important in promoting growth and organogenic development in many embryo and tissue cultures (*see* Wardlaw, 1965a, b, for résumé; and *see* p. 195 *et seq.*).

5. According to the concentration of IAA supplied, differences can be induced in the relative rates of growth in the hypocotyl and cotyledons of embryos, and there is sometimes inhibition of root formation (Rietsema, Satina and Blakeslee, 1953) (Fig. 4.2). In studies of 'heart-shaped' *Capsella* embryos in culture, Raghaven and Torrey (1963, 1964) showed that there is a general increase in the growth of the hypocotyl and shoot system at low concentrations of IAA, especially under 'light-grown' conditions. Gibberellic acid (GA) is more effective in promoting *Capsella* embryo root growth than IAA, but it inhibited the growth of embryonic leaves. Also, the characteristic effects of GA on shoot and leaf development reported by other workers were not observed. However, Brown and Gifford (1958) had already noted similar effects of GA on pine embryos. Miller (1961)

found that kinetin tends to accentuate, or promote, shoot and bud initiation but inhibits root growth. Similar results were obtained with *Capsella* embryos. Adenine sulphate made for premature leaf expansion and inhibited root growth.

6. From the work so far published it appears that in embryo growth there is a sequence of chemical phases which determine the normal course of organogenesis and differentiation. At each successive phase there are syntheses, to critical physiological concentrations and as part of a regulated

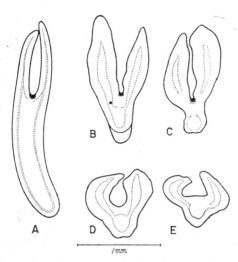

FIG. 4.2. *Datura stramonium.* Cultured embryos, after 9 days, showing the effects of 1 mg./l. of IAA in the medium. A, control. B–E, Embryos variously modified by IAA in medium. (After J. B. Rietsema, S. Satina and A. F. Blakeslee, *Proc. Nat. Acad. Sci., Washington,* 1953.)

system, of various enzymes, other proteins, hormonal substances, general metabolites, etc. But it is still an open question if any single substance is *uniquely*, rather than necessarily, involved in any particular organogenic development; i.e. the reaction system is a flexible one, of many components, in which the concentrations of major metabolites may vary in different circumstances, with different organogenic results (Veen, 1961, 1962, 1963; Rietsema, Satina and Blakeslee, 1953).

7. Sugar concentrations have marked effects on embryo growth and organogenesis, and so also have amino acids and other nitrogenous metabolites (Rijven, 1952; Rietsema, Satina and Blakeslee, 1953). The results of the relevant investigations indicate the complexity of the developmental situations. For example, many amino acids, known to be present in plant tissues, actually inhibit growth; and there have been other unexpected

C

observations. Sanders and Burkholder (1948) reported that excised *Datura* embryos can be grown to healthy seedlings on nutrients containing only inorganic salts and sucrose. Development was slower in culture than in the seed, and premature differentiation of roots and shoots occurred (Wardlaw 1965b, for review).

8. Various organic compounds stimulate embryo growth and retard premature differentiation. When casein hydrolysate with cysteine and tryptophane, mixtures of amino acids or single amino acids, were added to nutrient solutions for embryos ($\pm$0·2 mm. in length) of *Datura innoxia* and *D. stramonium*, the best growth was obtained with casein hydrolysate *plus* cysteine and tryptophane, and with a mixture of amino acids approximating to the composition of casein hydrolysate. The results indicated interactions between the acids in their effect upon embryo growth; some are stimulatory, others inhibitory. Moreover, the embryos of the two species responded differently to individual amino acids. In *Capsella*, Rijven (1952) found that some amino acids, e.g. tryosine and glycine, are unsuitable as nitrogen sources in culture. Although glutamine, apparently the prevailing amide in the seedlings of *Brassica* spp., supported good growth, Rijven thought that there may be yet other amino acids, or related compounds, that promote embryonic growth. In this general context Steward and his co-workers (*see* Bibliography) stated that there were still some twenty unidentified substances in this category. The failure of asparagine, a homologous compound, to promote growth in *Capsella* embryos is perhaps surprising when one recalls the importance of this substance in protein synthesis in various Leguminosae. Also, while protein synthesis can proceed from glutamine, even in very young embryos, experimental studies have shown that asparagine may actually be inhibitory in its action (Rijven, 1952).

9. Several substances are now known which affect the number of cotyledons formed by an embryo. In some species, e.g. in *Pinus* spp., the number of cotyledons (from 6 to 16) is related to the actual size, or bulk, of the embryo apex, i.e. to its general nutritional status. In other species the presence of some particular metabolite in the culture medium may result in polycotyledony; in yet other instances the ontogenetic pattern, sometimes including an increase in the number of cotyledons, may be modified by particular substances. (*See* below, and Wardlaw, 1955, 1965a, b, for review.)

EFFECTS OF VARIOUS CHEMICAL TREATMENTS *in ovulo* AND RELATED PHENOMENA

The embryos of *Eranthis hiemalis* and of some other Ranunculaceae do not become fully differentiated in the ovule, i.e. they do not develop fully until after seed maturation. Accordingly, they afford useful experimental materials, e.g. for studying the effects of injecting special substances into the embryo sac. Haccius (1955 *et seq.*) has described some very interesting modifications of the embryogenesis induced in this way. For example, when solutions of lithium carbonate (0·06–0·25% Li_2CO_3) were injected into *Eranthis* ovules, with club-shaped embryos, various anomalous developments, and, in particular, a curious, one-sided syncotyly, resulted. The injection or other application of 2,4-dichlorophenoxyacetic acid

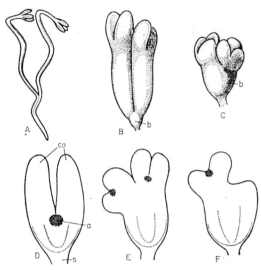

FIG. 4.3. *Eranthis hiemalis.* Various effects induced in young embryos by treatment with 0·1 per cent 2,4-dichlorophenoxyacetic acid. A, twin seedlings; B, C, twin embryos removed in September and towards the end of June (×110 and ×220 resp.); D, E, F, longitudinal sections showing common basal region (*b*) as in C; *a*, shoot apex, *co*, cotyledons. (After B. Haccius, *Nature*, 1955.)

(2,4-D), phenylboric acid (PB) and other substances, again into *Eranthis* ovules prior to cotyledon formation, resulted in departures from the normal course of embryogenesis (Fig. 4.3). Some of the techniques used were simple: freshly collected seeds were submerged for 12–14 hours in solutions of the active substances, or the seeds were planted out in flowerpots in groups of a hundred each and 50 ml. of solution applied. Embryos with more than two cotyledons and other anomalous features were observed (Fig. 4.3). Syncotyly, in various degrees, was frequently obtained after treatment of young, club-shaped embryos with 2,4-D (Haccius, 1955a; Haccius and Trompeter, 1960). A solution of 2,4-D, of 0·1 per cent caused almost 100 per cent cotyledon anomalies (syncotyly and pleiocotyly of all degrees); in untreated material there was only 0·37 per cent. Some twinning was also induced, the twins being typically fused at the base in varying degrees, and there were frequent cotyledon anomalies (Fig. 4.3). Anatomical studies indicated that twin embryos had probably originated from pear-shaped young embryos by regenerative growth. Where normally two primordial cotyledons would be expected, occasional embryos with three cotyledons each were observed (Fig. 4.3).

Haccius (1955a) considered that the still undifferentiated embryo of *Eranthis* already manifests apical dominance. The group of cells out of which the shoot apex will later be organized inhibits the formation of further apices. When these apical cells of the pear-shaped embryo are damaged by the action of synthetic growth substances their regulative influence disappears; and cells from which the cotyledons would normally originate become organized as new shoot apices.

Caujolle and Bergal (1949, 1950a, b) showed that phenylboric acid solutions have regulative effects on seed development and seedlings in various species of dicotyledons. By soaking May ovules (seeds) of *Eranthis* in solutions of phenylboric acid ranging from 150 to 2,500 mg./l., Haccius (1959a, 1960) demonstrated that PB exercises regulative morphogenetic effects on the undifferentiated young embryo. More than half of the treated seeds contained embryos with only a single cotyledon, the next visible primordium being that of a foliage leaf. Others were acotyledonous, the first primordia being those of foliage leaves, and yet others showed anisocotyly. Mention may here be made of work by Pellegrini (1957) in which embryos and seedlings of *Dianthus caryophyllus* were observed with one to three cotyledons. Pellegrini related these developments to the presence of a peripheral ring of meristematic tissue at the nascent apex of the club-shaped embryo. In different instances one or more active growth centres developed, yielding the cotyledons as described (*see* p. 122).

Maleic hydrazide is known to inhibit cell division at low concentrations and to restrict both cell division and elongation at higher ones; it may also cause a collapse of the phloem and lead to enlargement and extensive vacuolation in meristematic cells. When it was applied, at concentrations from 0·030 to 0·750 per cent, to developing embryos of *Avena sativa*, by hand-spraying the flowering panicles 3–4 days after fertilization, the embryogenesis was affected over the whole of this range, but especially at the higher concentrations (Mericle *et al.*, 1955). At the lower concentrations fewer cells were formed and maturation was precocious. At the higher concentrations, and in relation to the size of the embryo at the time of treatment, the normal course of embryogenesis was more or less seriously modified or disrupted, young embryos being most affected. Embryos at an intermediate stage did not form fully differentiated functional roots, or suffered from early root abortion.

In young embryos of *Eranthis hiemalis*, Haccius (1957a, b, 1959a, b) reported the effects of treatments with 0·1 per cent maleic hydrazide (MH) and 0·2 per cent isopropyl-N-phenylcarbamate (IPC) – sometimes described as antimitotic substances. When ovules, with their club-shaped embryos, were treated at the beginning of May, various regenerative and anomalous developments were noted (Fig. 4.4). The cells of the young

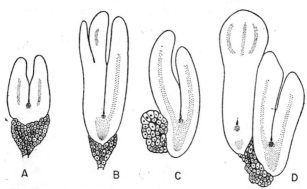

FIG. 4.4. *Eranthis hiemalis.* Embryos, treated in May with maleic hydrazide, as seen in November: these have all shown a characteristic regeneration from the more basal tissue of the young embryo. A and C, dicotyledonous embryos; B, a tricotyledonous embryo; D, twin embryos. (After B. Haccius, *Beitr. Biol. Pflanz.*, 1957.)

embryos became conspicuously enlarged and rounded, and showed signs of degeneration and anomalous nuclear behaviour, e.g. fragmentation, enlargement and a multinucleate condition in cells. However, by July and August more than 70 per cent. of the embryos exhibited regenerative activity in the basal region, with cell division and eventually the growth and organization of new embryos. Some of these were normally dicotyledonous, but others had cotyledons of unequal size. Also, some embryos were tricotyledonous, and twin embryos were sometimes formed (Fig. 4.4). In older treated embryos, i.e. with nascent cotyledons, further development was irreversibly blocked.

When excised ovaries of *Phlox drummondii* were grown in a suitable culture medium, with and without the addition of 0·15 per cent colchicine, Anantaswamy Rau (1956; and see also Miller and Wetmore, 1945) noted that nuclear changes had been induced in the young embryo and endosperm. Individual cells of the embryo exhibited hypertrophy, irregular mitosis and a nodular organization. Ovaries left on the colchicine medium for 12–14 days had considerably malformed seeds with abortive embryos within. The general pattern of the embryo development, however, was not altered by the growth of the ovary in artificial media. Haccius (1957a) also reported that incompletely formed embryos of *Eranthis hiemalis in ovulo* yielded evidence of regeneration after colchicine treatment.

EMBRYO TRANSPLANTS AND CROSSABILITY

Michurin, the Russian plant-breeder, used an embryo-grafting technique – described as 'vegetative approximation' – to facilitate certain difficult sexual crosses. Earlier workers in this field had excised embryos of various Gramineae and successfully implanted them in the endosperm of species of other genera. For example, it was found that *Triticum vulgare* embryos grew better when implanted in the endosperm of *Secale cereale* than when implanted in those of *Triticum durum* and *T. turgidum* (see Wardlaw, 1965a). An investigation by Hall (1954, 1956), undertaken primarily to verify some Russian claims, may be briefly noted here. Pissarev and Vinogradova (1944) reported increases in the crossability of wheat and rye by transplantation of wheat embryos to rye endosperm. Hall repeated this work on an extensive scale and, in his largest experiment, obtained 400 hybrid kernels from 2,897 pollinations with rye when he used wheat plants raised from embryos which had been transplanted to rye endosperm, as compared with only 75 hybrid kernels from 2,813 similar pollinations of wheat plants, raised from wheat embryo/wheat endosperm transplants. Also sixty plants of the wheat/wheat group, when pollinated with rye, were entirely without kernel, while only twenty-eight of the wheat/rye group showed this condition. It thus appears that the rye endosperm from which the young wheat seedling had drawn its nutrients had an important effect on the subsequent capacity of the plant to intercross with rye, i.e. some subtle metabolic change had been induced. Hall (1956) also found that the endosperm of a Chinese wheat – which is known to offer virtually no crossing barrier to rye – behaved like rye endosperm as indicated above. It would be interesting to know how specific are the effects of the kind described above.

Although we know that genetical systems have very considerable stability, it now appears that the reaction system in the young embryos of some species can be changed in subtle but important ways. The relevant biochemistry, however, is still not known and may, indeed, be exceedingly difficult to discover.

POLYEMBRYONY

Polyembryony, connoting the presence of more than one embryo in the embryo sac, affords a rich and varied field for the study of morphogenesis. This phenomenon may, indeed, be regarded as affording a link between normal embryogenesis, the formation of buds on shoots and leaves, and

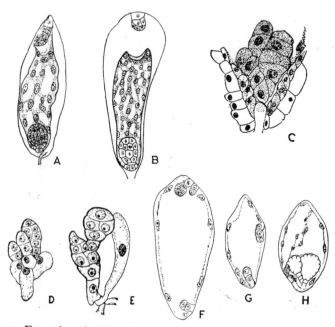

FIG. 4.5. Examples of polyembryony. A, B, *Ulmus americana*. Normal and antipodal embryos (after Shattuck). C, *Erythronium americanum*. Proliferation of embryonic mass with formation of several embryos (after Jeffrey). D, E, *Eulophea epidendraea*. D, The zygote has formed a group of cells, three of which have given rise to independent embryos. E, A bud has been formed on the right-hand side of the embryo (after Swamy). F, *Elatostema sinuatum eusinuatum*. A zygotic embryo and three antipodal embryos (one undergoing its first division). G, *Elatostema eurhynchum*. Zygotic and lateral embryos. H, *Elatostema acuminatum*. Compound embryo-sac formed by the fusion of two embryo-sacs; that on the right has two well-developed embryos; that on the left has two small embryos (F–H, after Fagerlind). (From C. W. Wardlaw, *Embryogenesis in Plants*, 1955.)

the induction of buds, single or multiple, in tissue cultures. Thus, in the flowering plants polyembryony may result from: (*a*) cleavage of the ovum; (*b*) the formation of additional embryos from the synergids or the antipodals; or (*c*) localized activation of cells of the nucellus or integuments.

Some examples are illustrated in Figs. 4.5, 4.6 (for a review of the literature, *see* Maheshwari and Sachar, 1963). The gymnosperms also afford numerous examples of polyembryony as a feature of the normal development (*see* Fig. 3.16).

Each of the several kinds of polyembryony in angiosperms raises its own problem of causality. In reviewing this aspect, Maheshwari and Sachar

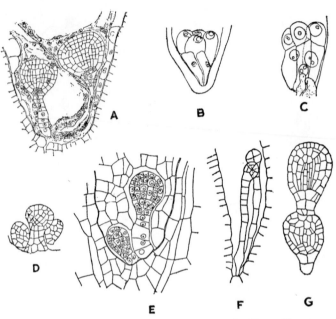

FIG. 4.6. Further examples of polyembryony. A, *Potentilla aurea* (after Lebègue). B, *Crepis capillaris* (after Gerassimova). C, *Sagittaria graminea* (after Johri). D, *Spathiphyllum patinii* (after Schurhoff). E, *Bergenia delavayi* (after Lebègue). F, *Arabis lyalli* (after Lebègue). G, *Lobelia syphilitica* (after Crété). (From C. W. Wardlaw, *Embryogenesis in Plants*, 1955.)

(1963) have referred to the several theories so far advanced, but still insufficiently validated. In different instances polyembryony has been ascribed to hybridization, the effect of particular genes, e.g. recessive genes, the presence of 'necrohormones' released from dying cells, which stimulate cell division, as in the formation of nucellar embryos and so on. In various experimental treatments of ovules the results to date have been largely negative; but some positive results have also been obtained (*see* Maheshwari and Sachar, 1963, for details). Some observations of special interest may be cited here. Fagerlind (1946) applied 1·0 per cent IAA in lanolin paste to the pistils of *Hosta* and induced adventive embryos. As the endosperm was not formed, the embryos did not develop further. This indicates that, in some species, adventive embryos can be induced by chemical treatment. When Rangaswamy (1958, 1959) cultured the nucellus tissue of *Citrus microcarpa* on Nitsch's medium with casein hydrolysate he induced tissue masses, or groups of 'pseudo-bulbils', which gave rise to normal seedlings – a valuable method for obtaining genetically uniform, i.e. clonal, plantlings in abundance (Maheshwari and Rangaswamy, 1958; *see also* Sabharwal, 1962, who found that in *C. aurantifolius* multiple embryos were *not* directly of nucellar origin but were formed as proliferations of proembryos of adventive origin). By devising appropriate culture media, Johri and Sehgal (1963) were able to induce polyembryony in excised ovaries of *Anethum graveolens*. By culturing excised proembryos on White's medium with casein hydrolysate, Maheshwari and Baldev (1962) induced polyembryony in *Cuscuta reflexa*; and Johri and Bajaj (1963) obtained similar results with *Dendrophthoe falcata*.

INTERLUDE: ON INTERPRETATION IN EMBRYOGENESIS

Let serious students (and others) relax and enjoy this section! Investigators of flowering plant and gymnosperm embryology have now seen so many strange and unexpected developments that virtually anything seems possible! The phase of free nuclear division, after fertilization, that is characteristic of many gymnosperms, is typically not present in the angiosperms. However, in 1957 Yakolev and Yoffe described what they regarded as a phase of free nuclear division, i.e. with no wall formation, following the fertilization of the ovum in *Paeonia*. This unique observation commanded a considerable amount of attention. In the coenocytic unit thus formed the nuclei were disposed round the inside of the wall, the central region consisting of a large vacuole. Wall formation took place later, and certain peripheral cells, of special meristematic activity, gave rise to embryo primordia. The close resemblance of the peony embryogeny, thus described, with developments in such gymnosperms as *Ginkgo* was, of course, noticed and regarded as being of phylogenetic significance. Cave *et al.* (1961) published confirmatory evidence relating to *P. californica* and *P. brownii*; and Yakolev and Yoffe (1961) reiterated their confidence in their earlier observations, emphasizing the importance of the phylogenetic inferences. However, in a close and critical study of the post-fertilization developments in six species of *Paeonia*, Murgai (1959, 1962) demonstrated that the division of the zygote nucleus was followed by the formation of a transverse wall, as in normal angiosperm embryogenesis (Fig. 4.7). Free nuclear divisions now follow in the enlarging, basal, suspensor cell. The apical, or distal, cell divides only occasionally, or rarely. This cell appears to degenerate later, though its remnants can be seen for some time (Fig. 4.7). The embryo proper is eventually derived by meristematic activity in a region of the new basal cell complex. The mature, small embryo is dicotyledonous and surrounded by an extensive endosperm. We may yet hear more of the peculiarities of *Paeonia*!

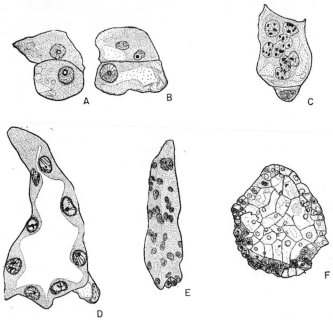

FIG. 4.7. Embryology in *Paeonia* spp. A, *Paeonia* sp., 2-celled proembryo. B, *P. actiflora*, 2-celled proembryo, the basal cell with two nuclei. C, *P. delavayi* proembryo; the basal cell has eight nuclei. D, *P. bakeri*, showing the basal cell with eight peripheral nuclei and an undivided apical cell. E, *Paeonia* sp., showing the large, multinucleate suspensor haustorium and the apical cell which has now divided. F, *P. delavayi*, cellular embryo. (After P. Murgai, in *Plant Embryology*, 1962.)

THE INVESTIGATION OF EMBRYOIDS (PSEUDO-EMBRYOS)

The terms 'embryoid', or 'pseudo-embryo', are comprehensive in their application. An embryoid is defined as an embryo-like structure which has its origin in a cell other than a zygote. Pseudo-embryos have been described from shaken tissue cultures of single cells or small cell groups. It is doubtful if the two terms can be separated in any absolute sense. In a broad sense the topics to be considered in this section pertain to the general phenomenon of regeneration; they also pertain to bud inception and development; and, not least, to the comprehensive and pervasive phenomenon of organization. Even to the least imaginative, the subject matter to be reviewed is of a most engaging interest; for we are concerned, in materials produced by experimentalists, with the potentialities and *organization of isolated single cells*, on the one hand, and the inception of the level of organization characteristic of higher plants, on the other. Between, we now have knowledge of a not inconsiderable assemblage of neo-plant-entities. (For reviews and refs. *see* Steward and Steward *et al.*, 1952 *et seq.*; Maheshwari and Sachar, 1963; Vasil, 1963; Konar and Nataraja, 1964, 1965; Wardlaw 1965a, b; Mohan Ram and Mridul Wadhi, 1965.) (*Caveat*: By the time this book is published, there will undoubtedly be much more information on this topic: we appear to be at a moment of efflorescence!)

THE INDUCTION OF PSEUDO-EMBRYOS IN CULTURE

In tissue culture investigations, the classical aims of Haberlandt (1902) have at length been achieved, namely, to grow tissues and whole plants from single cells under controlled conditions.

When Steward *et al.* (1952 *et seq.*) grew carrot phloem tissue in shaken deep culture, in a medium containing coconut milk, the inoculum tissue separated into single cells and clusters of cells. By sampling such cultures it was possible to pick out 'stages', seemingly the result of division of a single cell, which resembled the 'stages' in normal embryogenesis *in ovulo* (Fig. 4.8). Some of the more massive of these 'pseudo-embryos' were apparently developing as radially organized, multi-layered masses. When such masses were removed to a stationary medium of the same composition they developed as polarized structures, i.e. an axis, with nascent shoot and root apices. On further growth some of these bodies developed into leafy, rooted plantlings. As well as the 'pseudo-embryos', in which the segmentation pattern of young embryos was simulated, various anomalous segmenting structures were also noted (Fig. 4.8). These observations are interesting and important: by experimental procedures it has been possible to induce a developmental process, beginning with a single cell, or a small group of cells, which, at least superficially, resembles the development of the zygote *in ovulo*.

In Reinert's (1959, 1962, 1963) work, in which carrot tissue was also used – actually a tissue culture strain which had been maintained in the undifferentiated state for several years on a medium containing 7 per cent coconut milk and 10 mg./l. IAA – cultures were transferred to a completely synthetic medium of complex composition. A notable decrease in the growth rate ensued, and hard, nodule-like structures were formed on the surface of the tissue. When such cultures were transferred to an auxin-free medium, but otherwise with the same ingredients as before, there was an initial phase of considerable root formation followed by the appearance of increasing numbers of small shoots. The latter originated from densely protoplasmic single cells, with a thick membrane, usually located in or near the surface of the hard nodules. These cells divided into two, then four, and subsequently developed into larger multicellular structures. Eventually, on further development, these structures yielded a shoot apical meristem, a hypocotyl, leaves and a root. On the synthetic medium the growth of the plantlets was soon arrested; but on being transferred back to the original medium containing coconut milk and IAA, they grew

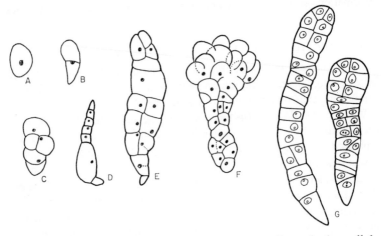

FIG. 4.8. *Daucus carota* (carrot). A–F, Embryo-like bodies and other cellular groups obtained by the culture of individual cells (from phloem tissue) in media of known composition. (After F. C. Steward *et al.*, *Amer. Jour. Botany.*) G, Normal embryos. (After H. A. Borthwick, *Bot. Gaz.*)

into robust and typical young carrot plants. In passing, it may be noted that the mode of inception of buds in Reinert's carrot-tissue cultures is not unlike bud inception in the root cortex and stem pith in *Ophioglossum vulgatum* as described by Wardlaw (1953).

These very stimulating discoveries raise their own problems. For example, what is the status of organization in isolated single cells, or in multicellular clusters, taken from a previous callus culture (*see* pp. 79, 84)? Is isolation of cells a prerequisite for pseudozygotic behaviour (*see* pp. 77, 82)? What of the establishment of polarity? Halperin and Hensen (1967) have illustrated the ultrastructure in a polarized 4-celled 'proembryo' from a carrot cell culture (Plate 4).

Further investigations have shown that the seeming 'stages' of pseudo-embryogenesis described by Steward and his co-workers call for some re-evaluation. A point of critical importance that has been urged is that the pseudo-embryos which developed into leafy plants probably did not originate from isolated single cells but from cellular aggregates: single cells kept under constant observation did not yield the successive stages of pseudo-embryogenesis. However, Kato and Takeuchi (1963) obtained plantlings from single carrot root cells (Plate 5).

In a study of single free cells of carrot (*Daucus carota*) and of *Haplopappus gracilis*, taken from suspension liquid cultures and grown on agar plates, Blakely and Steward (1964) showed: (i) that many single cells may not, or cannot, divide; (ii) that about 30 per cent of them are capable of division; and (iii) that only about 4 per cent of them can be induced to grow into viable cellular masses. Coconut milk, and the presence of other cells or tissue masses in proximity, greatly promoted this effect in carrot cells. In *Haplopappus* both naphthaleneacetic acid (NAA) and coconut milk – which are known to interact synergistically – are required for cell growth and division. From these investigations it may now be inferred that, even in the best media so far known, there are still metabolic deficiencies *vis-à-vis* the plant species under consideration. In a free cell culture it appears that there are unknown metabolic factors, produced by the cells themselves, which stimulate cell growth and proliferation (*see* below). So after many years, as a result of these and cognate investigations, we stand, perhaps, on the threshold of understanding 'what a single isolated cell requires in order that it may give rise to a colony in which differentiation may occur. This is, after all, what is so successfully accomplished by the zygote' (Blakely and Steward, 1964, p. 789).

With observation of time relationships, Blakely (1964) showed that single cells from secondary phloem carrot-root cultures can grow independently, and in complete isolation from other single cells, on an agar medium and form macroscopic colonies. The rate of growth and frequency of cell division in single cells may vary according to the species. Bergmann (1960) observed greater growth in cells of *Phaseolus vulgaris* than those reported for carrot; and Gibbs and Dougal (1963) also reported high percentages of growth and division in tobacco cells. So it appears that cultural techniques may well improve to the point where viable single cells will readily manifest totipotency. A further significant result of these studies is that isolated single cells have a considerable range of behaviour during growth in culture. They respond to what one would normally regard as stimuli of quite small magnitude. This is perhaps a lesson of some importance that we should apply to the development of cells in their normal tissue environment. Isolated single cells in culture will almost certainly yield many further surprises. Thus, Torrey (1957) and Jones et al. (1960) found that isolated cells could remain alive for several weeks, though they showed no tendency to divide; and Blakely and Steward (1964) observed that single cells on agar remained seemingly passive for about three weeks and then, unpredictably, began to divide. These are odd and thought-provoking reports.

In elongated growing carrot cells which formed tissue masses ('colonies') in culture, Blakely (1964) and Steward et al. (1964) recognized three stages:

1. There is a growth-induction phase of four or more days, and the cell prepares for division. During this phase cells become adjusted to the new culture environment and synthesis of new protein, nucleic acid, etc., may be expected; the DNA content per cell is very constant; and RNA increases to a high level just prior to the first cell division and thereafter quickly declines, under the influence of the coconut-milk stimulus, to a somewhat lower level characteristic of growing and dividing cells. (This content of RNA, however, is still greater than that in cells of the storage root.)

2. Several divisions now follow, with little or no increase in the size of the parent cell, the duration of a cell generation being as little as 24 hours.

3. These new cells enlarge to a varying extent, and division may cease temporarily; but, later, cell divisions and enlargement proceeded more or less together, and a globular colony was formed.

In these studies the authors have specially emphasized the great range in the growth forms obtained from single cells taken from the same cell suspension, and also the conspicuous differences in the development of adjacent cells in the same filament or colony; e.g. whereas some cells became greatly enlarged, others divided. Where a cell expanded and burst – a common occurrence – the adjacent cells died; and other curious and enigmatic observations were made. Evidently, the forms of cells grown in free culture are very different from those observed in coherently differentiated tissues within the plant body. Once again we see that, in the normal development, due weight must be given not only to the effects of genetical factors but also to those which become incident as a result of the organismic development and to extrinsic factors. Both of the last two contribute to the immediate environment in which a cell grows. If these investigations can ever be extended to the point where cultured free cells can be induced to conform to their normal histological development we shall be able to explain how essentially extrinsic factors modify the inherent totipotency of cells. Bonner and Huang (1962) suggested that histones are closely involved in these histological phenomena, and Jacob and Monod (1961) invoked special, but hypothetical, 'regulator' and 'operator' genes to account for them. Halperin (1966) obtained globular and heart-shaped 'pro-embryos', with 'suspensors', in wild carrot cell suspensions (Plate 3).

The nature and extent of variation in carrot (*Daucus*), *Haplopappus* and other tissues which have been held in culture for long periods is important (*see* Blakely and Steward, 1964, for discussion). Thus, whereas one strain of carrot-tissue culture grew with a compact habit, its parent strain was very friable. Also, in the former, the arrangement of dividing cells was quite different from that in the parent strain. By changing the medium, *Haplopappus* cultures were reversibly altered in their pigmentation and form; and conspicuous changes in their nitrogen metabolism were recorded in response to metabolic factors. Other tissue-culture strains of *Haplopappus* consistently differed from the parent strain, in respect of their nitrogenous compounds, even when grown under the same conditions. The nitrogenous constituents of stock cultures also changed spontaneously with time. Chromosome differences were noted in some of the spontaneous variant strains; and hence, as a reasonable inference, the observed changes in the metabolism and morphology of the cultures. (For fuller information on single-cell culture, *see also* Muir *et al.*, 1954, 1958; De Ropp, 1955; Torrey, 1957; Bergman, 1959; Nickell, 1956; Steward *et al.*, 1964; Wetherell and Halperin, 1963; Halperin and Wetherell, 1964; Kato and Takeuchi, 1963; Mohan Ram and Steward, 1964; Mohan Ram and Mridul Wahdi, 1965: Schroeder *et al.*, 1962; Guha *et al.*, 1964; Tulecke, 1957, 1959; Tulecke and Sehgal, 1963; Konar, 1963.)

Embryoids in Kalanchoe pinnata. Within the limitations of this book, justice cannot be done to the rapidly expanding information on embryoids. But a few examples may be mentioned. In cultural studies of explant leaf buds of *Kalanchoe pinnata*, for example, Mohan Ram and Mridul Wahdi (1965) have described how they obtained certain callus cultures which gave rise to cells and cell clusters of characteristic conformation; in fact, embryoids which, set out as a series, are strongly reminiscent of typical 'stages' in the normal embryogenesis (Fig. 4.9).

Suspensors in Embryoids. Haccius (1965) has cogently asked: do tissue culture 'embryos' possess a suspensor? It has long been accepted that the suspensor is that part of the proembryo which does not participate actively in the formation of the embryo proper. As already noted (p. 47 and Fig. 3.12), the suspensor in angiosperms may be slight or relatively conspicuous. In the latter instance there may be a more or less strong tendency towards polyembryony. If the embryo proper degenerates, either in the course of nature or as a result of experimental treatment (*see* p. 69), new, adventive, embryos may be formed from the suspensor (Fig. 4.10). Haccius has also called attention to the fact that, in adventive embryos which have been formed from the nucellus or from cells of the integument, a more or less considerable suspensor-like cell group is often present (Fig. 4.10), even though, in the normal embryogeny, the suspensor is small and filamentous. Haccius regards the embryoids which have been obtained from single-cell or from callus cultures as being typical adventive embryos, the embryo

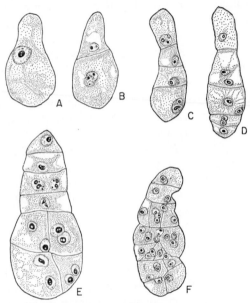

FIG. 4.9. *Kalanchoe pinnata*. Embryoids from leaf tissue cultures. A–F, Stages in the development of embryo-like structures on WB + CM + 2,4-D (5·0 ppm) (×100). (After H. Y. Mohan Ram and M. Wadhi, in *Tissue Culture*, 1965.)

proper typically having its origin in a massive, basal, suspensor-like tissue mass (also described as a 'proembryo'). Accordingly, she considered that it is unwarranted to look for a close morphogenetic identity between zygotic and adventive embryos in any particular species (*see* Plates 3, 4).

Many nucellar and integumentary embryos originate as a multicellular outgrowth. So also do some of the embryoids which develop from callus tissue (Fig. 4.10). In these developments, although a suspensor-like basal region is present, it is not possible to delimit a suspensor, as in normal embryogenesis. The interpretation of these structures therefore remains an open question (Haccius, 1965).

Embryoids in Ranunculus sceleratus. The scope for research on the regenerative properties of individual cells (or cell groups) in reactive species
has been demonstrated by Konar and Nataraja (1964, 1965). Flower
primordia of *Ranunculus sceleratus* were isolated, sterilized and implanted
in a standard agar medium with various additives. This is evidently an
unusually active species in its regenerative potentialities. Interesting
morphogenetic effects were obtained on a modified White's basal medium,

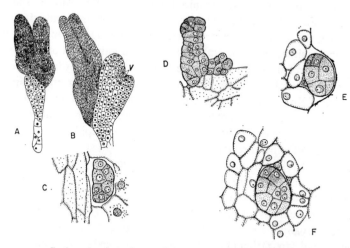

FIG. 4.10. Induced adventive embryos. A, B, *Eranthis hiemalis:* embryos
were selectively killed, by treatment with acid buffer solution, pH 4·5, leaving
the suspensor viable. On a suitable medium, the suspensor proliferated,
forming adventive embryos. The original embryos are dark, the new ones,
clear; *v,* apex of new embryo. (After B. Haccius, *Planta,* 1965.) C, D, *Opuntia
dillenii:* nucellar embryos at different stages of development. (After P.
Maheshwari and R. N. Chopra, *Phytomorph.,* 1955.) E, F, *Daucus carota:*
these are considered to be early stages of adventive embryos obtained *in
vitro* in callus tissue culture. (After B. Haccius and K. K. Lakshmanan,
Planta, 1965; and B. Haccius, *Bericht. deutsch. bot. Ges.* 1965.)

supplemented by 10 per cent coconut milk and 1 p.p.m. IAA. The growth
of the explant buds, with abundant cell division, was rapid. In the
course of 20 days a soft, white, friable callus was formed. After 20–25 days,
6–10 small roots, and 1–5 shoots with many leaves, appeared almost
simultaneously on a callus. These new plantlings were of normal morphology and, after 10 weeks, had terminal flower buds on the main axis.
The friable callus also yielded embryoids. These consisted of loose cell
groups in which the histological configuration was comparable with early
stages in normal embryogenesis. Older callus materials yielded globular
and heart-shaped embryoids and, later, normal dicotyledonous plantlings

were obtained. Tricotyledonous plantlings also occurred. These embryoids, which are described 'as emerging from the surface of the callus mass', developed into normal seedlings; and embryoids isolated and grown as separate cultures behaved in a similar manner. The finding of general interest is that the cells of a young flower bud are still totipotent.

In liquid media small masses of undifferentiated tissue grew at the periphery of the culture, and embryonal budding took place. Many of these buds became detached and organized into embryoids with a shoot, cotyledons and root. In turn, buds developed on those embryoids. It thus appears that the pattern of zygote growth, though undoubtedly related to the metabolic situation in the embryo sac, can be induced in other ways, and in other circumstances. In fact, we may now recognize that a kind of embryogenesis may be undergone by vegetative cells. An interesting feature of the work of Konar and Nataraja (1965) – and an important one – is that a plantling (c. 4 cm. in length), obtained in the manner described above, has been observed to yield abundant embryoids from the epidermis. Initially these appear in the basal region of the hypocotyl, but, subsequently, they are also formed higher up. Characteristic stages, beginning with the division of a single epidermal cell, are illustrated in Fig. 4.11. Similar developments were observed and described by earlier workers in species which readily yield adventitious buds, e.g. by Crooks (1933) and by Link and Eggers (1946) in *Linum usitatissimum.* (*See* p. 107 and Fig. 5.10.)

Steward *et al.* (1963) thought that a cell has to be freed from its surroundings and provided with special metabolites before it can behave like a zygote. But Konar *et al.* have now shown that in *R. sceleratus*, even in the absence of that important ingredient, coconut milk, the development of accessory embryos goes on. Nor have they found it essential that a cell must be freed from its surroundings if it is to become organized as a plantling. (*See also* Reinert, 1959; and Haccius, 1965.)

Again using *Ranunculus sceleratus*, Konar and Nataraja (1965b) have shown that mature anthers, placed in a culture medium consisting of White's basal medium, coconut milk and 2,4-D, can also form callus embryoids. In this instance, it appears that the mature cells of the connective still retain meristematic potentiality and can readily be activated.

When the callus formed from excised flower buds of *R. sceleratus*, grown in culture, was shaken into free cells and cell groups, embryoids and plantlings were obtained (Konar and Nataraja, 1965b).

Embryoids in Biota orientalis. The induction of embryoids, *in vitro*, on the cotyledons of *Biota orientalis* (Cupressaceae) has been reported by Konar and Oberoi (1965). (For cultural details, *see* ref.) Subcultured young embryoids yielded normal shoots with spirally arranged leaves.

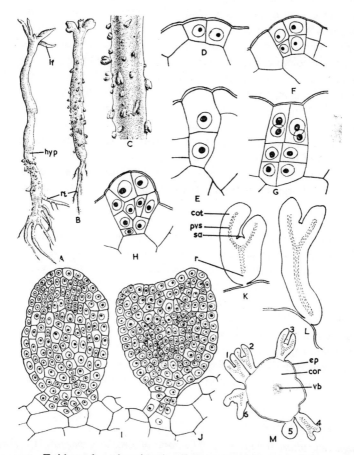

FIG. 4.11. Epidermal embryoids in *Ranunculus sceleratus*. (*cor*, cortex; *cot*, cotyledon; *ep*, epidermis; *hyp*, hypocotyl; *lf*, leaf; *pvs*, pro-vascular strand; *r*, radicle; *rt*, root; *sa*, shoot apex.)

A, B, 1-month-old seedlings bearing accessory embryos on the basal part (A) and all over the stem (B) (×2·5). C, Portion enlarged from B to show the epidermal embryos (×2). D, Two epidermal cells which would give rise to embryos (×918). E–G, 2-, 4- and 8-celled proembryos (×1,083, 700 and 666 respectively). H, Same, advanced stage (×958). I, Globular embryo (×337). J, Young heart-shaped embryo (×322). K, Embryo with developing cotyledons and shoot apex (×83). L, Same, advanced stage showing provascular strands (×79). M, Diagrammatic representation of t.s. of stem to show several developing embryos (×46) (After R. N. Konar and K. Nataraja, *Phytomorph.*, 1965.)

Some Recent Work. For recent work on the induction of embryoids in media of known composition, readers are referred to Reinert (1963a, b; 1965) and Reinert *et al.* (1966). A general aim in these studies was to obtain embryoids and plantlings from tissue cultures growing in simple synthetic media, i.e. without using such complex components as coconut milk. Another aim was to control the kind of organ-formation induced by varying the components in synthetic media. Among other important findings, Reinert (1963) reported that organogenesis is much more dependent on the interplay of chemical factors than on physical factors such as light, liquid as compared with semi-solid, agar media, etc. Although the effects of IAA on cultures of different ages on different media has been explored with some thoroughness, the relationships between the metabolic complex and organogenesis are still, in many respects, rather obscure.

Products of Sugar γ-Radiolysis. In a study of the effects of irradiating free cell cultures of carrot with a cobalt-60 source, with the aim of studying the induction of mutations, Holsten, Sugii and Steward (1965) made the surprising discovery that some of the effects could be just as great if the culture medium was irradiated before the non-irradiated cells were placed in it. This led to a close examination, in particular, of the effects of γ-radiation on solutions of sucrose, as being one of the principal ingredients of tissue and cell culture media. In fact, a number of γ-radiolysis products were obtained, one of which inhibited the growth effect normally obtained with coconut milk, but stimulated it at lower concentrations. These observations have many important biological implications.

A CRITICAL NOTE

Single cell culture from leaf mesophyll cells of Arachis hypogaea. It is always interesting to know of new techniques and of useful reactive materials. Ball and Joshi (1965) have been critical of statements about single-cell cultures derived from a callus culture, i.e. the method of Steward and his co-workers, and they have advocated the use of cultures derived from 'normal cells', e.g. from a mesophyll cell of an angiosperm. As a matter of information, considerable difficulty was experienced in selecting favourable materials. However, mesophyll scrapings of *Arachis hypogaea*, yielding individual cells, were grown in liquid culture and some interesting developments were recorded by time-lapse photomicrography.

During the 3–5 days after inoculation a palisade cell showed cytoplasmic streaming, but this only moved the large chloroplastids back and forth. Thereafter, a localized or more general enlargement of the cell took place. In the former a spherical structure with a filamentous end was formed; in the latter an egg-shaped or almost spherical body developed. In both instances there was a loss both of polarity and histological specificity; the chloroplasts increased in size and lost much of their green colour. Ball and Joshi have described some of the details of cell division. Here it may be noted that the new wall had no consistent orientation to the original axis of the enlarging cell, and it was often curved (*see* D'Arcy Thompson, 1917). In the derivative cells the divisions also seemed to be without recognizable orientation, and the cell-mass subsequently formed had no resemblance to a young embryo. The palisade parenchyma 'property' of the parent cell had no permanence. However, the cells which did divide were exclusively from the palisade layer; the spongy mesophyll cells showed little change other than plasmolysis. Ball and Joshi have recorded that similar observations were made on leaf materials of *Aster* sp., and from shaken cultures of *Erigeron* sp. and *Oenothera* sp. However, whether their contention that 'from every botanical viewpoint, it behoves the investigator of all morphogenesis to start his experiments with a normal cell' has been validated, seems to the writer to call for a suspension of judgement. After all, what is a 'normal cell'? Moreover, *any living cell*, of whatever origin, and however 'normal' or otherwise, always confronts the investigator with so many 'unknowns'.

SUMMARY OF CHEMICAL EMBRYOGENESIS

From the foregoing observations on embryos and embryoids, it may justly be claimed that the study of chemical embryogenesis in plants and of single cells in culture is at length on its way. Beginning with the zygotic organization, and thence onwards through embryogenesis, a vast amount of new work – and opportunity – awaits the perceptive student. Many skills and qualities will be needed and, not least, in the writer's submission, intuitive insight into the complex physico-chemical reactions, or interactions, between the growing, and subsequently disintegrating, endosperm and the enlarging germ. Many curious relationships exist between the nutrition and growth of the embryo, perhaps of hybrid origin, and the triploid endosperm, the maternal tapetum and the nucellar tissues. In some instances, for example, a nucleus from a pollen-tube other than that which brought the sperm to the ovum may be involved in endosperm formation, with concomitant physiological–genetical effects on the metabolic materials available to the developing zygote. There are also important problems relating to the possible uptake by the embryo of large molecules, synthesized in the endosperm or elsewhere in the embryonic environment. Not least, there are phenomena that seem to be mainly of a biophysical kind. Thus, at a certain stage of development, the spherical embryo becomes bilateral, indicating the inception of transverse as well as longitudinal polarity.

NEOMORPHOSIS IN SEED PLANTS

Some curious observations, described by Waris (1957, 1959, 1962) and Miettinen and Waris (1958) on the induction of 'neomorphs' in species of *Oenanthe* (Umbelliferae), are reminiscent of embryoids. Since amino acids are essential constituents of proteins, morphogenetic changes might be expected to occur when the normal balance of protein synthesis was intentionally upset by an excess of a particular amino acid. In other words,

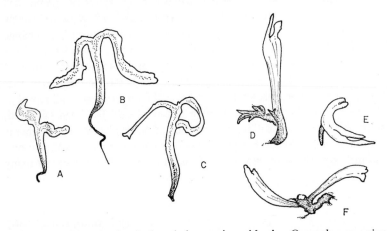

FIG. 4.12. Neomorphs induced by aminoacids in *Oenanthe aquatica*. A, B, C, Seedling-like neomorphs (×3) formed from plants grown in a medium containing 0·4 per cent glycine. D, E, Neomorphs obtained in a medium containing 0·01 per cent glycine. F, A broad-leaved neomorph grown in a medium containing 0·00063M of arginine nitrate. (After H. Waris, *Physiol. Plantarum*, 1959.)

it might be possible to interfere in some characteristic way with metabolic reactions in the apical meristem. Waris (1957) tested this hypothesis, making use of aquatic plants as having evident advantages. Young plants of *Oenanthe aquatica* were grown aseptically from seed in a basic nutrient medium, with the addition of 10 g. sucrose and 1–4 g. glycine per litre. The plantlings were initially of normal appearance, but during three to four months they stopped growing and seemingly became moribund. After some time, however, a number of fresh, vigorously growing, green plantlings, of a *Vallisneria*-like appearance, developed in the culture flasks (Fig. 4.12). These 'neomorphs', which were unrecognizable as *O. aquatica* and of very reduced differentiation, had originated from small nodules, constricted and detached from lateral root tips of the morbid plant. The nodules showed polarity with evidence of distinct shoot and root poles. In some concentrations of glycine thalloid structures were formed. A further formation of neomorphs took place from cell groups which were spontaneously detached from colourless, epidermal outgrowths of the green leaves. These cell groups gave rise to colourless embryo-like structures which subsequently became green and developed a configuration like a normal seedling, though sometimes more than two 'cotyledons' were present. On further development, narrow leaves, a few millimetres wide and a few centimetres long, appeared, but the final size of the individuals was only a few centimetres. These neomorphs were capable of submerged growth. On being transferred to nutrient solutions containing sucrose but no glycine, the new conformation remained unchanged for several months, though there was some evidence of growth promotion, especially in the roots (which was poor in the presence of glycine). After about four months, however, normal leaves began to appear in some plants; but growth after transfer to inorganic solutions was unsuccessful (Fig. 4.12).

Waris interpreted these observations as evidence of physiological adaptation in this species to glycine, though not involving any irreversible change in the genotype. However the results may be understood, significant metabolic changes seem to have taken place in the embryonic tissues; and this, indeed, was shown in biochemical studies by Miettinen and Waris (1958). They found that the neomorphs contained much larger quantities of free amino acids than normal plants. Similar changes were subsequently induced with amino acids in *Oenanthe lachenalii* and *Daucus carota* (Waris, 1959, 1962). Waris found that the transition of neomorphs to normal growth was accelerated by ribose, although sugar inhibited growth in size. (*See also* Waris, 1965, 1967.)

APOGAMY

In essentials, the apogamous formation of young sporophytes on the prothalli of ferns is another instance of bud formation from a centre of active metabolism. Thus, at some distance behind the growing point of the prothallus the tissue begins to divide and a noticeably thick region develops. After some time a young plantling is formed in precisely the same spatial relationships with the long axis of the prothallus as the normal young embryo. Whittier and Steeves (1960, 1962) have now demonstrated that the prothalli of a considerable group of fern species (seven species, fourteen strains) can be induced to form apogamous sporophytes, under aseptic cultural conditions, in media of known composition, provided the right concentration of sugar is present. Sucrose proved more effective than glucose, probably in relation to osmotic effects. Optimal concentrations for the several fern cultures were not established, and the possible effects of other metabolites are not precluded. Whittier and Steeves considered that

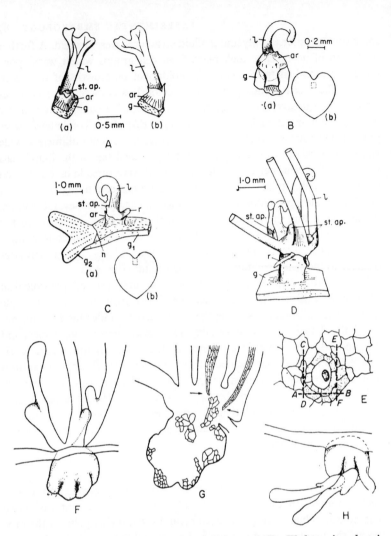

FIG. 4.13. Surgical treatments of fern embryos. A–D, *Thelypteris palustris*. A, Embryo 36 days old, excised from the gametophyte 5 days after fertilization; drawing as placed on the medium, ventral surface of the gametophyte uppermost: (*a*) from the side originally adjacent to the anterior side of the gametophyte; (*b*) from the opposite side; *ar*, archegonium; *g*, gametophyte; *l*, leaf; *st. ap.*, stem apex. Ba, Embryo 27 days old, the archegonium excised from the gametophyte before fertilization. The dotted line indicates the position of the foot and stem apex determined by sectioning. Drawn as placed on medium, ventral surface of the gametophyte uppermost; indications as in A. B, Diagram showing original position of archegonium; distance between anterior margin of fragment of gametophyte and base of notch, 0·8 mm. Ca, Embryo 22 days old, the archgonium excised from the gametophyte before fertilization but with the apical notch attached and active.

the additional carbohydrate nutrition of the prothallus by the sucrose, e.g. at 2–3 per cent, led to the thickening of the prothallial tissue and from that on to the inception of buds.

SURGICAL EXPERIMENTS

If one envisages the zygote as a reaction system, in which factors in the environment also participate, then by complete or partial isolation of the zygote from its gametophyte tissue environment, changes in the embryonic development might be expected to be induced. So far, the amount of experimental work of this kind is small, but some information of very considerable interest has been obtained. Thus, when a fern zygote is excised from the gametophyte tissue, it is removed from the nutrients, physiological gradients, pressures, etc., in which it normally develops. Ward and Wetmore (1954), Jayasekera and Bell (1959) and de Maggio (1963) have reported on investigations of this kind (Fig. 4.13).

Fern Studies: Phlebodium. In delicate surgical experiments, using the fern *Phlebodium aureum*, and involving the incision of the prothallus close to a fertilized archegonium, Ward and Wetmore (1954) effected a partial 'release' of the young embryo (Fig. 4.13 E–H). As a result, the normal course of embryogenesis was modified in various ways. The young embryo

---

Drawn as placed on the medium, ventral surface of the gametophyte uppermost; n, original position of apical notch; g_1, original fragment of gametophyte; g_2, new growth of gametophyte. Cb, Diagram showing position from which fragment of gametophyte was removed. D, Cylindrical body developing from zygote 70 days after fertilization following removal of the archegonial neck on the fifth day after fertilization. Drawn as placed on the medium, the dorsal surface of the gametophyte uppermost. (From R. D. E. Jayasekera and P. R. Bell, *Planta*, 1959.)

E–H, *Phlebodium aureum.* E, Diagram to show position of incisions made in a prothallus in one of the experimental treatments. Dotted lines indicate the places where cuts were made to release the embryo from the restraint of the prothallial tissue. F and G, Tuberous bodies resulting from single zygotes after surgical treatment. Massive growth in F is about 50 days old and bears three young shoots on the upper part, above the surface of the prothallus. In G, the vascular connections from two of the leaves (arrows) are shown diagrammatically from sections of tuber in E. Below the ends of the vascular trace is an arrangement of columnar tissue in the former foot region of the tuber. Variation in size and shape of the parenchymatous cells of the tuberous body is indicated in a few isolated areas. The apical notch is to the right in both figures. H, Young leafy shoots on the under side of a tuberous body, becoming orientated towards the apical notch to the left. (From M. Ward and R. H. Wetmore, *Amer. Jour. Botany*, 1954.)

outgrew the calyptra precociously and developed as a slow-growing tissue mass without definite shape. This structure was initially without appendages, but later it formed a stem and leaf, as in the normal development; however, it remained rootless. In such 'released' embryos an extreme effect was the formation of an enlarged, amorphous, slow-growing, tuberous, non-vascularized, parenchymatous tissue mass. Some of these masses eventually gave rise to three apparently normal plantlings (Fig. 4.13 F). In embryos which had been isolated from the prothallus apex by transverse incisions, development was very slow as compared with those which had been isolated in other ways. This was attributed to the interruption of the known basipetal auxin gradient (Albaum, 1938). These observations indicate that formative effects are normally induced in the developing embryo by the prothallus, the archegonium and the derived calyptra.

Fern Studies: Thelypteris. In experiments in which pure cultures of the gametophyte of the fern *Thelypteris palustris* were used, Jayasekera and Bell (1959) induced notable departures from the normal embryogenesis by various surgical treatments of the archegonium containing the fertilized ovum (Fig. 4.13 A–D). Archegonia with fertilized eggs can be recognized from the third to the fifth day after fertilization by the expansion of the tissue at the base of the neck. By using a micro-manipulator, the venter of the archegonium was excised on a minute cube of prothallial tissue; this was then transferred to the surface of a mineral–agar culture medium. In some experiments small cubes of prothallus were excised from just behind the apex. These typically bore about three mature archegonia. Such pieces of tissue were placed in a suspension of antherozoids for 24 hours and then transferred to the surface of an agar medium. In other experiments, in which archegonia were inseminated, the piece of prothallus was so excised as to include the base of the sunken apical notch; and, for comparison, similar pieces, with the apex removed, had auxin (IAA) applied in its place. In yet other experiments results of great interest were obtained when necks were excised from archegonia-containing zygotes.

In the normal development the zygote of *T. palustris* divides by a wall at right-angles of the long axis of the prothallus about the fifth day after fertilization; in fact, in its embryogenesis, it is comparable with other polypodiaceous ferns (*see* pp. 51, 52). With the exception of specimens in which the neck of the archegonium had been removed, the development of the embryos after the several treatments was approximately normal, though some consistent differences in the rate and order of development were noted. Jayasekera and Bell concluded that auxin diffusing from the apex of the prothallus promotes the general differentiation of the embryo and, in particular, the formation of the first root. They also considered that the mechanical restraint imposed on the young embryo by the intact archegonium contributes to differentiation in general, and that it is responsible for the orientation of the embryo in relation to the surface of the prothallus. Thus, when the archegonium neck was excised, with a concomitant release of pressure, the embryo emerged from the upper (dorsal) surface of the prothallus when the ventral surface of the latter was next to the medium – a result not obtained from any other treatment (Fig. 4.13 D). When the ventral surface of the prothallus faced upwards the embryo also developed upwards. The intact archegonium neck is thus a factor which affects the orientation of the embryo.

Pteris and Marsilea. Thomson (1934) reported that if young embryos of *Marsilea* are excised and grown in culture solution changes are induced in the shape of the foot. When Rivières (1959) grew aseptically isolated, embryo-containing archegonia of *Pteris longifolia* on a Knop medium with trace elements he obtained sporophytes with increasingly differentiated leaves but without roots. He inferred that the developing embryo normally receives root-forming factors from the prothallus.

Divided Embryos: Sesamum. That the normal ontogenetic pattern can be disturbed by surgical treatments is not unexpected. When Hanawa and Ishizaki (1953) divided *Sesamum indicum* embryos longitudinally they obtained viable half-embryos which showed various transitory morphological abnormalities. In an equally divided embryo each half grew on and formed a double leaf. Some temporary phyllotactic abnormality was noted. The incised cortex was regenerated from the vascular region. In unequally divided embryos the smaller portion formed an abnormal foliar member, and no apical growing point was reconstituted.

Cuscuta. Maheshwari and Baldev (1962) observed the induction of adventitious buds in cultured embryos of *Cuscuta reflexa*.

These and other experiments show that by removing an enclosed zygote or young embryo from its normal tissue environment, more or less conspicuous modifications may be induced in the normal morphogenetic development. In other words, within limits, the reaction system in the developing young embryo shows some flexibility. Quite considerable, and sometimes surprising, modifications of the normal course of embryogenesis have been observed. It may well be that this finding can be exploited both for academic and practical ends. But perhaps one should not expect too much: as experience has shown, the genetical system has considerable flexibility in some respects but great stability in others.

ELECTRON MICROSCOPY

So far, presumably mainly for technical reasons, very few studies, using electron microscopy, have been made of the maturing ovum, the zygote, the two-celled polarized embryo, and the proembryo. Here an important and diversified field awaits exploration: in the molecular biology of higher plants, it will be no bad thing to begin at the beginning, i.e. with the single generative cell.

IRRADIATION EFFECTS

The effects of irradiating mature embryos in seeds have been studied in some detail. There have, however, been few investigations in which the histological changes in young embryos, as the result of irradiation, have been closely observed. Chlorophyll abnormalities in bean seedling leaves, after irradiation of immature embryos, were noted by Rabideau (1954). Mericle and Mericle (1957) observed the effects of X-rays on embryogenesis in an inbred line of barley. Various anomalous histological developments increased in number and severity as radiation levels were raised. The youngest proembryos were less sensitive, or reactive, than the next slightly older ones; but, as embryogenesis advanced, the radio-sensitivity was inversely related to the degree of differentiation. A complete degeneration of embryos was unusual at the radiation intensities applied. Multiple proliferations with attendant disturbance of the normal pattern of organogenesis were features of the experimental materials. The scutellum, shoot and root loci of pre-differentiation embryos appeared to be about equally radio-sensitive; but, in embryos treated during differentiation, the root region was found to be considerably more sensitive than the other two regions. In fact, some specimens were rootless. Embryos just prior to differentiation were critically sensitive, especially in respect of the subsequent formation of the coleoptile: if irradiated at this stage an anomalous cleft coleoptile developed. A curious finding was that although irradiated zygotes and proembryos did not yield subsequent histological aberrations, they were highly sensitive as judged by the post-germination behaviour of the plantlings and plants formed from them. These effects, obscured, or not manifested during embryogenesis, are regarded as being due to gene or chromosome aberrations. Such plants subsequently afforded evidence of lethal or semi-lethal effects, in more or less severe and persistent dwarfing of the plant, absence of tillering, tubular leaves and other anomalous foliar conditions.

Haccius and Reinholz (1953) found that when undifferentiated embryos of *Eranthis hiemalis* were subjected to X-rays (125–32,000 r) the developing embryos showed syncotyly, tricotyly and tetracotyly (125–800 r). Many of the embryos remained strongly inhibited or became abortive (2,000–32,000 r). As already noted (p. 66), comparable effects were induced by injecting ovules with growth-regulating substances.

Anomalous developments, including syncotyly, anisocotyly, tri- and tetracotyly, and multiple embryos, have been induced in *Arabidopsis thaliana* by irradiating young embryos (200–16,000 r) (Reinholz, 1954). In this species, however, the age of the embryo treated and the dosage seem to be of less critical importance than in some other species. In these irradiation experiments the effects are probably of several kinds, e.g. effects on chemical reactions at lower dosages, and direct injury to cells and tissues at higher dosages.

CONCLUSION

In embryogenesis in plants we may inquire, with a view to further investigations, what are the great 'unknowns'? At this stage and time the general answers seem to the writer to be: (i) the nature of the zygotic organization; (ii) the biochemical subtleties of early embryogenesis, and (iii) the biophysics of the whole embryonic development.

CHAPTER V

The Shoot Apex

All plants above the organizational level of the Bryophyta exemplify the phenomena of the growth and differentiation of a vascularized axis, bearing regularly disposed lateral organs, typically leaves and branches (or buds). The formation of the leafy-shoot, its evident developmental harmony and its distinctive organogenic and histogenic patterns are primarily due to regulated activities in the distal region – the shoot apex. As used here, the

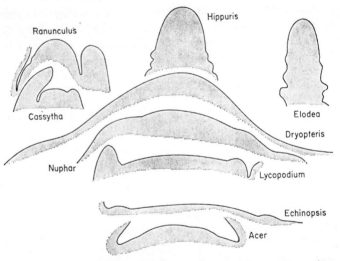

FIG. 5.1. Outlines of various shoot apices, as seen in longitudinal median section, to illustrate the very varied distribution of growth in different species (all × 150). (After C. W. Wardlaw, *Amer. Jour. Bot.*, 1957.)

shoot apex comprises both the *apical meristem* and the subjacent regions of expansion and maturation. Important as it is as *the* primary formative region, the apical meristem cannot be treated as a thing apart. The activities of the apex, both temporally and functionally, include its growth, the formation of lateral organs and the *differentiation* of the several tissue systems: from an early stage, e.g. as seen in a cross-section of the stem below the apex, the differentiating tissues afford evidence of *specific pattern*. As these phenomena of ontogenesis can be observed in quite different phyletic lines, they may be recognized as constituting some of the great *homologies of organization*, or *parallelisms of development*, in the Plant Kingdom. Moreover, as we shall see, the matter is still more remarkable when we consider how very different in size, shape and histological constitution are the apices of species of different genetical affinities (Figs. 5.1–5.4).

Since it is the most accessible embryonic region, the shoot apex has been extensively used in studies of morphogenesis. Accordingly, in this chapter factual information and ideas on which experimental work may be based are considered.

HISTOLOGICAL CONSTITUTION

More than one hundred years ago Naegeli and Hofmeister demonstrated that, in many vascular cryptogams, the development of the shoot is the result of growth and division in a conspicuous apical cell and its segments, followed by the expansion and maturation of the resulting tissues. Since then, much effort has gone into the examination of the cellular constitution of apices. During the latter part of the nineteenth century and, more recently, from about 1930 onwards, excellent descriptive studies of apices in all classes of plants have been published. On the basis of cellular organization, at least seven different 'types' of apex can be specified in vascular plants. In many of these studies, especially in the gymnosperms and angiosperms, much attention has been paid to the number of discrete cell layers that can be distinguished at the summit of the apex and to the propriety of interpreting the histological arrangements observed in terms of the *histogen layer* concept of Hanstein, or of the *tunica-corpus* concept of Schmidt (*see* Foster, 1939; Wardlaw, 1952a, b; 1965a, b; Cutter, 1965; Esau, 1965a; Newman, 1956 *et. seq.*, and other reviews).

Histologically, the shoot apex of any particular vascular plant can be referred to one of the following 'types' (Fig. 5.3): (1) a single conspicuous apical or initial cell, to which all cell lineages can be traced; (2) several definite but rather less conspicuous cells; (3) inconspicuous but definitely superficial initial cells; (4) a weakly zoned or layered construction; (5) a fluctuating layered construction; (6) a highly definite layered construction; and (7) a radiating construction, apparently originating from a distal and central but sub-surface group of mother cells. The first three groups indicated above comprise pteridophyte apices and the remaining four the apices of seed plants. Group (7) includes the apices of cycads, some conifers and some angiosperms (*see* Popham, 1951). Some of these apical types are illustrated in Figs. 5.3–5.9.

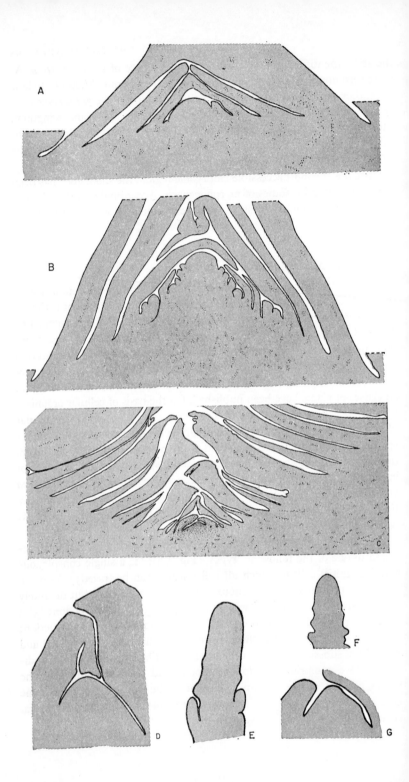

Apices in Malvaceae. Tolbert and Johnson (1966) have examined the structure of the vegetative shoot apex in forty species of the Malvaceae. These apices, like the apices of the angiosperms at large (Wardlaw, 1956), exhibit a wide range in size, shape and histological construction. In a majority of the species studied the tunica consists of a single layer of cells; but stratification in the outermost region of the corpus is common. These investigators have introduced a new term, or concept, to describe the shoot apex, namely, the *metrameristem*. This region is defined as comprising the initials of the tunica and corpus, and it gives rise to the flanking meristem and the pith meristem. How useful, or valid, this concept may be remains to be seen. Tolbert and Johnson noted that there appears to be a correlation between the growth habit of the species and the evident distinction between the metrameristem and the contiguous tissues. In the herbaceous species examined, the metrameristem was usually less clearly evident, or distinct, than in the shrubs and trees. Within a single genus, e.g. *Hibiscus*, in which there is a wide range in growth habit, this generalization was found to hold good.

The shoot apex thus presents initial problems of considerable variety and complexity. How can we account for the different cellular patterns? How does an apex maintain itself as a formative region? And how does it grow and give rise to the several organs and tissues? The first stage is to ascertain, with precision, the visible morphological and histological features of the apex in the species selected for study. But one must not become obsessed by any particular aspect! For example, no one would deny the importance of cell division in the apex, or of the plane, or planes, in which the new partition walls are laid down. Yet, as it appears to the writer, this is really evidence of a more basic phenomenon: *the distribution of growth* is the major phenomenon, of which the planes of cell division are resultant manifestations. Hence de Bary's aphorism: Organs make cells, not cells organs. Here, we impinge on one of the great 'unknowns' in biology. How is the distribution of growth determined? In the end it is a biophysical phenomenon, in that matter is being moved in characteristic ways and utilized in new conformations (*see* p. 110). Thus the observed cellular organization is not simply an anatomical phenomenon. Indeed, in studies of morphogenesis one must constantly think in terms of the movement and

---

FIG. 5.2. Outlines of various apices of monocotyledons, as seen in median l.s. (various magnifications). A, B, *Musa* sp. (Gros Michel banana). A, Vegetative apex; B, an early stage in the formation of the inflorescence (×12). C, *Elaeis guineensis* – the oil palm (×12). D, *Cocos nucifera* (×45). E, *Agropyron repens*. F, *Elodea canadensis*. G, *Iris pseudacorus* (×70). (D, after K. Periswamy, *Australian Jour. Bot.*, 1965; E, after B. C. Sharman, *Bot. Gaz.*, 1945; the others by author.)

D

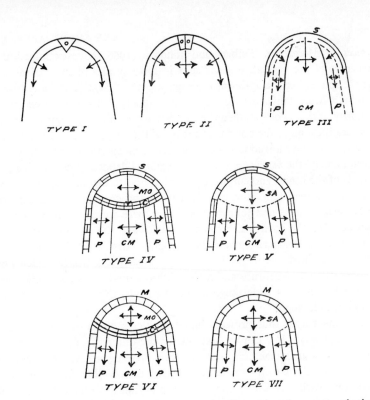

FIG. 5.3. Shoot apical 'types', diagrammatic, illustrating the seven principal types of histological organization among vascular plants. *S*, surface meristem; *M*, mantle; *Mo*, central mother cells; *C*, cambium-like zones; *SA*, subapical initials; *CM*, central meristem; *P*, peripheral meristem. (After R. A. Popham, *Ohio Jour. Sci.*, 1952.)

FIG. 5.4. Histological details of some apices of Gramineae, as seen in longitudinal median sections. A–F, *Saccharum officinarum* (sugar cane). A, B, Var. 'NC 25'. A, Young shoot described as being without a tunica. B, Ditto, but with a tunica; the internode has elongated. C, D, E, Var. 'Cavengerie'. C, Young shoot apex without a tunica. D, Ditto, with tunica. E, Older shoot apex, with tunica. F, Var. 'Badila'. Young shoot apex with a tunica (all ×150). (After C. Thielke, *Planta*, **62**, 1964.)

G, *Agropyron repens* (couch grass). Shoot apex showing leaf primordia at different stages of development. *d*, dermatogen; *h*, hypodermis; *sh*, subhypodermis; *lb*, sheath of next leaf below. (After B. C. Sharman, *Bot. Gaz.* **106**, 1945.)

H, *Phyllostachys nigra* (black bamboo). *ad*, dermatogen initial; *d*, dermatogen; apl^1, apl^2, plerome initials; *ap*, periblem initials; br^1, br^2, loci of branch buds; n^1, n^2, upper limits of first and second nodes; l^1, l^2, l^3, rudiments belonging to the same sheath leaf; *pc*, procambial elements; *p*, periblem; *pl*, plerome. The dotted line indicates the probable disposition of the first enclosing leaf sheath. (After W. M. Porterfield. *Bul. Dept. Biol.* Yenching Univ., **1**, 1929–30.)

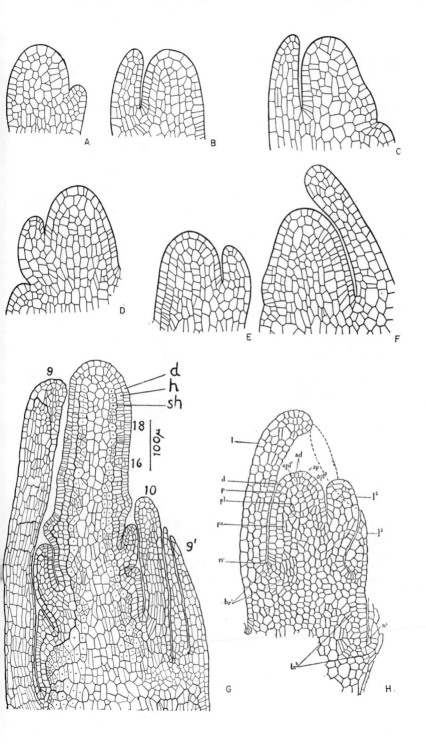

utilization of metabolic substances in embryonic regions, such as the shoot apex, viewed as a genetically specific and integrated whole. The spatial relationships and the changing sizes and shapes of growing regions also enter into our thinking, and it becomes evident that we must also study the apex as a dynamic geometric entity.

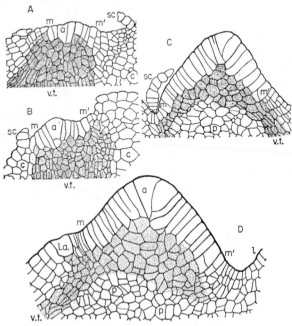

FIG. 5.5. Shoot apical ontogenesis in a fern, *Matteuccia struthiopteris*. Longitudinal median sections (semi-diagrammatic) of shoot apices of different sizes: the essential features of the organization of the apical meristem, with its conspicuous apical cell, as established in the young sporophyte or a bud, (A), are retained as the meristem increases in size; but there are evident changes in cell size and in the distribution of growth and of tissues, e.g. the transverse component is conspicuous in the subapical region of large shoots in which a pith is present. *a*, apical cell; *m–m'*, apical meristem; *vt.*, vascular tissue (incipient); *c*, cortex; *p*, pith; *sc*, scale. (×50.) (After C. W. Wardlaw *Annals of Botany*, 1944.)

An important preliminary exercise in the study of the shoot meristem is to ascertain the facts concerning its changing cellular constitution during ontogenesis. So far, this has been done for only a small number of species (*see* Wardlaw, 1965a; Philipson, 1949; Figs. 5.5, 5.6 and p. 106). Botanists have long been aware of the fact that although the apices of different species have very different cellular patterns, nevertheless they all grow and function in very much the same way; i.e. they remain embryonic during the vegetative phase of ontogenesis and they give rise to a vascularized axis with lateral organs. So, for the moment, let us liberate our minds from the details of cellular pattern. Fig. 5.1, illustrates diagrammatically a selection of apices, of species of different taxonomic affinity, as seen in longitudinal median section and *all drawn to the same scale*. This kind of representation could, of course, be very greatly extended. At a glance, it can be seen that shoot apices vary greatly in their sizes and shapes. The shape is the result of the way in which the metabolic materials are distributed in the growing region and utilized in the formation of the more rigid skeletal materials. In some apices it is evident that the *vertical component of growth* (or growth in the longitudinal direction) is much greater than the *radial* or *transverse* component; in other apices, e.g. those of *Dryopteris* (a fern) or *Echinopsis* (a cactus), it is the radial component that is conspicuous. Although the several apices illustrated are all specific and distinctive in their cellular organization, yet, when viewed as dynamic geometric constructions, they appear to be much more in the nature of 'variations upon a theme', rather than entities that are different one from another in any fundamental way. A task for students of morphogenesis, therefore, is to search for valid relationships between genetical constitution, environmental factors, overall morphology and cellular constitution. An acceptable system of ideas should evidently possess interpretive value both for the general phenomenon of apical growth and for the specific constructional features of any particular apex. To this end, apical organization and activity may now be considered in relation to: (i) the genetical constitution; (ii) the ontogenetic development; and (iii) the impact of environmental factors.

GENETICAL FACTORS AND APICAL ORGANIZATION

When allowance has been made for the effects of environmental factors, and for organismal factors which become incident as ontogenesis proceeds, there remain features of apical organization and reactivity which must be ascribed to genetical factors. (Of course, directly or indirectly, genetical factors are involved in every aspect of development.) Thus, although the several facets of apical construction and activity can be investigated by appropriate techniques, they must also to some extent be accepted as 'given'. Genetically determined apical 'characters' include the following:

(1) *The size and protoplasmic constitution of the cells of the meristem.* In the ontogenetic development of any species there is no absolute size for meristem or embryonic cells. Nevertheless, the size of meristem cells is related to genetical factors (Wardlaw, 1952b, 1953a). This statement is intended to convey a general truth, namely, that when a plant of a particular species has reached a certain stage in ontogenesis, under the usual conditions of

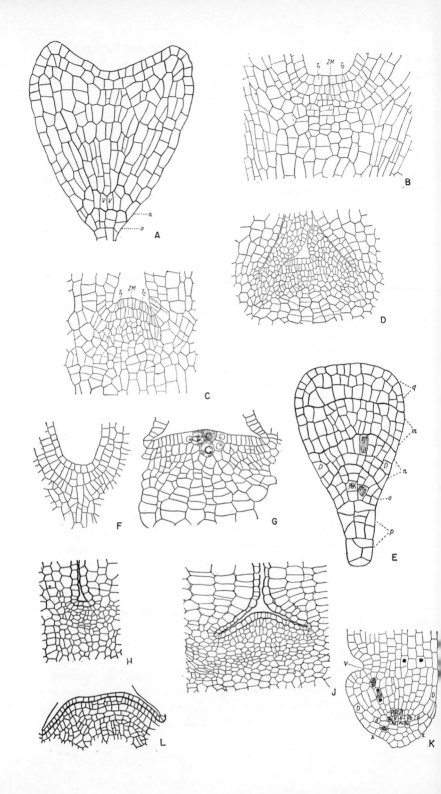

growth, its apical meristem cells will be found to be of a characteristic size.

(2) *The relative rates of growth in the vertical and transverse planes.* This important relationship determines the shape of the apical and subapical regions. In conjunction with cell size and constitution, the specific distribution of growth largely determines the characteristic cellular constitution, or pattern, of the apex, i.e. the disposition of embryonic cells in a characteristic number of histogenic layers, or whatever the cellular pattern may be. Qualifications of the kind indicated in (1) will also apply here.

(3) *The absolute size of the apex.* Embryo apices are initially of small size; but whereas in some species the apex undergoes a relatively small ontogenetic increase in size, in other species, e.g. in ferns and cycads, it eventually becomes greatly enlarged. The genetical constitution is closely involved in these phenomena, but environmental and other factors, which may affect the supply of nutrients to the apex, must be given due weight (Figs. 5.5, 5.6).

(4) *Growth centres.* The concept of growth centres, i.e. loci of special metabolism, is essential in morphogenesis. Thus, a leaf primordium typically develops in the meristem from a discrete locus of special metabolism. The positions of growth centres are specific and characteristic of the species. Thus a growth centre may be high up or low down on the meristem; and it may comprise cells pertaining to relatively superficial or relatively deep-

---

FIG. 5.6. Shoot apical ontogenesis in flowering plants. A–D, *Helianthus annuus.* A, Young embryo. *v*, the developing connecting cells (Verbindungszellen). B, C, D, The inception of the epicotyl, and progressive organization of the shoot apex in successively older seedlings; T_1, T_2, the two layers of the tunica; *ZM*, the central meristem. E, F, G, *Anoda triangularis.* E, Young embryo, showing beginning of arched hypophysis at *O*; the beginning of dermatogen (*D*) splitting is seen at *n*. F, G, Further organization of the shoot apex. In F the first periclinal division can be seen in the subdermatogen. In G the tunica and some conspicuous central cells are evident. The corpus is also considered to originate from one of the inner central (or apical) cells. Other active cell divisions are giving rise to a flank meristem. (After H. v. Guttenberg, J. Burmeister and H.-J. Brosell, *Planta,* **46**, 1955.)

H, J, *Impatiens glandulifera.* Formation of the shoot apex in a young embryo and in an older stage. (After Steffen.)

K, *Allium giganteum.* Older embryo, as seen in l.s., showing the shoot apex, *v*, the primary dermatogen (*D*), the secondary dermatogen, *d*. The first root is becoming organized: $K_{1, 2, 3}$, the root apex histogen; *Pl*, *Pb*, plerome and periblem initials (after v. Guttenberg, Heydel and Pankow).

L, *Allium porrum.* Shoot apex with single tunica layer; the subdermatogen is showing periclinal divisions (after Rüdiger). (H–L, From H. v. Guttenberg, I, *Die Angiospermen, Encyclopedia of Plant Anatomy,* 1960.)

seated histogenic layers. These positional relationships will affect the size and shape of primordia and their phyllotaxis.

(5) *The apical reaction system.* The shoot apex, like any active embryonic region, is the seat of many complex but inter-related chemical reactions, all the necessary metabolic substances being contained in the embryonic cells, or supplied from below. As many of the components of an apical reaction system are directly or indirectly gene-determined, each system is specific in character; but as many of the major metabolic processes and extrinsic factors are common to all green plants, certain components are likely to be common to different reaction systems. Accordingly, apical reaction systems will yield both general (or common) and specific morphogenetic effects.

The foregoing statements are unavoidably of a rather general character. However, they do indicate that the diverse apical configurations can be brought into some working relationship with the underlying factors.

FIG. 5.7. The shoot apex in (A) diploid and (B) tetraploid *Vinca rosea* as seen in longitudinal section ($\times 370$). (After G. L. Cross and T. J. Johnson, *Bull. Torrey Bot. Club*, 1941.)

The literature relating apical histology to genetical constitution is still meagre. But what has been achieved leaves little doubt that further relevant studies can hardly fail to be rewarding. Of particular interest is the work of Cross and Johnson (1941), Randolph, Abbe and Einset (1944), Satina, Blakeslee and Avery (1940), Bain and Dermen (1944), and others. (*See* Figs. 5.7–5.9.)

Cross and Johnson compared the apices of colchicine-induced polyploids and related diploids of *Vinca rosea* with that of *V. minor* (Fig. 5.7). The tetraploid *Vinca* was characterized by a more massive stem than the diploid, and by thicker and greener leaves and larger flowers. The several vegetative differences can be directly correlated with histological features of the respective shoot apices. In *V. minor* the apex consists of a three-layered tunica surrounding a central corpus, whereas in *V. rosea* the tunica is only two-layered. In the two apices, however, growth and organogenesis are generally comparable. In each species the three outer layers of the meristem make essentially the same contribution to the developing leaf primordia and axis. In the colchicine-induced tetraploid of *V. rosea* the shoot apex is comparable histologically with that of the parent. It is, however, considerably

broader, *due to an increase in average cell width*; but the depth (i.e. longitudinal dimension) is the same as in the parent. In fact, cell width in the
outermost tunica layer was increased by 68 per cent, that of the second
layer by 43 per cent, and that of the first layer of the corpus by 59 per cent.
The nuclei in the tetraploid meristem were approximately one-third larger
than those of the diploid. In this instance the effect of doubling the
chromosome complement was to modify both the shape and size of embryonic cells at the meristem; i.e. *the distribution of growth* in the apical
meristem had been modified in a characteristic manner.

Randolph, Abbe and Einset (1944) investigated shoot apices in diploid
and auto-tetraploid maize plants, their comparisons being based on apices

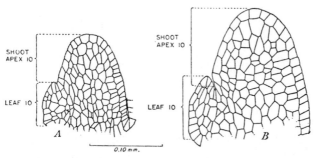

FIG. 5.8. The shoot apex and the primordium of leaf 10 in (A) diploid and
(B) tetraploid maize. (After L. F. Randolph, E. C. Abbé and J. Einset,
Jour. Agr. Res., 1944.)

which were forming the tenth leaf primordium. They observed that corresponding shoot apices in diploid and tetraploid maize (Fig. 5.8) had the
same number and arrangement of cells, but the volume of the nuclei and
cells was doubled in the latter. Leaf initials were also correspondingly wider,
this difference being maintained throughout development. The absolute
rate of increase in both width and length was, however, slower than in the
diploid. At maturity the tetraploid leaf was approximately of the same length
as the diploid, about 1·16 times as wide, 1·35 times as thick and 1·6 times
the volume. Differences in the total numbers of cells in the mature leaf
blade of diploid and tetraploid plants were of doubtful significance. The
average cell volume in the tetraploid was approximately 1·6 times that of
the diploid, but detailed analysis of cell size from one tissue region to
another indicated that this relationship was not constant.

By using colchicine, Satina, Blakeslee and Avery (1940) obtained apical
meristems of *Datura* in which the three layers of the tunica consisted of
cells with nuclei of different chromosome number; i.e. cells might have

normal diploid nuclei, or their nuclei might be tetraploid or octoploid. According to the disposition of these layers, containing $2n$, $4n$ or $8n$ chromosomes, so was the apical meristem modified in size and cellular constitution (Fig. 5.9). Although three histogenic layers are present, the data do not

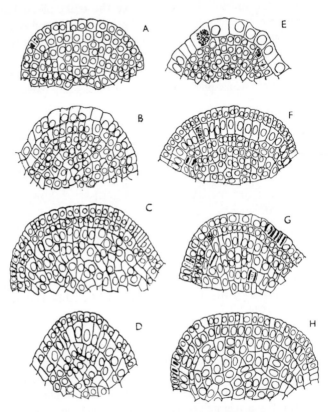

FIG. 5.9. Shoot apices of colchicine-induced chimaeras in *Datura stramonium*. A, control, 2n, 2n, 2n; B, 4n, 2n, 2n; C, 2n, 2n, 4n; D, 2n, 8n, 4n; E, 8n, 2n, 2n; F, 2n, 4n, 2n; G, 4n, 2n, 4n; H, 2n, 4n, 4n ($\times$270). (After S. Satina, A. F. Blakeslee and A. G. Avery, *Amer. Jour. Bot.*, 1940.)

support in detail Hanstein's (1868) views as to the contribution which these layers make to the several tissue systems; but they are in accord with the tunica–corpus conception of the apical meristem as advanced by Schmidt (1924). Important observations on induced chimaera polyploids have also been made by other investigators. (*See also* Satina and Blakeslee, 1941, and Satina, 1944.)

THE SHOOT APEX DURING ONTOGENESIS

This important topic can only be dealt with briefly here. (*See also* pp. 100–102.) Whether we are investigating a developing, globular proembryo, a nascent embryoid plantling or a growing adventitious bud, the essential initial task is to observe the inception of organization in an active meristematic entity or locus: we must be in at the genesis of morphogenesis! In general terms, it has been ascertained from anatomical studies that a cell (or a small group of cells) in a particular locus, e.g. distally in the dicotyle-

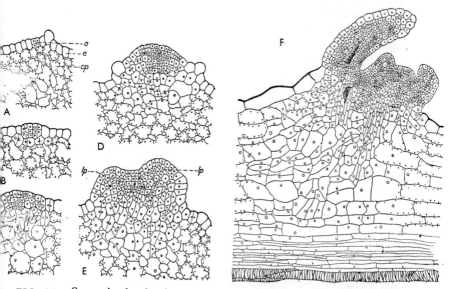

FIG. 5.10. Stages in the development of adventitious buds in flax (*Linum*). A–C, Regeneration begins at (*a*) by division of one of the epidermal cells (*e*), and spreads to the cortical parenchyma (*cp*); D–F, A meristematic outgrowth – a bud – is formed; it gives rise to leaf primordia (*lp*) and to a basipetally differentiating vascular strand. (After D. M. Crooks, *Botanical Gazette*, 1933–34.)

don embryo or superficially as in the adventitious buds of *Linum* (Fig. 5.10), becomes specially active, divides repeatedly and so constitutes a 'physiological sink', i.e. a locus of active utilization of the substances of growth processes. In fact, this *nascent meristem* becomes a focal point to which a general flow of metabolic materials is directed. It also affords evidence of being in a *regulated*, or perhaps *complementary*, relationship with the adjacent tissues. Polarity is soon established, perhaps in relation to metabolic gradients; but this phenomenon is still obscure. At any rate the direction of development of the long axis of growth soon becomes determined. For the reasons already suggested (p. 101), the embryonic cells which are of a characteristic size, and in response to the biophysical forces of growth, become disposed in a pattern of some regularity, e.g. the convex, layered configuration of many flowering-plant apices. (The foregoing, it need hardly be said, is merely a tentative working outline.)

In the ferns the apical meristem and its constituent cells undergo considerable enlargement as the young sporophyte develops into a plant of adult stature. And similarly in some gymnosperms, e.g. cycads; and in angiosperms, e.g. *Nuphar* and *Nymphaea* spp., etc. But in many flowering plants the shoot apex attains to its maximum size quite early in ontogenesis, e.g. at the young plantling stage, and thereafter it remains more or less unchanged until the onset of the flowering phase (p. 310).

Although the plant as a whole typically undergoes a considerable enlargement during ontogenesis, the morphogenetic activities of its apex during the vegetative phase remain generally unchanged qualitatively, though they may change quantitatively. There may, for example, be gradual changes in phyllotaxis, or in heteroblastic leaf development (*see* p. 209) and so on. But these are not changes of a fundamental organogenic nature. They are, however, closely related to the supplies of nutrients reaching the distal growing region and to other ontogenetic developments (*see* p. 310).

ENVIRONMENTAL FACTORS

The morphological appearance of a plant – of any plant – is the resultant of its genetical constitution, during ontogenesis, in interaction with environmental factors, e.g. the changing seasons, vicissitudes in supplies of water and nutrients, growth in full sunshine or shade, or under conditions of etiolation, and so on. One has only to compare the sun and shade habits of some species, or the land and water habits of others, to see how much the phenotypic expression may be affected by environmental factors. Our immediate task is to consider to what extent the organization of the shoot apex is modified by environmental factors.

In fact, the literature on this aspect is still rather scanty. There are, however, indications that although the fundamental and characteristic configuration of the apex remains unaltered, certain changes can be referred to external factors. In a study of the land- and water-forms of the fern *Marsilea drummondii*, Allsopp (1955) showed that the shoot apices in water-form plants, cultured in media with 1 and 2 per cent glucose, differed from those of land-forms, cultured in media with 4 and 5 per cent glucose. The latter were more obtuse in outline and expanded more rapidly in the subapical region. Apices of water-forms showed a more gradual subapical expansion.

However, it is doubtful if any significant differences were induced in the histological constitution or morphogenetic activities of the apical meristem by the different environmental conditions. It is also known that apices can be considerably modified in size and shape by the plant being grown under 'starvation' conditions; and other, more radical, changes may result in some species from ageing. Disorganization effects can also be induced in the apical meristem by the direct application of various substances (*see* p. 177; and Cutter, 1965, for an extended general review).

The incidence of light, which usually has conspicuous effects on the nature and extent of leaf development (for recent reviews, *see* Mohr, 1962; and Hendricks and Borthwick, 1963), may have comparatively little or no visible effect on apical histology. In broad-bean seedlings, for example, the size of the apical meristem and the distribution of mitotic figures was the same in the darkness and in light (Butler and Lane, 1959); and similarly for peas (Thomson and Miller, 1962). In *Elodea canadensis*, however, Dale (1957) found that the apices of lateral shoots formed in darkness were smaller and had fewer cells than those formed in light. The several changes induced by variations in light intensity in the subapical regions and in developing leaf primordia have been reviewed by Cutter (1965). Butler (1965) has demonstrated the phenomenon of endogenous mitotic rhythm in the shoot apical meristem of *Vicia*.

It thus appears that, in its cellular organization, the shoot apical meristem, though subject to some changes, is remarkably stable. Many of the phenotypic changes, associated with the action of environmental factors, are induced in the *subapical* and *maturing* regions. Nevertheless, the apical meristem can also undergo critical organizational changes, in particular as a result of stimuli proceeding from below. Such changes are seen at the onset of flowering in angiosperms (*see* p. 310).

THE SHOOT APEX IN MONOCOTYLEDONS

So far, experimental work on shoot apices has largely been confined to ferns and dicotyledons. Of course, many monocotyledon apices, e.g. those of Gramineae, have been closely examined anatomically. In general, they show a considerable range in size and shape due to differential growth, as already noted in other apices (Fig. 5.2). Some monocotyledon apices are of rather distinctive configuration. In species of Gramineae, for example, as also in some aquatic species, e.g. *Elodea canadensis* (Hydrocharitaceae), the apical dome (or meristem) is a thin, elongated organ, extending a considerable distance above the youngest leaf primordia. Here, in parenthesis, we may note the close resemblance in general configuration between *Elodea*, a monocotyledon, and *Hippuris vulgaris*, an aquatic dicotyledon (Hippuridaceae; Lythrales) (Figs. 5.1, 5.2). Other monocotyledon species are characterized by the formation, during the vegetative phase, of a close assemblage of leaves, often with more or less completely clasping bases, these enveloping the apex. In species such as the banana (*Musa* sp.) the successive leaf primordia of the vegetative phase are separated by lateral rather than by vertical intervals. In palms, such as the oil palm (*Elaeis guineensis*), while the apical meristem is itself a raised dome, it occupies a depression in the midst of numerous encasing leaf-bases (Fig. 5.2). A further point of special interest in bulky monocotyledons, which either form massive trunks as in the palms, or large fleshy rhizomes as in bananas, is the 'secondary thickening' in the subapical and maturing regions. This is the result of active augmentation of the cortical and medullary tissues by a region of subapical tissue which persists in an actively meristematic state.

Symmetry. In the monocotyledons, as in some dicotyledons, apices of bilateral symmetry are known. In ferns, such as the bracken (*Pteridium aquilinum*), the shoot apex is of dorsiventral symmetry. A majority of the apices of vascular plants, however, are of radial symmetry.

DIFFERENTIAL GROWTH IN THE SHOOT APEX

The distribution of growth in the shoot apex, or indeed, in any growing region, has been described as one of the great 'unknowns' in biology. Some light, however, is beginning to break through: relevant observations are now accumulating from different sources. Here, one must ask if the direction of growth of a cell, or tissue, is directly affected by the presence of some particular metabolite, or system of metabolites; i.e. as an immediate endogenous effect, or as a result of translocation from other parts of the plant. Some important information is now becoming available.

It has been known for some time that IAA is closely involved in the elongation of shoots, buds and foliar organs. Several workers have recently found that auxin induces cell elongation only if there are concurrent syntheses of protein and RNA (*see* Nooden and Thimann, 1963, 1965; Key, 1964; Nitsan and Lang, 1965). Quite simply, we are concerned with whole cell processes, or phenomena.

Some reference to experimental studies of differential growth in the subapical region in angiosperms has its place here (*see* summary in Wardlaw, 1965a). In a tall (normal) and dwarf variety of tomato (*Lycopersicum esculentum*), Bindloss (1942) reported that whereas, in 9-day-old seedlings, cell divisions only took place a few microns below the apex, in 38-day-old plants the zone of active cell division extended 4–5 mm. below the apex. Moreover, in the tall variety this zone was at least 1 mm. longer than in the dwarf. Sachs and Lang (1961) assessed the incidence of mitosis in the apices of several species. In vegetative rosette plants, e.g. species of *Hyoscyamus* and *Samolus*, they noted that the zone of mitotic activity was quite limited; but in elongating rosette plants and in caulescent species there was a mitotic zone of 5–10 mm. Now these dividing cells in the subapical region eventually become more or less extensively elongated. Accordingly, conspicuous effects on the configuration of the leafy shoot follow as a natural consequence. Investigations of the GA effects on stem elongation in dwarf varieties and in rosette plants, e.g. by Basford (1961), Lang (1957, 1959), Lang *et al.* (1959), Sachs and Lang (1957, 1961), and Sachs *et al.* (1959, 1960), all indicate the importance of differential growth in contributing to the eventual morphology of the plant. In species characterized by elongated stems GA does not exercise these effects. But applications to the subapical region of growth-inhibiting substances, e.g. various carbamates (Amo-1618), result in a dwarf or rosette configuration, though with normal leaf formation and phyllotaxis, in normally caulescent species. This effect, however, can be offset by applications of gibberellin (for refs. *see* Wardlaw, 1965b). Sachs and his co-workers reported that Amo-1618 inhibited mitosis in the shoot subapical region of *Chrysanthemum*; but if GA was applied either simultaneously or later it reversed this effect. In these several experiments the growth and morphogenetic activities of the apical meristem were but little affected.

Gorter (1961) investigated three dwarf and one 'normal' tall variety of *Pisum sativum* and concluded that dwarfism is determined by light. In the dark the four varieties grew to the same height: in the light their growth was reduced, but more so in the dwarfs than in the tall variety. In white and yellow light, of equal incident energy, the several varieties showed different responses. Thus, the dwarfs showed considerably higher sensitivity to white light by the reduction in their growth than did the tall variety. In yellow light the tall variety underwent no reduction in its growth and it showed no response at the higher intensities; but at the lower intensities it developed a 'yellow-etiolation'. The dwarfs showed less growth at all intensities. Gorter found that GA counteracted these light-induced reductions in stature; i.e. GA-treated intact plants of all four varieties grew to the same size. Although isolated internode sections of the four varieties responded only a little to GA, their growth was increased by additions of sucrose and indoleacetic acid, the latter apparently contributing more to this effect than the GA. Gorter considered that there were no synergistic activities of GA, IAA and sucrose.

In a wild type groundsel (*Senecio vulgaris*), in comparison with a radiation-induced dwarf, differing from the parental type by a single gene only, Basford (1961) reported that the dwarf could be induced to grow to approxi-

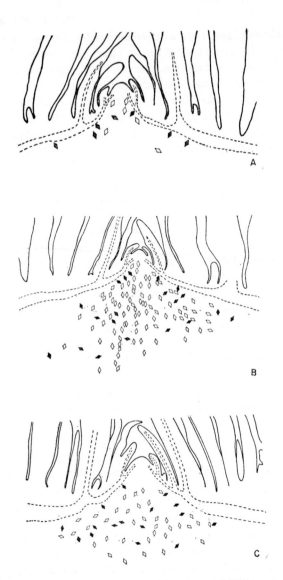

FIG. 5.11. Differential growth in the shoot apex of *Hyoscyamus niger*, as ascertained from a study of the number and direction of the mitotic spindles: vertical spindles, light; horizontal spindles, dark. The 'maps' show the distribution and orientation of mitotic spindles in intact and defoliated biennial *Hyoscyamus* plants after treatment with gibberellin. The maps were prepared as described in Sachs *et al.*, 1959, except that each mitotic spindle is represented by a diamond, showing its actual position and direction in the central 64 *u* of the pith meristem. The divisions in the pro-meristem are *not*

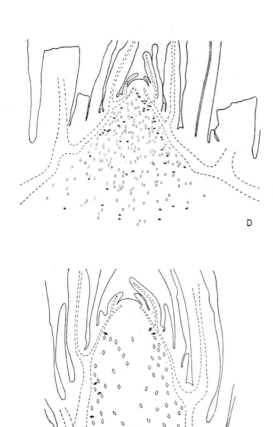

shown because they cannot be represented at the same scale; however, their number and orientation do not differ significantly in the various treatments, except that no divisions were present in this region in the 96-hours defoliated plants. Stippled lines show the limits of the prevascular tissue. A, untreated control, zero time. B, intact, gibberellin-treated, 24 hours C, defoliated, gibberellin-treated, 24 hours. D, defoliated, gibberellin-treated, 48 hours. E, defoliated, gibberellin-treated, 96 hours. (After M. Negbi, B. Baldev and A. Lang, *Israel Jour. Bot.*, 1964.)

mately the same size as the normal wild type by applications of GA. However, although the several morphological features of the treated dwarf were closely comparable with those of the wild type, some significant differences of detail were noted.

Negbi, Baldev and Lang (1964) studied the orientation of the mitotic spindles in the shoot apex of *Hyoscyamus niger*, with and without defoliation, and with application of gibberellic acid (GA$_3$) to promote mitotic activity (Fig. 5.11). (These diagrams, in fact, do not indicate mitotic divisions in the apical meristem proper nor in the nascent and developing cortex; but they afford an interesting insight into the general distribution of growth in the distal region of the axis.) Spindle orientation was assessed as being *vertical*, i.e. in the longitudinal axis of the stem, or *horizontal*, i.e. at right-angles to the stem axis; spindles parallel to the procambial strand, i.e. in the nascent or developing pith, were also assessed as being *vertical*, and those at right-angles as being *horizontal*. As spindle orientation affords an indication of the *direction* of growth, the purpose of the exercise is evident. The orientation of the mitotic figures was expressed as a percentage of the vertical spindles – the latter being indicative of the vertical component of growth. A solution of gibberellic acid (50 micrograms per plant) was applied directly to the exposed apices of defoliated plants and at the base of the youngest leaves, close to the apex, in the intact plants. (For full experimental details and criteria, *see* the original paper.)

As in the earlier studies of Sachs *et al.* (1957 *et seq.*), the application of GA did not change the number of mitotic figures in the apical meristem, but it greatly increased the amount of nuclear division in the subapical region. In the intact plants (also treated with GA) about 80 per cent of the spindles were vertical. In the defoliated plants, irrespective of the extent of defoliation, the number of dividing nuclei was diminished; and the percentage of vertically orientated spindles decreased proportionately with the extent of defoliation. However, the presence of one 3-mm. leaf primordium, or of a single young adult leaf, maintained a substantial number of vertical spindle orientations. Forty-eight hours after treatment defoliated plants showed a rapid increase in their mitotic activity, exceeding that in intact, GA-treated plants. Thereafter there was a decline, not, apparently, because of a GA shortage but, more probably, because of a general decrease in growth in the defoliated plants. The amount of vertical spindle orientation in defoliated plants generally followed these growth changes.

An increase of vertical spindle orientation in defoliated plants, 48 hours after gibberellin treatment, was also observed in several other rosette plants, e.g. *Raphanus sativus*, *Samolus parviflorus* and *Crepis parviflora*. These investigators concluded: (*a*) that nuclear division and spindle orientation are dependent on metabolic substances which are normally synthesized in the leaves, and (b) that the substances affecting the two processes are separate and independent. In their view, the factor which limits nuclear division 'recovers' in the defoliated plant more rapidly than that which determines spindle orientation. Some evidence has thus been obtained which bears closely on the phenomenon of differential growth in the sub-apical region. But *how*, as a physical phenomenon, the factors proceeding from young leaves into the axis determine the *direction of growth* has still to be ascertained.

Nitsan and Lang (1965) described experiments in which lettuce seedlings were grown with and without applied gibberellin (GA$_3$), in solutions which also contained different inhibitors of DNA synthesis. The GA increased hypocotyl elongation in the dark, and both hypocotyl and cotyledon elongation in the light. 5-fluorodeoxyuridine (FUDR), applied at 3×10^{-7} M, was attended by a 50 per cent inhibition of growth. The inhibition resulting from FUDR applications at 10^{-7} to 10^{-5} M was completely reversed by 10^{-4} M thymidine, but not by uridine. An inhibition due to amethopterin (50 per cent at 10^{-7} M) was only partly reversed by thymidine; and similarly for 10^{-5} M of mitomycin C, and 2×10^{-3} M of phenethyl alcohol. Both cell division and cell elongation were suppressed in the inhibited tissues. In other experiments using decapitated lentil seedlings, in which epicotyl growth is chiefly by cell elongation, such elongation was increased by application of GA$_3$ and was inhibited by FUDR at 10^{-7} to 10^{-5} M. This inhibition was reversed by thymidine, but not by uridine (Nitsan and Lang, 1965). From these experiments it may be inferred that there is a direct relationship between the synthesis of DNA and cell elongation as well as cell division.

Further information on differential growth can be found in the work of Kaufman (1965a). Kaufman used the intercalary meristem in the internode of *Avena sativa* in a study of the effects of gibberellins on cell division, enlargement and differentiation. Already, Kuraishi and Muir (1964a, b) and others had shown that the amount of diffusible auxins in various tissues and organs is increased by exogenous GA. The conclusion of special interest here from Kaufman's work is illustrated in Fig. 5.12. This shows that IAA and GA have rather different effects on the distribution of growth, and therefore on the pattern of cell division. In the intercalary development of *Avena* internodes IAA markedly increases longitudinal growth in the light and decreases it in the dark. But IAA also substantially augments transverse growth (*pathway 2*, Fig. 5.12), especially in the light. At comparable concentrations GA accelerates longitudinal growth in both light and dark, but it has little effect in augmenting the transverse component of growth (*pathway 3*, Fig. 5.12). Kaufman has discussed the possible mechanisms of action of GA and IAA in these growth phenomena in terms of the relevant biochemistry. As already emphasized, an adequate interpretation should also include a consideration of the biophysical aspects of metabolic processes. As tentative general conclusions, it appears that some metabolic

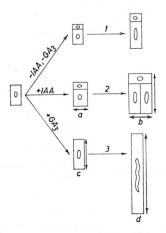

FIG. 5.12. Indoleacetic acid and gibberellin in differential growth. Comparison of patterns of cell expansion and first stages of cellular differentiation in *untreated* intercalary meristem epidermal cells (*pathway 1*) with those in internodes incubated in IAA and GA₃ (*10 mg./l.*) in pathways 2 and 3, respectively. (After P. B. Kaufman, *Physiologia Plantarum*, 1965.)

substances chiefly affect the vertical component of growth, while others affect both the vertical and transverse components; but in that DNA synthesis is also involved, it may be inferred that differential growth is essentially a holistic process.

CHAPTER VI

An Introduction to the Study of Meristems

INTRODUCTION

With some of the facts of embryogenesis and of the histological constitution
of the shoot apical meristem before us, we may now consider how new
ideas and new observations and experiments are advancing our knowledge
of morphogenesis. Indeed, as compared with thirty years ago, there is a
great deal to be discussed.

As already noted, the developing leafy-shoot in *any* higher plant – fern,
gymnosperm or angiosperm – may be envisaged as a dynamic geometrical
system: an actively growing apex gives rise to an axis and to lateral members in an orderly and characteristic sequence. If, now, to this simplified
statement we add Sachs' chemical concept of morphogenesis, i.e. that
specific metabolic substances are present in the loci or sites in which particular organs originate, it might perhaps appear to the detached, non-
biological observer that it should not prove unduly difficult to account for
the vegetative organization of higher plants. Some of the problems can be
indicated in fairly simple terms, namely, to elucidate the physico-chemical
basis of organization in single generative cells and in apical meristems; to
ascertain the factors which determine the inception of regularly spaced
growth centres; the nature and activity of the substances in these loci and
in the adjacent tissues; and the nexus of factors which determines whether
a primordium shall develop as a leaf or a bud. Somewhat similar considerations also apply to the inception and development of the several organs of
the flower. However, although work on plant growth substances is now
very extensive (*see Encyclopedia of Plant Physiology* for comprehensive reviews), no one has yet detected or isolated a specific 'leaf-forming', 'bud-
forming', or 'flower-forming' substance (*but see* p. 203). Nor do we have
much direct information on the accumulation and reactions of metabolic
substances, whether general or specific, in growth centres. In brief, our
knowledge of the metabolic reactions of organogenesis is still very slight.
Accordingly, when one attempts to indicate factually some of the basic reactions, e.g. the presence and activities of specific enzymes, the regulation
of enzyme activity, RNA relationships, etc., in apical growth, bud and leaf
induction, etc., there is still relatively little that can be said. From morpho-

genetic investigations it is now quite clear where solutions to problems of organogenesis must be sought, but we do not yet possess microchemical and other techniques of sufficient precision and delicacy to deal with the inception of specific metabolism in small growth centres in apical meristems. However, a review of some recent and contemporary investigations and conjectures may be helpful.

DISTRIBUTION OF METABOLIC SUBSTANCES

Some simple ideas regarding the movement of metabolic substances into and out of the apical region enable us to draw inferences of considerable importance in morphogenesis. They may also serve as a guide to pertinent analytical and experimental investigations.

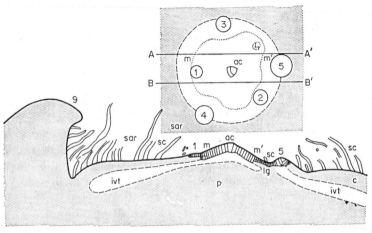

FIG. 6.1. *Dryopteris dilatata*₉ the morphological and histological organization of a fern apex; the apical cone as seen from above and in median vertical section (AA′–BB′). The interrupted line separates the base of the cone from the subapical region (stippled). Leaf primordia, 1, 2, 3, etc., in order of increasing age; I_1, position of next primordium to be formed; *ac*, apical cell; the apical meristem (*m–m′*) does not cover the whole surface of the apical cone but extends a variable distance down its sides; *ivt*, incipient vascular tissue below apex and primordium; *sar*, subapical region; *c*, cortex; *p*, pith; *sc*, scales; *lg*, leaf gap. (Semi-diagrammatic) (×20). (After C. W. Wardlaw, *Phil. Trans. Roy. Soc.*, 1949.)

In the ferns the *incipient vascular tissue* (or *prevascular tissue*) can be traced upwards from the older, mature conducting tissues into the shoot apex to a point immediately below the apical cell group and the associated prism-shaped calls and the youngest leaf primordia (Fig. 6.1). In many flowering plants the pre- or pro-vascular tissue (or procambium) can also be followed upwards from mature regions to the bases of the youngest leaf primordia; and in some instances, e.g. *Hippuris vulgaris*, the central column of prevascular tissue can be observed in the apex above the level of insertion of the youngest leaf primordia. These prevascular tissues, however feeble their differentiation, afford incipient pathways of translocation and are functionally important in organogenic developments in the apex, Fig. 6.2 (Wardlaw, 1956a; Wardlaw & Cutter, 1954, 1956). A typical mature vascular strand, i.e. consisting of fully differentiated xylem and phloem tissues, to each of which specific translocational functions have been ascribed, is enclosed within an impervious endodermal sheath in some species. In the

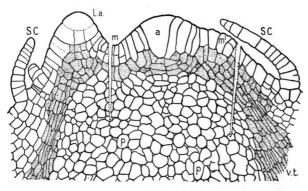

FIG. 6.2. *Dryopteris dilatata*. A small shoot apex as seen in median longitudinal section. *m–m'*, apical meristem, consisting of distinctive prism-shaped cells and a large apical cell, *a*; *sc*, scale; *l.a.*, leaf apex; *v.t.*, incipient vascular tissue; *p*, pith. The vertical incisions by which the meristem can be isolated are shown. The isolated meristem has a thin layer of incipient vascular tissue and is seated on a plug of pith parenchyma (×200). (After C. W. Wardlaw, *Annals of Botany*, 1944; *Phil. Trans. Roy. Soc.*, 1947.)

shoot apex, however, the xylem and phloem have not yet become differentiated and the radial walls of the endodermis have not yet become suberized. So, in the subapical and apical regions, we may envisage the ascending metabolic solutions, hitherto retained within the vascular tissues by the endodermis, and possibly by other agencies, as diffusing laterally into the developing cortex and pith, and upwards into the apical meristem and its recently formed primordia (Fig. 6.3). We may reasonably conjecture that some of the metabolic substances are drawn from the incipient vascular tissue to regions of active utilization; or they may perhaps diffuse passively outwards from the vascular tissue in which concentrations are high. However, on this important aspect of plant physiology we have surprisingly little information. As a generally acceptable hypothesis in plant physiology, it is assumed that metabolic materials move from regions of higher concentration, e.g. loci of production, to regions of lower concentration, or to loci of active utilization. In different ways, and in different degrees, the several regions of an actively growing apex may be envisaged as loci of utilization. This general argument could have an important application to

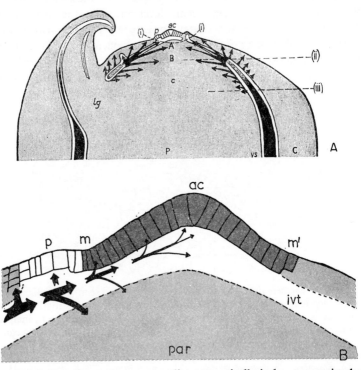

FIG. 6.3. A fern shoot apex, as seen diagrammatically in l.s., suggesting how metabolic substances may move into the growing region from the older mature regions of the axis (*see* text). A, (i) the apical region; (ii) the subapical region; (iii) the maturing region. The arrows suggest a conception of the distribution of nutrients from the mature and immature vascular tissues. c, pith; C, cortex; *vs*, vascular strand; *l.g.*, leaf-gap. B, detail of apex: *ac*, apical cell; *m–m′*, apical meristem; *p*, leaf primordium, *ivt*, incipient vascular tissue. (After C. W. Wardlaw, A, *Amer. Jour. Bot.*, 1957; B, *Annals of Botany*, 1952.)

all morphogenetic developments. If a particular metabolic substance, e.g. a sugar, is being actively utilized in the subapical region of rapid cell expansion there will be less sugar available for growth in the more acropetal regions progressively closer to the distal meristem. This could also be true of the ascending solutions of amino acids and other important metabolites. One may also envisage a differential utilization of different substances, e.g.

different balances of amino acids, hormones, etc., at different levels in the apex. Moreover, in relation to synthetic processes in the apical meristem, or in young primordia, certain substances, synthesized in excess of local utilization, will tend to diffuse from the locus of high concentration to other regions of the apex and basipetally into more mature regions. If, now, we accept the existence of both acropetal and basipetal metabolic gradients it will be seen that no two contiguous cross-sectional levels in the apex can be quite identical; and a metabolic situation of this kind, in terms of Sachs' concept of chemical morphogenesis, may be the basis of the characteristic organogenic or histogenic development perceived at any particular level (*see* Figs. 6.1–6.3). For further consideration of differential growth, *see* p. 110.

PROTEIN METABOLISM IN MERISTEMATIC TISSUES

It will already be apparent that, in practice, it is very difficult to relate the distinctive morphology of an organ to its metabolism during development. Yet it seems reasonable, not to say inescapable, to suppose that metabolic differences are involved in the formation of leaf and bud primordia, i.e. that morphological differentiation is determined by metabolic differentiation. The investigation of metabolism in root and shoot apices by Brown and Robinson (1955), Heyes and Brown (1956, 1965), and Sunderland *et al.* (1956, 1957) have revealed differences in the metabolic characteristics of: (i) the tunica and corpus; (ii) the distal region of the meristem and the organogenic region; (iii) young leaf primordia and their related stem segments and so on. It was found that the vacuolating and enlarging cells of the corpus are of higher metabolic activity than the smaller and more densely protoplasmic cells of the tunica; and a somewhat similar relationship holds for a young leaf primordium and its associated stem segment. The corpus, in fact, may be an important source of synthesized metabolites, some of which pass outwards, i.e. move centrifugally, and contribute to the activities of the superficial tissues and organs.

From the work of Wetmore (1953 *et seq.*) and of Steward, Wetmore *et al.* (1954, 1955), on the amounts of amino acids present in the various regions of the shoot apex, i.e. the most distal region of the meristem, leaf primordia, unexpanded and expanded leaves, cotyledons and stem, it has been inferred that there may be a sequential or phasic utilization of different amino acids at successive stages of growth, histogenesis and morphogenesis; i.e. a phasic synthesis of different proteins, chiefly enzymes, with concomitant differential metabolism in growing tissues, growth centres and primordia, may, together with other factors (*see* below), determine the eventual morphological differences between organs. This general concept could also be applied to the interpretation of heteroblastic development, i.e. the development of different leaf forms during ontogenesis and at critical stages, such as the transition to flowering (*see* p. 209).

If, now, we apply the idea of sequential protein synthesis to organogenesis in the shoot apex, bearing in mind that in both ferns and flowering plants *leaf primordia are usually formed spatially higher up on the meristem and temporally earlier than buds*, it is possible that the morphological differences between these organs may be due to subtle differences, both quantitative and qualitative, in their protein synthesis and related metabolism. Furthermore, the essential contiguity in which the growth centres of leaf and bud primordia originate in the apical meristem suggests that some complementary relationship may exist between 'leaf' proteins and 'bud' proteins. The inception of such complementary metabolic relationships may, indeed, be an important part of the differentiation process. According to the initial constitution of the physico-chemical reaction system in an embryonic region and how it is stimulated to activity, certain differential accumulations of metabolites may be expected to ensue and organogenic relationships to be established, e.g. that of leaf and bud. Specific substances, e.g. auxins or hormones, could have accelerating, delaying or inhibiting effects on the phasic protein metabolism and related organogenic developments. The complementary organogenic development mentioned above would be in accord with D. Thoday's (1933, 1939) concept of developmental and functional harmony.

GROWTH CENTRES AND LEAF PRIMORDIA

If the shoot apex of a fern or a flowering plant is laid bare by dissecting off all the older leaves and leaf primordia, the apical meristem can be observed as a convex, glossy region, on which outgrowing mounds of tissue – the leaf primordia at various stages of development – can be observed. In all phyla

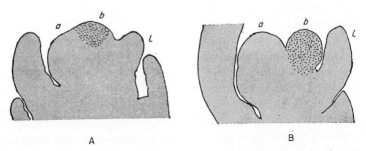

FIG. 6.4. *Hydrocharis morsus-ranae*. A and B illustrate two stages in the formation of a bud (*b*) in the apical meristem (*a*); *l*, leaf primordium. (Redrawn, diagrammatically, from E. G. Cutter, *Amer. Jour. Bot.*, 1964.)

of vascular plants, including very ancient fossil species, the formation of leaf primordia is the principal and primary manifestation of organogenic activity in the apical meristem (Wardlaw, 1956b). Buds may also originate in the meristem and, in some species, may develop to considerable size while still in proximity to the most distal region of the shoot (Fig. 6.4). More generally, however, the growth of a bud rudiment occurs some distance below the apical meristem. Since both leaf and bud primordia originate in the shoot apical meristem, investigation of one usually invokes consideration of the other.

Leaf Growth Centres. A leaf primordium becomes recognizable on the apical meristem because of active growth in a localized site of characteristic size and shape, i.e. a restricted region of special metabolism, conveniently described as a *growth centre*.[1] In the fern *Dryopteris*, with its large conical apex, the leaf growth centres are relatively small and occur in situations low down on the flanks of the apical meristem. In some flowering plants similar relationships may be observed; but in others the growth centres originate very close to the tip of the meristem (Figs. 6.5, 6.6). Because growth centres differ in number, position, size and shape, in species from different taxonomic groups, very considerable diversity in primordium morphology and phyllotaxis follows as a natural consequence. (Wardlaw, 1956d, 1957c.)

In ferns the nascent leaf primordium results from the growth of a group of some 8–10 conspicuous, superficial, prism-shaped cells of the apical meristem, together with active division in the underlying cells (Fig. 6.7). Although the histological details are different, the inception of a leaf primordium in flowering plants is similar in its main features, the growth centres typically comprising both surface and sub-surface cells of the apical meristem (Figs. 6.7, 6.8). The microphylls of *Psilotum* and *Lycopodium* also originate from comparable multi-cellular growth centres (Wardlaw, 1957a). The histological account of leaf inception could evidently be greatly extended, but the main points are clear: (1) in all vascular plants the inception of leaf primordia exemplifies a remarkable homology of organization; and (ii) within the general system of relationships in shoot apical meristems indicated above, there is great scope for the inception of morphological diversity in leaf formation.

In a study of leaf inception in species of Rosaceae, with opposite and

---

[1] *Growth centre.* The writer should make it clear that, in his view, a *growth centre* which becomes a primordium is not necessarily a 'centre' in any strict mathematical sense. Rather it is a *locus* or *site* which may comprise a group of cells in which, as compared with the surrounding cells, there has been an accumulation of those metabolic materials (enzymes, substrates, growth-regulating substances, etc.) which, in appropriate circumstances, will make for rapid growth.

alternate leaves, Rouffa and Gunckel (1951) found that primordia originated on the flanks of the apical meristem from two to five cells below the
surface but usually in the second tunica layer. There was a concomitant
differentiation of procambium during the plastochron. The changes in the

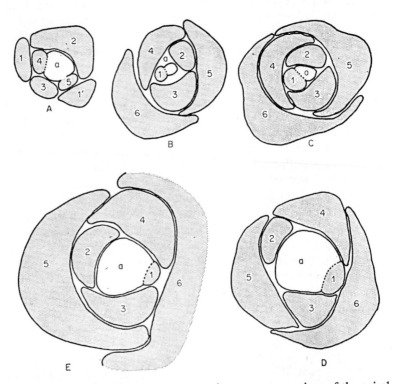

FIG. 6.5. Leaf primordia at apex as seen in transverse sections of the apical
meristem. Various apices cut in transverse section at or near the axil of the
youngest primordium. Except in A, where the oldest leaves are indicated as
l, l', the leaves are numbered in the order of their increasing age, i.e. 1, 2, etc.
A, *Lycopodium selago*, young plant from a bulbil. B, *Cassytha filiformis*, a
parasite with 'reduced' scale leaves on the adult shoot. C, *Rosa multiflora*.
D, *Cuscuta americana*, a parasite with greatly 'reduced' scale leaves on the
adult shoot. E, *Ranunculus acris*. (All ×67.) (After C. W. Wardlaw, *Annals
of Botany*, 1957.)

size of the apical meristem were not accompanied by significant fluctuations
in the stratification of the tunica. However, when an apical meristem was at
its minimal volume the tunica layers on its flanks were less stable. Some
typical stages in the inception and early development of leaf primordia are
illustrated in Fig. 6.8.

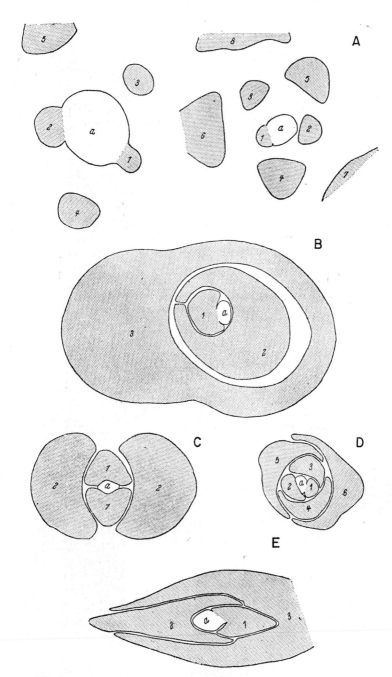

FIG. 6.6. Leaf primordia at apex. A, (left) *Dryopteris dilatata*, (right) *Nuphar luteum*. B, *Magnolia lennei*. C, *Phoradendron flavescens*. D, *Rosa multiflora*. E, *Iris pseudacorus* (all ×50). (After C. W. Wardlaw, *The Growth of Leaves*, 1956.)

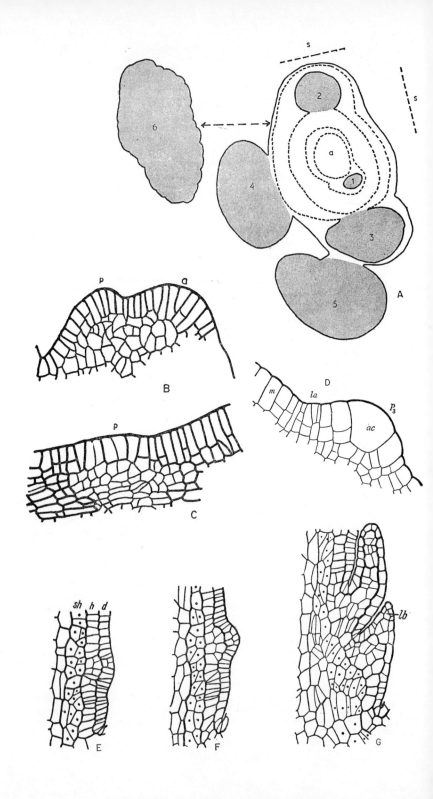

Leaf Symmetry and Orientation. Since a primordium originates on the flank of a conical or paraboloidal apex, with differentiating tissue below and embryonic cells above, or, to state the matter in more general terms, in a growing system in which there is an acropetal falling off in the growth rate, it follows that the growth relationships and rates of differentiation on the adaxial and abaxial sides of the primordium are different from the outset. The factors which determine this distribution of growth, together with other regulative factors, may determine leaf symmetry and orientation. In a leaf growth centre it is conceivable that, because of its positional relationships as described above, a differential adaxial/abaxial pattern of metabolites is established at a very early stage.

Both in pteridophytes and seed plants, the vertical growth of a young primordium is primarily due to the activity of a centrally placed, superficial initial cell, or cells. A conspicuous leaf apical cell is present in ferns, but in the flowering plants there is a group of small, superficial initial cells. Here again, within a general morphogenetic pattern, there is scope for great diversification in the further development of the foliar members. Not least, the growth of a young primordium is attended by the differentiation of an uninterrupted, acropetally developing strand, or strands, of prevascular tissue, whereby it is brought into a functional continuity with the vascular system of the parent axis. In different instances, according to the relative growth activities of the leaf primordia and the shoot apex, the vascular system of the leafy shoot may range from being predominantly foliar to predominantly axial in origin; many flowering plants illustrate the former, whereas microphyllous pteridophytes exemplify the latter state of affairs.

The development of very young leaf primordia may also be affected, or regulated, by endogenous factors proceeding from older leaves with which they are in vascular continuity (Fulford, 1965, 1966). In mature shoot systems of apple (Roach, 1939), and of tobacco (Shiroya *et al.* 1961), it was shown that, with three-eighths phyllotaxis, a particular leaf exported most

---

FIG. 6.7. Inception of leaf primordia as seen in t.s. and l.s. of shoot apices.
A, B, *Psilotum nudum.* A. Superimposed serial transverse sections of a vegetative shoot apex, showing that the eventual scale-like microphylls begin as substantial primordia at the apex ($\times 50$). B. Longitudinal median section of apex, showing a leaf primordium (*p*) and the shoot apex (*a*) ($\times 112$).
C, D, *Dryopteris dilatata.* C. l.s. of a very young leaf primordium (*p*), both surface and sub-surface cells being involved in its formation; shoot apex to right. D, older primordium ($\times 112$). (A–D, after C. W. Wardlaw, *Annals of Botany,* 1957.)
E, F, G, Leaf inception in a grass, *Agropyron repens.* *d*, dermatogen; *h*, hypodermis; *sh*, sub-hypodermis; *lb*, leaf sheath of next leaf. (After B. C. Sharman, *Bot. Gaz.,* 106, 1945.)

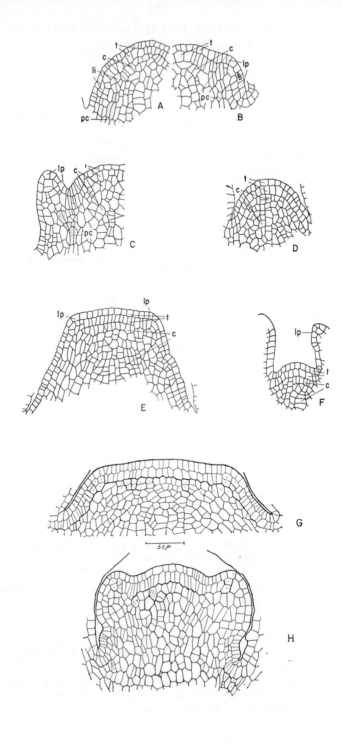

50μ

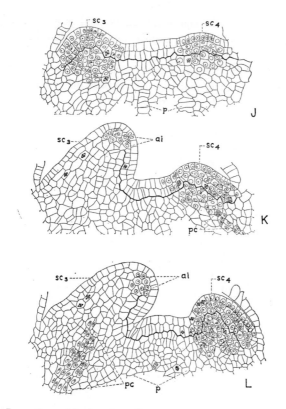

FIG. 6.8. Inception of leaf primordia as seen in l.s. of the shoot apex of species of Rosaceae and other families.

A, B, C, *Spiraea latifolia*. (Alternate leaves, and apex with 2 or rarely 3 tunica layers.) t_1, t_2, t_3, tunica layers; c, corpus; lp, leaf primordium; li, region of leaf inception; pc, procambium. In A, the apex, seen in l.s., is at its maximum volume just before the inception of a new leaf primordium in t_2 or t_3. The procambium is differentiated concomitantly with the primordium. B. A young primordium (lp) has appeared and the shoot apex is at its minimum volume. C. The primordium and the apex have both enlarged.

D, E, F, *Rhodotypos scandens*. In this species, with opposite leaves and 2 tunica layers, the apex is seen at its maximum size in D, with young primordia in E and enlarging leaves, with minimum apical diameter, in F. (After A. S. Rouffa and J. E. Gunckel, *Amer. Jour. Bot.*, 1951.)

G, *Veronica longifolia*, showing median l.s. of vegetative apex, with inception of leaf primordia.

H, *Veronica teucrium*, with primordia, in autumn. Both species have a two-layered tunica. (After U. Hamann, *Ber. deutsch. bot. Ges.*, 1960.)

J, K, L, *Carya buckleyi* var. *arkansana*. Inception of scale leaves (Sc_3, Sc_4) at the vegetative shoot apex and stages in their further development. ai, leaf apical initial cells; p, pith; pc, procambium.
(After A. S. Foster, *Amer. Jour. Bot.*, 1935.)

E

dyes or assimilates to the eighth leaf above, and proportionately less to other primordia with increasing angular divergence from it.

Discreteness of Growth Centres. A nascent leaf primordium becomes visible in a geometrically regular position on the apical meristem, as a localized, discrete outgrowth, of characteristic shape and size for the species and for

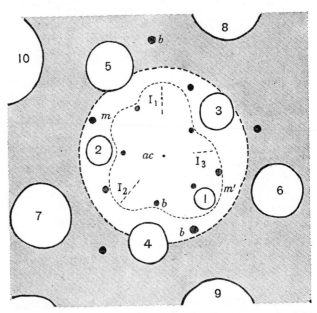

FIG. 6.9. *Dryopteris dilatata.* Diagram of a large shoot apex as seen from above. *ac*, apical cell; *m–m′*, apical meristem; the circular broken line indicates approximately the base of the apical cone; 1, 2, 3, etc., leaf primordia, in order of increasing age; I_1, I_2, I_3, positions of new leaf primordia, as yet invisible, in the order of their appearance; *b*, bud positions (×30). (After C. W. Wardlaw, *Growth*, 1949.)

the stage reached by the plant in its ontogenetic development. The observational and experimental evidence is consistent with the view that the visible outgrowth of primordia is preceded by the inception of growth centres. In large apices of *Dryopteris*, for example, three growth centres (those of I_1, I_2 and I_3)[1] are already present when the last formed primordium (P_1) is still in early plastochrone (Fig. 6.9). These growth centres

[1] Common practice sanctions the use of the symbols P_1, P_2, P_3 for the youngest leaf primordia on the apex of a plant, and I_1, I_2, I_3, etc., for the incipient primordia, the spaces at which they will have their origin being already recognizable. From oldest to youngest, in the order of their occurrence, the series would be P_3, P_2, P_1, I_1, I_2, I_3, etc.

occupy positions on the meristem somewhat above the level of P_1. It is now necessary to discuss the inception of growth centres and the primordia formed from them. Various ideas, some of them seemingly opposed, have been advanced to interpret the observed developments. But whatever view may eventually be considered valid, some basic assumptions are essential at this stage. One is that the whole shoot-apex, or some particular region of

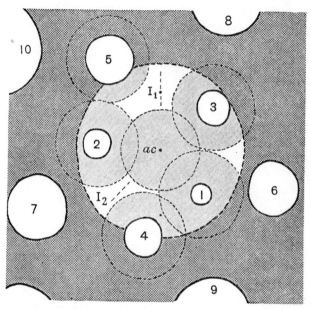

FIG. 6.10. The growth centre and field concept as it applies to the apex of *Dryopteris*. *m–m'*, apical meristem; *ac*, apical cell; 1, last-formed leaf primordium, near base of apical cone; 2–9, older primordia; *sc*, scales; *sar*, subapical region; *ivt*, incipient vascular tissue; *p*, pith; *lg*, leaf-gap; *c*, cortex (×28). (After C. W. Wardlaw, *Growth*, 1949.)

it, is a complex bio-physico-chemical reaction system, the working of this system being such that it gives rise to an orderly sequence, or pattern, of growth centres (*see also* p. 133). An amplification of these ideas leads to the further concept of 'fields' of physiological activity (Fig. 6.10).

THE APEX AS A SYSTEM OF INTER-RELATED ZONES

A comprehensive conception of the shoot apex is that it is a continuous system of integrated zones. On the evidence of experimental work (Wardlaw, 1949c, 1950b), based on Schoute's (1936) inferences from anatomical studies, the following regions of zones, in basipetal sequence, may be indicated (Fig. 6.11):

(1) *The distal region* (i.e. the summit or centre of the meristem) comprises the apical cell group in ferns, or a group of embryonic initial cells, in one or more layers, in seed plants; this is the centre or focal point of the meristem on which the integrity and, in some measure, the sustained development of the primary axis depend. For cogent reasons, it is a slow-growing region, so much so that it has mistakenly been described by some observers as being totally inert during the vegetative phase. Direct observations show

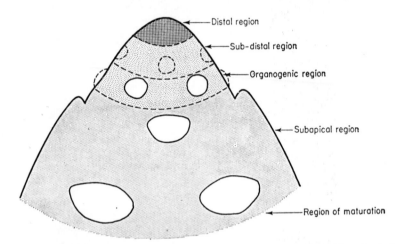

FIG. 6.11. Diagrammatic representation of a shoot apex with whorled phyllotaxis, as a system of contiguous inter-related regions or zones. (After C. W. Wardlaw, *Amer. Jour. Bot.* 1957.)

that it is not inert (Ball, 1963; Soma and Ball, 1963; Ball and Soma, 1965; Newman, 1956).

(2) *The sub-distal region* of the apical meristem consists of a superficial layer or layers of meristematic cells and, according to the species, of embryonic or differentiating cells within. This is the region in which the inception of growth centres takes place.

(3) *The organogenic region* subjacent to (2) is that in which the outgrowth of leaf primordia takes place and tissue differentiation has its inception or becomes more conspicuous. In the ferns this region occupies the base of the apical cone; in the flowering plants, in different instances, it may be high up, or low down, on the shoot apex.

(4) *The subapical region*, subjacent to (3), is usually characterized by: (*a*) a considerable widening and elongation of the shoot; (*b*) a conspicuous

enlargement of the primordia; and (c) active formation of a parenchymatous cortex and pith and further differentiation of the vascular tissue.

(5) *The region of maturation.*

THE INCEPTION OF THE ORGANOGENIC PATTERN

In the foregoing account of the apex the *sub-distal region* (2) is deemed to be of special importance, since, in it, the growth centres have their inception. In 1913 Schoute suggested that a growth centre is first determined and a leaf primordium subsequently organized round it. He also held that a specific substance is produced by these centres which inhibits the formation of others in the immediate vicinity; hence new primordia only arise between older ones when the space has become sufficiently large. The inhibition of new growth centres by the apical cell (or group of apical initial cells) was also postulated: hence the position of a new primordium on the flanks at some characteristic distance from the apical cell group. Support for the concept of growth centres has been given by various contemporary investigators. In surgical experiments, Wardlaw (1949) and Sussex (1951–55) showed that there is substantial evidence of the real existence of growth centres and that young primordia do exercise mutually regulative effects (Fig. 6.10).

Bünning (1948, 1952, 1965) ascribed the patternized distribution of growth centres to the mutual incompatibility of regions of vigorous protoplasmic growth. In his view, competition for nutrients cannot be the decisive factor underlying or determining the distribution of growth centres; rather it is that 'a certain type of embryonic growth will not allow the same type of growth to take place nearby'; but a different type of embryonic growth may proceed unimpeded. The processes in question are probably enzymatical; i.e. in the inception and development of a growth centre a particular enzyme may become quantitatively predominant, and this will lead to a diminution of the corresponding substrate in the surrounding field (Bünning). With a wealth of illustration, based on the facts of development and differentiation in cryptogams and higher plants, and comprising such anatomical features as the distribution of stomata, vascular tissues, fibres, medullary rays, etc., Bünning (1965) has done much to substantiate his views.

While Bünning's ideas may be applicable to a shoot apex in which organs have already been formed, it may be questioned if they enable us to explain how a patternized distribution of metabolites could be brought about in a new embryonic region in which no organs or tissue systems have yet been formed or differentiated. This, of course, is one of the great problems in morphogenesis. In this connection Turing's (1952) diffusion reaction theory of morphogenesis is of special interest and importance, for he has indicated that an initially homogeneous physico-chemical reaction system may become heterogeneous and give rise to a regular patternized distribution of metabolites, and thus provide the basis for a regular and characteristic morphological or histological development. As Wardlaw, (1953d; 1955b; 1965a) has pointed out, this theory, or some similar theory resting on a physico-chemical basis, is of the kind that could have a wide and general application to the phenomena of morphogenesis. It may, for example, afford a means of interpreting the orderly inception of growth centres in the sub-distal zone of the apex.

Turing's theory could enable us to account for whorled phyllotaxis, e.g. in species of *Galium,* in which four, five or more evenly spaced primordia have their inception simultaneously in the shoot meristem. In such species the members of consecutive whorls usually alternate, and hence it may be inferred that the eventual equilibrium of the reaction system in the sub-distal zone is affected by the next older primordia immediately below. The number of new growth centres produced at any particular stage in the development of the shoot is, however, determined by the state of the reaction system in the sub-distal zone. During the ontogenetic increase in size of the apex in some species with whorled phyllotaxis there is an increase in the number of primordia in successive whorls (Wardlaw, 1955a, 1965a). Any whorl with more, or fewer, primordia than the whorl below cannot absolutely alternate with it, but it seems probable that the disposition of primordia will be such as to make for equilibrium in the apex as a whole.

If Turing's theory applies to whorled phyllotaxis it may also be expected to apply to spiral and other systems. In this connection the writer now suggests, as a working hypothesis, that the inception of primordia in characteristic and usually predictable positions is due partly to the activity of the reaction system located in the sub-distal region of the apex and partly to effects exercised by the adjacent older primordia. On this basis, one can understand that an apical reaction system which gives rise to a simple pattern at an early stage in the ontogeny is likely to yield more complex variants of the same pattern during its subsequent enlargement; and that asymmetries in proximity to the reaction system, e.g. the presence of adjacent developing organs and tissues, may induce characteristic asymmetries in the system and in the patterns to which it gives rise. In large apices of *Dryopteris dilatata* the experimental evidence indicates that the growth centres of the next three primordia to be formed, i.e. I_1, I_2 and I_3, are already determined, but that the I_4 and I_5 positions can be modified by appropriate surgical treatments. In some dicotyledons, as the work of M. and R. Snow (1947, 1948) has shown, it appears that only I_1 is so determined. Critical changes in some of the components of the reaction system may affect the patterns to which it gives rise. Lastly, variations in the histological patterns that have been observed in the vegetative apex, and the transition from the 'vegetative' to the 'floral' meristem, must sooner or later be attributed to quantitative and/or qualitative changes in the substances that are being synthesized in other parts of the plant and which, on being translocated to the apex, become components of the apical reaction system.

Like any active physico-chemical system, the apex, comprising the several zones indicated above, will constantly tend towards a state of equilibrium, and this will contribute to the harmonious development of the leafy axis to which it gives rise. The apex, thus envisaged, is essentially holistic in nature.

CYTOLOGY AND APICAL ORGANIZATION AND ACTIVITY

Plantefol (1946 *et seq.*), Buvat (1952, 1953, 1955), Bersillon (1955) and others have shown that, as judged by the number of dividing nuclei, some regions of the apex are meristematically much more active than others; for example, leaf sites and the basal (or organogenic) region of the apical cone (or dome) are demonstrably more active than the cells near the tip or centre of the meristem. Indeed, these workers have asserted that, during the vegetative phase, the tip of the meristem is virtually inert, that it largely owes its origin to the subjacent region and is simply carried upwards by its growth. Some of the views elaborated in the foregoing sections, together with what follows, may perhaps enable us to evaluate the cytological contribution (Fig. 6.12).

If an apical meristem is of large size relative to its nascent leaf primordia its conformation will be but little affected by primordium formation, and a comparatively small amount of growth, with concomitant cell division, in the most distal cells will suffice to keep pace with more active cell division lower down and to maintain the paraboloidal or conical apex at its characteristic size. But if, on the other hand, the nascent primordia are of large relative size and are formed close to the tip or centre of the apical meristem, the meristem will undergo very considerable changes in size and shape at the formation of each primordium. In such cases active growth and cell division can be observed at, and close to, the tip of the meristem. Newman (1956) showed, by the direct study of living apices of *Tropaeolum* and *Coleus*, that divisions do take place in the apical initial cells. Gifford (1954) advanced cogent criticisms of the French school; and Wardlaw (1957e) discussed the cytological contribution to our knowledge of apical organization in some detail against the general background of information obtained from anatomical and experimental investigations. Wardlaw's conclusion was that detailed cytological and cytochemical investigations will almost certainly yield important new information but that the emphatic statements made by the French workers concerning growth in the apical meristem are open to substantial criticism. In recent studies, Ball (1960, 1963, 1965), and Soma and Ball (1963) kept individual apices under close observation, using time-lapse photography. They demonstrated conclusively that marked cells at the summit of the apical meristem do divide and that they and their daughter cells move outwards to the flanks of the apical meristem. (Plate 6.)

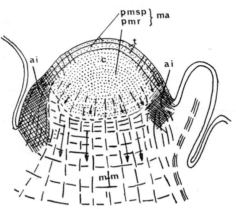

FIG. 6.12. The interpretation of organization in the vegetative shoot apex of *Lupinus albus*, according to Plantefol and Buvat. *ai*, anneau initial (initiating ring); *mm*, medullary meristem; *ma*, méristème d'attente (the resting or inactive meristem) comprising *pmsp*, the sporogenous promeristem and *pmr*, the receptacle promeristem; *t*, tunica; *c* corpus. (After C. Wibaut, *Rev. Cytol. Biol. Veg.*, 1965.)

However, there is much truth in the contention of the French workers. Cytological and histochemical studies, e.g. of DNA synthesis, indicate clearly that the *anneau initial*, i.e. the region of primordium inception, is one of great activity relative to the most distal region of the apex.

No matter how the overall organization of the shoot apex, including the spatial arrangement of leaf primordia, is to be understood, or interpreted, there can be little doubt that the region, zone or ring (*anneau initial*) on the flanks of the apical meristem, in which leaf primordia originate, is one of active metabolism, growth and organogenic activity. Histochemical studies by Buvat (1952, 1955); Gifford (1960); Gifford *et al.* (1963); Bernier and Bronchard (1963); Bernier (1964, 1966); Bernier and Jensen (1966); Brown *et al.* (1964); Nougarède and Bronchard (1965); Tillandier (1965); Lance-Nougarède (1965), etc., bear this out. But it is no less clear that the upper regions of the apical meristem, though evidently less active in the several respects mentioned above, are in no sense inactive. Gifford (1960), for example, showed that when a solution of tritiated thymidine was applied to the terminal bud of *Chenopodium album* it was taken up by the young leaves and the shoot apical meristem and that labelled nuclei were present in proximity to the most distal region.

THE ULTRASTRUCTURE OF THE SHOOT APICAL MERISTEM

Only a small number of investigations of the ultrastructure of the shoot apical meristem have so far been reported (Buvat, 1958; Lance, 1958; Hohl, 1960; Marinos, 1962, 1963; Gifford, 1965; Bowes, 1965). Whaley *et al.* (1960), however, had already described and illustrated the ultra-structure of meristematic cells in the root apex of maize; and their account has now been found to be of wide applicability. Bowes (1965) examined the apex of *Glechoma hederacea* which he had previously studied with the light microscope (Bowes, 1963). In this species the tunica consists of a single layer of cells, in which occasional, isolated, periclinal divisions can be observed. In this layer the cells have greater density of cytoplasm and nucleoplasm than the underlying cells. This is clearly shown in some of Bowes' electron micrographs. At the summit of the central initiation zone the cells are characterized by small vacuoles and proplastids. In fact, they closely resemble the root meristem cells illustrated by Whaley *et al.* (1960) and Marinos (1962, 1963). The cells of the procambium are similar in organization. Those of the rib meristem show a progressive basipetal vacu-olation. Bowes found that it was difficult to distinguish between the cellular organization in the central initiation group and the flank meristem, al-though marked differences are usually evident under the light microscope after haematoxylin staining: the density of staining in flank meristem cells is regarded as evidence of higher concentrations of RNA in the cytoplasm. In a study of the seedling apex of *Chenopodium album*, using pyronin stain-ing, Gifford and Tepper (1962) demonstrated higher RNA in the cells of the flank than in those of the distal meristem.

Vacuolation is one of the more conspicuous features of cellular differenti-ation in apical regions. Mühlethaler (1960) and Sitte (1961) interpreted vacuolation, as observed in ultramicroscopic preparations, as the result of a localized hydration of the cytoplasm, the tonoplast developing later. Buvat (1961) and Poux (1962) considered that vacuoles originated in the endo-plasmic reticulum by the separation of the two unit membranes; and Marinos (1963) ascribed their development to the enlargement of the intra-membranous space of a Golgi cisterna. Explanations along the lines of the last three workers would account for the presence of a single membrane. Vacuole formation may also be due to degeneration of mitochondria and plastids (Bell and Mühlethaler, 1962, 1964). Esau and Cheadle (1962) stated that the endoplasmic reticulum and Golgi bodies may develop vesicles. In a close study of this phenomenon in the shoot apical meristem of *Glechoma hederacea*, Bowes (1965) concluded that vacuoles originate in the endoplasmic reticulum as a result of localized accumulations of certain metabolic substances. In non-meristematic cells vacuole development is traceable to degenerating cell organelles and to the breakdown of the cytoplasmic 'ground substance' and of the nucleoplasm. In *Chenopodium album*, as studied by Gifford and Stewart (1965), the distal, axial cells of the shoot apical meristem have an ultrastructure that is common to other apical meristems in flowering plant species (*see also* p. 316).

EXPERIMENTAL APPROACHES

It has long been known that, if the shoot apex is damaged, e.g. by puncturing, damaging or excising the most distal region, lateral buds, or bud

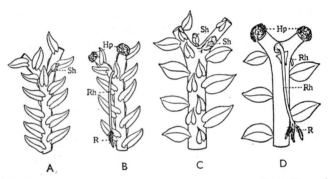

FIG. 6.13. Correlation phenomena in *Selaginella Martensii*. A, Decapitated, untreated length of shoot: a shoot (*Sh*) has developed from one of the angle meristems; B, decapitated length of shoot, treated with indoleacetic acid in lanoline paste: a rhizophore (*Rh*) giving rise to a root (*R*) has developed from the angle meristem. C, *S. Lobbii*, decapitated but untreated, has given rise to a shoot; D, *S. Lobbii*, decapitated and treated with indoleacetic acid, has given rise to a rhizophore (×1·2). (After S. Williams, *Nature*, 1937.)

rudiments hitherto dormant, become active and grow out as lateral branches. An interesting instance of the correlative inhibition of bud rudiments was demonstrated by S. Williams (1937) in species of *Selaginella* (Fig. 6.13). In some species, near the point of bifurcation of the shoot, there are two small regions of residual meristematic tissue, known as angle meristems. These may remain dormant, or they may grow downwards as root-bearing organs, or rhizophores – described by Bower as organs of indeterminate nature. If, however, the main shoot apex is damaged the angle meristem, or incipient rhizophore, grows upwards as a negatively geotropic leafy-shoot. If, again, the main shoot apex is excised and treated with IAA in lanoline, positively geotropic rhizophores are formed. (*See also* p. 180.)

An important advance was made when it seemed to some investigators that it might be possible to carry out minute but closely controlled surgical treatments of the apex. In other words, if small incisions could be made in particular positions it might be possible to observe the resulting effects on organogenesis, phyllotaxis, tissue differentiation and so on. Some of the earliest critical studies were made by Pilkington (1929) and M. and R. Snow (1932 *et seq.*) on phyllotaxis. Subsequently, others also have entered the field of *direct* apical experimentation, both by surgical techniques and by the direct or indirect application of auxins, vitamins, inhibitors, DNA precursors, etc. Others, again, have explored the possibilities of excising and culturing the apical meristem and individual leaf primordia; and different regions of the apex have been excised for micro-chemical and physiological study. As already noted (p. 135), there has recently been a considerable intensification of cytological and cytochemical observation; and time-lapse photography and electron microscopy are becoming increasingly important. Each of these approaches has its merits and its limitations. Nevertheless, the collective effect of the past 25 years of work has been to widen and deepen our understanding of the constitution, functioning and potentialities of the shoot apex. Similar and parallel investigational procedures have been, and are being, effectively applied to the meristems of roots and of inflorescences and flowers.

CHAPTER VII

The Shoot Apex: Experimental Investigations

INTRODUCTION

In this chapter, by reference to experimental studies of the shoot apex, the author will attempt to show: (i) how one significant observation, or idea, can lead to another; (ii) how old ideas, as well as new ones, can be made the basis for experimental investigations; and (iii) that crucial experiments, with predictable results, can be devised in experimental morphology, just as they have been in the physical sciences. The writer will be largely, but not exclusively, concerned with surgical experiments, these being necessarily based on close morphological and anatomical observations. This approach has its defects and limitations, but so also have other approaches. All may contribute to a synthesis. Lastly, as this book is intended to be a short introductory text, not all recent work can be mentioned.

THE FERN APEX AND DETACHED MERISTEMS

In the sections that follow, the results obtained from observational and experimental studies are treated in chronological order, in the hope that this may be helpful and encouraging to research students who venture into these complex and difficult fields.

In tentative, preliminary observations on the ostrich fern (*Matteuccia struthiopteris*) and on *Onoclea sensibilis* (both Onocleoid ferns), the writer noticed that when the apex of the horizontal rhizome was excised the lateral buds always originated in quite definite positions, or sites, along the rhizome, i.e. near the abaxial basal region of a petiole and high above the axil of an older leaf. Anatomical studies of untreated rhizomes showed that these sites are occupied by a small region of quiescent superficial, prism-shaped cells, resembling the characteristic prism-shaped cells of the shoot apical meristem. They are protected by an overarching, peripheral scaly development, Fig. 7.1. These potentially meristematic regions, *bud rudiments*, or *detached meristems*, which indeed had originally constituted part of the shoot apical meristem, were found to occupy *interfoliar* positions on the apical meristem, Fig. 7.2. In relation to the distribution of growth, they were not used up in the very considerable parenchymatous development of the shoot cortex and leaf-bases in the subapical region. They also occupied positions of minimal tensile stress at the apical end of a closing leaf-gap. Now, whereas many of the earlier investigators of the fern shoot

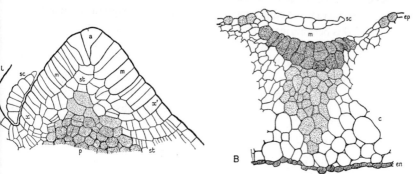

FIG. 7.1. *Matteuccia struthiopteris* – the ostrich fern. A, L.s. rhizome apex, showing apical cell (*a*), and meristematic cells (*m*) of the apical meristem extending down the flanks of the cone to *x* and *x'* (×255). *st*, differentiating stelar tissue; *p*, pith; *sc*, scale; *l*, leaf. B, T.s. rhizome (semi-diagrammatic), showing meristematic cells (heavily stippled) in groove, at commencement of plantling development; cells showing similar staining reaction below (lightly stippled). (×180.) *m*, detached meristem; *sc*, scale; *en*, endodermis; *ep*, epidermis; *c*, cortex. (×120). (After C. W. Wardlaw, *Annals of Botany*, 1943.)

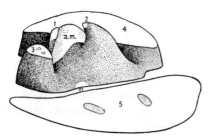

FIG. 7.2. *Matteuccia struthiopteris*. Reconstruction, from serial transverse sections, of a rhizome apex; *a.m.*, apical meristem; *m*, detached meristem; 3, 4, 5, leaves cut transversely; 1, 2, primordia of most recently formed leaves. (×27.) (After C. W. Wardlaw, *Annals of Botany*, 1943.)

apex had been mainly preoccupied with the conspicuous apical cell, its segmentations and its cell lineages, it seemed to the writer that, in interpreting morphogenetic developments, it was essential to take cognizance of the morphological and structural organization of the whole shoot apex and, in particular, of the *apical meristem*. It was noted: (1) that the prismatic cells of the apical meristem tapered out downwards towards the axils of the primordia, i.e. the outline of the meristem was undulating and did not coincide with the base of the apical cone; (ii) that a very considerable tangential expansion of the bases of the young leaf primordia and of the shoot took place close to the base of the cone; and (iii) that under the apical meristem there was a continuous sheet, or layer, of incipient vascular tissue, but that this became interrupted by leaf-gaps as soon as the afore-mentioned tangential enlargement of leaf-bases began (*see* Figs. 6.1, 7.2). On reflection, it seemed to the writer that, from anatomical observations, some very important inferences could be drawn. Still more important was the possibility that the ideas might be tested, and even validated, by crucial experiments. (For refs. *see* Wardlaw, 1952a, b; 1965a, b; Cutter, 1965;

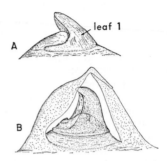

FIG. 7.3. *Musa* sp. – the banana. A, The central apical dome with the youngest leaf. During its growth the primordium encircles the axis and overarches the apex. B, The central apical dome showing the origin of leaf primordia and a completely overarching primordium. (After W. G. Barker and F. C. Steward, *Annals of Botany*, 1962.)

Allsopp, 1964a, b.) The general idea outlined above has been found applicable to some dicotyledons (*see* Garrison 1949 *et seq.*). Fig. 7.3 shows the apex and its extensive basipetal expansion in a moncotyledon – the banana (Barker and Steward, 1962).

DICTYOSTELY TO SOLENOSTELY: A PREDICTED RESULT

In a fern such as *Dryopteris dilatata*[1] the incipient vascular tissue typically originates in contiguity with the active meristems of shoots, buds, leaves and roots. The incipient vascular strand of a very young leaf primordium becomes conjoined with the uninterrupted layer of incipient shoot vascular tissue; and there are no leaf-gaps (Fig. 7.4). But lower down small gaps begin

[1] This much named and very useful species is also referred to as *D. aristata* and *D. austriaca*.

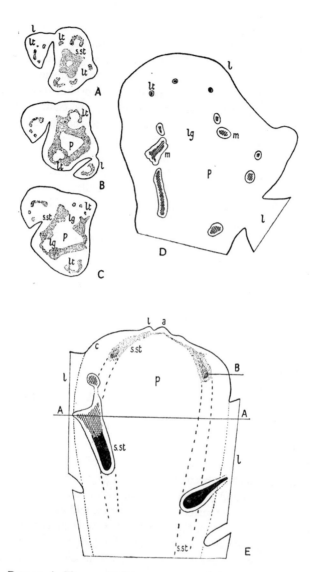

FIG. 7.4. *Dryopteris dilatata*. E, Diagram of a longitudinal median section of a rhizome apex. *a*, apical meristem; *l*, leaf primordium or leaf-base; *s.st*, tissues of the shoot stele, in an incipient condition just below the apex; *c*, cortex; *p*, pith. The discontinuities of the vascular column, or leaf-gaps, occur at the insertion of the leaf-bases. (×13.) A–D, Successive transverse sections of an apex like that in E. Just below the apex, the column of incipient vascular tissue is not interrupted by the insertion of the leaf-traces (*lt*), but, lower down, leaf-gaps, (*lg*) begin to appear. *l*, leaf; *p*, pith. (×13.) (After C. W. Wardlaw, *Annals of Botany*, 1945.)

to appear at the point of conjunction ('insertion') of the now dividing leaf-trace (i.e. the vascular system of the petiole) on the shoot stele. As the primordia enlarge, so also do their respective leaf-gaps; and as the leaves are set on the shoot in a close spiral arrangement, the shoot stele in the mature adult region is seen to be an open meshwork (or dictyostele) with wide, overlapping parenchymatous leaf-gaps. In the centre is parenchymatous pith. In short, the facts of anatomy indicate that there is a close and obligate relation between the stelar structure of the shoot and the enlargement of the leaves. An anatomical analysis also shows that, in growing leaf-bases, there is a very considerable tangential enlargement, due chiefly to an increase in the volume of the cortical and medullary parenchyma. Concomitant with these developments, the leaf-trace, which is initially a crescentic mass of cross-section, is pulled apart into four or five separate strands, with parenchyma in between. In brief, the distribution of growth in the leaf-base is such that the initially crescentic vascular trace is disrupted by being subjected to tensile stress. The cylindrical, still undifferentiated, stele of the shoot is also affected by this tensile stress, and hence the formation of leaf-gaps.

With these anatomical observations in mind, a simple experiment, with a predictable result, suggested itself, namely, that if all the very young leaf primordia being formed at the apex were destroyed, and their growth and tangential expansion thereby precluded, the associated region of the shoot would be devoid of leaf-gaps and its stele would remain a continuous uninterrupted cylinder, or solenostele, in marked contrast to the normal dictyostele. When the appropriate experiments, using *Dryopteris dilatata* and *D. filix-mas*, were carried out, the predicted result was obtained (Fig. 7.5). This simple experiment can easily be *repeated and confirmed* by anyone who exercises a little care and refinement of manipulative technique. Comparable results have been obtained with *Angiopteris evecta*, and species of *Osmunda*, *Todea* and *Primula*. Solenostelic vascular developments have been observed in other materials, both natural and experimental, e.g. in *Onoclea sensibilis* (Fig. 7.5), the normal foliar development has either not taken place or been suppressed. By other techniques it has also been possible to obtain solenosteles and even protosteles from dictyosteles (*see* p. 146 and Figs. 7.7, 7.10 and Plate 2).

In the simplified account given above, tangential stress has been indicated as the proximal factor determining the formation of leaf-gaps. In other words, incipient vascular tissue, on being subjected to tensile stress, undergoes a parenchymatous development. A considerable body of evidence supports this contention. But, in a growing system, tangential stress cannot be the primary factor: it becomes incident in relation to the tangential distribution of growth in the leaf-base and shoot cortex. So the basic question is: what factors determine this characteristic distribution of growth? As it now appears, in the orderly growth, development and differentiation of the shoot apex and its lateral organs, a whole nexus of factors is involved. Wetmore and Pratt (1949), for example, have shown that in the fern *Adiantum pedatum* there is a basipetal movement of auxin

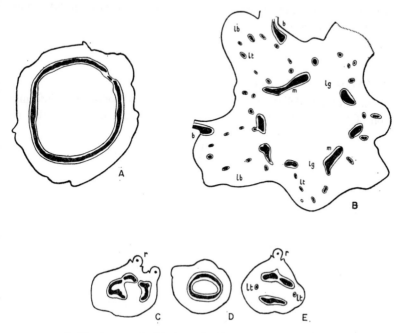

FIG. 7.5. A, B, *Dryopteris dilatata*. A, Transverse section of a stout erect shoot from which all leaf primordia had been systematically removed: the stele is a solenostele. B, Lower down in the same shoot, showing the fully developed and normal dictyostelic structure prior to the experimental treatment; *m*, meristele; *lb*, leaf-base; *lt*, leaf-trace; *lg*, leaf-gap; *b*, bud. (×3.) C, D, E, *Onoclea sensibilis*. Transverse sections of a rhizome illustrating a transition from dictyostelic structure to solenostelic structure and a return to dictyostely. *lt*, leaf-trace; *r*, roots. (×8.) (After C. W. Wardlaw, *Annals of Botany*, 1944.) (*See also* Plate 2.)

from leaf primordia into the shoot; and this may partly account for the very considerable parenchymatous developments already noted. In dicotyledons there is now abundant evidence of the basipetal movement of auxin from the petiole into the stem (*see* p. 296). But we are still very far from an adequate knowledge of the totality of the phenomena under consideration. Exciting opportunities for new work remain.

Inception of Primary Vascular Tissue

Although exceptions are known, e.g. in tissue cultures, leaf venation in some species, etc., the inception of primary vascular tissue is typically associated with active meristems of shoots, buds, leaves, roots, flowers and sori. Accordingly, in studies of morphogenesis, as we are deeply concerned with meristems in all their aspects, the phenomenon of vascular differentiation presents itself in a constant and pervasive fashion (*see* p. 293 and Esau, 1965b).

ISOLATION OF THE APICAL MERISTEM

A simple though delicate technique which has been productive of information of considerable interest consists of isolating the apical meristem by

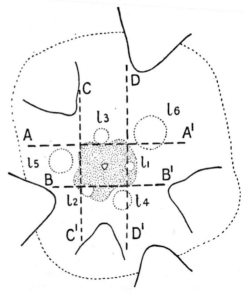

FIG. 7.6. Downward view of a small apex of *Dryopteris dilatata*, showing the apical meristem (stippled) and a succession of young leaf primordia (l_1, l_2, etc.). The apex is isolated by a system of vertical incisions (AA^1, BB^2, etc.) ($\times 54$.) (After C. W. Wardlaw, *Phil. Trans. Roy. Soc.*, 1947.) (*See* Fig. 6.2).

three or four vertical incisions from the adjacent, lateral organs and tissues (Figs. 7.6, 7.7, 7.8, 7.9). This procedure has the effect of severing the incipient vascular tissue, so that the apical meristem is seated on a plug of pith parenchyma. Both in ferns (Wardlaw, 1947, 1949, 1950, 1952a) and in flowering plants (Ball, 1948, 1952a) the apical meristem, thus isolated, continued to grow and formed a vascularized shoot with new leaf primordia in the normal phyllotactic sequence. In the ferns the newly differentiated vascular tissue did not become conjoined with that of the parent shoot below (Fig. 7.7). In *Lupinus* and *Primula* the vascular system of the isolated

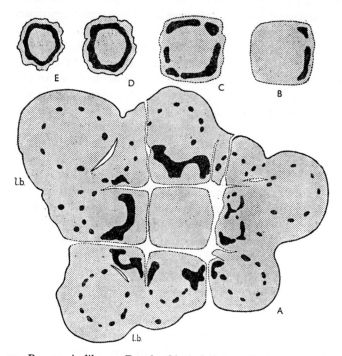

FIG. 7.7. *Dryopteris dilatata*. Result of isolating the apical meristem, as seen in serial transverse sections; the isolated meristem has grown on and given rise to a short vascularized shoot. A, Taken near the base of the experimental region, shows the system of incisions whereby the apex was isolated on a plug of non-vascularized medullary parenchyma; the dictyostelic vascular system and leaf-traces of the normal shoot are indicated; *l.b.*, leaf base; in B and C, progressively higher up than A, vascular tissue is present; in D and E still higher up, a complete vascular ring, or solenostele, has been differentiated below the growing apex (×7). (After C. W. Wardlaw, *Phil. Trans. Roy. Soc.*, 1947.)

shoot was at first completely separate from the vascular strands of the parental shoot, but, on further growth, as a result of a basipetal differentiation of new vascular tissue, i.e. downwards through the pith, a conjunction with the parental vascular strands was effected. Some interesting conclusions can be drawn from this simple experiment. Provided an apical meristem is in contact with an appropriate source of nutrition below, it is capable of normal growth and morphogenesis and behaves as a self-determining morphogenetic region. This important conclusion has been validated by the results of cultural experiments reported by Ball (1944a, 1946a, b), Wetmore and Morel (1949), and Wetmore (1950, 1953, 1954). Wetmore showed that if the apical meristem of the fern *Adiantum pedatum* is excised on a minimal panel of tissue, and grown in a suitable culture medium, a new plant, eventually capable of being 'potted-up' and grown to adult size will be obtained. The suggestion sometimes made that the older organs or tissues are the *primary* determiners of morphogenesis at the shoot apex is ruled out by those findings. This, of course, is not to deny that they have any effect. The older regions evidently supply the nutrients on which the apex depends; and important regulative effects are exerted by older leaves on younger ones, especially when they are in vascular continuity. The important phenomenon of phyllotaxis, in fact, depends to a considerable extent on acropetal effects. In general, we should probably look for reciprocal relationships between the apex and older regions of the leafy shoot.

The experimental evidence also indicates that the inception of vascular tissue is primarily determined by metabolic activities in the apical meristem, either by the basipetal diffusion of some particular substance, or by the removal of something from the subjacent cells, or by both of these processes. The active meristems of the shoot apex and of leaf primordia may be regarded as 'physiological sinks' which set up incipient pathways of translocation (*see* p. 119). The basipetal differentiation of vascular tissue in the pith of *Lupinus* and *Primula* and also in relation to developing buds and detached meristems, mentioned above, affords indisputable supporting evidence. But, in fact, in a normal elongating axis the differentiation of prevascular tissue is acropetal. It is the causation of its differentiation that is basipetal (*see also* p. 293).

In the fern experiment, where vascular continuity between the new and the parental shoot was not established, the materials required to sustain new apical growth can evidently pass across a limited zone of pith parenchyma.

In these and in cognate experiments an interesting relationship between the cross-sectional outline of the vascular column and that of the shoot has been established. Both in *Dryopteris* and in *Primula*, it was found that where the apical meristem was isolated on a triangular panel of tissue the resulting solenostele was triangular in cross-sectional outline; and where the panel was rectangular the solenostele also was of rectangular outline (Figs. 7.7, 7.8). These observations led naturally to two further experiments with predictable results. (i) If incisions could be made very close to the apical cell group, without damaging it, it should be possible to reduce the large *Dryopteris* dictyostele to a protostele at a single operation. This result was

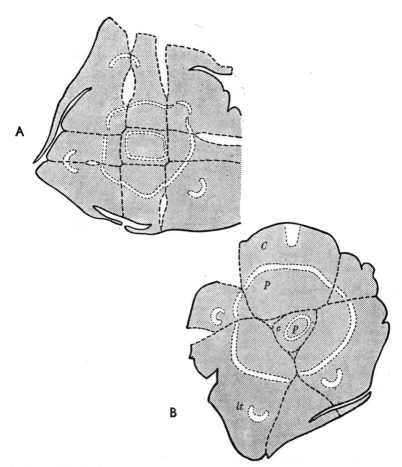

FIG. 7.8. *Primula polyantha.* Cross-sections of shoots in which the apex was isolated A, by four and B, by three vertical incisions. In each instance a new vascular column was differentiated in the isolated plug of pith parenchyma, the contour of this column being in conformity with the outline of the plug (×14). (After C. W. Wardlaw, *Phil. Trans. Roy. Soc.,* 1950.)

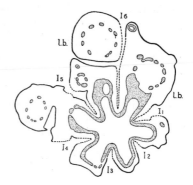

FIG. 7.9 *Dryopteris dilatata.* Stellate stele, as seen in a transverse section of the shoot, on the further growth of an apex which had been incised radially: the outline of the stele is in close conformity with that of the shoot. I_1, I_2, etc., radial incisions; *lb*, leaf-base. (×10.) (After C. W. Wardlaw, *Phil. Trans. Roy. Soc.,* 1947.)

obtained, Fig. 7.10 (Wardlaw, 1949). Numerous large solenostelic buds were formed in the regions outside the incisions. (ii) If the apical meristem is subjected to several radial incisions, without destroying its capacity for further growth, a stellate soleno-dictyostele should develop. This result

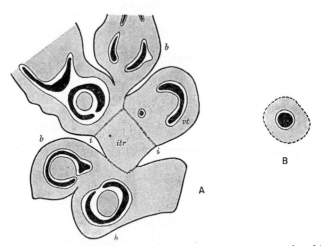

FIG. 7.10. *Dryopteris dilatata.* A, Transverse section of an apex in which the apical meristem had been isolated on a very small panel of tissue by four close, vertical incisions. The isolated terminal region (*itr*) developed as a miniature shoot, with a protostele as shown in B. Outside the incisions (*i*), in the subapical region, large solenostelic buds (*b*) were induced. (After C. W. Wardlaw, *Phil. Trans. Roy. Soc.*, 1949.)

was also obtained; Fig. 7.9. illustrates a typical record. Similar vascular configurations have been obtained experimentally in dicotyledons (Ball, 1952b).

THE EFFECT OF SUBDIVIDING THE APICAL MERISTEM

Pilkington (1929) demonstrated that the shoot apices of *Lupinus* and *Vicia* could be vertically bisected and remain viable – a pioneer discovery – and that two new apices developed from the flanks of the original meristem. Using the same technique Ball (1948, 1950, 1952b) observed the effects of vertically dividing the apex of *Lupinus* into quarter and even smaller segments. He found that such apical segments can survive and are capable of further growth; and that, eventually, each can give rise to a small leafy shoot. A one-sixth segment was about the smallest size from which regeneration could take place.

In Ball's experiments the fact that each apical segment grew on independently was regarded as further evidence of self-determination in the apical meristem. The differentiation of vascular tissue on the cut inner sides of the new shoots, prior to the appearance of new leaves, affords evidence that the inception of some of the tissue is determined by the shoot apex. Thus, while leaves have an important effect on the vascular development of the shoot, some truly axial or cauline vascular tissue is also differentiated, i.e. not all the shoot vascular tissue is merely an extension of decurrent leaf-traces, as has sometimes been suggested. But in some species it may be so.

Sussex (1952) demonstrated that regeneration could be obtained from one-sixth of a vertically incised potato shoot apex; and, when the rest of the meristem was removed, pieces of meristem not exceeding one-twentieth of the normal apical area could regenerate. He concluded that competition for nutrients by the constituent cells is part of the regulatory mechanism which conserves the organization of the apical meristem. M. & R. Snow (1953) suggested that inhibition of regeneration might be due to hormonal effects and not to competition for nutrients. However, Sussex (1953) reported effects relating to deeper incisions, involving also the undercutting of the isolated panel of the apical meristem. With these deeper cuts, regeneration was more frequent and the undercut panel grew less than the other part of the apex. In some experiments the growth of the main apex was apparently inhibited by the small regenerating panel. Sussex regarded these experimental observations as providing validating evidence for his thesis on the importance of nutritional competition in apical organization. Other investigators who, like the author, envisage the apex and its component regions as 'physiological sinks', i.e. as loci of active utilization of the metabolic substances of growth, recognize that competition for nutrients may not only contribute to the maintenance of apical organization but may afford a basis for an adequate interpretation of apical dominance (for refs. see Cutter, 1965). In any growing region it is difficult to separate the effects of hormones and nutritional competition; both are contributory to the normal orderly development.

In this section it is appropriate to note that the *in vitro* culture of apical regions has contributed relevant information. Wetmore (1956) investigated the capacity for development of different regions of the shoot apex of *Helianthus annuus*. When the central region of the apical meristem, which consists of large, superficial, vacuolated cells overlying a pith meristem, was excised and cultured it did not grow; but excised tissue from the more densely staining, sub-distal region, i.e. the flanks of the meristem, grew and developed a leaf, i.e. if a primordium was already present on the explant; and the new entity often formed roots.

THE APICAL MERISTEM AS A FIELD SYSTEM

The problems of leaf and bud formation, of phyllotaxis, and of the orderly development of the leafy shoot can be approached from several points of view. Here we shall follow a course of ideas and discoveries based on: (i) direct observation of the normal morphogenetic activities of the fern apex; (2) modifications that can be induced in it by particular treatments; and (3) a useful hypothesis proposed by Schoute (1913).

Hypotheses relating to formative activities in the fern apical meristem that have now been validated by experimental evidence are as follows: (1) the apical cell of the fern shoot (together with its adjacent segments), as also each young leaf primordium, is a growth centre with a surrounding physiological field; new growth centres can only originate in regions of the apical meristem which lie outside the existing fields; (2) no fundamental metabolic differences exist between shoot and leaf apices; but there may be differences in the extent or intensity of their fields; (3) the physiological field round a growth centre is established at an early stage.

The application of these ideas to the apex of *Dryopteris* is illustrated in Figs. 6.9, 6.10. The positions of the existing leaf primordia ($P_{1, 2, 3}$, etc., in order of increasing age) and of primordia yet to be formed (I_1, I_2, I_3, in the order of their appearance) are shown. Approximate bud positions (b), situated some distance above the axils of the leaf primordia, or in lateral or interfoliar positions, are also indicated. In respect of their distance from the apical cell, it will be noted that some bud positions are thus closely comparable with those of recently formed leaf primordia. Nevertheless, bud rudiments remain inhibited, whereas leaf primordia grow out. The growth centre hypothesis, as it may apply to the fern apex, is indicated in Fig. 6.10. The physiological fields of the apical cell group and of the adjacent leaf primordia ($P_1 - P_5$) are suggested in a simplified and purely arbitrary fashion. Of course, other, different, representations are possible. It is improbable that the fields associated with primordia of different ages, and occupying different positions on the meristem, are equivalent in shape, size and physiological properties. The fields, moreover, should be regarded as three-dimensional. As shown in the diagram, the next area of the apical meristem – the 'first available space' of M. and R. Snow – which is free from the inhibitory effects of adjacent growth centres, and in which a primordium could develop, is the position normally occupied by I_1; the next space to become available after that is that normally occupied by I_2; and so on. Bud positions, on this hypothesis, are subject to inhibition by the young leaf primordia, i.e. the inhibition of buds at the apex is not solely due to the shoot apex.

The foregoing hypothesis can be subjected to experimental tests: by isolating particular regions of the apical meristem it should be possible to observe whether or not the inception and growth of primordia are inhibited.

Effects of Isolating Position I_1, and P_1, P_2, etc. It is improbable that the inhibitional fields shown in Fig. 6.10, have definite boundaries, especially if diffusion gradients are involved; but when a primordium originates in the I_1 position, it is probable that its growth is affected, or regulated, by the adjacent primordia, P_3 and P_5. If, therefore, the I_1 position is isolated from P_3 and P_5 by deep radial incisions, the rate of growth of the primordium developing there should be increased. This expectation has, in fact, been

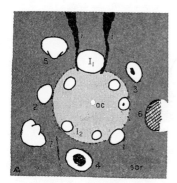 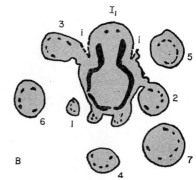

FIG. 7.11. *Dryopteris dilatata*. The effect of isolating a leaf primordium, or site, by deep radial incisions. A, An apex, laid bare, as seen from above. Here the isolated I_1 has outgrown primordia several plastochrones older. (Redrawn from photograph.) B, The same apex some time later. Serial sections confirmed that I_1 had become the largest primordium in proximity to the apex. (After C. W. Wardlaw, *Growth* (Supplement), 1949.)

realized: the new primordium soon became larger than P_2, i.e. a primordium two plastochrones older (Fig. 7.11). In other apices, either P_1, P_2 or P_3 was isolated by deep radial incisions from the adjacent, older primordia. In each instance the isolated primordium soon increased in relative size. Histological studies showed that the increase in size was due to growth of the primordium and not to a rapid wound reaction.

Effect of Incising I_1 and I_2. If radial incisions are made through primordia $P_1 - P_5$ the positions occupied in due course by the new primordia $I_1 - I_4$ are the normal phyllotactic positions (Wardlaw, 1949). This is what would be expected if fields are established round young primordia soon after their inception and if they persist for some time after the destruction of the primordium. But what would happen if the I_1 and I_2 positions were incised, i.e. so that the development of their inhibitional fields would be precluded? In the ferns a primordium does not develop if its presumptive position is damaged. Accordingly, no primordium will be formed at I_1 or I_2; but I_3, arising in relation to P_1–P_3 will occupy a normal position; I_4 will originate in a position remote from P_2, by whose field it will be affected, i.e. it will be displaced towards the incision through I_1. I_4 may also be expected to grow rapidly. Results in keeping with these expectations have been obtained.

Isolation of I_1 by a Tangential Incision. In a fern such as *Dryopteris dilatata*, a new leaf primordium originates a little above the base of the apical cone;

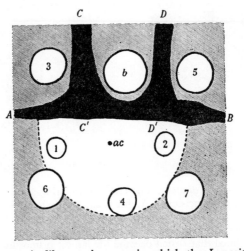

FIG. 7.12. *Dryopteris dilatata.* An apex in which the I_1 position has been isolated from the apical cell region (*ac*) by a deep tangential incision (AB) and from leaf primordia 3 and 5 by radial incisions (*CC″, DD″*). A bud, *b*, was formed in what is normally a leaf position. ($\times$30.) (After C. W. Wardlaw, *Growth* (Supplement), 1949.)

and, as already noted (p. 127), the growth rate in such a location is greater on the abaxial than on the adaxial side. The latter may also be subjected to inhibitive effects proceeding from the distal region. Hence, if the incidence of these factors results in an early fixation of a dorsiventral organization in the primordium meristem, the dorsiventral symmetry of the resulting foliar member will tend to follow as a natural consequence. Accordingly, it was thought that if the I_1 position was isolated from the apical meristem by a deep and wide tangential incision, inhibitive effects proceeding from the apex would be precluded, and there might also be a levelling up of the growth rates on the abaxial and adaxial sides. In these circumstances a primordium of radial symmetry, i.e. a lateral shoot bud, might be expected to be formed at I_1.

In fact, when I_1 positions were isolated by deep tangential cuts shoot buds were usually formed; i.e. in each instance a bud was induced in what is normally a leaf position or site (Fig. 7.12). In other experiments the position I_1 was isolated from the apical cell by a tangential incision and from P_3 and P_5 by radial incisions; in a majority of the specimens shoot buds were formed in the I_1 position (Fig. 7.12). These buds were characterized by their rapid relative growth and by the presence of a solenostelic vascular system from the outset (Wardlaw, 1949).

Isolation of P_1, P_2 and P_3 by Deep Tangential Incisions. In critical experiments, Cutter (1954, 1956) extended the foregoing studies by isolating the youngest visible primordia, P_1, P_2, P_3, etc. Especially in the younger treated primordia P_1 and P_2, but including some P_{3s}, buds were frequently induced (Fig. 7. 13). Cutter was able to demonstrate that, once the conspicuous lenticular apical cell had been formed in a primordium, it could no longer be induced to develop as a bud. The formation of a leaf apical cell may take place during the first plastochrone in some apices, or not until the third plastochrone in others. But once the nascent or actual *dorsiventral organization* of the *leaf apical meristem* (i.e. the conspicuous, lens-shaped apical cell, its immediate lateral segments and contiguous cells on the adaxial and abaxial faces) had been established, the course of development of the primordium into a foliar organ could not be changed. By marking the central region of isolated young primordia, still without a visibly enlarged apical cell, Cutter concluded that the apex of the bud developed from the central region of the primordium. In the writer's view the formation of the large apical cell is evidence of the establishment of a characteristic histophysiological organization in the primordium apex as a whole; i.e. its dorsiventral pattern, or symmetry is now irreversibly determined.

In other experiments (Wardlaw, 1949, 1950) it was found that leaf primordia could be induced in what are normally bud positions. (*See* p. 162.)

On the evidence of these and other experiments, the orderly development of lateral members is referable to: (*a*) the continued activity of the apical cell and its segments, and (*b*) to the organization of the apical meristem, one feature of which is the regulated inception of growth centres. There is also evidence of reciprocal relationships between different regions of the growing apex; for whereas the positions and rates of growth of new leaf primordia are, in part, determined by the older primordia – an acropetal effect – the inhibition of inter-foliar members, i.e. buds, is partly due to the distal region of the apical meristem and to young primordia – a basipetal effect. The effects of older primordia on younger ones had already been reported by Goodwin (1937). He showed that, in the basal rosettes of *Solidago sempervirens*, the elongation of an older leaf retards the

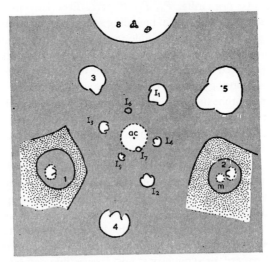

FIG. 7.13. *Dryopteris dilatata*. Isolation of P_1 and P_2 by four deep vertical incisions. Above: An apex in which P_1 and P_2 were isolated by four deep vertical incisions, as observed 43 days after this treatment: P_1 and P_2 had developed as conical organs, of radial symmetry. Below: After 106 days: buds, or incipient buds, have been formed in the leaf sites. (After E. G. Cutter, *Annals of Botany*, 1956.)

development of the younger ones; and Albaum (1938) observed that the first leaf of the fern sporophyte, which is apparently the primary source of hormones in the plant, inhibits the growth of the younger leaves. If this leaf is removed and its cut petiole surface is smeared with IAA in lanoline the younger leaves are inhibited.

APICAL TOTIPOTENCY

That the fern apex is totipotent in respect of organ formation has been demonstrated by the accumulated results of experimental studies. In further experiments, where both the main shoot and leaf apices were punctured, leaf primordia developed in some of the presumptive leaf positions and buds in others. It thus appears that very little is needed to tip the balance from leaf formation to bud formation, or vice-versa. If there are indeed no fundamental metabolic differences between leaf and bud primordia, i.e. if no special 'leaf-' or 'bud-forming' substances are involved, then the symmetry and configuration of an organ must be directly related to the organization of the apical meristem and to the physical and physiological factors in the tissue environment of the primordium. If, on the other hand, it is assumed that specific 'organ-forming' substances are involved, then it becomes necessary to explain how these substances come to be located, at critical concentrations, in particular positions. In the experimental materials under consideration there would be the added difficulty of demonstrating how, in some instances, a 'bud-forming' substance has become localized in what is normally a leaf site, and vice-versa. Any general hypothesis of the kind that leaves inhibit leaves and buds inhibit buds – though it offers attractive possibilities – raises similar difficulties. Hence, as it seems to the writer, it is to the mechanics and genic control of growth in the plastic meristematic region that we must look for an explanation of the characteristic form and structure of the shoot and its lateral members.

A general view which emerges from these experiments is that the integrated organization of the leafy shoot can be understood in terms of the comparatively simple and unified concepts of (a) an apical reaction system; (b) the growth centres to which it gives rise and their associated physiological fields; and (c) the distribution of growth. Incipient and developing organs are thus seen to have a functional aspect, the orderly or regulated development of the leafy shoot being largely referable to the physiological effects which proceed from them. These tentative views are, it need hardly be said, a very considerable but unavoidable over-simplification of a highly complex situation. (For a full account of the field concept, see Weiss, 1939, and Wardlaw, 1965a.)

In the earlier literature leaves and shoots were assigned to different fundamental morphological categories, or their specific characters were regarded as having been evolved during the course of descent. As we now see, there are no immutable fundamental morphological categories: in favourable materials, e.g. some ferns, it is possible to induce buds in leaf positions and leaves in bud positions; and other 'transformations' are known. Moreover, leaf primordia can be induced to form in positions

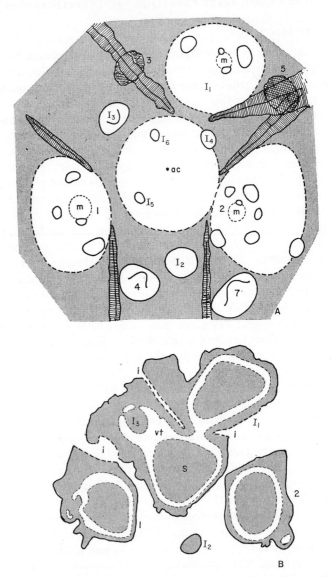

FIG. 7.14. *Dryopteris dilatata*. A, Illustrates the growth of an apex in which tangential incisions, leaving a 'bridge' of intact tissue, had been made above primordia P_1 and P_2 and the site of I_1. (Indications as in previous figures; *m*, apical meristem of induced buds.) The basal regions of P_1 and P_2 became greatly enlarged, the original primordium being visible on the top of the tissue mound. On further growth, it can be seen that large buds have been formed (*m*), each with several leaf primordia. I_1–I_6 have now appeared. (Semi-diagrammatic, ×14.) B, Transverse section of the specimen il-

other than their normal phyllotactic positions. The apical meristem in leptosporangiate ferns, then, is totipotent, any region being potentially capable of originating leaf or bud primordia. The individual lateral organs are thus held to be an expression of growth in the shoot apex: they are not specifically predetermined either by the hereditary constitution of the plant or by the pre-existence in the race of organs of different fundamental categories.

MORPHOGENETIC EFFECTS OF THE SHOOT APICAL CELL REGION

In view of the attention that the conspicuous fern shoot apical cell has attracted to itself, one may well inquire as to its actual effects in organogenesis. The writer (Wardlaw, 1955) showed that if only small deep incisions are made immediately above the axils of young leaf primordia (P_1, P_2) or I_1 sites, buds are not induced. But if two wide and deep lateral incisions are made on either side of the primordium, so as to leave a bridge of intact tissue above the primordium, some buds may be obtained (Fig. 7.14). These observations indicate that, in considering the experimental induction of buds, attention must be directed to the whole nutritional–hormonal system in the treated sector of the apex. (*See also* p. 173.)

FUNCTIONAL ACTIVITY OF THE PREVASCULAR TISSUE

In the experiments so far considered, deep incisions were used to ensure the complete severance of the incipient vascular tissue. As already noted, the facts of apical anatomy, and especially of the induction of incipient vascular tissues in relation to active meristems, suggest that this nascent tissue may serve as a pathway for the movement of nutrients, hormones, etc. In fact, when young primordia were isolated adaxially by wide shallow incisions, i.e. penetrating only a single layer of cells and not severing the prevascular tissue, or in which the whole apical meristem was isolated by similar shallow incisions, buds were not formed (Fig. 7.15) (Wardlaw and Cutter, 1954, 1956; Wardlaw, 1956). It may therefore be inferred that the regulative effects of shoot and leaf regions, of older primordia on younger

---

lustrated in A. Cortex and pith, stippled; *s*, axis and stele of main shoot; *i*, *i*, incisions; *vt*, vascular tissue. It will be noted that the large solenostelic bud which developed in the I_1 position is in vascular continuity with the main axis, *s*. Similarly, in sections lower down, the solenostelic buds formed from P_1 and P_2 are seen to be in vascular continuity. At that level the pith of bud I_1 is confluent with that of the main axis. (Semi-diagrammatic, ×17.) (After C. W. Wardlaw, *Annals of Botany*, 1955.)

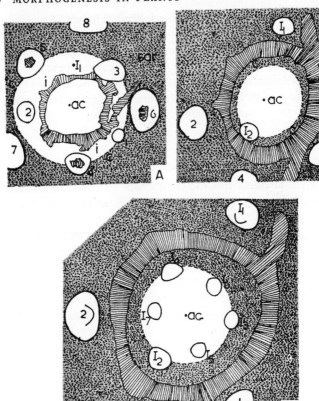

FIG. 7.15. *Dryopteris dilatata.* Isolation of the apical meristem by shallow incisions. A, B, C, Stages in the growth of an apex, as seen from above, in which the apical meristem had been ringed or isolated by shallow incisions, i.e. not severing the incipient vascular tissue. *1–8*, existing leaf primordia; I_1, position or site of next primordium to be formed; *ac*, position of apical cell of shoot; *c*, base of apical cone and region of transition to the sub-apical region; *i*, shallow incision, made above the level of I_1 (radial line shading). A, Five days after the experimental treatment. B, C, Successively later developments; no buds have been induced outside the shallow incisions. (After C. W. Wardlaw, *Phytomorph.*, 1956.)

ones, etc., are mediated through the prevascular tissue. This affords further evidence that developing organs and tissues may have important functional activities.

LEAF AND BUD FORMATION IN PUNCTURED APICES

In *Dryopteris dilatata* and other leptosporangiate ferns, buds are not normally formed on the apical meristem. But they can be induced to form there, either from young primordia, e.g. P_1 or P_2, from leaf sites, e.g. I_1, I_2 and I_3, or from the bud sites in interfoliar positions (p. 130). These developments are usually a concomitant of injury to the apical cell region; but new leaf primordia, as well as buds, may also be formed, some of these originating in close proximity to the distal necrosed apical cell group. In a comprehensive study of injured apices, ranging from the slightest injury to the

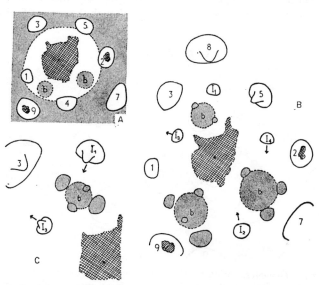

FIG. 7.16. *Dryopteris dilatata*. Apex with considerable necrosis round punctured apical cell. A, Four days after experimental treatment, buds are being formed above the axils of P_7 and P_9. B, Twenty-three days later: the two original buds have now become conspicuous, a bud has appeared above the axil of P_3, and new leaf primordia I_1–I_4 have appeared. At this stage I_1 and I_2 appear to be normally orientated towards the original shoot apex, but I_4 has become orientated towards the bud of P_7 while I_3 is directed outwards and away from the shoot apex. C, As observed 15 days later, shows that I_1 has, in fact, become orientated towards the bud of P_3, while I_3 is clearly directed outwards. ($\times 14$.) (After C. W. Wardlaw and E. G. Cutter, *Annals of Botany*, 1955.)

apical cell (or cell group) to severely damaged, the various assemblages of new leaf and bud primordia on the apical meristem were recorded (Fig. 7.16) (Wardlaw, 1949, 1950; Wardlaw and Cutter, 1955).

In extensively damaged apices buds were formed quickly, usually close to the base of the apical cone, while new leaf primordia appeared higher up. Where the injury was very slight, i.e. causing necrosis in the apical cell and its immediate segments only, bud formation was much slower, but was

F

again near the base of the cone. In some instances a leaf primordium, occupying its normal phyllotactic position, subsequently developed as if it belonged to a new, induced bud (Fig. 7.16). Other leaf primordia, formed high on the cone, i.e. close to the distal region of necrosis and rapid wound-healing, had their normal circinnate curvature reversed, i.e. away from the apical cell region. Cutter (1965) has reviewed the corresponding records for angiosperms (*see* p. 171). From the collective evidence from flowering plants and ferns it may be inferred that, although the group of initial cells

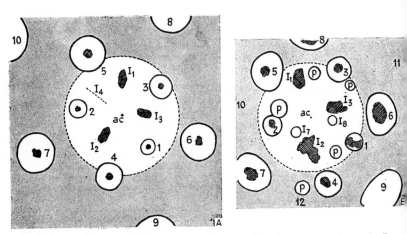

FIG. 7.17. *Dryopteris dilatata*, the induction of leaves in bud sites. A, Indicates the experimental procedure: in a shoot apex which had been laid bare, the apices of the existing top cycle of leaf primordia, P_1-P_5, were punctured and the sites of the next primordia to develop, i.e. I_1, I_2 and I_3, were lightly incised. ($\times 20$.) B, An apex treated as in A after further growth. Interfoliar leaf primordia (p) have been formed between the primordia P_1-P_5 in what are normally bud sites. It can be seen that these primordia are supra-axillary to older leaf primordia, e.g. P_8-P_{12}. No new leaf primordia have been formed in the expected I_4, I_5 or I_6 positions, but I_7 and I_8 occupy approximately normal positions. (After C. W. Wardlaw, *Annals of Botany*, 1950.)

occupying the summit of the meristem is important in the overall growth and organization of the apex, its destruction does not preclude the formation of leaf primordia. In fact, in *Dryopteris* new primordia continued to be formed until the apical meristem, limited in extent by the distal wound, was used up.

When the apices of P_1-P_5 and the sites of I_1-I_3 were punctured, leaf primordia developed in what are normally bud sites (Fig. 7.17; Wardlaw, 1950).

BUD FORMATION AND VASCULAR DEVELOPMENT

As we have seen, many of the surgical treatments of the fern shoot apex resulted in bud formation. Buds were also induced in detached meristems.
Anatomical studies of these materials have shed light on the organization
of new apical meristems and on the differentiation of vascular tissues.

THE FORMATION OF BUDS

A central problem for botanists is to understand shoot organization; for it
is characteristic of all vascular plants and may even be held to include some
bryophytes. A cognate problem arises in relation to the larger and more
complex brown algae, since these, too, have an apical growing point, the
activity of which yields an axial construction, sometimes with lateral organs.
The study of embryos has taken us some way towards our goal. The study
of buds provides additional information. They typically occur laterally on
the shoot; they may be formed on leaves and roots; and they can be induced in some tissue cultures under controlled conditions. In fact, the
study of buds is one of the principal means of investigating certain morphogenetic processes.

In the ferns and in some flowering plants buds arise from bud rudiments,
these consisting of small superficial groups of cells which at one time formed
part of the apical meristem and which have retained their meristematic
potentialities (Fig. 7.1). In other instances there is a renewal of growth in
parenchymatous cells, followed by active cell division, the organization of
an apical meristem and, on further growth, the development of a bud (Fig.
5.10). Thus, a bud, which is simply an embryonic shoot, can originate
from a small group of meristematic cells. Because of their readily accessible
superficial position, buds, as in the ferns, afford useful material for observational and experimental studies. The nutrition of a bud is typically derived
from a parent shoot or other tissue, and here we encounter factors which
have still to be more fully investigated.

Some features of bud formation may be briefly reviewed. In a fern such
as *Onoclea sensibilis* or *Matteuccia struthiopteris* detached meristems (or bud
rudiments) are present in specific positions along the rhizome. Each such
meristem consists of a small area of superficial quiescent, prism-shaped
cells (p. 140). When the inhibition exercised by the rhizome apex is removed, these cells begin to grow and divide, and a period of sustained
meristematic activity ensues. Nutrients are drawn from the cortical parenchyma of the parent shoot, since at this early stage there is no vascular
connection between the nascent bud and the rhizome stele; and indeed,
in some buds there may never be. The developing bud at first grows out as

a mound of tissue, with a distal but incompletely organized meristem, below which differentiation of a strand of incipient vascular tissue begins. This small-celled tissue is quite distinct from the surrounding large-celled cortical parenchyma, in which cell division has also been induced. As the bud elongates, its vascular system traversing the cortex of the parent

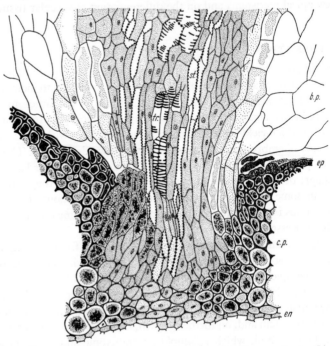

FIG. 7.18. Development of a detached meristem in *Matteuccia struthiopteris*. The stele of the new, seen in l.s., bud traverses the parental cortex, seen in t.s., and makes a still incomplete conjunction with a meristele of the parental shoot. *bp*, bud parenchyma; *ep*, rhizome epidermis; *cp*, cortical parenchyma; *en*, endodermis; *tr*, tracheids in bud; *st*, sieve tubes. (After C. W. Wardlaw, *Encyclopedia of Plant Physiology*, XV/I, 1965.)

rhizome becomes increasingly important in the translocation of materials to its actively growing apex and to its basal regions which are becoming rigid as a result of the deposition of cell-wall materials (Figs. 7.18, 7.19). As growth proceeds, the bud apex becomes more highly organized: one of the more centrally placed prism-shaped cells becomes a large apical cell, and from it, by successive divisions, all the new tissues of the shoot subsequently originate. About this time the first leaf is formed and others follow in a regular phyllotactic sequence (Wardlaw, 1952a). Comparable developments can be observed in flowering plants and in tissue cultures. At every stage of bud development we are concerned with growth and with a whole system of reacting and interacting factors. Bud development is thus essentially an *epigenetic* one, each phase being affected by the antecedent phases. Here it may be noted that, in theories of the leafy-shoot as propounded by comparative morphologists, a pre-existent axial structure or shoot was taken for granted. In the epigenetic approach nothing is taken for granted but a capacity for growth in meristematic cells in contact with a source of nutrition.

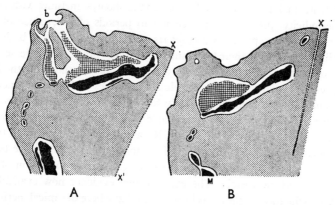

FIG. 7.19. *Dryopteris dilatata.* Transverse sections of an experimentally treated shoot, showing a large induced solenostelic bud. A, The bud in longitudinal section showing the incomplete conjunction of its vascular tissues with those of the parent shoot; B, lower down: the bud stele lies outside the meristele of the parent shoot. *b*, apex of bud. (×15.) (After C. W. Wardlaw, *Phil. Trans. Roy. Soc.*, 1947.)

In the ferns truly adventitious buds are rare. There is, accordingly, a unity of meristematic tissue throughout the fern plant and the various positions of buds described by Bower (1923), lateral, basal, on the petiole, etc., represent displacements of the detached meristems during the process of growth. Where the inception of bud rudiments has been closely studied in flowering plants there is evidence of a not dissimilar organization (cf. Garrison, 1948).

VASCULAR DIFFERENTIATION IN INDUCED BUDS IN FERNS

When buds are induced close to the shoot or rhizome apex, i.e. in a region where tissue differentiation is still at an early stage, there is usually a complete conjunction of the bud and the parental vascular tissues, i.e. phloem-to-phloem and xylem-to-xylem continuity can be observed. But if a bud originates farther away from the shoot apex its stele may be more or less incompletely conjoined with the parental stele (Fig. 7.19). In some instances the bud stele may lie along the outside of the endodermis of the parent meristele, or there may be a partial union. The endodermis may undergo dedifferentiation with subsequent vascularization (Fig. 7.18) (Wardlaw, 1946). Lastly, when buds are induced in mature regions of the shoot the basipetally differentiating bud stele may fade out in the parent cortex; and no conjunction with the shoot stele is effected.

An interesting field observation may here be noted. In the normal development, small fern buds are formed on the shoot, sometimes with a certain periodicity, presumably in relation to periods of quiescence of the main apex, e.g. in species of *Dryopteris* and *Matteuccia*. These buds are typically protostelic at their base, and only a small protostele traverses the cortex to become conjoined with the stele of the parent shoot. As the bud elongates and enlarges, the protostele also enlarges and becomes medullated; and solenostely and dictyostely follow. In fact, the stelar development in a lateral bud is closely comparable with that of a young sporophyte. Botanists who support the Theory of Recapitulation have regarded these stelar developments as being of special importance, the protostele being held to be a necessary antecedent development for the formation of the solenostele and dictyostele. The experimental evidence now available is contrary to the theory; for it has been found that where the apical meristem has been isolated by vertical incisions, as already described (p. 146), the buds which are formed in the subapical region are of very large size and are solenostelic from the outset (Figs. 7.10, 7.19). So also are buds induced on the apex as a result of puncturing the apical cell. It has also been noted (p. 150) that a dictyostele can be 'reduced' to a solenostele or even to a protostele by a single operation (Fig. 7.10).

A Further Property of Detached Meristems. If, in decapitated rhizomes of *Matteuccia* and *Onoclea*, the superficial tissue containing a detached meristem is removed, the tissue immediately below may regenerate and give rise to a bud. But it is uniquely in these regions, and nowhere else on the rhizome, that buds can be so induced. The parenchymatous tissue of the outer cortex, in contiguity with a detached meristem, thus retains some meristematic potentiality. The outermost cells begin to divide actively, a mound of meristematic tissue is formed, its distal region becomes organized as a meristem and bud formation, as already described, ensues. Such developments apart, the writer knows of no buds on the fern shoot or rhizome that are truly adventitious.

In flowering plants a somewhat comparable condition has been observed in callus buds, e.g. in species of *Nicotiana*. When the shoot is cut across, a callus, or pad of meristematic tissue, is formed, and this may give rise to a crop of shoot buds. If these are removed a new crop will be formed, and this may continue until eventually the shoot is impoverished.

Effects of O_2, N_2 *and* CO_2. Wardlaw and Allsopp (1948), and Allsopp (1949) showed that, in bud induction, no abnormal morphogenetic developments ensued when apices of *Dryopteris* or detached meristems of *Matteuccia* and *Onoclea* were held in different partial pressures of oxygen, nitrogen and carbon dioxide. Growth may be totally arrested, or it may be accelerated, or diminished, but no important changes in the form of organs or the differentiation of tissues was observed. In some experiments where the rate of growth was greatly reduced the detached meristem gave rise to small hemispherical or subspherical masses of callus. Later, under conditions which are specified, these callus masses gave rise to an abundant crop of buds, the effect being closely comparable with that obtained in some tissue-culture experiments.

THE CONTINUITY OF THE VASCULAR SYSTEM

In the normal development of a higher plant the vascular system is continuous, from the base of the stem (and including the roots) right up into the apex. The vascular column, or stele, may be periodically interrupted by more or less numerous leaf-gaps or perforations, but the conducting system as a whole is essentially a continuous one and, accordingly, permits of the uninterrupted movement of solutions. In fact, we take the continuity of the vascular system for granted. Nevertheless, this continuity is a phenomenon of growth and differentiation in the apical region and occasional instances of interrupted or discontinuous vascular columns have been encountered. These are of especial interest to the student of morphogenesis.

Holloway (1939) described an interesting example of an interrupted vascular system in a large prothallus of *Psilotum triquetrum*. The vascular column, a protostele, was periodically interrupted by intervening regions of parenchyma (Fig. 7.20). Holloway noted that growth in these prothalli was intermittent, a period of active apical growth, with differentiation of vascular tissue, being followed by a period of inactivity when all but a few of the terminal apical and subapical cells are transformed into large-celled parenchyma. On the renewal of apical growth, vascular tissue was again differentiated. Hence, in an old, elongated, columnar prothallus a discontinuous vascular system resulted.

Somewhat similar effects were induced experimentally in *Onoclea sensibilis* (Wardlaw, 1945). Rhizomes which normally lose their adult leaves and become inactive in winter were kept growing during that season at an abnormally high temperature and in feeble illumination. For some time apical growth continued with unrolling of leaves and the formation of new primordia. Eventually, however, normal apical activity ceased, the last-formed leaves being small, non-laminate, awl-shaped organs, while the dis-

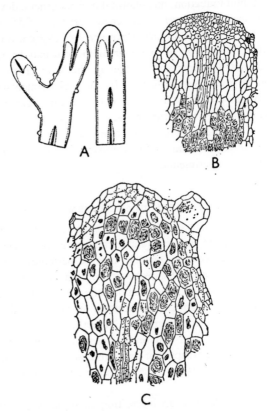

FIG. 7.20. *Psilotum triquetrum*. A, Distal portions of two large prothalli, in longitudinal median section, showing the discontinuous vascular system. B, An actively growing apex below which a vascular strand is being differentiated. C, An inactive apex in which almost all the meristematic cells at the distal end have become parenchymatous; no vascular tissue is differentiated. (A, ×10; B, C, ×50.) (After J. E. Holloway, *Annals of Botany*, 1939.)

tal region of the shoot became swollen and parenchymatous (Fig. 7.21). In such anomalous rhizomes an anatomical study showed that the original dictyostele had become solenostelic and eventually protostelic towards the distal end. This protostele gradually diminished in size, almost to the point of complete disappearance, in the 'parenchymatized' apical region of

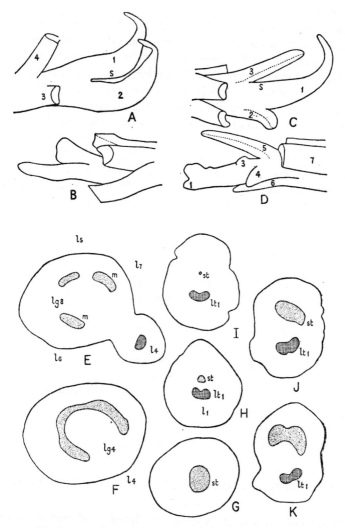

FIG. 7.21. *Onoclea sensibilis:* A–D, The terminal regions of greatly reduced plants, the awl-like leaves being numbered in basipetal sequence. *S,* approximate position of inactive shoot apex ($\times 5$).

E–K, Transverse sections, in acropetal sequence, of the reduced plant illustrated in D above.

E, Oldest region: dictyostele with reduced leaf-trace (*l4*).

F, Nearer the apex, the stele is solenostelic.

G, The stele (*st*) is now protostelic. H, I, The stele (*st*) has almost completely disappeared. J, K, Nearer the apex, in which there has been a renewal of growth: the protostele (*st*) has increased in size and the leaf-trace (*lt₁*) of the last-formed leaf primordium can be seen. ($\times 18$.) (After C. W. Wardlaw, *Annals of Botany,* 1945.)

the shoot – a result not unlike that found in the *Psilotum* prothallus. When some of these attenuated *Onoclea* rhizomes were subsequently grown under conditions of improved illumination they showed a renewal of apical activity, and approximately normal small leaves were again formed. Anatomical studies of these materials showed that the stele had either become discontinuous between the two regions of the rhizome or that it was continuous by virtue of an exceedingly small and tenuous strand of vascular tissue (Fig. 7.21). Cutter (1965) illustrated very considerable diminutions in the size of the shoot stele associated with apices of *Dryopteris* which had been progressively starved. These several observations support the view that the inception of vascular tissue is primarily determined by the active apex of the main shoot and its growing leaf primordia.

FURTHER EXPERIMENTAL INVESTIGATIONS OF ANGIOSPERM APICES

The success which attended the initial surgical treatment of angiosperm apices, such as those of *Epilobium*, *Lupinus*, etc., by M. & R. Snow; and of the large and convenient apices of ferns such as *Dryopteris dilatata* and *D. filix mas* (Wardlaw; Cutter) encouraged investigators to study morphogenesis in other angiosperm apices by similar means and greatly to extend the scope of the work by using the techniques of tissue culture. As a result, the literature on apical morphogenesis is now considerable. Here, reference can only be made to recent investigations which confirm main conclusions already stated, or which have opened up new and important avenues for thought and work. (The use of surgical methods in the study of phyllotactic systems is discussed later: *see* p. 236.)

ORGAN CULTURE AND SELF-DETERMINATION IN THE SHOOT APEX

The validity of this concept has been more firmly established by investigations in which the shoot apical meristem, on a larger or smaller panel of subapical tissue, was excised and grown under aseptic conditions *in vitro*, on media of known composition. Among the principal contributions are those of Ball (1944, 1946, 1960) on *Lupinus* and *Tropaeolum*, and later (1950, 1955, 1959) on Ginkgo; Loo (1945, 1946) and Galston (1948) on asparagus and the dodder (*Cuscuta* sp.); Wetmore and Morel (1949, 1951), Wetmore (1950, 1954, 1956) and Wetmore, Nitsch and Morel (1954) on *Adiantum*, *Osmunda*, *Pteridium*, *Selaginella*, *Equisetum*, *Cucurbita* and *Lupinus*; Allsopp (1951, 1952) on *Marsilea*; Al-Talib and Torrey (1959) on *Pseudotsuga*. Biochemical aspects of apex and organ culture are considered later (p. 203). Here it may be noted that, in many instances, whole plants with roots were eventually obtained from such excised, cultured apices. An intriguing and probably a very important observation is that whereas large angiosperm apical explants grew readily, smaller ones were difficult to culture, even in sophisticated media (*see* Wetmore, 1954; and Wardlaw, 1965a, b, for review). In angiosperms in particular, the size of the excised apical region, and the number of leaf primordia on it, appear to be of critical importance if continued growth is to be obtained. For example, in Ball's earlier experiments with *Lupinus* the meristems were excised with the two or three youngest leaf primordia. These apices grew well and eventually yielded rooted plants. When he repeated his experiments, using apical meristems excised without primordia, some growth took place in a basic medium containing gamma-aminobutyric acid; and shoots about 1 cm. long and bearing three to five leaf primordia were obtained. Similar explants, when supplied with the range of amino acids known to be present in the apex, failed to grow. On media with added coconut milk and gibberellic acid good growth was obtained: shoots 5–10 cm. developed, bearing 7–9 leaves. When he attempted the culture of excised apices of *Tropaeolum* and *Lycopersicum* on a number of sophisticated media Ball had no success. This leads to the view that the apices of particular species have special nutritional needs. Ball suggested that the maintenance of an active apical meristem is dependent on substances moving acropetally from the subjacent region and that the recently formed primordia may have important functional activities in this relationship.

While the results of surgical and cultural experiments indicate that the *shoot apex* is a self-determining region, as is also the *apical meristem* in some of its major activities, the concept still requires cautious statement and further research. Given a supply of nutrients from below, the fern apical meristem is demonstrably a self-determining region. In the flowering plants an apical meristem, like a young embryo at the globular stage, appears to have rather more special and delicately balanced nutritional and hormonal requirements. Further investigations may show that the regulation of 'appropriate' metabolism is largely mediated through the growing tissues of the subjacent region and by young leaf primordia, all of these being component parts of the holistic shoot apex (*see* p. 135).

LEAF AND BUD PRIMORDIA IN ANGIOSPERMS

In the ferns the experimental evidence is compatible with the view that the inception of a leaf primordium in a particular position on the apical meristem, its dorsiventral symmetry, acropetal orientation and morphological development are all referable to the organization and growth of the holistic apical region. In particular, it is possible to induce buds to develop in leaf sites, and vice-versa. In the dicotyledons, although instances are known of buds (vegetative and floral) developing naturally in leaf sites (p. 187), it has not yet been possible, for example in surgical treatments of apices, to induce bud formation in leaf sites or from young leaf primordia.

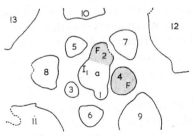

FIG. 7.22. *Nuphar lutea*. Transverse section of the apical meristem in which it can be seen that flower primordia (F_2, F_4) originate in what are normally leaf sites in the genetic spiral. 1, 3, 5, etc., leaf primordia; *a*, centre of apical meristem ($\times 40$). (Drawing by courtesy of Dr. E. G. Cutter.)

Species of *Nuphar* and *Nymphaea* are of special interest in that their flower buds originate in leaf sites and constitute part of the normal phyllotactic sequence (Fig. 7.22) (Wardlaw, 1956; Cutter, 1957, 1958).

Isolation of Primordia in Solanum. Sussex (1951) showed that surgical techniques which had been usefully applied to fern apices, especially in the investigation of leaf and bud primordia, can also be used in investigating similar problems in the flowering plants. When the apical meristem of *Solanum tuberosum* was isolated by four vertical incisions the primordium which formed in the I_1 position was an awl-shaped, centric leaf. Similarly, if the I_1 position was isolated by a tangential incision a centric leaf was formed. As the illustrations show, the dorsiventrality of the leaf is in some way related to activities in the apical meristem; and hence, when a subsidiary apical meristem is induced by an appropriate incision the primordium at I_1 becomes orientated towards it (Fig. 7.23).

Radial and Centric Leaves. In flowering plants, as also in ferns and lycopods, apices which had been subjected to various incisions gave rise to awl-like organs of feeble or restricted growth and of radial, or nearly radial, symmetry (for refs. see Wardlaw, 1952; 1965a, Cutter, 1965). These organs, described as radial and centric[1] leaves, have a cylinder or ring of vascular

---

[1] *Radial* leaves are organs of circular cross-sectional outline; *centric* leaves have a truly centric distribution of tissues.

tissue, whereas the stele in a normal petiole is crescentic. Since ferns and flowering plants show some interesting parallelisms in the matter of centric leaves, examples will be cited from both classes.

Primordia of *Dryopteris dilatata*, e.g. P_1–P_4, which have been closely isolated by four deep vertical incisions, usually develop as radial leaves; and similar organs have been obtained by direct chemical treatments of the apical meristem (Wardlaw, 1957). Radial leaves are quite distinct from buds, especially in their potentiality for development. The developing primor-

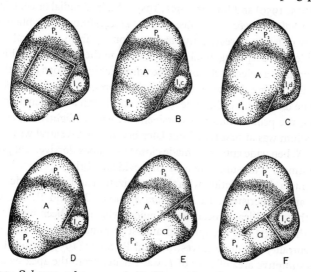

FIG. 7.23. *Solanum tuberosum*. A–F, Illustrating diagrammatically the apex after surgical operations (*see* text). P_1 and P_2, the two youngest leaf primordia present at the time of the operations. I_1, the first leaf to appear after the operation (not drawn to the same scale). I_1c, centric organ developed in the I_1 position. I_1d, dorsiventral leaf developed in the I_1 position. A, main apex; a, induced apex. By comparing D, E and F it can be seen that the symmetry of the new primordium is affected by the adjacent shoot apex. (After I. M. Sussex, *Nature*, 1951.)

dium loses its active marginal meristems, and its characteristic tangential widening is thereby precluded. The apex also loses its embryonic character and becomes an attenuated parenchymatous region. These anomalous organs in ferns are thus foliar primordia in which the normal lateral growth has been suppressed; in fact, some of them may show a brief renewal of lateral growth. As Cutter (1956) noted, the three potential developments of a lateral organ on a shoot apex have been realized in *Dryopteris*, viz. buds, radial and dorsiventral leaves; and she suggested that there may be three critical phases in the normal development of a leaf primordium, namely its inception as a growth centre, its determination as an organ of limited growth and its development as an organ of dorsiventral symmetry. As a result of certain treatments, leaf apices lose their capacity for active growth and fail to enter on the third phase. Such primordia come to maturity as small radial leaves. The nutritional relationships of these radial organs are not known, but they are considerably different from those of buds, in which a nascent meristem soon develops to large relative size.

In surgical treatments of angiosperm apices M. & R. Snow (1931, 1935, 1953, 1955, 1959) and Sussex (1951, 1955) obtained radial or centric leaves. Thus, in *Solanum tuberosum*, Sussex (1951 *et seq.*) frequently obtained radial leaves by isolating a presumptive leaf position (I_1) from the apical meristem by a wide and deep tangential incision close to the leaf site (*see* Fig. 7.23). (In *Dryopteris* a solenostelic bud almost invariably develops after this treatment.) By varying the size of the cut in *S. tuberosum*, it was possible to alter the shape of the primordium developing at I_1: with a very small tangential incision, the primordium was dorsiventral; with a slightly larger cut, the primordium was at first radial but later became dorsiventral with a narrow lamina. When wide cuts were made close to the apex dorsiventral primordia were formed. The summation of this evidence brings primordium symmetry into a direct relation with the organization and physiological activity of the apical meristem. In *Epilobium hirsutum*, M. and R. Snow (1935) noted that radial leaves occurred in apices which had been incised in such a way that a leaf site occupied an almost terminal position. In a study of dorsiventrality in potato leaves, M. and R. Snow (1959) found that when the presumptive area of I_1 or of I_2 was isolated from the apex by a vertical cut the isolated regions usually formed dorsiventral leaf primordia, whereas *E. hirsutum* apices, similarly incised, yielded radial leaves, but also some dorsiventral ones. Radial leaves were also formed when P_1 primordia, in early plastochrone, were isolated on small areas of meristem tissue. M. and R. Snow concluded that, in *E. hirsutum*, the normal dorsiventrality may be induced by the apex; the small size of the tissue panel isolated may also be a factor in the formation of radial leaves. In *Lupinus albus* isolated I_1 and I_2 areas never yielded radial leaves (M. and R. Snow, 1931), perhaps because of the very early establishment of dorsiventral symmetry in primordia.

Axillary Buds. Bud morphogenesis is considered in greater detail in the following chapter. Although axillary buds are ultimately referable to developments at the shoot apical meristem, and although, because of their prevalence in flowering plants, they are a commonplace of botanical observation, the factors determining their inception and further development are by no means clearly known or understood. At this point we may examine some views based on morphological observation and experimental treatments. (For reviews, *see* Sifton, 1944; Philipson, 1949; Garrison, 1949; Gifford, 1951; Cutter, 1965.)

In some species axillary buds are of very general occurrence: in others they are occasional only. For example, only occasional vegetative buds may be observed in the leaf-axils in *Nuphar lutea*; but, as in many other flowering-plant species, they can be induced to form if the potential bud sites are isolated from the shoot apical meristem (Cutter, 1958). Cutter (1965) has reviewed the information available on the relation between the shoot apical meristem and also the subtending leaf primordium on bud inception and development. It is common knowledge that the outgrowth of axillary buds is typically inhibited by an actively growing shoot apex. In some species of herbaceous dicotyledons the subtending leaf primordium appears to be necessary for the formation of an axillary bud. In other species, however, buds are formed on the axis even when their subtending leaf has been isolated at a very early stage. In *Hydrocharis* buds occur only in the axis of every other leaf. Cutter (1963, 1964b) showed that the close spatial relationship between bud and subtending primordium persisted even when the position of the latter was altered by treatment with gibberellic acid. Other species afford further evidence of a possible, perhaps essential, metabolic relationship between a bud and its axillant leaf. In *Gleditschia*, a woody genus, the leaf axils have normally a basipetal series of buds. If, however, very small leaf primordia (less than 1 mm. long) are destroyed their axillary buds become abortive or parenchymatous (Neville, 1961). Further information of the same general kind is also afforded by leaf primordia and their associated buds in the reproductive phase. In *Primula bulleyana*, for example, Cusick (1959) found that no flower buds developed after excision of P_2 and younger bracts; but the removal of older bracts, e.g. P_4, etc., did not preclude the development of the flower primordia.

Cutter (1965) stated that the experimental work to date suggests that, in both the vegetative and reproductive phases of some species, axillary bud inception and development 'are dependent on some activity of the subtending leaf primordium'. Here, the writer would interpose the general idea that, in discussing axillary buds, as distinct from adventitious ones, one should bear in mind that any axillary bud is part of an integrated, harmoniously developing system, in which any contiguous organ, be it shoot apical meristem or young leaf primordium, which can exercise regulative effects may act as a controlling factor. According to the species, the kind and extent of this control may vary widely. There may even be variation during ontogenesis. Thus, in *Ipomoea* Kuse (1961) reported that whereas the growth of an axillary bud was inhibited by a young subtending leaf, it was actually promoted by a fully expanded one.

CHEMICAL TREATMENTS OF THE APICAL MERISTEM

Let it be freely admitted: the results of surgical experiments have been regarded, not without an element of suspicion, by some investigators as being no more than teratologies. But, to date, as a means of ascertaining something of the potentialities of the apical meristem and the relationships of parts during morphogenesis have they, in fact, been surpassed by other techniques or procedures? Experimentalists, it may be agreed, must do better – and still better! But the critics, if their words are to be heeded at all, must also do better and better! They must show, if they can, where new constructive ideas and practical procedures can be sought.

An avenue that can be explored, though it brings its own difficulties, relates to the effects that can be induced in the apical meristem by direct applications of hormonal and other stimulatory, regulatory or nutritive substances. Many reports are available of the eventual effects on primordium formation of applying specific substances to the older leaves. (For refs. *see* Wardlaw, 1952, 1965a; and *Encyclopedia of Plant Physiology*, Vol. XV, 1965.) Among the induced developments are the formation of double, or tangentially fasciated, leaves, reduction in lamina surface, changes in shape, abnormal torsions, curvatures, etc. Many of these interesting anomalous materials still await morphogenetic and anatomical examination.

M. and R. Snow (1937) reported on the effect of applying IAA in lanoline to particular positions on angiosperm apices, e.g. below I_1, in *Lupinus* and *Epilobium*. The treated young primordia and primordium sites grew considerably more rapidly. Contiguous primordia, which also enlarged conspicuously, tended to grow together from a common base. Concomitantly there was a modification in the phyllotaxis. In *Epilobium hirsutum*, a decussate species, spiral phyllotaxis was induced. Ball (1944) reported various effects when IAA (in lanoline) was applied to the apex of *Tropaeolum major*. In the cells at the extreme tip no visible reaction was observed; but the organogenic region showed an abnormal formation of axillary buds, hypertrophy in tissues and primordia, the formation of 'fused' or multiple leaves and some departure from the normal phyllotaxis. When small blobs of lanoline with IAA were applied below the I_1 and I_2 positions on the apex of *Dryopteris dilatata* the nascent and adjacent primordia became conspicuously enlarged (Wardlaw, 1957), i.e. as in comparable treatments of angiosperms.

The reactivities of the several regions of the fern apex were explored by observing the effects of applying various physiologically active substances directly to the large apical meristem of *Dryopteris dilatata* (Wardlaw, 1957). Apices which had been laid bare were treated for periods up to twenty days with representative solutions of physiologically active substances such as

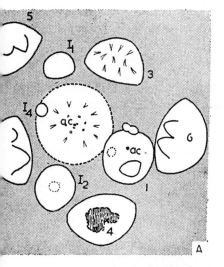

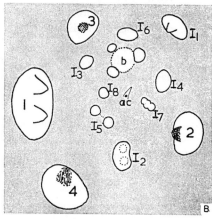

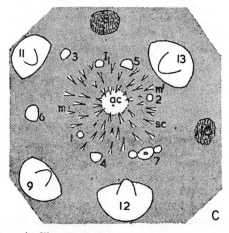

FIG. 7.24. *Dryopteris dilatata*. Apices were laid bare except for the inner group of leaf primordia and solutions of various substances applied directly. A, An apex after treatment with dinitrophenol. P_1 was transformed into a bud, one of its primordia being double; other primordia, 2, 5 and 6, have become double; I_2 developed as an awl-like leaf; P_3 became scaly to the summit of its apex; scales have also developed right up to the apical cell region (*ac*); no primordium was formed in the I_3 site, but one has appeared in the I_4 site. (×20.) B, An apex after treatment with maleic hydrazide. The apical cell has developed as a spiny scale (*see Fig. 25A*); a bud (*b*) has developed above the axil of I_6; P_1 (*left*) has developed as a double primordium; I_2 and I_7 show anomalous orientation. (×20.) C, An apex after treatment with yeast extract: the new leaf primordia are very small and the apical meristem has become scaly almost to the summit. (×13.) (After C. W. Wardlaw, *Annals of Botany*, 1957.)

IAA, 3-indoleacetonitrile, dinitrophenol, maleic hydrazide, thiamine (vitamin B_1) hydrochloride, yeast extract, glutamine, etc., and kept under daily observation. Even changes of a transitory nature could thus be detected.

Although only a few substances have so far been tested, some reaction has usually been obtained; and developments of some morphogenetic interest have been noted. These include: (1) an increase in growth rate in the subapical region; (2) an arrest of growth in the apical meristem; (3) the formation of flattened, sunken and cup-shaped apices; (4) the formation of double, treble and quadruple leaf primordia; of two primordia in a single leaf site; and of centric (or radial) leaves; (5) the occasional suppression of

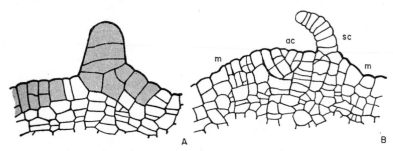

FIG. 7.25. *Dryopteris dilatata*. Apices in longitudinal median section after direct chemical treatments. A, As in Fig. 24B, after treatment with maleic hydrazide: the apical meristem has become disorganized and can no longer be recognized; the apical cell has become much divided and has grown out as a large, deeply staining, spine-like scale. (×112.) B, An apex which has become disorganized and scaly to the summit as a result of direct treatment with thiamine hydrochloride. *ac*, disorganized apical cell region; *m–m*, apical meristem; *sc*, scale close to apical cell. (×112.) (After C. W. Wardlaw, *Annals of Botany*, 1957.)

primordia; (6) a reversal of the phyllotactic spiral; (7) the induction of buds on meristems with an apparently uninjured apical cell; (8) the promotion of root formation and growth; (9) the formation of scales on the apices of young leaf primordia and leaf sites; the precocious formation of scales, over the apical meristem, including the apical cell; and (10) the precocious parenchymatization of the meristem, including the apical cell (Figs. 7.24, 7.25).

As shown by Wardlaw and Mitra (1957, 1958), applications of various kinetin solutions to the exposed apex of *Dryopteris dilatata* may result in the disappearance of the youngest primordia and the failure of new primordia to be formed. Kinetin stimulated cell division and the formation of parenchyma throughout the whole apical region; and the apical organization became so modified that the characteristic tissue pattern disappeared.

Extensive morphological changes may thus be induced in apices by direct (and indirect) chemical treatments. Some of the solutions applied may be well beyond the 'normal physiological range'. In the usual environment of the species the apical meristem exemplifies a remarkable stability; and, indeed, some of its characteristic morphogenetic activities are not readily modified (Wardlaw, 1957).

Effects of 2-Thiouracil. In experiments in which this substance was supplied, at low dosage, by way of leaves, Heslop-Harrison (1962) found that it progressively slowed down apical growth and leaf formation in young plants of *Cannabis sativa*. The leaves formed during the treatment afforded evidence of inhibited cell differentiation, but there was not a parallel diminution in the expansion of the lamina. Considerable anomalous changes in leaf morphology and phyllotaxis became evident later, and apical dominance was temporarily in abeyance. When the treatment was stopped, apical growth continued and development was approximately normal, though in some leaves the lamina continued to show anomalous features.

EFFECTS OF IONIZING RADIATIONS

Many curious and interesting departures from the normal morphological development can be induced in plants by exposing their seeds or embryonic regions to ionizing radiations. In different instances the effects induced are described as being genetical, cytological or physiological. These aberrant materials could be of rather special interest to students of morphogenesis: they have not yet been sufficiently analysed! In fact, some of the anomalous developments associated with radiation exposure are similar to those which occasionally occur in Nature. This may perhaps suggest that any particular species can only respond to external stimuli (and injuries) in a limited number of ways. In other words, the course of morphogenesis, in a particular species, is restricted to a limited number of developmental pathways. Experimentally induced morphogenetic developments in embryonic regions, in some instances, constitute a drift towards more or less complete disorganization, though partial or more complete recovery is also known. (This topic has been comprehensively reviewed by Gunckel (1965) and Gunckel and Sparrow (1965).) Other aspects of abnormal developments, due to other agencies, have been surveyed by Bloch (1965).

D'Amato (1965) has discussed in genetical terms the changes that may be induced in the organization of the shoot apex by mutagenic agents, leading to the formation of chimaeras. (*See also* Holsten *et al.*, 1965.)

CHAPTER VIII

Leaves and Buds: Further Observations

Every morphogenetic development, e.g. the formation of leaves and buds, involves the process of growth, i.e. the accumulation of metabolic substances in embryonic regions; and, accordingly, new factors become incident and new relationships are established. Localization of growth typically results in the formation of a new organ in a particular position; and different rates of growth in different directions contribute to its distinctive morphology (*see* p. 110). In fact, unorganized tissue masses excepted, growth and morphogenesis are inseparable, so that any analysis of a morphogenetic situation involves a consideration of growth. As already noted, some knowledge of the general physiology of growth will be taken for granted as part of the essential background to our inquiry – e.g. that protein synthesis largely takes place in embryonic and adjacent regions, that maturing regions are characterized by vacuolation and the deposition of more or less rigid skeletal materials, that metabolites essential to growth are synthesized in some parts of the plant and translocated to others, etc. – and attention will be concentrated on the action of particular substances which are known to be important in morphogenesis. Before extending the discussion of leaf and bud morphogenesis, some consideration must be given to the very general and much studied phenomenon of apical dominance.

APICAL DOMINANCE

Apical dominance is one of the most familiar and, indeed, most important examples of correlation in plants: in different degrees, according to the species, its state of development and other circumstances, the active shoot apex controls the development of the lateral buds. This control, or regulation, of branch formation and development has profound effects on the overall appearance of the plant, e.g. a single main shoot, or a much-branched shrubby conformation. If the apex is excised, punctured or arrested in its growth the lateral buds begin to develop or to show more rapid growth. Students of botany are familiar with the phenomenon of apical dominance; and they know that if auxin (IAA) is applied in place of an excised shoot apex the lateral buds usually remain inhibited. Many different hypotheses have been proposed to interpret these observations (see Wardlaw, 1952; Audus, 1953; Cutter, 1965, etc., for reviews). The contemporary position, based on experiments of different kinds, including bud formation in tissue cultures, is that when auxin is present, at a critical concentration for the species (and in relation to the concentrations of certain other metabolites), in the immediate locus of a bud primordium, bud growth is arrested. So, in a growing leafy-shoot, the problem of apical dominance resolves itself into: (a) the synthesis of auxin in the shoot apex; (b) the basipetal translocation of auxin to the loci of axillary buds more or less distant from the apex; (c) its accumulation to a critical concentration and its effective action; (d) other sustaining conditions, e.g. presence of various nutrients, etc. The results of some recent investigations may now be considered.

In a reassessment of apical dominance, Gregory and Veale (1957) pointed out that, in flax, the lateral buds along the axis develop to a different extent and have different growth potentials. The size of a bud and the degree of development of its vascular connection with the conducting system of the axis appeared to be important factors in its correlative inhibition by the main apex. Gregory and Veale suggested that auxin moving basipetally from the apical region impedes the differentiation of the bud vascular connection with a consequential arrest of growth. Although this interpretation is now inappropriate, these observers did a service by focusing attention on the growth, morphology and anatomy of nascent, growing and arrested buds. In fact, contemporary investigators now seek evidence of the direct inhibition of bud growth by auxin, i.e. as a component of the reaction system in the bud rudiment.

Already, in 1959, Jacobs et al. found that, in Coleus, applications of native auxin (IAA) were not a complete substitute for the apex which had been removed, i.e. in inhibiting the outgrowth of lateral buds. In green Alaska pea, as studied by Scott et al. (1965), when an application of IAA was substituted for the apex, the outgrowth of the axillary buds was suppressed for three days only. When GA, which had been extracted from this species was substituted for the apex, the result, as expected, was an extra elongation of the lateral buds. However, the curious observation was made that when the GA was applied together with the IAA, the period of bud inhibition was increased by two days. In experiments in which radioactive IAA was applied, the GA increased the amount of ^{14}C at the level of the inhibited buds. It was ascertained that most of the ^{14}C was still present in the IAA. These authors concluded that both IAA and GA are involved in the classical phenomenon of apical dominance, and that the presence of GA increases the effective concentrations of IAA at positions distant from its sites of formation. Furthermore, Jacobs and Case (1965) demonstrated that an application of GA *plus* IAA, in place of the shoot apex in *Pisum*, was more potent than an application of IAA alone. Translocation studies of IAA supported the general finding set out above. It thus appears that the presence of IAA, *at a critical concentration in the bud locus*, is closely involved in bud inhibition.

GROWTH-REGULATING SUBSTANCES

It has now been known for some time that certain metabolic substances, even when present in very small amounts, are directly or indirectly involved in the differentiation of organs and tissues, and in the integrated development of the organism as a whole. In the absence of such substances, organ formation does not take place. Where a close and obligate relationship of this kind exists, the substance is said to be morphogenetic in its action. These growth-regulating substances have sometimes been described as morphogenetic hormones. We have thus to inquire where these important substances are synthesized, how they become localized in specific positions, and how their presence there contributes to the observed organogenic result. The appropriate terminology for these specific activating substances in plants has been much discussed (*see* Wardlaw, 1952–3). The substance indole-3-acetic acid, formerly referred to as heteroauxin, is now known to be the most common growth-regulating substance in plants; it is commonly referred to as auxin (IAA). Other naturally occurring growth-regulating substances are now known, and include the vitamins, hormones, kinins and gibberellins. A very considerable number of synthetic organic substances, not known to occur in living plant tissues, can also induce morphogenetic effects, sometimes of a very remarkable kind.

The study of the biological action of 'morphogenetic substances' is beset with difficulties. For one thing, they never act alone and, almost invariably, the morphogenetic problems have proved to be considerably more complex than had at first appeared. In fact, we recognize that the relation between metabolism and the assumption of form is still one of the great mysteries of biology. Not every cell can react, or will react, in the same way to a growth-regulating substance: so there is a further major problem, namely, to understand what constitutes the competence of a cell to react to a specific substance.

The physiology of hormonal substances – the term is used in a general sense – is dealt with in most standard texts and encyclopaedias, often with some account of the historical development. The foundations of the subject, in its botanical aspect, were laid by Sachs, who formulated a theory which covered most of the facts of correlation and of morphogenesis. He attributed the differences between organs to differences in their chemical composition: even though these were not readily detectable, they were held to be already present at the time of organ inception. Thus, the existence of root-forming, flower-forming and other organ-forming substances, and their movements in different directions through the plant, were assumed; and the general theory, comprising these several ideas, appeared to afford a reasonable means of interpreting many morphological developments. The work of Beijerinck on galls, of Vöchting on morphological polarity in correlation phenomena, and of Goebel on nutrition and organ formation, advanced our knowledge of biochemical factors in plant morphogenesis and did much, both factually and conceptually, to prepare the way for the contemporary phase of active research.

The auxins, which comprise a wide range of organic substances, have been identified in various animal tissues, including carcinoma. In the higher plants they are typically produced in meristematic regions, the seat of protein synthesis. Rapidly growing plants, rooted in soil with abundant available nitrogen, tend to have high auxin production. Auxin-like action is also shown by substances such as indole-butyric acid and alpha-naphthalene-acetic acid.

The Calines. Went (1938) advanced the theory that specific morphogenetic substances, which he referred to as *calines*, are specifically involved in the inception of the several types of plant organs. Thus *rhizocaline*, formed in the terminal shoot bud, moves down the stem and induces root formation; *caulocaline*, formed in the root, moves upwards and induces shoot development; and *phyllocaline* is responsible for leaf formation. That such specific morphogenetic substances have a real existence is doubted by some observers. The odd fact, as we go to press, is that the question is still an open one.

In common with some other investigators, Went regarded the known action of auxins as being insufficient to account for the formation of the several categories of plant organs: 'All effects of auxin other than cell elongation must be called secondary . . . they can all be accounted for if we assume that other specific substances – the calines – are activated in one way or another by auxin.' In short, although auxin is necessary for certain phases of growth, it is not the only specific biochemical factor in organ formation. Other hormone-like substances, i.e. the calines, are essential for the formation of roots, leaves and shoots. These substances move from their regions of synthesis, through the living tissues, auxin being essential for establishing the path of translocation. Went maintained that although the existence of calines has not been directly proven, the available evidence makes their existence seem highly probable; and, moreover, the caline hypothesis 'offers the simplest explanation of many other effects related to growth and development of plants'.

From experimental observations of a rather different kind Gregory (1928) also concluded that a special factor necessary for leaf growth is formed in the older leaves under the influence of light; this factor is not directly related to carbohydrate photosynthesis. On the basis of tissue-culture studies, however, both White (1939) and Skoog (1944) rejected the caline hypothesis as being unnecessary. From tissue cultures which had been maintained in the undifferentiated condition for long periods and during many transfers they were able, by appropriate experimental treatments, to induce the development of leafy shoots and roots. What, then, they asked, was the source of the caulocaline and phyllocaline? Perhaps this argument is not quite so devastating as it at first seems: the productive cultures did have special substances added to their media.

Thimann's Interpretation. Thimann (1938, 1949) suggested a rather different interpretation of the action of morphogenetic substances. Growth acceleration and growth inhibition (he said) may be aspects of the same general phenomenon. Root formation, for example, requires the presence of auxin, but all but the lowest concentrations inhibit root elongation, i.e. root tissue behaves like bud tissue. Very low concentrations of auxin actually stimulate root development and, in Thimann's view, this finding may also be applied to the effect of auxin on buds. Auxin not only stimulates cell enlargement but also rapid cell division, as in cambial activity (*see also* p. 306). Thus there does not appear to be 'so clear a distinction between the factors causing division and those causing enlargement as was formerly thought'. Moreover, the effects which result from auxin action, whether of growth or inhibition, depend on the kind of cell involved and its physiological state. Also, auxins and related compounds have very different powers of movement through the plant. Indene-acetic acid, for example, causes excellent rooting of cuttings, but moves very slowly through the tissues. Cumaryl-acetic acid spreads evenly down a stem and causes growth but not curvature. 'Hence (said Thimann) we are dealing with properties which are not essential for growth activity, but which control the way in which the growth comes to be manifested.' The ability of a specific substance to be linearly transported is of evident importance in formative processes.

In relation to the foregoing views, the writer would now express his own as follows. Certain specific growth-regulating substances – auxins, calines, etc. – are capable of reacting together, in the presence of general metabolic substances such as sugars, amino acids, etc., and of substances present in the embryonic cells. Collectively, all these substances constitute a reaction system, operating in a particular organ or tissue environment, or locus. Differently constituted reaction systems will give rise to different patternized distributions of metabolites, these underlying and being antecedent to the formation of specific organs, shoot, leaf, root, etc.

LEAVES AND BUDS: THE RANGE OF MATERIALS

In this chapter some special aspects of leaf and bud morphogenesis have been selected for fuller treatment. In particular, the biochemical basis of organogenesis will be examined, partly as a direct contribution to botanical knowledge and partly to illustrate the inner complexity of common plant organs with which every botanist is familiar.

A brief survey shows that there is really a surprising variety in the categories of leaves and buds. One can scarcely fail to be impressed by the rich and intriguing array of materials that are available for observational and experimental study.

LEAF PRIMORDIA

Leaf primordia originate in the shoot apical meristem in characteristic positions for the species and in a regular phyllotactic sequence (*see* p. 226). In angiosperm embryos the inception of the cotyledon primordia in relation to a histologically organized shoot apical meristem may be not at all evident. Nevertheless, an apical growth centre, as a potent metabolic locus, is established at a very early stage in ontogenesis. (This is as much as to say that, if we could, we should look to the biochemistry rather than the histology of embryonic regions.) In many gymnosperm embryos, e.g. those of *Pinus* spp., leaf primordia originate round the margin of an organized shoot apical meristem. Even where the apical meristem of the embryonic axis may be very small and histologically ill-defined, as in some eusporangiate ferns, species of *Lycopodium*, etc., it nevertheless becomes evident, as ontogenesis proceeds, that an apex, which is the source of the whole leafy-shoot development, has been present from the outset. In brief, leaf formation begins with the inception of growth centres and young primordia in the shoot apical meristem. Furthermore, in *all* vascular plants a leaf primordium typically originates from a group of superficial and sub-surface cells in the apical meristem. In relation to the genetical constitution of the species, the stage reached in ontogenesis, and factors in the environment, both phyllotaxis and adult leaf morphology may show great diversity, e.g. leaves may vary in size, shape, symmetry, presence or absence of a petiole, or lamina, etc. Such foliar differences are readily

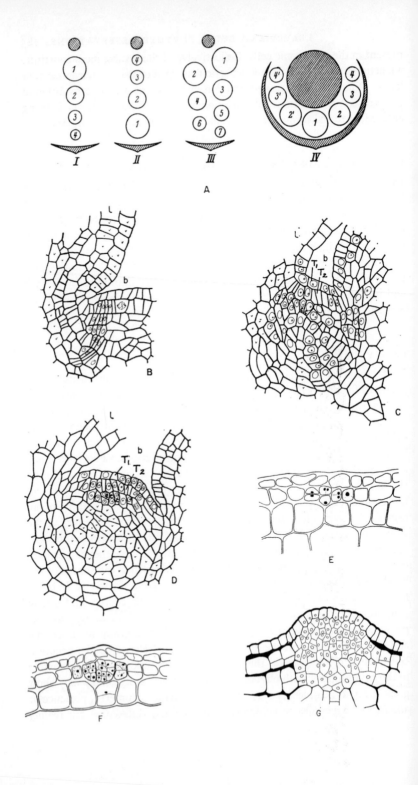

apparent in comparisons of different species, but they are also evident in the development of the individual plant, especially in those species which show heteroblastic development, i.e. variation in leaf size and shape along the stem (*see* p. 209 *and* Figs. 8.8 *et seq.*). Lastly, students of botany need scarcely be reminded of the many modifications in the form and function of leaves, e.g. protective and storage scales, tendrils, spines, phyllodes, the pitchers of insectivorous species, etc. – all wonderfully interesting materials for morphogenetic investigations. Although leaves are usually of dorsi-ventral symmetry, radial and centric leaves may occur naturally or as the result of experimental treatment (*see* p. 172).

BUD PRIMORDIA

In respect of their position of origin, time of formation and further development, buds also present a surprising range of diversity. In some species bud primordia may originate in the apical meristem, or from embryonic tissues that, at an earlier stage, had formed part of the apical meristem; whereas in other species they may be truly adventitious and either exogenous or endogenous in origin (Fig. 8.1). Again, in many flowering plants the axillary bud is a common feature, but a wider survey shows that there are species in which the buds are interfoliar, as in many ferns, supra-axillary, and in various serial, multiple-bud systems, in and above the axil. In such instances the problem of bud inception is, as it were, compounded; but the evidence of orderly development is emphasized. In some genera, e.g. species of *Nymphaea* and *Nuphar*, occasional buds, both vegetative and floral, occur in the genetical spiral, i.e. in what are usually leaf sites (Fig. 8.2). So, also, the bulbils in *Lycopodium selago* occupy leaf sites. In the Hydrocharitaceae a somewhat different facet of bud formation presents itself. In some species, e.g. *Hydrocharis morsus-ranae*, a bud, demonstrably formed in the apical meristem (Fig. 6.4), is present with great

---

FIG. 8.1. Aspects of bud development. A, Diagrams illustrating the various modes of origin and the patterns of multiple 'axillary' buds (Beiknospen). (After W. Troll, *Vergleichende Morphologie der hoheren Pflanzen*, 1935 *et seq.*) B, C, D, *Drimys Winteri* var. *chilensis*. Successive stages in the inception and early development of an axillary bud (*b*); *l*, axillant, or subtending leaf; T_1, T_2, the tunica layers; *c*, corpus initials; *v*, vacuolated cells. ($\times$230.) (After E. M. Gifford Jr., *Amer. Jour. Bot.*, 1951.) E, F, G, *Euphorbia peplus*. E, The inception of an adventitious bud in the hypocotyl in subepidermal cells. F, A later stage: longitudinal section of hypocotyledonary bud; the epidermal cells now show divisions by anticlinal walls. G, A massive bud has now developed from a single subepidermal locus. (After M. Champagnat, J. Marichal and Y. Cailleux, *Bull. Soc. Bot. France*, 1962.)

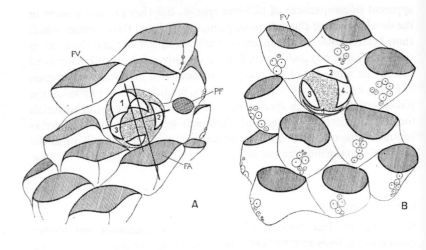

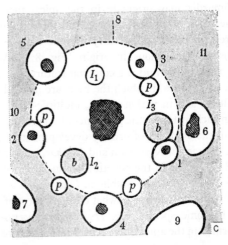

FIG. 8.2. Buds in (?) leaf sites. A. *Nuphar luteum*. B. *Nymphaea alba*.
PF, floral peduncle; FV, vegetative leaf; FA, axillant leaf. (After J. F.
Chassat, *Bull. Soc. Bot. France*, 1962.) These have been regarded by some
investigators as buds in leaf sites and by others as axillary buds. It is evident
that, whatever the morphological interpretation, a growth centre with the
'bud type of metabolism' has supervened upon a leaf, or nascent leaf, locus.
C. *Dryopteris dilatata*. Shoot apices were exposed and the apices of leaf
primordia P_1–P_7 and of the shoot were punctured. I_1 is developing as a leaf
primordium, but I_2 is developing as a bud (*b*). No primordium had developed
in the I_3 site, but close by a bud, supra-axillary to P_6, has been formed. Some
leaf primordia (*p*) are developing in what are normally undeveloped bud
sites. ($\times 27$.) (After C. W. Wardlaw, *Proc. Linn. Soc. London*, 1950.)

regularity in the axil of *every other* leaf primordium (Loiseau and Nou-garède, 1963; *Cutter*, 1963, 1964); whereas, in other species, e.g *Stratiotes aloides*, buds occur rather irregularly, e.g. in the axil of about every tenth leaf primordium; and other species manifest intermediate conditions. These non-adventitious organogenic developments have their inception in the apical meristem.

Since buds can be induced in undifferentiated tissue cultures by the incorporation of certain combinations of growth substances in the medium, the phenomena of bud induction are different in scope from those of leaf induction. It may also be recalled that vegetative propagation – one of the mainstays of horticulture – is often based on the induction of adventitious buds in leaves, petioles, etc. There are also the many instances of root buds, in species as far apart as *Ophioglossum* and *Linaria* (see Chapter X).

Some reference to recent studies of bud morphogenesis is appropriate at this point.

Hypocotyledonary Buds in Euphorbia. Champagnat *et al.* (1962) demon-strated in *Euphorbia peplus* and related species that hypocotyledonary bud rudiments can be induced to develop into leafy and flowering branches by suppressing the epicotyl. The first localized cell divisions, leading to bud inception, take place in parenchymatous subepidermal cells which, initi-ally, do not become conspicuously dedifferentiated (Fig. 8.1). Periclinal divisions are followed by anticlinal divisions, or vice-versa, and a mariste-matic mass of tissue begins to be formed. More slowly, anticlinal divisions appear in the epidermal cells and the bud rudiment becomes visible on the hypocotyl as a small mound (Fig. 8.1). The divisions in the epi-dermal cells are apparently not merely passive – e.g. a result of tension exercised by the expanding tissue within – but are a response to the growth stimulus in the bud site, described as a wave of dedifferentiation and mitosis. Meanwhile, the growth stimulus has also affected the more deeply seated cells. Many such bud rudiments proceed no further in their development and remain invisible externally. Their number is apparently not affected by excision of the epicotyl; but their further induction and development can be obtained by a comprehensive removal of all the young branches on the axis. This endogenous (sub-epidermal) origination of buds in *Euphorbia* spp. has led to conjectures regarding the inability of the epidermal layer to become the locus of new growth, as in the adventitious, hypocotyle-donary root buds in other flowering plants, e.g. in *Alliaria officinalis*, as described by Champagnat *et al.* (1962), (Fig. 10.19, Chapter X).

Axillary Buds in Cucurbitaceae. In species of the Nymphaeaceae, vegetative and flower buds may occupy leaf sites or they may be axillary. In *Victoria cruziana* (Fig. 8.3) it will be seen that the flower bud, though axillary, is somewhat lateral; in fact, it originates in the anodic or acropetal direction of the genetic spiral of leaf primordia. Snow (1965) reported that, in *Cucurbita pepo*, the axillary buds are also eccentric. In fact, as in those of *Victoria*, they are 'much displaced in the anodic or uphill direction of the

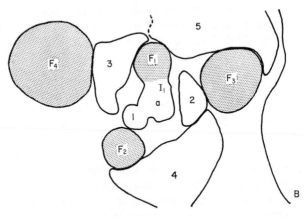

FIG. 8.3. *Victoria cruziana*. Transverse section of a rhizome apex, showing the apical meristem (*a*), leaf primordia, *1–7*, and flower primordia, F_1, F_2, etc., these being formed in interfoliar positions above leaf margins. On the genetic spiral, F_2 may be regarded as being anodic to *leaf 4* and F_1 to *leaf 3*. (Drawing by courtesy of Dr. E. G. Cutter; after C. W. Wardlaw, *Growth in Living Systems*, 1961.)

genetic leaf spiral' (Fig. 8.4). It can be seen that the angles between successive leaves are unusually large in this species. Both of these unusual morphological features are present in young seedlings, beginning with the third leaf from the base. By making a radial vertical incision in the apical meristem on the kathodic side of P_1, or of I_1, the respective buds were often median or nearly so. By other surgical treatments of the apex, Snow was able to obtain subeccentric or nearly median axillary buds. He concluded that the normal anodic locus of an axillary bud is probably due to a hormone, originating in an older leaf primordium, which has a 'repelling' effect on bud inception. A further inference is that this substance moves upwards in the direction of the leaf spiral: hence the effectiveness of a cut on the kathodic side of a young leaf primordium. Snow further considered that changes observed in the positions of certain younger leaves due to the formation of median or nearly median buds in experimental materials is consonant with 'an explanation of the large angles between successive leaves, based on a space-filling theory of phyllotaxis. This explanation is that the position in which any leaf n is determined is displaced in the anodic direction by the anodic axillary bud of leaf $n - 3$, which encroaches from the kathodic side upon the space available for n between $n - 3$ and $n - 2$.

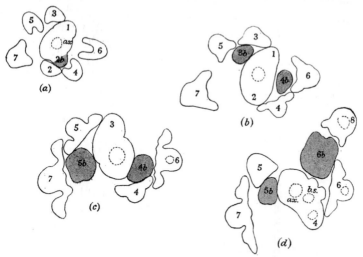

FIG. 8.4. *Cucurbita pepo*. The formation of pseudo-axillary, anodic buds. Transections in collodion through the shoot apex of a normal seedling of *Cucurbita pepo* from the level of the youngest two leaves downwards. The leaves are numbered downwards 1, 2, 3, etc., and their axillary buds, when present, 2*b*, 3*b*, etc., *b.s.*, bud stele; *ax.*, contour of xylem of axis. (*a* to *c*, ×66; *d*, ×55.) (After R. Snow, *Phil. Trans. Roy. Soc.*, 1965.)

When the bud $n - 3$ is median or nearly so, the position of n is much less far anodic.'

A Note on Tendrils. As well as morphologically evident leaves and buds, there are many lateral organs which are ontogenetic modifications of one or other of these organs. Some of these have been the subject of interesting morphogenetic investigations. Here, a recent study has been selected as an indication of the way in which the morphogenetic approach can add to our knowledge of classical problems. (*See* Plate 1.)

In an investigation of tendrils on long shoots of *Parthenocissus inserta*, Millington (1966) observed that these organs originate with regularity opposite the alternate distichous leaves at two successive nodes of each three nodes (Fig. 8.5); but the nodes immediately above and below are without tendrils. A tendril has its inception on the flank of the shoot apex, in an essentially axillary position, during the second plastochrone, but it becomes separated from its axillary leaf by internodal growth. As a result, it eventually occupies a position opposite the next younger leaf above. In a rhythmical pattern of organogenesis, different lateral organs are formed at the shoot apex at each of a group of three nodes as follows, in acropetal sequence: (1) a node without a tendril but with a leaf which subtends an axillary bud complex which in turn subtends a tendril; (2) the leaf at the lower tendril-bearing node directly subtends a tendril; and (3) the leaf at the upper tendril-bearing node subtends an axillary bud (Fig. 8.6). Millington was unable to induce tendril primordia to develop as foliaceous shoots in decapitation experiments or when he cultured them *in vitro*. It thus appears that the chemical basis for tendril

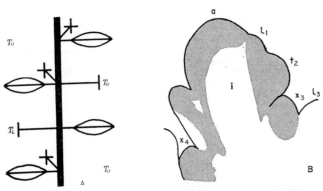

FIG. 8.5. *Parthenocissus inserta*, the formation of tendrils. A, Diagram showing the positional relationships of the lateral organs. +, axillary bud, or buds; *Tu*, upper tendril; *TL*, lower tendril; *TO*, node without a tendril. B, Long shoot as seen in longitudinal median section, showing a, shoot apex; l_1, most recently formed leaf primordium above the tendril (t_2); t_2, primordium of lower tendril, subtended by axillary bud (X_3) and leaf 3 (l_3). (×125.) (After W. F. Millington; B was traced from a photograph. *Amer. Jour. Bot.*, 1966.) (*See also* Plate 1.)

inception is established early at a locus in the shoot meristem. Although the tendril of *Parthenocissus* is shoot-like in its general conformation, Millington regards it as an organ *sui generis*, possibly with an inflorescence relationship. (For other literature on morphogenesis in climbing organs, *see* Bugnon, 1949, 1953; Moens, 1956; Chadefaud, 1949; Shah, 1960.)

Shah (1962) reported on the origin and development of tendrils in the Vitaceae (Fig. 8.7). These organs, which may be branched or unbranched, usually occur at a node, opposite a leaf. In *Cissus* spp. tendril inception begins by periclinal divisions in the second or third sub-surface layer. In *Cayratia* similar divisions occur in the second or third tunica layers. At an early stage a single abaxial procambium trace may be observed. The elongation of the tendril primordium is ascribed by Shah to the activity of a group of subapical meristematic cells and to generalized intercalary growth. In the Vitaceae a tendril is apparently a modified lateral branch, the extra-axillary development of which is related to the vegetative and reproductive phases of the shoot.

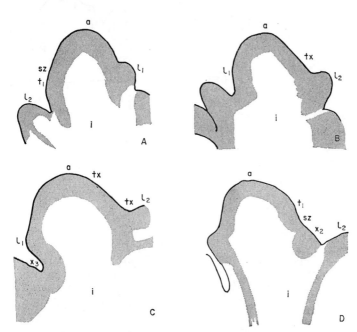

FIG. 8.6. *Parthenocissus inserta*. Various illustrations of tendril formation (tracings from photographs). A, Initiation of an *upper* tendril (t_1) above its subtending leaf (l_2). Note limited shell zone activity (sz) at upper limit of tendril and vacuolation of cells delimiting tendril above and to the interior. ($\times 80$.) Number of cells here has been increased, largely by periclinal division. B, Site of initiation of a *lower* tendril and bud (tx) axillary to leaf 2 (l_2). Initiation of leaf 1 (l_1) at left. ($\times 80$.) C, D, Progressive development of *lower* tendril and associated axillary bud during the second plastochron. Axillant leaf, l_2; tendril-bud complex, tx; tendril, t_1; axillary bud, x_2; shell zone, sz. (After W. F. Millington, *Amer. Jour. Bot.*, 1966.)

All these developments are the result of regulated growth and the inception of organogenic patterns in particular loci. Accordingly, we may consider what has been ascertained or conjectured about the underlying metabolic processes (*see* p. 195 and Dore, 1965).

Thorns and Spines. Many thorns and spines typically originate in leaf axils and may be regarded as modified buds. In *Lycium chinense*, a member

G

of a Solanaceous genus with thorny twigs, Fujita (1965) observed that, in spring, some of the axillary buds develop as thorns, bearing a pair of prophylls and some 10–12 minute scale leaves. Initially the apical meristem of this axis consists of a normal tunica and corpus of densely protoplasmic

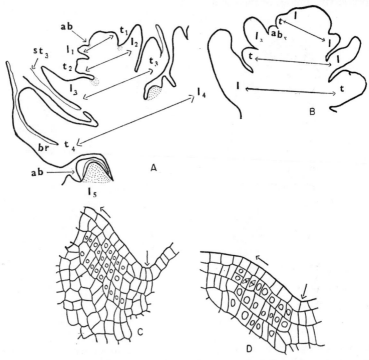

FIG. 8.7. Tendril formation in Vitaceae. A, *Cissus* sp. B, *Cayratia auriculata.* C, D, *Cissus* sp. (*ab*, axillary bud; *br*, bract-like scale; *l*, leaf; *st*, stipule; *t*, tendril. Numerals indicate the number of the leaf or tendril primordium from the shoot apex.)

A, *Cissus sp.* l.s. terminal bud. (×50.) B, *Cayratia auriculata*, l.s. terminal bud and shoot apex. (×50.) C, D, *Cissus* sp. l.s. sector of shoot apex showing tendril inception. The ascending arrow is towards the shoot apex and the vertical arrow delimits the peripheral meristem. (×380.) (After J. J. Shah, *Proc. Summer School of Botany – Darjeeling*, 1962.)

cells, but, later, the tip turns from green to yellow and eventually brown, loses its histological organization, collapses and becomes necrotic, as do also the scale leaves in a basipetal sequence. With the lignification of the lower parts of the axis, the thorn-like character is established. Other examples of shoot tip abortion have also been described (*see* Arnold, 1959, on *Hymenanthera*; Garrison and Wetmore, 1961, on *Syringa*; Millington, 1963, on *Ulmus*).

In *Ulex europaeus* in which axillary buds may become differentiated as spines, Bieniek and Millington (1967) reported that axillary buds originate from detached meristems, i.e. from portions of the shoot apical meristem. The lateral buds which are formed in the axils of juvenile seedling leaves typically develop as leafy shoots. On the other hand, those in the axils of adult leaves usually become spines, or thorns. Even on the same axis, however, the presumptive spines may manifest various degrees of vegetative development; i.e. they may form a variable number, 3–9, of bracteal leaves. If the successive lateral buds along a shoot are examined it can be seen that there is a sharp, or critical, change from the foliose to the spiny condition. In other words, the lateral meristem ceases to form leaf primordia and the metabolic events that determine the spiny development supervene. The process of sclerification proceeds basipetally. A point of considerable interest is that although no new leaf primordia are initiated at the transformed spine apex, prevascular strands traceable to the potential leaf sites, i.e. to leaf growth centres, are differentiated.

METABOLISM IN GROWTH CENTRES

Growth centres or *discrete loci of special metabolism* (i.e. as compared with contiguous regions of the shoot apical meristem which do not grow out as lateral primordia, but differentiate into the tissues of the axis), have already been considered in terms of their outgrowth as leaf or bud primordia. But what can be said of their inception and of the position in which they occur? What factors determine their further development and differentiation, either as leaves or as buds? And what factors control the range in leaf size and shape which one can observe in many species?

In discussing the metabolism of apical growth and morphogenesis, it is accepted that the distal embryonic region is supplied from the older organs and regions below with the basic materials required to sustain its activities, i.e. with mineral nutrients, carbohydrates, amino acids, hormonal substances, etc. Endogenous, i.e. locally produced, metabolites are also likely to be involved. As active growth centres of both leaf and bud primordia soon show evidence of enlargement, it may be inferred that our primary concern is with the stimuli which induce cell growth and division in a localized group of surface and sub-surface cells of the meristem. However, we have little definitive information on this point: we still do not know how some particular substance(s) reaches a critical concentration in a small region of tissue in a particular position in the apical meristem. Experimental investigations of phyllotaxis indicate that the position of a new growth centre – in the 'next available space' on the meristem – is determined by the two or more adjacent, or contiguous, older primordia (*see* p. 237). In trying to account for the inception of growth centres, it is not absolutely necessary to postulate the presence of stimuli proceeding from adjacent older leaf primordia: in *Pinus* spp., for example, the club-shaped young embryo, with its massive apical meristem, typically gives rise simultaneously to 6–16 primordia without the intervention of older primordia. In fact, general experience indicates that the organization and reactivity of shoot apical meristems are such that they give rise to regularly spaced growth centres.

According to contemporary observations and conjectures, auxins, gibberellins, kinins and other substances still to be detected may all have effects in stimulating cell division, i.e. by affecting the metabolism of enzymes or their precursors. (Relevant literature has been surveyed and discussed by Heslop-Harrison, 1963; Allsopp, 1964; and by others.) So far, no absolute specificity in the stimulation of cell division in growth centres has been demonstrated for any of these substances acting alone. Auxin and kinetin are known to affect both nucleic acid and protein metabolism; DNA synthesis may be activated by kinetin and IAA; and RNA by IAA alone. Kinetin has also been found to affect RNA and protein synthesis in other instances. When kinetin was applied locally to detached, ageing leaves at low concentrations Mothes (1960) observed that the treated areas remained green and became active loci to which free amino acids moved from other regions of the leaf. Osborne and Halloway (1960) showed that protein levels in detached autumn leaves may be increased by auxin. On the other hand, in auxin-inhibited lateral buds protein synthesis may be reduced. (Some important inferences may, perhaps, be drawn from this observation.) So far, there is little conclusive evidence that auxin affects metabolism in the cell nucleus; but its participation in protein and RNA metabolism is not precluded. Maciejewska Potapczyk (1959) reported observations which indicate that auxin may affect nucleic acid metabolism by regulating associated enzyme activities. In particular, it was noted, though in crude extracts only from bean hypocotyl, that IAA considerably increased the activity *in vitro* of deoxyribonuclease and ribonuclease extracts. As to the possible action of kinetin, Thimann and Laloraya (1960) suggested that its rapid immobilization when supplied to a tissue may be due to its rapid incorporation in an active nucleic acid molecule.

Although references to the gibberellins are prominent in the contemporary literature of morphogenesis, little can be said about their activity in promoting the inception of growth centres. One suggestion is that GA may enhance auxin activity by protecting it from the action of other substances (Heslop–Harrison, 1963).

To summarize: although critical information has still to be obtained, it seems probable that the inception of growth centres depends on a sub-stance, or perhaps a *system* of substances, which stimulates and maintains the synthesis and activities of DNA, RNA and their associated metabolites. (*See* also p. 202.)

In considering the inception and activities of a growth centre and the primordium to which it gives rise it will be important to discover which of the reacting substances are already present or synthesized in the constituent cells, and which of them diffuse into the locus from the adjacent older primordia or tissues of the shoot. This aspect may be examined in relation to auxin, gibberellic acid and kinetin, bearing in mind that the effective primary stimulus may be a substance not yet detected, perhaps one which quickly becomes immobilized by being incorporated in the nucleus or cytoplasm during metabolism.

Auxin and Growth Centres. Although indoleacetic acid and related sub-stances affect many basic morphogenetic processes, the mechanism is still not understood (Galston and Purves, 1960). Hence the various theories of auxin action, e.g. on the cell wall, in the cytoplasm, on enzymes, etc. Information on the effects of hormonal substances on nascent growth centres is still very slight, though certain conjectures are not unreasonable and may indeed eventually be shown to be valid. What we know about auxin in this connection is largely inferred from observations made on older primordia. Wetmore and Prat (1949), using *Adiantum,* and Jacobs (1954), working with *Coleus,* showed that young leaf primordia synthesize auxin, the quantity of free auxin produced increasing as primordia enlarge. In the group of most recently formed primordia only very small amounts of auxin could be detected. This has suggested that virtually no free auxin, i.e. at the assay level, is produced by the shoot apical meristem. In *Coleus,* Jacobs showed that auxin (IAA) moves from young primordia into the axis, where its further movement, though mainly basipetal, may also be acropetal. It seems probable that the incipient or differentiating vascular system affords the pathway for auxin movement. Other evidence of the acropetal movement of auxin has been reported by Leopold and Guernsey (1953). At the onset of flowering in *Coleus* they observed that, concomit-antly with the extensive morphological changes in primordia, there is a marked increase in the capacity of the shoot for the acropetal translocation of auxin. The regulation of the rate of development of younger primordia by older ones – a well-known phenomenon – may thus be due, in part at least, to the acropetal movement of IAA and its attendant reactions. This effect may also extend to the growth of the shoot apical meristem and its nascent and developing growth centres. That the application of auxin to very young leaf primordia, in both flowering plants and ferns, greatly enhances their growth is now well established (p. 176). Although auxin is involved in the inhibition of buds at variable distances below the apical meristem, we still have to face the curious fact that, when it is applied in a liquid, or semi-liquid, culture medium, it does not necessarily, or invariably, inhibit the formation or further development of buds.

Gibberellic Acid and Growth Centres. When GA is applied to older leaves, or if it is applied directly to the apex, it may, in various ways according to the species, affect the rate and extent of stem elongation and modify the morphological development of leaf primordia. How it affects the inception of growth centres has received little attention. When GA was applied directly to naked apices of *Dryopteris dilatata* variable results were obtained, including inhibition of primordium formation and formation of double primordia (Wardlaw and Mitra, 1958). The first of these effects, obtained with 100 mg./l. GA, could have been a concomitant of the general arrest of growth observed in the apex as a whole and not a specific GA effect on the reactions in growth centre loci. Where double primordia developed, as in a P_1, or in I_1 or I_2 sites, the site became tangentially enlarged, indicating enhanced meristematic activity in it. However, as in flowering-plant species, the main growth responses to GA were observed in the expanding sub-apical region. It is relevant that Yabuta and Hayashi (1939) reported an increased rate of leaf formation in tobacco seedlings treated with GA, i.e. initially an effect on growth centre inception. Further observations on GA effects on a variety of apices are evidently required.

Kinetin and Growth Centres. When apices of *Dryopteris dilatata* were laid bare and supplied with 10·0, 1·0 and 0·1 mg./l. kinetin – non-lethal concentrations – growth continued in the apical and subapical regions during the period of application (Wardlaw and Mitra, 1958). At 0·1 mg./l. there was a general stimulation of growth, but no special morphogenetic effects were observed. At higher concentrations the two youngest leaf primordia P_1 and P_2 completely disappeared, and P_3 became so modified and parenchymatous that it could only be recognized by its apical cell four plastochrones later. No new primordia were formed. As anatomical studies showed, these effects were due to a considerable stimulation of cell division, and to the induction of precocious and anomalous patterns of cell division and enlargement, both in the main apex and in young primordia. Similar evidence of activated and irregular cell division, resulting in a loss of the normal organization, after application of kinetin and IAA, have been reported by other investigators.

Denizci (1966) has described an investigation in which he repeated, with slight modifications, some experiments of Wickson and Thimann (1958) on the effect of kinetin and IAA on the growth of axillary buds of *Pisum*. When applied separately, kinetin had initially some suppressive effect on bud growth; but after 3–4 days an increase in growth was recorded in some instances. The suppression of bud growth by IAA was only partly removed by kinetin.

Effects of Other Substances. Substances such as 2,3,5-tri-iodobenzoic acid (TIBA) may cause various anomalous developments in shoots and young leaf primordia of flowering plants, e.g. ring fasciation in tomato (Gorter 1949, 1951). The effects on nascent growth centres, however, have not been closely specified. In *Dryopteris dilatata* the writer (Wardlaw, 1957) showed that apical organization may be greatly modified and the inception of primordia more or less precluded by direct application to the apical meristem of solutions of various physiologically active substances (*see* p. 176). Thus, solutions of yeast extract and thiamin hydrochloride led to a scaly and parenchymatous development of the apical meristem, including the apical cell; in fact, to the loss of its normal histological organization. However, small leaf primordia continued to be formed in normal positions for some time, suggesting that their reaction systems have considerable stability. Buds, which do not occur in the normal intact apical meristem of *Dryopteris*, were sometimes induced in these experimentally treated apices (*see* p. 177 and Figs. 7.24, 7.25).

Dinitrophenol (DNP) caused some arrest of growth in the apical meristem, and the youngest leaf primordium, P_1, developed as a bud; the next primordia to appear, I_1 and I_2, showed an anomalous scaly, foliar development. After 64 days no primordium had originated in the I_3 site, but a small one had appeared in the I_4 site. In other apices treated with DNP there were scaly developments of the apical meristem and delays and irregularities in the formation of the new primordia. However, the DNP effects on different batches of apices, showing different rates of growth, were variable. Maleic hydrazide, when applied directly to exposed apices of *Dryopteris dilatata*, resulted in a more or less considerable arrest of growth in the apical meristem. New primordia continued to appear, but their further development was usually modified, and they were sometimes obliterated as a result of the development of blister-like outgrowth of superficial cells.

To summarize: various substances, when applied in solution directly to the apical meristem, may affect its growth and morphogenesis activity in a number of ways. Some substances prevent the inception of growth centres, but others do not, though the ensuing primordial development may be anomalous and primordia may sometimes become obliterated. As a tentative view, it appears that the reaction system in a growth centre can be disturbed by the introduction into it of substances which interfere with any of its major components, e.g. hormonal substances, enzymes, etc.

THE OUTGROWTH OF PRIMORDIA

Investigations by Veen (1963) and by Humphries and Wheeler (1964) indicate that rapid changes in growth substances accompany cell division, enlargement and differentiation in active loci. Thus, the rate of cell division in an enlarging leaf decreases as the IAA disappears. Although many of the metabolic substances in a growth centre are probably also essential to its outgrowth as a primordium, one cannot assume that the hormonal and other substances in the developing primordium remain qualitatively or quantitatively unaltered. A developing leaf primordium is characterized by meristematic activity, a steady acceleration of growth and increasing differentiation as it becomes separated from the apical meristem. The transitions from the growth centre phase to the young and older primordial phases are continuous and harmonious; accordingly, it may be inferred that the factors which affect the synthesis of enzymes, other cytoplasmic and nuclear proteins, and processes such as cell vacuolation and elongation, etc., remain active until the mature or adult state is reached.

The growth of primordia in ferns may be accelerated or augmented by direct applications of IAA and of 3-indole-acetonitrile (IAN) (Wardlaw, 1957). When IAN was applied in solution to the exposed apex of *Dryopteris dilatata* the organs and tissues of the subapical region became enlarged and some of the nascent and newly formed primordia on the apical meristem became tangentially extended and developed as double primordia; i.e. IAN stimulated growth in the meristematic tissues of growth centres and young primordia. When indoleacetic acid (IAA) was applied to lanoline just below the I_1 and I_2 positions in *Dryopteris*, i.e. below the sites of growth centres, evident responses were obtained. I_1 (and also I_6 in its vicinity) and I_2 developed as conspicuously enlarged leaf primordia. Earlier, Snow and Snow (1937) and Ball (1944) had shown similar stimulatory effects of auxin (IAA) on young primordia in species of flowering plants, e.g. *Tropaeolum major*.

The effects of gibberellic acid on young fern leaf primordia were variable and dependent on the state of growth, active or less active, in the apex. While these observations may support the view that GA and IAA effects on growth are closely interrelated, more precise information is required.

When kinetin was applied to the apex of *Dryopteris dilatata*, all meristematic tissues tended to be stimulated to excessive division, with concomitant departures from the normal organization (p. 178). In particular, young primordia, such as P_1 and P_2, sometimes disappeared.

The collective experimental information suggests that substances such as IAA, IAN, GA and kinetin contribute to the normal development when they are present in growth centres or in young primordia in certain concentrations, together with the other metabolic substances necessary for growth; i.e. they behave as normal components of a regulated and balanced reaction system. In experimental treatments, however, a single substance may easily be applied in excess: as a result, the normal working of the reaction system is modified and primordium development may be more or less considerably disturbed.

LEAVES AND BUDS: SPECIFIC FORMATIVE ACTIVITIES

A major topic for students of morphogenesis is why some primordia develop with the characteristic dorsiventral symmetry and definitive growth of leaves, whereas others develop as organs of radial symmetry and potentially indefinite growth, i.e. as buds.

Leaf- and Bud-forming Substances. Although no convincing evidence of specific 'leaf-forming' and 'bud-forming' substances has yet been obtained, it need not be concluded, or inferred, that they do not exist. However, if they do, they have consistently escaped detection and isolation. The analyses by Steward et al. (1954, 1955) of nitrogenous constituents of the shoot apex may be mentioned as important and indeed essential beginnings; but, in themselves, they add little to our understanding of apical organization and the distinctive organogenic processes associated with it. One might, perhaps, try to simplify the problem by saying that lateral buds, being simply smaller replicas of the parent shoot, have the same metabolism, and that the task remaining is to account for the particular metabolism involved in leaf formation. Of course, since leaf primordia are outgrowths of the shoot apical meristem and organically continuous with the axis, it could be argued that many of the metabolic processes in the two morphological regions are likely to be identical. Such arguments do not get us very far. The subtlety of the metabolic phenomena in leaf and bud formation has already been indicated by reference to experimental studies with *Dryopteris*: young leaf and bud primordia are closely comparable histologically and, by simple surgical techniques, buds may be caused to originate in leaf sites and leaves in bud sites. In the ferns at least it thus appears that a growth centre is undetermined metabolically: its reaction system either does not comprise a specific leaf- or bud-forming substance or the organogenic action of such a substance is readily modified by other metabolic changes in the growth centre. So far, comparable observations, after surgical treatments of the apical meristem, have not been obtained with dicotyledon apices; but the immediate contiguity of induced leaf and bud primordia on the shoot apical meristem has again been observed (Cutter, 1958; Sussex, 1951).

Other enigmatic problems of leaf and bud differentiation have already been exemplified by reference to species of *Nymphaea* and *Nuphar*. In them, vegetative buds and flower buds originate in what are typically leaf sites in the phyllotactic spiral. As already noted and illustrated (p. 122), in *Hydrocharis morsus-ranae*, an axillary bud is formed in the apical meristem, just above the axil of *every other* leaf primordium with a truly remarkable order of regularity. This bud demonstrably originates close to the summit (or centre) of the shoot apical meristem, its early histological development being comparable with that of a leaf primordium. It seems inescapable that growth centres, whether they develop into leaf or into bud primordia, must all draw on the general metabolic resources available at the summit of the shoot. So, one may ask, should a particular kind of morphological development be referred to the accumulation of certain specific metabolites in a growth centre? Or is the characteristic form of a leaf or a bud due to the regulation of differential growth in a primordium, according to its position on the axis and its relationship with other developing organs?

In *Nymphaea*, *Nuphar* or *Hydrocharis* a growth centre which is destined to become a leaf, a vegetative bud or a flower bud proceeds on its characteristic metabolic and developmental pathway from an early stage, perhaps even from the outset; and similarly for leaf primordia and induced buds at the apex of *Dryopteris*. If, now, in *Dryopteris*, one examines *all the circumstances* of leaf and bud primordia from their inception one may note that leaf primordia usually and typically originate *higher up* on the shoot apical meristem than do buds, i.e. their metabolic relationships may be different for the reasons already stated (p. 118). Moreover, the rates of growth of the two kinds of primordium are different and there are differences in their allometric growth patterns. In both ferns and flowering plants, as a simple dissection will show, leaf primordia grow more rapidly than the axis that bears them, especially in the vertical direction. Is anything known of specific substances and reactions which could contribute to such differences? (*see* p. 110).

LEAF AND BUD METABOLISM BASED ON CULTURAL TECHNIQUES

The techniques of tissue, organ and embryo culture have yielded a considerable amount of information on the nutritional requirements of excised shoot and root meristems, excised leaf primordia, flower buds and embryos (see pp. 62, 342). Although information is now available on the special growth requirements of some root and shoot apices *in vitro*, the different metabolic needs of leaf and bud primordia have still not been ascertained. However, some morphogenetic developments associated with certain substances may now be considered. Caution must evidently be exercised in applying the conclusions from such studies to the more massive apical meristem.

Bud Formation in Tissue Cultures. Relatively high auxin concentrations stimulate root formation but inhibit bud formation. In both woody and herbaceous cuttings buds are typically formed on the acropetal callus and roots on the basipetal callus, the movement of auxin being basipetal. However, species are known in which auxin applications do not inhibit bud formation, and there are others in which bud formation is promoted. Very different interpretations of the action of auxin in bud formation and inhibition have been proposed. It can be said with justice that the evidence for a direct and specific effect of IAA in bud formation is scanty and inconclusive.

In particular strains of undifferentiated tobacco tissue culture, Skoog and his co-workers 1944–57 (see Wardlaw, 1965a, b, for résumé) showed that roots, or shoot buds bearing leaves, may be induced more or less at will according to the balance of IAA, adenine and kinetin present in the basic medium: IAA tended to inhibit bud formation, whereas adenine tended to promote it. From the evidence, it appears that a delicate quantitative balance between these and other substances is critically important in organogenesis. Skoog and Miller (1957) stated that, at the molecular level, 15,000 molecules of adenine are required to offset the inhibitory effects of one molecule of IAA on bud formation. Although similar results have not been obtained in all tissue cultures, these are undoubtedly very interesting and important observations. Nevertheless, they do not provide the information we seek on factors which specifically determine leaf as against shoot inception: appropriate balances of the specific substances resulted in the formation of leafy-shoots and perhaps, as Sachs stated long ago, the two are part of an indivisible unit.

Jablonski and Skoog (1954), Skoog and Miller (1957), Miller (1961), Miller and Skoog (1953), and other investigators, in an important sequence of discoveries, demonstrated that both IAA and kinetin must be present in tobacco-pith cultures for the continued active synthesis of DNA, and for mitosis and cell division. Whereas IAA alone yields cell enlargement, the morphogenetic effects of kinetin and IAA together are numerous and subject to modification by other factors and conditions. Kinetin, like adenine, was found to be important in the inception of buds in undifferentiated tobacco tissue culture. On a modified White's medium, in which IAA was present at a constant concentration of 2·0 mg./l., cultures exhibited cell enlargement and the formation of some short roots; with kinetin at 0·02 mg./l. added to this medium, abundant root formation was obtained; at 0·2 mg./l. kinetin, the growth of undifferentiated callus was the main feature; but, at 0·5 and 1·0 mg./l. kinetin, bud formation was conspicuous and root formation was absent. These are very interesting and significant observations. However, if they are to be adequately interpreted the reactions of IAA and kinetin with genetically determined substances, which are already present in the cells of the tobacco species or strain used, must also be ascertained.

According to the present writer's interpretation, we have here a strong indication that, in a reaction system in an embryonic tissue, high relative IAA concentration determines a chemical pattern which, later, we recognize as that of a root primordium, whereas high relative kinetin concentration determines one that shall become a bud primordium. It is conceivable that some particular balance of metabolic components determines leaf primordium formation at the shoot apex. If so, perhaps it is to a quantitative rather than a qualitative relationship that we should be looking in our attempts to interpret leaf as distinct from bud organogenesis. This, indeed, was the general conclusion reached by Skoog and Miller (1957); i.e. they reject the concept of specific organogenic substances. However, as we shall see below, some other avenues remain to be explored.

Skoog and Miller (1957) also found that casein hydrolystate stimulated bud formation, but only when it contributed essential basic metabolites, tyrosine being indicated as the most important component promoting bud formation.

Various combinations of kinetin and adenine have also been found to be effective in increasing growth and bud formation in tobacco tissue cultures, the several organogenic effects obtained being dependent on the strain of tobacco used; i.e. gene-determined metabolites affected the reactions leading to organ inception. Thus, whereas some strains of Turkish tobacco grew as an undifferentiated tissue mass, others formed buds and yet others roots. A 'non-differentiating' strain of tobacoo gave rise to buds when suitable combinations of kinetin, adenine and tyrosine were present in the medium; but if kinetin were not present the other two substances alone were not effective in promoting bud formation, i.e. buds have apparently a multiple growth-factor requirement.

Other workers have made significant contributions to this theme (see Wardlaw, 1965a, b for résumé). Of special relevance to the present work are the findings of Paulet and Nitsch (1959). By using leaf discs of Garda-

mine pratensis, the materials being so selected as not to include certain preformed undifferentiated meristems, they found that buds could be induced by a whole series of substances, including gibberellins. In particular, they noted that the other substances had one property in common, namely, that *they were all related to nucleic aicd metabolism*. Thus they included purine and pyrimidine bases (adenine, guanine, cytosine and thymine); certain precursors, nucleic acid derivatives or analogues (kinetin and 6-succinylaminopurine); and substances such as nicotinic and folic acids which are known to be involved in the biosynthesis of nucleic acid.

To summarize, it appears that, indirectly or directly, IAA, GA, kinetin, adenine, etc., are involved in nucleic acid metabolism and in organogenesis, *endogenous metabolic factors being contributory in different degrees according to the genetic constitution of the species*. The latter concept seems to the writer to bridge the gap between the views of observers like Skoog and Miller (1957), who regarded organ inception as being determined by *quantitative interactions*, i.e. the *ratios*, rather than the *absolute levels* (concentrations) of the substances participating in growth, and those of others, such as Mayer (1956) and Stichel (1959), who regarded the *concentration* of auxin (NAA) rather than the adenine/auxin ratio as being of critical importance in organogenesis. (They found that whereas the presence of adenine or guanine in the medium determined the *number* of organs formed by *Cyclamen* tuber tissue, the type of organ formed, i.e. buds or roots, was exclusively determined by the concentration of auxin (NAA) in the medium.)

That information of the kind set out above is relevant to normal bud inception at the shoot apex may perhaps be accepted, but how precisely it is to be applied is considerably less evident, because of the sheer complexity of the situation there. In the latter connection, Audus (1953, 1959) suggested that, in the normal inception of any typical axillary bud, the subtending or associated leaf primordium might supply one essential metabolic component, the shoot apical meristem another and the developing axis yet a third. The pattern of gradients which would develop might then provide the balance of nutrients, i.e. the components of a reaction system, essential for bud formation. However, such a concept does not really account for the inception of the distinctive morphological features by which buds are usually characterized.

Isolated Shoot and Leaf Culture. Related to the foregoing discussion, information is available on the growth, in media of known composition, of excised shoot apical meristems and of individual leaf primordia. With various additions and modifications, the media used were based on those which had proved successful in plant tissue-culture studies. Leaf-culture media, for example, typically contain the main and trace inorganic nutrients, a carbohydrate source such as sucrose, various amino acids, vitamins and growth-regulating substances, either auxins of known composition or coconut milk (in which all the ingredients are not yet known). Low and high concentrations of sugars have been shown by various investigators to have important effects on the subsequent development of leaf primordia, i.e. yielding simple or relatively complex laminal developments respectively in different instances. Treated collectively, the information to date from cultural investigations is that the recipes used admit of more or less normal growth and development of embryonic tissues, e.g. excised shoot apices or young excised leaf primordia; but it does not enable us to explain why one primordium develops as a foliar organ whereas another develops as an axial organ.

Leaf and Bud Primordia in Osmunda cinnamomea. In investigations of the growth of excised young leaf primordia of *O. cinnamomea* in culture (*see* Sussex and Steeves, 1953), Steeves (1957 *et seq.*) reported that buds could not only be obtained from P_1, P_2 and P_3, as in *Dryopteris dilatata*, but also, though not invariably, from older primordia, e.g. $P_4 - P_9$; in fact, progressively older primordia yielded an increasing proportion of leaves; and P_{10} always developed as a dorsiventral leaf. Roots were formed at the bases of the shoots or leaves. The type of organ which developed from the excised leaf primordium was not affected morphogenetically by any particular component of the culture medium. From these observations, Steeves concluded that, in this fern, primordia remain undetermined for a considerable time, the foliar character being gradually induced by a leaf-forming substance. Cutter (1965) has adopted a somewhat cautious attitude towards Steeves' interpretation of his observations. (For further investigations of leaf–bud interrelationships, *see also* Kuehnert and Steeves, 1962; and Cutter and Wardlaw, 1963.)

LEAVES AND BUDS: GENERAL DISCUSSION

Evidence from Embryos. The subject of embryo culture has already been considered in Chapter IV, p. 62. Very young embryos, like the most distal region of flowering plant apices, are difficult to culture, and have, as it seems, special nutrient and other physiological requirements (*but see* Raghavan and Torrey, 1964). Our special concern here is with such light as cultural studies of embryos may shed on nutritional factors which differentially affect the growth of the shoot apex and the cotyledons. Substances which make for precocious or extensive development of the embryonic shoot apex, or which increase the number of cotyledons, will evidently be of interest here. However, it should perhaps be noted, as a caution against over-optimism, that where an embryo apical meristem becomes abnormally enlarged, or metabolically disturbed, an increase in the number of cotyledon primordia not infrequently follows as a natural consequence.

To date, conclusive evidence of the specific organogenic action of individual substances has not been obtained. This result may be interpreted in various ways: (1) that such 'morphogenetic' substances do exist, but being present in very small amounts, they are difficult to detect in complex tissue extracts; (2) that they are very labile and difficult to isolate in their biologically active state; (3) that they react for a brief period only, i.e. at a particular phase of development and, thereafter, are incorporated into larger molecules; i.e. like certain gene products, they act as transitory components of a changing reaction system; (4) that specific organ-forming substances have no real existence. With regard to (4), it is neither reasonable, nor desirable, to be final (or dogmatic) at the present time. Notwithstanding a great deal of close analytical work, there are still many active ingredients of plant extracts of which we do not know the chemical composition; and many substances, not yet diagnosed, may be present in apical meristems and young primordia. Some of these may eventually be shown to be a *sine qua non* in organogenesis.

Of course, it is conceivable that, in seeking individual 'organ-forming' substances, we are not looking for 'the right thing'. Perhaps, as suggested in (3) above, we should be trying to envisage *reaction systems* both in the shoot apex as a whole and in growth centres. Thus, in a nascent and developing growth centre, according to its position in the shoot apex (*see* p. 123), i.e. its local tissue environment, basic metabolic substances such as sugars, amino acids, inorganic nutrients, etc., would be fed or drawn into the system in variable quantities according to various conditions; and, again according to the overall growth of the apex, different concentrations of organogenically important growth substances, IAA, IAN, GA, kinetin, adenine, enzymes, etc., would determine the nature of the new organ being formed. In the organogenic situations with which we are confronted, an acute difficulty is to know how much of some important regulating substance, e.g. IAA, GA or kinetin, is already present within the cells of the nascent organ and how much is diffusing in from adjacent more highly differentiated tissues and organs. At the moment it is not apparent how this difficulty is to be overcome.

When one considers the formation of a bud in a particular locus in a hitherto undifferentiated tissue culture, or adventitiously in the intact plant, a reasonable inference is that some active metabolic substance has accumulated to a critical concentration in that locus and has stimulated cell division and growth. As the cells must have been in such a physiological state that they were competent to react to the stimulus, it is clear that we must think of the organogenic development as the manifestation of the working of a reaction system. It may readily be conceded that to think about organogenesis in this way is a task of a different order of complexity than to think in terms of the effects of single 'organ-forming substances'. Yet it is the writer's conviction that this is the situation which we must face. In practice, of course, one proceeds analytically, step-by-step. But to attempt to interpret root, leaf or bud formation, each with its distinctive form and structure, in terms of special 'organizing' effects of single substances, and not more comprehensively in terms of systems of which the substances are components, seems likely to obscure rather than to reveal the truth.

This point of view may be expressed in other ways. Thus, for example, while it is not too difficult to understand how a specific substance could stimulate growth in a group of cells, it is exceedingly difficult to envisage how a substance, hypothetical or real, e.g. a 'leaf-forming substance', could bring about the characteristic dorsiventral symmetry in a multicellular primordium. Such symmetry is demonstrably the result of *differential growth*, i.e. more rapid growth in the abaxial as compared with the adaxial region of the primordial cellular mass; and the factors which determine such growth differences are at work both in the primordium and in the surrounding tissues; for the leafy-shoot develops as a harmoniously integrated whole, with older leaf primordia regulating the rate of growth of adjacent younger ones.

Earlier experiments by the writer and by E. G. Cutter (already discussed in Chapter VII, p. 154) showed that if leaf sites and very young leaf primordia in the fern *Dryopteris dilatata* are separated from the more distal region of the shoot apical meristem by a deep and wide tangential incision, the primordium developed as a bud and not as a leaf. This finding can be further analysed in terms of the main differences in leaf and bud growth. The following observations are relevant:

(1) The superficial area of a very young leaf primordium is small relative to that of an induced bud; the latter, in fact, quickly broadens out into a more or less conspicuous, dome-like shoot apical meristem. So, in buds, we are concerned with the nutrition and growth of a larger distal meristem.

(2) After its inception as a low mound on the apical meristem, the vertical component of growth in a leaf primordium is evidently considerably greater than its transverse component, whereas the reverse is the case in a bud primordium. Accordingly, in the differentiation of the

two kinds of organs we are concerned with substances and reactions which affect differential growth. The rapid elongation of a leaf primordium, for example, may be attributable to the rapid synthesis of auxin in its more distal tissues.

(3) Leaf and bud primordia, from an early stage, usually show conspicuous differences in symmetry, the former being typically dorsiventral in their construction, the latter radial. Such symmetry differences are strongly indicative of differences in the regulation of growth in the primordium by the circumambient tissues of the apical meristem. The organization of a leaf primordium as an organ of dorsiventral symmetry is established in a region of the apical meristem that is undergoing active growth, the rate of growth being evidently much greater on the abaxial than the adaxial side. The effects of deep adaxial, tangential incisions on organ formation in *Dryopteris* has already been discussed (*see* pp. 154, 159 *et seq.*).

The abaxial side participates in the rapid growth which is characteristic of the expanding axis with which it is in organic continuity; the adaxial side, which participates in the slower rate of growth characteristic of the upper region of the shoot apical cone, also appears to be regulated by substances moving basipetally from the more distal tissue mass. The regulating substance apparently moves in the incipient vascular tissue which, in *Dryopteris*, underlies the prismatic cells of the apical meristem. Thus, if only shallow tangential incisions are made, so that the incipient vascular tissue is left intact, buds are not induced.

On the evidence at present available, it may be doubted if different, individual 'special substances' are necessarily involved in the formation of leaves and buds. This, however, does not preclude the action of specific substances in other organogenic situations, e.g. in the formation of the several floral organs. But, in so far as leaves and buds are concerned, positional relationships at the time of primordium inception, and associated quantitative, and possibly qualitative, metabolic differences, especially those which affect, or determine, differential growth, appear to be the essential clues.

HETEROBLASTIC DEVELOPMENTS

Leaf form not only varies from species to species but, during the ontogenesis of particular species, the successively formed leaves usually show increases in size and sometimes more or less conspicuous changes in shape (Figs. 8.8–8.15).

In angiosperms the onset of flowering is often attended by progressive

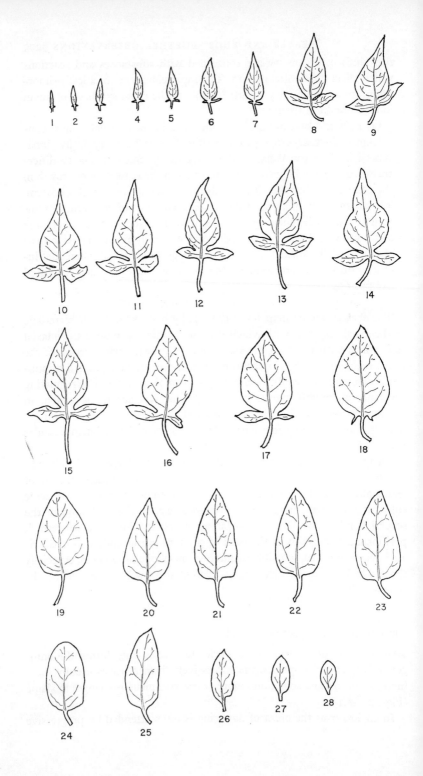

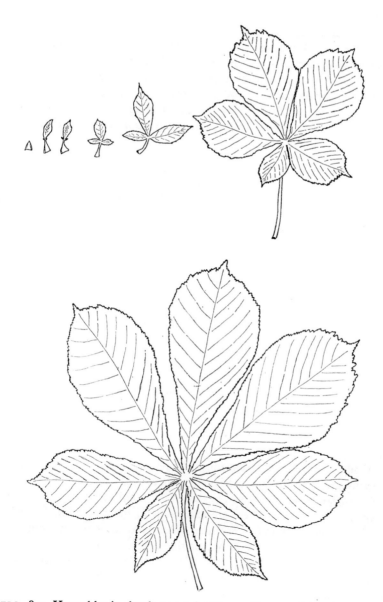

FIG. 8.9. Heteroblastic development in Horse Chestnut (*Aesculus hippo-castanum*), illustrating the acropetal sequence of leaves formed on a lateral branch growing out from a trunk or large branch.

FIG. 8.8. Heteroblastic development in *Solanum dulcamara*. Acropetal sequence of leaves along an axis with terminal flower buds.

diminutions in leaf size and by simplifications in their shape. Also, under contrasted environmental conditions, and in relation to experimental treatments, notable changes in leaf size and shape may be induced. Such characteristic ontogenetic or induced changes in the configuration of organs, including the shoot, were designated by Goebel (1898) as *hetero-blastic developments* (*blast*, from the Greek, meaning a sprout, shoot or germ), as distinct from *homoblastic developments* in which the differences are relatively slight.

FIG. 8.10. Heteroblastic development in *Trollius europaeus*.

While morphological and anatomical aspects of leaf formation in angio-sperms, gymnosperms and pteridophytes have been examined in consider-able detail, experimental study, in view of the wealth of materials, has been comparatively slight. (There are exceptions to this statement. Goebel's books contain a fund of information, often based on some experimental treatment.) Yet leaf shape is one of the most conspicuous and evident characteristics of vascular plants. (For an earlier review of the main causal aspects, *see* Ashby, 1948; and, more recently, Allsopp, 1965; Cutter, 1965.)

FIG. 8.11. Heteroblastic development in species of *Senecio*. A, *S. aquaticus*. 1–17, illustrating the sequence of leaves from the base to the apex of a flowering shoot; the small leaves 15–17 are bracts in the floral region. B, *S. sylvaticus*. C, *S. Jacobaea* (ragwort). D, *S. vulgaris* (groundsel). E, *Senecio* sp.

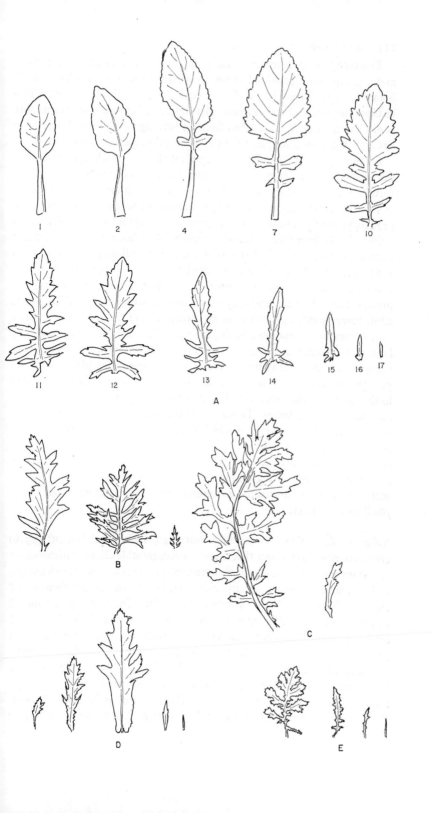

A

B

C

D

E

The comparison of leaves of different species, genera and larger systematic groups have provided materials of special interest to phylogenetic botanists (e.g. Bower, in the ferns), ecologists, geneticists and physiologists and to experimental morphologists interested in questions of causality (e.g. Goebel). Fig. 8.12, is taken from an investigation in which leaf form has afforded a meeting point for these several branches of botany.

In some species relatively small genetical changes, or changes in growth during ontogenesis, may result in quite extensive changes in successively formed leaves (Figs. 8.8, 8.12). In young fern plantlings, e.g. in *Phyllitis scolopendrium*, the leaves are cordate, because of an early arrest of apical growth, probably in relation to limitations in the supplies of particular metabolites. In the later formed leaves, when the plant has increased in size and nutritional potential, apical growth in a leaf primordium is sustained for a longer period and the characteristic ligulate lamina is formed. In the monocotyledon species *Sagittaria sagittifolia* the extent of surface growth in the juvenile leaves is small, and they have a narrow, ribbon-like outline. But in adult leaves surface growth is more extensive, and the lamina becomes a broad arrowhead structure. Again, in species in which the adult leaves are large and of compound structure, e.g. horse chestnut, ash, strawberry, etc., the juvenile leaves are typically small and of simple, undivided outline. In yet other species the characteristic heteroblastic development may be seen in the degree or marginal serration, depth of lobing, number of segments, etc., in successive leaves. To complete this very brief survey, it may be noted that, in those species in which the leaves have undergone profound modifications to form tendrils (*Lathyrus*), spines (*Ulex*), phyllodes (*Acacia*), etc., whereas the juvenile leaves are of 'normal' appearance, there may be abrupt transitions, during ontogenesis, to the modified form. In all these materials there are associated anatomical changes, e.g. in venation, mesophyll formation, etc.

'Climatic' Leaf Types. Some fifty years ago, Bailey and Sinnott (1916) called attention to the fact that there is a recognizable climatic distribution of certain leaf types among the flowering plants; i.e. there are relationships, to be defined, between certain ecological, i.e. climatological, factors and leaf morphogenesis. In an extensive survey these investigators assembled comprehensive, specific information on the geographical distribution of leaves and leaflets with entire and non-entire margins. The latter comprised the numerous categories used by taxonomists, e.g. crenulate, crenate, serrulate, serrate, denticulate, dentate, lobed, incised and so on. Space does not permit of a detailed recapitulation of this interesting study, but the following were among the main conclusions and inferences. A well-defined correlation exists between leaf-margin ('entire' or 'non-entire')

and environment in the global distribution of dicotyledons. Thus, species with entire leaves and leaflets are characteristic of, and predominant in, low-land-tropical regions. Species with non-entire margins predominate in mesophytic, cold-temperate areas. In tropical regions species with non-entire margins are found in moist uplands, equable environments and, generally, in habitats that are protected and comparatively cool. In cold-temperate regions species with entire margins are characteristic of arid or physiologically dry habitats. These correlations are more evident in trees and large shrubs than in herbs. Bailey and Sinnott also pointed out that

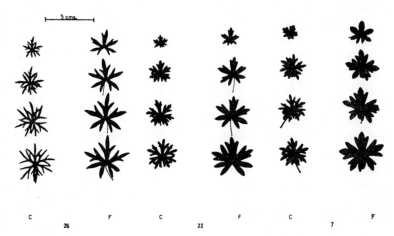

FIG. 8.12. *Geranium sanguineum*, illustrating heteroblastic development, the diversity of leaf shape in varieties occurring in different regions, and the effects of different experimental growth conditions. The numbers refer to the strain numbers; acropetal sequences of leaves are shown from plants grown (C) in a cactus house and (F) in a fern house. (After T. W. Böcher and M. C. Lewis, *Biol. Skrift. Kongel. Danske Vidensk. Selsk.*, 1962.)

by ascertaining the percentages of entire and of non-entire leaves in Cretaceous and Tertiary dicotyledonous floras it should readily be possible to infer the prevailing climatic conditions.

The present writer's reflection on the foregoing is simple: wherever the observant (and knowledgeable) botanist goes in our beautiful green world, he can perceive and enjoy 'morphogenesis by the wayside'.

Earlier Experimental Investigations. Changing morphogenetic developments of the kind observed in heteroblastic phenomena have provoked a considerable output of ideas. In a review of the evidence for and against the idea that the ontogeny of heteroblastic leaf development reflects, or recapitulates, the phylogeny of leaf shape in the race, Ashby (1948) showed how the protagonists of this view lost ground as a result of the experimental evidence and physiological concepts advanced by Goebel (1898, 1908) and Shull (1905). In Goebel's view, the shape of a leaf could be related in a simple way to the nutritional status of the apex or of the shoot on which it developed: juvenile leaves were essentially arrested organs. Schneider (1952) showed that anatomical studies largely support this thesis. The effects of differential or allometric growth, as expounded by Huxley (1932), on the shapes of leaves of different sizes, but beginning from essentially the same juvenile state, also support Goebel's concept. Other investigators (cited by Ashby), however, demonstrated that juvenile leaf shape may not merely be a consequence of poor nutrition; e.g. there appears to be a relationship between leaf shape and sexual maturity; and it has been observed that external conditions which hasten flowering also promote the transition from juvenile to adult leaf shape.

Ashby pointed out that, when leaf form is approached as a problem of causality, the eventual shape may be envisaged as the product of three determinants: (i) the shape of its primordium; (ii) the number, distribution and orientation of cell divisions; and (iii) the amount and distribution of cell enlargement. Both environment and heredity affect these determinants, each of which may eventually be expressed in terms of biochemistry and biophysics. Ashby (1948) showed that there are various methods by which leaf shape can be given quantitative description and reviewed the literature on leaf shape and cell size, leaf shape and external and internal environmental factors, etc. The relevant problems are thus seen to include an account of differences in leaf shape in terms of developmental anatomy, the investigation of the cytochemical differences which underlie these differences in shape, the elucidation of anatomical and chemical changes which cause changes in leaf shape from node to node, and the investigation of rate of change in leaf shape in relation to the rate of ageing of the plant. On this last aspect Krenke (1940, reviewed by Ashby, 1948) made the interesting observation that heteroblastic development may be a photoperiodic response, spring and autumn leaves being alike and differing from summer leaves. Harder and von Witsch (1940) also found that leaf shape in *Kalanchoe Blossfeldiana* is affected by length of day; in plants exposed to 'short-days' the leaves are sessile, succulent and with entire margins, whereas 'long-day' leaves are petiolate, thinner and with notched margins. On the basis of this and other experiments, they suggested that a diffusible chemical substance – *metaplasm* – which affects leaf shape, is produced when plants are exposed to certain photoperiods. More recent work by various investigators tends to validate the hypothesis that, in some species, leaf shape is a function of photoperiod. But not all changes in leaf shape are necessarily to be referred to this factor: the determination of leaf shape is evidently a complex and multifarious problem. In fact, no brief account can do justice to the relevant fund of contemporary information.

Mutant and hybrid forms have yielded abundant evidence that leaf shape is subject to modification by particular factors in the genotype, e.g. in strains of *Gossypium arboreum* (Fig. 8.13), reported by Hammond (1941).

Reversion to Juvenile Forms. When a leaf form is described as being 'juvenile' the implication is that it is characteristic of the early stages of onto-

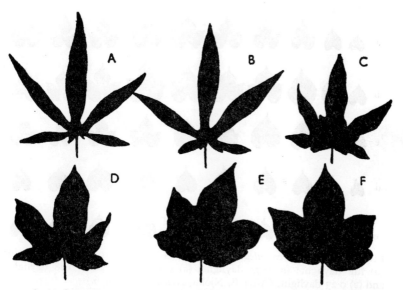

FIG. 8.13. *Gossypium arboreum.* Typical leaves of plants differing in genes of the multiple allelic series for leaf shape. A, 'laciniate'; D, 'intermediate broad'; E, 'recessive broad'; and F, 'mutant broad'. D, E and F have the same genetic background. ($\times c. \frac{1}{4}$.) (After D. Hammond, *Amer. Jour. Bot.*, 1941.)

genesis. Yet many leaf forms, equivalent to juvenile forms, may be observed in the adult plant. Goebel and Troll have cited many such instances (*see* Allsopp, 1965, for refs.). It is a simple and common observation that the first leaves formed on a lateral branch are closely comparable in shape with those in the young plant; and similar 'juvenile' leaf forms can readily be induced by particular treatments, e.g. increase in temperature, defoliation, various 'starvation' procedures, etc. Here, assuredly, is a rich vein for further exploration. The relevant investigations show that the anatomical developments are in general accordance with the size status of the leaf.

FACTORS IN HETEROBLASTIC DEVELOPMENT

Some of these have already been indicated in general terms. Pervasive and specific genetical factors apart, changes in leaf form are determined by organismal factors which become incident as ontogenesis proceeds (*see* below) and by environmental factors. The latter include temperature, light, water and nutrient supply.

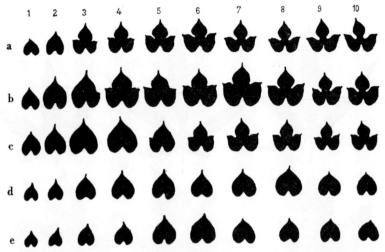

FIG. 8.14. *Ipomoea coerulea*. Examples of leaves 1–10 of plants grown in: (*a*) full daylight; (*b*) 0·74 daylight; (*c*) 0·56 daylight; (*d*) 0·28 daylight; and (*e*) 0·23 daylight. (After E. Njoku, *New Phytol.*, 1956.)

The effects of light may be either of a nutritional or a photoperiodic character. In *Ipomoea coerulea*, Njoku (1956) found that the heteroblastic leaf development could be more closely related to light intensity rather than to the duration of exposure to it (Fig. 8.14). Accordingly, he concluded that a substance responsible for leaf-lobing is synthesized in the light. The present writer would prefer to say that a substance is formed which stimulates meristematic activity of lateral meristems of the developing primordium.

Derivative 'Simple' Forms. In some species the later-formed vegetative leaves are the simpler, as in species of *Lacunaria* described by Foster (1951). In *Lacunaria* the early seedling leaves are deeply pinnatifid, whereas the adult leaves are simple (Fig. 8.15). The transition from the pinnatifid to the simple foliar state is due to the reduction and ultimate suppression

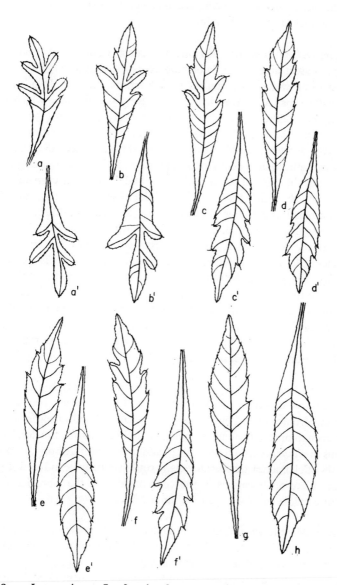

FIG. 8.15. *Lacunaria* sp. Leaf series from a seedling collected near Vigia, Para, Brazil, showing the transition from pinnatifid to simple leaves. Only one member of leaf-pairs *g* and *h* is represented. Note progressive increase in number of secondary veins in this series. (After A. S. Foster, *Bull. Torrey Bot. Club*, 1951.)

of the lateral lobes, this being accompanied by a conspicuous increase in the number of secondary veins.

Organismal, or Regulative, Factors. The effects of older leaves on younger ones, as ascertained from defoliation experiments, was largely considered in terms of 'water deflection' by the earlier investigators. In other words, the older expanded leaves deflect water from younger ones which are still developing higher up on the stem. However, Goodwin (1937) demonstrated that the removal of a rapidly expanding leaf in the basal rosette in *Solidago* accelerated the enlargement of the next succeeding leaves and that an application of auxin to the leaf stump had a regulative effect similar to that of the original intact leaf. These and many other cognate observations indicate clearly that the effect of older leaves on younger ones is due to hormonal action (*see* Allsopp, 1965, for details). Many interesting examples could be cited. Early in the growing season Dostál (1960) removed the leaves from young, current-year shoots of several woody species (*Aesculus hippocastanum, Fraxinus excelsior, Tilia platyphylla, Syringa vulgaris*). In the replacement shoots which were thereby induced, leaves of the juvenile type were formed. From a survey of defoliation experiments, Allsopp concluded that water supply is only a minor factor in heteroblastic leaf development, and that more work is necessary to distinguish the extent of the regulative effects that are due to nutritional as distinct from hormonal factors.

Nutritional Factors. Many investigations, in which the techniques of tissue and embryo culture *in vitro* have been used to advantage, bear witness to the importance of carbohydrates (various sugars) and nitrogen sources in the growth of the shoot apical meristem and in heteroblastic development. Thus in *Adiantum* (Wetmore, 1954), and in *Marsilea* (Allsopp, 1953 *et seq.*) leaves of characteristic size and shape could virtually be induced at will by appropriate modifications in the concentration of the ingredients of the culture media (*see* Allsopp, 1965 for refs.).

Specific Morphogenetic Substances. Heteroblastic development in leaves has been ascribed by some workers not only to the regulative effects of auxin but to the action of more specific morphogenetic substances. As Allsopp (1965) noted, the virtual absence of lamina development in etiolated plants is indicative of some light-induced stimulus, or specific substance, determining normal leaf expansion. So far, however, no clear evidence of specific morphogenetic substances, e.g. affecting the extent of leaf-lobing, has been obtained. But, as already noted, there is indisputable evidence that variations in leaf size and shape are profoundly affected by sugar concentration.

In the matter of lobing, the present writer suggests that the organization and activities of the distal and marginal meristems of leaf primordia, under different nutritional conditions, would repay detailed study. When auxin, other growth-regulating substances, gibberellic acid, etc., have been applied to plants, various heteroblastic leaf effects have been induced. In some instances juvenile leaves have been obtained: in others, adult types of leaves have been formed precociously. The several interpretations in terms of hormonal action have been discussed by Allsopp: he inclines to the view that the observed changes in leaf form can probably be referred to the carbohydrate supplies available for growth. For example, Robbins (1957, 1960) found that when GA was applied to a species of ivy (*Hedera* sp.) the plant showed a considerable increase in growth, and some of its branches developed with completely juvenile characters. Robbins' suggestion that GA is a specific 'juvenility hormone' is rejected by Allsopp, who has indicated that the increased growth rate would lead to a decreased concentration of available sugar, with consequential effects on leaf size and shape.

Physiological Age. Heteroblastic developments have been ascribed by some workers to a 'physiological ageing' of the plant. Certainly, particular types of leaf development seem characteristic of, or a concomitant of, the attainment of a particular stage – and age – in ontogenesis, i.e. they are related to a particular physiological state of the plant. Allsopp (1965) has suggested that the formation of thorns, at a particular stage of development in some species, depends on the establishment of a certain sugar concentration within the plant. In a considerable memoir, Schaffalitzky de Muckadell (1959) stated that most of the successive developments in woody species are due to an ageing process in the apical meristems. Changes in meristems undoubtedly do occur, with concomitant morphogenetic developments. For example, apices may become disorganized. But whether a physiological change, correctly described as *ageing*, does occur in apical meristems is still an open question. Various observations suggest that meristems of different ages may exemplify different degrees of maturation. In *Hedera helix*, for example, there are relatively stable juvenile and adult stages which retain their characteristic morphological features when propagated as grafts and cuttings. Molisch (1929–38) used the term *topophysis* to denote the phenomenon in which the behaviour of an isolated shoot is determined by its position on the parent plant. For a fuller account of morphogenetic effects associated with physiological ageing, the reader is referred to Allsopp (1965) and Wangermann (1965).

SPECIAL PROBLEMS OF LEAF ORIENTATION

As previously noted (p. 127), the leaves of virtually all classes of vascular plants are typically of dorsiventral symmetry and, at the primordial stage if not later, they are orientated directly towards the shoot apical meristem from which they originated. In fact, the symmetry and orientation of leaves are determined at a very early stage in their development. Although these statements are of great generality, some intriguing exceptions are known. We have already seen that not all leaves are of dorsiventral symmetry. Arber, for example, indicated that, if one surveys the field sufficiently, there

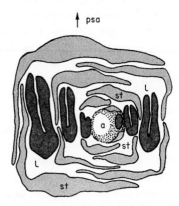

FIG. 8.16. *Zelkova carpinifolia* (*Planera richardii*), illustrating the curious leaf orientation in the *axillary buds*. *l*, leaf; *st*, stipule; *a*, shoot apex with last-formed leaf primordium with its lateral stipules. The apex of the *parental shoot* (*psa*) is on the upper side (arrow). (After W. Hofmeister, *Allgemeine Morphologie der Gewachse*, 1868.)

is quite a degree of convergence between the symmetry of shoots and leaves. However, at this point the writer's aim is to call attention to species, some of which have now been examined morphogenetically, in which the orientation of young leaf primordia is *not* towards their own initiating shoot apex.

As long ago as 1846, Henry had shown that the *orientation* of the leaves in the *axillary buds* of some dicotyledonous species is not towards their own initiating apex but *towards the shoot apex from which the axillary bud itself had originated* (e.g. in *Platanus orientalis*, *Magnolia umbrella*, *M. tripetala*, *Ulmus campestris*, *Corylus avellana*, *Prunus laurocerasus* and *Tilia glabra*). Hofmeister (1868) verified and amplified these observations, and further illustrated the phenomenon by reference to *Ulmus effusa*, *Zelkova carpinifolia* (*see* Fig. 8.16) and *Begonia fagifolia*. He pointed out that, in these species, the symmetry of the bud is bilateral. (The present author would now suggest that, metabolically, it is dorsiventral.) Other examples of buds of bilateral symmetry have been cited by Troll (1937). The early investigators of unusual leaf orientation did not, however, study the phenomenon in its developmental aspect. Recently Soma (1965) has presented a detailed account of leaf inception and development in the axillary buds of *Zelkova serrata* (Ulmaceae) (Fig. 8.17 and Plate 7).

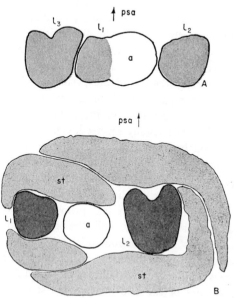

FIG. 8.17. *Zelkova serrata*. Formation and orientation of leaves. A, Transverse section of apex showing the apical meristem (*a*) and young leaf primordia (*l*). In the early stages the origin and orientation of *l* to *a* are in no way anomalous. B, Transverse section of shoot apex showing *a*, the shoot apical meristem of an axillary bud; l_1, l_2 young leaf primordia, orientated *not* towards *a* but towards the parental shoot apex (*psa*); *st*, stipules. (After S. Soma, *Jour. Fac. Sci. Univ. Tokyo*, 1965.)

In *Z. serrata*, in which the leaves are distichous, there are no specially distinctive or remarkable histological features in the shoot apical meristem or in the mode of inception of leaf or bract primordia. The nascent axillary bud first forms two opposite scale-leaves, or prophylls, one of which is a little larger than the other and early develops an axillary bud. Somewhat comparable observations were made by Foster (1928) in *Castanea pumila* and by Mauney and Ball (1959) in *Gossypium*. About eight other scale-leaves are now formed in *Z. serrata*, and then a leaf with stipules is differentiated. In some instances the petiole and lamina may remain rudimentary.

All the early stages of primordium formation are as in other dicotyledons; and, in all, some six distichous leaf primordia, but no further buds, may be present in the axillary bud. In the bud thus formed all the developing laminae are orientated, not towards their own apex but towards the main (parental) stem apex (Fig. 8.17). In other words, the young leaf primordium does not develop with an adaxial and an abaxial side in relation to its own apex as in flowering plants in general. At a certain size, it is a side of the primordium at right-angles to the normal adaxial face, and facing the main stem, which becomes the morphologically upper side of the nascent leaf. This is clearly shown in the illustrations. In the early stages the development of the stipules, which is rapid, is as in other flowering plants. However, as illustrated, one stipule typically outgrows the other.

Now, these are very remarkable and unexpected morphogenetic developments. As noted elsewhere, normally dorsiventral leaves may be induced to develop as radial or centric leaves (p. 172); and the orientation of leaf primordia has been experimentally reversed, e.g. from its own apex to a neighbouring induced bud apex (p. 161). Also, as in fern species like *Pteridium aquilinum* (Dasanayake, 1960), or *Polypodium vulgare* (Wardlaw, 1963b), only the upper, or dorsal, region of the rhizome apical meristem normally gives rise to leaf primordia. Of the developments observed in *Zelkova*, Soma concluded: (1) that leaf primordium dorsiventrality is determined at a very early stage, i.e. while the primordium is still in close contiguity with the apical meristem from which it originated; (2) that lamina orientation as a result of growth torsion is not involved in this species; and (3) that there is a difference in the rates of growth of the stipules originating on the two sides of the bud apex. Soma stated that the factors which control leaf orientation and dorsiventrality 'are very complicated and are yet to be explained'. One cannot but agree. As it seems to the present writer, it is improbable that the lamina orientation in the later bud leaves can be determined in any *direct* manner by the parental main-stem apex. But the nascent axillary bud meristem could have a pattern of chemical dorsiventrality imposed on it by the parental apex; and this persisting pattern is imparted, in ways that we do not yet understand, to each newly formed leaf primordium. Even if we say that inherent, i.e. genetical, factors are the determiners of dorsiventrality and orientation in the bud leaves, this concept has still to be interpreted in terms of the pattern of growth metabolism. Lastly, it may perhaps be remarked that exceptional developments, like those in *Zelkova*, should not simply be regarded as occasional and interesting oddities – which, of course, in a way, they are – but rather as further evidence of our need to concentrate more thought on the metabolic events and, in particular, the spatial distribution of metabolites which underlies the subsequent morphogenetic developments.

OUTLOOK

In the study of 'typical' leaves and buds much still remains to be done. But the relevant problems do not end there. Both leaves and shoots show many remarkable morphological modifications, to each of which some adaptive function is usually ascribed. The scope for new and comprehensive morphogenetic investigations of such organs, e.g. pitchers of insectivorous plants, etc., needs no emphasis; and such studies may well be evocative of much new thinking.

H

CHAPTER IX

Phyllotaxis

INTRODUCTION

If one lays bare the apex of a daisy, a grass or a fern, so that the youngest leaf primordia (described as P_1, P_2, P_3, etc., in the order of their increasing age) are clearly visible it can be seen that they occupy positions of very considerable geometrical, or spatial, regularity, round the apical cone and downwards along the axis. So, in this phenomenon of leaf position, or *phyllotaxis*,[1] an evident manifestation of regulated growth and organogenesis, we encounter further problems of morphogenesis. The fact that leaves are formed in regular positions and patterns, e.g. alternate, decussate, spiral, etc. (Fig. 9.1), along the axis, is perhaps one of the first and simplest observations that a botanist makes. It is a chastening thought that, after so many decades of work, we still know so little of the factors which determine phyllotaxis and related phenomena.

The term phyllotaxis refers to the arrangement of the leaves on the shoot or axis and to the underlying geometrical principles. In fact, some of the earlier investigators of leaf arrangements regarded the problems as being almost purely mathematical ones. Phyllotaxis is sometimes rather neglected in standard texts, possibly because it is a difficult topic. Yet it must rank as one of the great classical themes in botany and, at the present time, is still of lively controversial interest, if only to a small number of investigators. The subject has been comprehensively reviewed in recent years (Snow, 1955; Cutter, 1959, 1965; Sinnott, 1960; Wardlaw, 1965a, b), and only a brief treatment will be attempted here.

Phyllotactic systems of different orders of complexity are of common occurrence. If one examines the naked apex in many common species, e.g. ferns, buttercups, etc., it can be seen that if the bases of the successively larger primordia were joined by a line that line would constitute a simple logarithmic spiral – known as the *genetic spiral*. On the other hand, if one

---

[1] Phyllotaxis is a very complex and abstruse phenomenon – the more so as, in some respects, e.g. in plants with alternate or decussate leaves, it gives the impression of being quite simple. Because it really is difficult, some students of botany, junior and senior, make the early discovery that it is dull and boring! The writer was tempted to give this Chapter the title of 'Phyllotaxis Without Tears!'

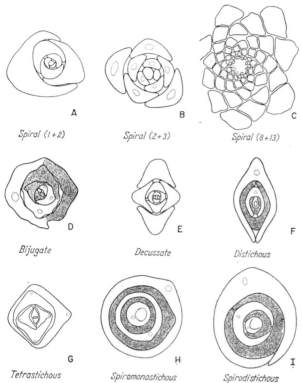

Spiral (1 + 2)   *Spiral (2 + 3)*   *Spiral (8 + 13)*

Bijugate   *Decussate*   *Distichous*

Tetrastichous   *Spiromonostichous*   *Spirodistichous*

FIG. 9.1. Some types of phyllotaxis. A, *Bellis perennis*. T.S. one-year-old rosette. A low spiral system (1 + 2). (After Van Iterson, 1907.) B, *Jasminum fruticans*. T.S. apex. Spiral (2 + 3). (After Van Iterson, 1907.) C, *Araucaria excelsa*. T.S. lateral branch. Spiral (8 + 13). (After Church, 1904.) D, *Dipsacus sylvestris*. T.S. apical bud of seedling just above the stem apex. Bijugate. One of the two genetic spirals is stippled. (After R. Snow, 1954.) E, *Syringa vulgaris*. T.S. bud. Decussate. (After Van Iterson, 1907.) F, *Bupleurum perfoliatum*. T.S. apex. Distichous. (After Van Iterson, 1907.) G, *Kniphofia tysoni*. T.S. apical bud. Tetrastichous. (After R. Snow, 1958.) H, *Costus cylindricus*. T.S. apex. Spiromonostichous (costoid). (After R. Snow, 1952.) I, *Rhoeo discolor*. T.S. apex. Spirodistichous. (After M. Snow, 1951.) In Figs. B, D, F, G, H and I the central vascular bundles of the leaves are shown. In Figs. F, H and I every second leaf is stippled for clarity. (After C. W. Wardlaw, *Encyclopedia of Plant Physiology*, XV/1, 1965, Springer.)

examined the apex in other common species, e.g. of *Labiatae*, *Epilobium*, *Acer*, etc., one would find that the primordia, as in the adult regions of the shoot, originate in pairs, each successive pair being at right-angles to the pairs above and below. Now, in these decussate species, if a sufficiently large part of the distal region is laid bare or if one inspects a considerable length of the adult leafy shoot, the primordia, developing and adult leaves, viewed collectively, will be found to lie along four vertical lines, rows or *orthostichies*. And similarly, if one views a sufficiently large part of a spiral system one will find that several regular but oblique, intersecting rows of primordia (or *parastichies*) can be distinguished. Such systems are now described by their contact parastichy relationships, e.g. $(1 + 2)$, $(2 + 3)$, $(3 + 5)$, $(5 + 8)$, $(8 + 13)$ and so on. Other systems of greater complexity, e.g. *bijugate* systems, in which pairs of equal leaves are disposed on a spiral, are also known, e.g. in *Dipsacus*. It is because of the high order of regularity in these systems that some investigators have tended to regard phyllotaxis almost entirely as a mathematical problem. As one aspect of the growth and organization of the leafy shoot, this approach is valid: it expresses mathematically that a growing region, as a dynamic system, constantly tends towards equilibrium, or steady state, and the whole process of growth is so regulated that the normal growing axis personifies harmonious development. Of course, it could be argued that the mathematician is only giving expression to the final resultant condition, and that the real problems are concerned with the process of growth. It now seems clear that what is needed is a physiological–mathematical approach. Nevertheless, it is an astonishing fact – to the writer at least – that, in spiral phyllotaxis, the numbers of contact parastichies are usually two adjacent members of the Fibonacci series – a series in which each term is the sum of the two preceding terms, thus,

$$1, 1, 2, 3, 5, 8, 13, 21, \ldots$$

systems of increasing complexity, being indicated by terms such as $(1 + 2)$, $(2 + 3)$, etc. (*See* Plate 8.)

Richards (1951) demonstrated that a mathematical analysis of the primordium arrangement at the apex, together with certain physiological concepts, can go some way towards a more adequate interpretation of phyllotaxis, whether this is of a high, or less high, degree of regularity, or whether the aim is to link the simpler leaf arrangements in the seedling with the more complex arrangements in the adult. Richards assumed that primordia originate from growth centres and pointed out that a precise description of any spiral system must include information about the *radial* and *tangential spacing* of primordia. More recent studies (*see* Cutter, 1965; and Wardlaw, 1965a) indicate the importance of measurements of the *vertical spacing* of primordia, especially in phyllotactic systems which are undergoing change. In fact, many plants show regular changes in phyllotaxis during ontogenesis. The paired cotyledons in many dicotyledon seedlings, for example, are followed briefly by a decussate arrangement which soon changes to a simple spiral system. Most monocotyledons begin with a distichous system which may become spiromonostichous as in members of the ginger family (e.g. *Costus* spp.). Simple observation indicates that the more complex foliar systems are derived from simpler ones. So the task is to understand the physiology of growth as it affects the dynamic geometry of the enlarging apical meristem.

THE MATHEMATICAL ANALYSIS OF PHYLLOTAXIS

General observation indicates that the direction of the genetic spiral is randomly determined, though qualifications must be made in some instances (*see* Wardlaw, 1965a). Earlier workers, who paid close attention to the spatial relationships of primordia, concluded that the position in which a new primordium originates is determined by the positions and shapes of the immediately adjacent primordia. In fact, a nascent primordium tends to be formed in the largest gap between and slightly above the previously formed primordia. Thus, van Iterson (1907) interpreted the phyllotaxis in any particular species in terms of the relative sizes of the young primordia and the apex, and the way the system began. He expanded the idea that the development of primordia on the conical apex may be regarded as being equivalent to a system of touching circles; and he demonstrated that, in terms of size relationships, only certain *contact systems* are possible. M. and R. Snow (1948) considered van Iterson's hypothesis to be valid. Other hypotheses, such as those stemming from Hofmeister, in which the next primordium to be formed was thought to originate as far away as possible from the last-formed primordia – the so-called Repulsion Theory of Phyllotaxis – are not supported by the experimental evidence. In critical experiments, involving the incision of the apical meristem in selected positions, M. and R. Snow furnished evidence that the next primordium to be formed originates in 'the first available space' on the apical meristem; i.e. in the first widening gap sufficiently large for this organogenic development. The position of the new primordium in the gap is determined by the immediately adjacent older primordia, and not by all the primordia of the top cycle. (*See* Figs. 6.9, 6.10, for the positions of I_1, I_2 and I_3, the sites of the new primordia to be formed, in that order.)

As a matter of causality, an *available space*, of itself, does not *do* anything; rather it is a necessary sustaining condition; it provides a locus in which important physiological activities leading to morphological developments may take place. Also, the organ which develops is distinctive and characteristic of the species; so, in ways that are subtle and still obscure, genetical factors contribute to the organogenic development in the 'available space'. They are the primary determiners of the *size* and *shape* of the shoot apex and of its primordia. What goes on in a widening space on the meristem, during a plastochrone, is the morphological expression of the regulated reaction system in the shoot meristem. These physiological–genetical activities, which periodically result in the formation of a new primordium in a regular position, lend themselves to mathematical analysis. In the end, we are concerned with physico-chemical laws applied to an organismal system. But, one might add, contemporary physical chemistry is helping the biologist considerably less than one might expect, or hope. Or, perhaps it would be more exact to say that the biologist has not yet learnt how to ask the questions that will arouse the sympathetic interest of the physical chemist.

With regard to the utilization of the 'next available space', Richards (1948) pointed out that, as a matter of geometry, confirmed by observation, the new growth centre occupies a position which lies at the point of inter-section of two equal circles based on the centres of the two adjacent pri-mordia. In a fern like *Dryopteris dilatata*, with its large and convenient apex, anyone who is prepared to bring a little skill and patience to the task can verify this point for himself. And similarly for angiosperm apices.

If some of these general ideas are accepted there still remains the problem of accounting for the transition from one Fibonacci system to another, e.g. from (1 + 2) to (2 + 3) to (5 + 8), etc. Richards' mathe-matical analysis led him to the conclusion that an adequate theory of phyllotaxis must explain: (i) the absolute distance of one primordium growth centre from another; (ii) the absence of primordia from the central region of the apical meristem; and (iii) the factors which determine the transverse size of the meristem at the time of leaf inception. From a general survey of shoot apical meristems it becomes evident that the larger a nascent leaf primordium is relative to the apex, and the closer it is to the summit of the apical meristem, the lower is the phyllotaxis (*see* Figs. 6.5, 6.6). This condition can be seen in *Acer* and in other species with decussate phyllotaxis. Conversely, the smaller the nascent primordium is, and the more remote it is from the centre of the apex, the higher is the phyllotaxis. This condition is exemplified by *Hippuris, Equisetum, Lycopodium, Dryop-teris*, etc. Between these extremes there are many intermediate conditions. We must also recognize that there are some notable exceptions. In the Gramineae, for example, the nascent primordia are small and quite remote from the summit of the shoot apex; yet the phyllotaxis is low, i.e. distichous or some modification thereof.

PRIMORDIUM SHAPE AND PHYLLOTAXIS

By simple diagrams, Richards (1951) demonstrated that apices with the same *divergence angle, plastochrone ratio* (see below), and ratio of *nascent primordium area* to *apical area*, may nevertheless have very different phyllotaxis systems (Fig. 9.2). This diversity stems from *the shape of the primordium*. For a given divergence angle, the contact parastichies depend on the plastochrone ratio and the primordium shape, both of which are dependent on the specific organization and reactivity of the apical meristem (Fig. 9.3).

For an adequate description of phyllotaxis three parameters are necessary: (1) the angle of the cone tangential to the apex in the region of the primordium; (2) the divergence angle; and (3) the plastochrone ratio (*P.R.*), which is given by

$$\frac{\text{Radius } P_2 - \text{Centre of apex}}{\text{Radius } P_1 - \text{Centre of apex}}$$

(Richards, 1951). This ratio is independent of primordium shape and is applicable to any theory of phyllotaxis. When the factors for leaf inception are constant the natural logarithm of the *P.R.*, divided by the plastochrone period, gives the relative rate of growth. For any particular divergence angle, the phyllotaxis is the resultant of two growth processes, namely, the rate of expansion of the apex and the rate of formation of primordia. A continuously varying function, referred to as the *phyllotaxis index* (*P.I.*), can be calculated from the plastochrone ratio. This index is rigidly related to the ratio of *primordium area* : *apical area* in the transverse plane, or projection (see below).

According to the magnitude of the divergence angle, the contact parastichies depend on the plastochrone ratio and the primordium shape, both inherent properties, but subject to modifications during ontogenesis or by environmental factors, e.g. nutrient supply. A knowledge of contact parastichies thus affords a good indication of what the primordium shape may be; but, as Richards wrote, 'phyllotaxis proper is uniquely defined by divergence angle and plastochrone ratio'. As the several systems (e.g. 3 : 5, 5 : 8, etc.) in Fibonacci phyllotaxis have closely comparable divergence angles, i.e. about 137·5°, the essential differences between them are due to their plastochrone ratios. As the *P.R.* approaches unity, the phyllotaxis rises.

In relation to Richards' mathematical analysis of phyllotaxis, it is of interest to note that when he measured the apices of the Snows' (1935) *Epilobium* experiment, in which a decussate leaf arrangement was changed to a spiral one by a median diagonal incision, he found no change in the plastochrone ratio (Fig. 9.4). In other words, the fundamental growth phenomenon was little changed.

The *phyllotaxis index* (*P.I.*), which is a resultant of transverse apical growth rate and plastochrone, is determined by the relative sizes of a new

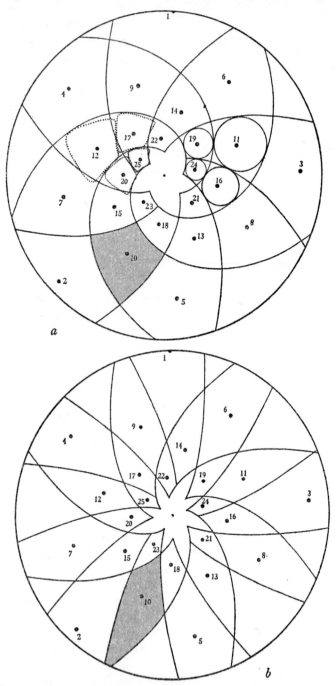

FIG. 9.2. a–d. Ideal representation of the transverse components of four regular Fibonacci phyllotaxis arrangements in all of which the 5-parastichies intersect the 8-parastichies orthogonally. In terms of contact parastichies these arrangements are as follows: a, (5 + 8); b, (8 + 13); c, (3 + 5); and

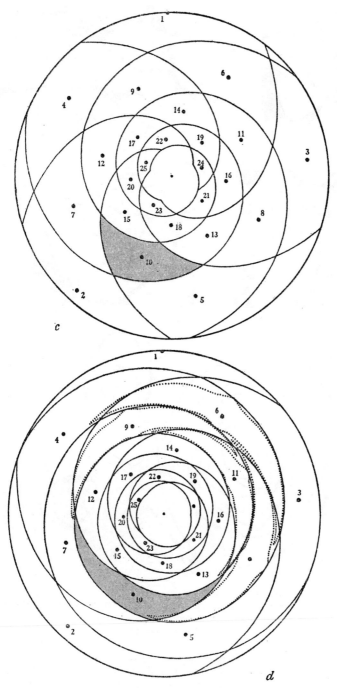

d, (2 + 3). Divergence = Fibonacci angle; plastochrone ratio = 1·07296. In each diagram *leaf 10* has been stippled for clarity. (After F. J. Richards, *Phil. Trans. Roy. Soc.*, 1951.)

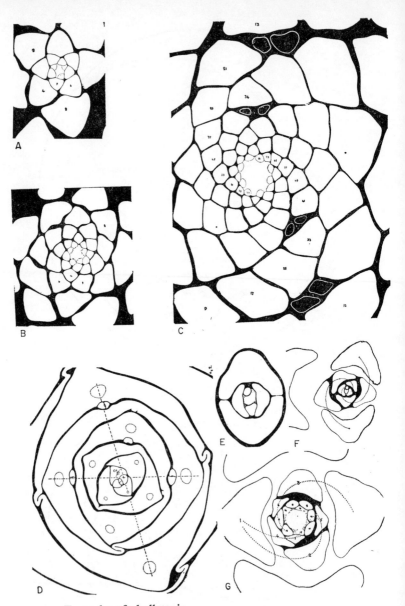

FIG. 9.3. Examples of phyllotaxis.

A, B, C, *Araucaria excelsa*, illustrating differences in phyllotaxis in cross-sections of apices of axes of different sizes: A, a lateral third order branch with phyllotaxis (3 + 5); B, a larger, second order branch (5 + 8); C, a still larger lateral branch (8 + 13).

D, *Dipsacus sylvestris*, illustrating bijugate phyllotaxis (2 + 4) in a perennating seedling, i.e. the system is well defined, or regulated, and 'results in the formation of alternating pairs of leaves in four spiral rows' (Church, 1904).

E, F, G, *Helianthus annuus*. Transverse sections of the apices of seedlings. The decussate arrangement of the cotyledons and young plumular leaves may persist until 3–5 pairs have been formed. E, departure from the

decussate system has begun with the fifth plumular leaf (the cotyledons lie outside the thick line). F, above a symmetrical pair of leaves a spiral system (2 + 3) has developed. G, a more complex system (3 + 5) has followed a decussate series and is already changing to a still higher system.

H, *Cyperus alternifolius*. Section of a shoot apex, as seen in November, illustrating a three-spiral leaf system (1 + 2), enclosing a spiral system of scale-leaves with (3 + 5) phyllotaxis.

J–M, *Lycopodium selago*. Sections at the level of the apex, illustrating various anomalous spiral phyllotactic series, commonly observed in species with xeromorphic characters. Of the several parastichy systems observed, the following are illustrated here: J, (5 +6); K, (5 + 5); L, (4 + 5); M, (4 + 4). (*N.B.* L and M were twin-shoots of a dichotomy.)
(After A. H. Church, *On the Relation of Phyllotaxis to Mechanical Laws*, Williams and Norgate, London, 1904.)

primordium and the apical meristem. If this size ratio is constant, so also is the phyllotaxis. Change in *area apex : area primordium* may be due to a change in one or other component, or in both, and will lead to a change in the *P.I.* Irrespective of primordium shape, Richards' calculations are valid; what is measured is not the projected transverse area of the primordium, but the actual area occupied by it on the meristem. In Richards' words: 'It is the maximal possible transverse size of a primordium ("primordial area") that can exist without compression in the particular phyllotaxis pattern.' The fact that the area may not be fully occupied relates to a

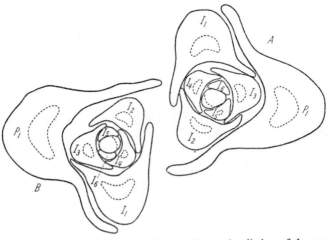

FIG. 9.4. *Epilobium hirsutum*. The effect of diagonal splitting of the apex in a decussate shoot. Two shoots, *A* and *B*, have developed, each showing spiral phyllotaxis (×40.) (From M. and R. Snow, *Phil. Trans. Roy. Soc.*, 1935.)

genetically determined specificity in the size and shape of leaf growth centres. The ratio of *mean apical area : primordial area* is described as the *area ratio*. It is the reciprocal of the relative transverse growth rate of the apex when time is measured in plastochrones.

It should not be assumed that plastochrone ratio is always a simple concept, in that it may comprise: (i) the rate of formation of primordia; (ii) the overall rate of transverse apical growth at the level of the youngest primordium; and (iii) the rate of change of transverse size of the apex within (or above) the primordium zone, these processes taking place simultaneously. If any one of them changes, the *P.I.* will change.

EXPERIMENTAL INVESTIGATIONS

Conceptions of phyllotaxis that have been studied experimentally – though certainly not definitively – include: (i) that the position to be occupied by a leaf primordium is determined by an acropetally developing, pre-existing leaf-trace; (ii) that the superficial layer of the shoot apex grows more rapidly than the tissues within, and so forms folds which become leaves; (iii) that new primordia are formed as far as possible from the margins of the existing primordia, the related factors being physiological (nutritional) or physical; (iv) that the next primordium to be formed originates in the first space of sufficient width above and between existing primordia of the top whorl; (v) that tensile stress, induced in the apex by the growth of leaf primordia, is a factor in phyllotaxis, the next primordium being formed in a position of minimal tensile stress; (vi) that the phyllo-tactic pattern can be referred to the regular inception of growth centres and their physiological fields. Some of these ideas no longer seem sufficiently tenable to be perpetuated (see Snow, 1947, 1948; Wardlaw, 1949).

As already noted, various experimental studies tend to validate: (a) the concept that a new primordium is formed in the 'next available space' (p. 229), and (b) the field concept of spatial regulation at the apex and primordium formation (p. 153). Each of these now seems complementary to the other: in a game there must be both ground and players, i.e. a suitable locus in which factors can react and interact. Accordingly, readers are referred to earlier reviews (Wardlaw, 1952); and here we may move on to a consideration of some recent ideas and experimental work on phyllotaxis. Three main topics will now be considered, namely:

(1) the size of a sector of the apical meristem that is essential for primordium formation;
(2) induced phyllotactic variability;
(3) the concept of foliar helices.

Minimum Area for Primordium Formation. In the vegetative shoot apex of *Lupinus albus*, M. and R. Snow (1933, 1952) noted that the minimum or primary arc of a leaf primordium is 122°. They also reported that when the greater part of an I_2 site was confined within vertical radial incisions 100° apart, a primordium did not form in that locus. However, in similarly incised apices approaching the onset of flowering, small primordia were formed. When the summit of the shoot meristem was destroyed, a leaf primordium was always formed between the afore-mentioned radial incisions. Experiments with *Euphorbia lathyris* yielded confirmatory results. In *Lupinus* apices, in which the centre of P_1 was excised or destroyed, the angles $P_2 - I_1$ and $I_1 - I_2$ remained unaltered, but the angle $I_2 - I_3$ diminished by 3·4°, indicating that I_3 originated closer than normal to P_1. M. and R. Snow considered that these results sustain their hypothesis of primordium inception in the next available space, for the species investigated, and possibly in the dicotyledons generally. They also argued that in *Lupinus*: (i) the centre of a primordium has no repellent effect on the centres of primordia which are about to be formed, and (ii) that primordia are determined as wholes, and not as centres round which a primordium will subsequently become organized. Their conclusion that the primordium centre is a secondary or later development is supported by the histological evidence both in seed plants (Esau, 1953) and ferns (Wardlaw, 1949a; Cutter, 1956). However, the possibility that the discrete locus, which we describe as a growth centre, may have its absolute inception in a single cell has not been eliminated.

Regulative Effects of Young Leaves. In further experiments on *Lupinus albus*, M. and R. Snow (1959) reported that, in relation to the excision of young leaves, the new leaves covered larger arcs of the axis circumference; i.e. young leaves regulate the secondary extension of still younger ones; whereas the summit of the shoot meristem affects the primary areas of the new primordia (M. and R. Snow, 1955). At least two factors are thus known to affect the size of the leaf arc: (1) the summit of the shoot increases the primary area of the apical meristem which is required for leaf primordium inception; and (2) young developing leaves decrease the secondary tangential extension of younger leaf-bases. In the view of M. and R. Snow (1955), these observations provide a physiological *rationale* for the need for a certain minimum free area for leaf formation. When M. and R. Snow (1959) used a different race of *Lupinus* in their experiments they found that the primary leaf arc was only about 90°, as compared with previous estimates of 124° or 122° in the race formerly used. In ferns, e.g. *Dryopteris dilatata*, a new primordium occupies only a small fraction of the space 'available' to it. But if a primordium, together with its surrounding physiological field, is regarded as a morphogenetic unit, the concept of the 'next available space' may be valid.

RECENT INVESTIGATIONS ON OTHER TYPES OF PHYLLOTAXIS

M. and R. Snow have also studied experimentally some of the less common types of phyllotaxis, including *spirodistichous* (M. Snow, 1951, 1955); *spiromonostichous* or *costoid* (R. Snow, 1952); *tetrastichous* (R. Snow, 1958); and *bijugate* (R. Snow, 1951, 1954). In the species exemplifying these systems, if the contacts of the leaf flanks, or sheaths, which are held to be important, are taken into account, the phyllotactic systems can be interpreted in terms of a space-filling theory. Only a few points can be dealt with here. It is surely a thought-provoking observation that, in some of the less-common types of phyllotaxis indicated above, the characteristic leaf arrangement is already present in seedlings (M. Snow, 1955; R. Snow, 1951, 1958).

The well-known bijugate phyllotaxis of *Dipsacus* was interpreted by R. Snow (1951) in terms of a junctional factor ascribed to the peculiar united rims of the paired leaf bases and of pressures exerted on the apex by the vertical parts of the P_2's. As Snow pointed out, bijugy in other plants may not be controlled by these factors. In *Dryopteris dilatata*, for example, in which bijugy is occasionally encountered, the leaf-bases are not at all in contact (Cutter and Voeller, 1959). The experimental details relating to bijugate and other less-common phyllotactic systems are somewhat complex. For a lucid summary and *critique*, readers are referred to Cutter (1965).

M. and R. Snow (1962) outlined a theory, based on the nature of the primary and secondary leaf arcs (p. 238), which would account for the precise regulation of phyllotactic systems and, in particular, their return to regularity after a disturbance. The transitions from Fibonacci spiral systems to spiral systems of the accessory series 1, 3, 4, 7, 11, . . . were interpreted by M. and R. Snow on space-filling principles. However, as Cutter and Voeller (1959) pointed out, such transitions are also explicable in terms of a field theory. They demonstrated that somewhat comparable transitions also occur in ferns in which neither primary nor secondary leaf arcs are in contact.

The phyllotaxis index, devised by Richards, enables different systems of phyllotaxis to be directly compared; and changes in *P.I.* are indicative of changes in growth in the apical meristem. *Dryopteris dilatata* usually exemplifies Fibonacci spiral systems of phyllotaxis. However, Voeller and Cutter (1959) showed that a proportion of natural populations is bijugate. When R. Snow's (1951) experimental procedure with *Dipsacus* was applied to bijugate specimens of *D. dilatata*, Cutter and Voeller observed an initial increase in divergence angle, which was comparable with Snow's results. More profound changes in phyllotaxis also ensued. In bijugate apices in which the younger primordia were not destroyed, but in which all the outer leaves and primordia were removed, to admit of continuous observation, comparable changes in phyllotaxis were recorded. Most of the initially bijugate apices became spiral, of the Fibonacci series 1, 2, 3, 5, 8, . . . but a few yielded a trimerous pseudo-whorled system or became spiral, of the accessory series 1, 3, 4, 7, 11, . . . (Fig. 9.5). When *Dryopteris* apices with spiral phyllotaxis were maintained under comparable conditions they reverted to the lower spiral systems seen in sporelings (Cutter, 1965).

In a comparative study of apical size, phyllotaxis index and rate of leaf inception in spiral and bijugate specimens of *Dryopteris dilatata*, Cutter

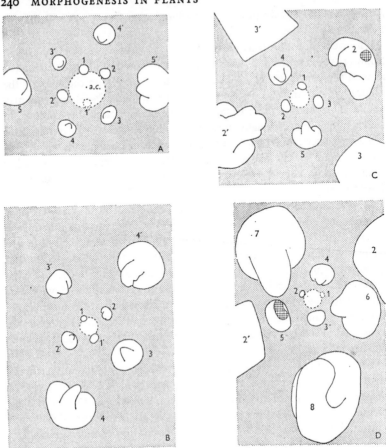

FIG. 9.5. Observations on bijugate phyllotaxis. *Dryopteris dilatata*. Specimen with bijugate phyllotaxis, maintained in the laboratory without surgical treatment. A, $4\frac{1}{2}$ months after the first observation. The phyllotaxis is still bijugate. B, 7 months after the first observation. The angle of divergence has increased, so that the phyllotaxis is nearly decussate. Note that primordia I and I' are not of equal size. C, 8 months after the first observation. Primordia 1-5 are in spiral sequence, older primordia paired. Primordia 4 and 5 represent I and I' of Fig. B, primordia 2, 2' and 3, 3' of that drawing being so numbered again. D, 3 weeks later. Three more primordia have been formed in spiral sequence. P_4 represents P_1 of Fig. C. (All $\times$ 13.) (After E. G. Cutter and B. R. Voeller, *Jour. Linn. Soc. (Bot.)*, 1959.)

(1964a) found the two systems to be similar; and in the apices of both groups these parameters underwent similar changes over a period of time. In the spiral apices, as already indicated, such changes resulted in an increase in the differences in size and stage of development between successive primordia. Cutter concluded that a similar effect on existing small differences between the two primordia of a pair in bijugate apices might account for the change to a spiral system. 'The observed changes in phyllotaxis would thus be indirectly attributable to progressive changes in the rates of the various components of growth in the apex occurring over a period of time' (Cutter, 1964a).

In *Dipsacus* plants treated with GA, Cutter (1964a) reported an increase in internodal elongation and a slight increase in the mean angle of divergence. Accordingly, she indicated the importance of the vertical component of growth in the apex as a factor in phyllotaxis. Phyllotactic changes were also induced in buds of *Hydrocharis* growing in a nutrient solution containing GA (Cutter, 1963). Here, again, the induced extensive internodal elongation may have been a factor associated with the observed changes. The changes in phyllotaxis which accompany the onset of flowering in many species are probably mediated, in part at least, through the elongation of the axis. In this connection, Schwabe (1963) described a change from decussate to spiral phyllotaxis in plants of *Epilobium adenocaulon* which had been maintained in daylength conditions just insufficient to induce flowering. Applications of various growth-regulating substances, in addition to GA, are now known to cause changes, not infrequently anomalous, in phyllotaxis. (For a fuller exposition and refs., *see* Cutter, 1965.)

APICAL ORGANIZATION AND FOLIAR HELICES

Since the middle 1940s, the literature relating to apices and to phyllotaxis has been greatly enlarged and, indeed, enlivened, by the ideas and observations of a group of French botanists – Plantefol, Buvat and their co-workers. Some of the ideas which they have advanced concerning apical organization and the concomitant morphogenetic activities are at variance with those long held by older, and also by some contemporary, observers.

According to Plantefol (1946, 1947, 1948); Buvat (1952, 1955); Camefort (1956); Loiseau (1955, 1962); and others, the cells in the most distal position in the vegetative shoot apex are more or less completely inert and virtually do not participate in, or contribute to, histogenesis or organogenesis. The summit, or centre, of the apical meristem, in this view, is a *resting* or *waiting meristem* (*méristème d'attente*), which becomes active and functional only at the onset of the flowering phase. The effective seat of growth, i.e. the locus of tissue formation and primordium inception, is a band of tissue, situated below the allegedly inert distal region. This meristematic band or ring – the '*anneau initial*', i.e. initial or initiating ring – is regarded as a self-perpetuating tissue and as the true vegetative meristem. As compared with the distal tissue, its cells are characterized by various cytoplasmic phenomena, increased synthesis of proteins, DNA, etc., and the relative abundance of mitosis. In the associated phyllotaxis theory – known as the Theory of Foliar Helices – it is held that the phyllotaxis in most plants can be referred to a relatively small number of foliar helices which wind round the stem. The upper extremity of a helix consists of a generative centre, occupying a position in the meristematic *anneau initial*. The periodic activity of this generating centre gives rise to all the leaf primordia on the helix. Where there are several helices, there are also several generative centres in the meristematic ring. The activities of the several centres are assumed to be harmonized by an organizer which is present in the apex. As explicitly stated by adherents of this theory, a generative centre is to be regarded as a physiological unit, rather than as a recognizable morphological unit. (*See also* p. 135 and Fig. 6.12.)

The theory of apical organization and multiple foliar helices, as proposed and elaborated by the 'French School', has undoubtedly had a stimulating effect on studies of the manner and mechanism of apical growth. There has been a considerable, and desirable, intensification of studies of the cytology, using electron microscopy, and histochemistry of the several regions of the apex. It cannot be denied that the *anneau initial* is a region of great activity – and the present writer makes no such denial; in fact, he agrees. Thus Taillandier (1965), in a histoautoradiographical study of the vegetative apex of *Pinus pinea*, using tritiated thymidine, demonstrated that, throughout a plastochrone, the lateral cells of the apical meristem, i.e. those of the *anneau initial*, had a much greater capacity for the synthesis of DNA than those at the centre, or summit, of the meristem. In an investigation of apical metabolism in the shoot of *Perilla nankinensis* during its several phases of development, Lance-Nougarède and Bronchard (1965) obtained evidence on RNA and DNA synthesis which was confirmatory of Plantefol's concept of apical constitution and formative activity. However, the notion that the 'apical cell region' (in pteridophytes) or 'apical initials region' (in seed plants) is an inert region, is not justified by the facts (*see* résumés in R. Snow, 1948; Gifford, 1954; Wardlaw, 1956, 1965; Cutter, 1959, 1965; Ball, 1960 *et seq.*). Loiseau (1962), in an investigation of the displacement of marks on growing apices of *Impatiens roylei*, reported that such displacement was most rapid on the flanks of the apical meristem but was not absent from the more central, or distal, region. Lance-Nougarède and Loiseau (1960) reported that in aquatic species, such as *Elodea, Hippuris, Ceratophyllum* and *Callitriche*, the apical meristem has neither an *anneau initial* nor a *méristème d'attente*. The shoot apex consists of a massive region of homogeneous cells and a prevascular strand which, as Wetmore (1946) noted, is differentiated higher up in the axis than the youngest leaf primordia. The latter originate without the so-called 'foliar buttress'.

In a large conical apex, e.g. of *Dryopteris dilatata*, it is evident, as a matter of geometry, that the structural organization and all the sustaining conditions are such that the rate of growth falls off steadily, acropetally, from the maturing region to the summit of the axis. In various paraboloidal apices the growth rate must fall off considerably more rapidly; and in flattish meristems the rate of growth at the centre of the system must be very slow indeed. As it seems to the author, these facts are unavoidable and indisputable.

Some direct observations on growth in the most distal region of the apical meristem are contrary to the theory of inertness, e.g. Wardlaw's (1949) demonstration that a film of lamp-black eventually becomes completely dispersed from the summit of the apex, though, as expected, this happens considerably more rapidly in the basal regions. Newman (1956) observed mitotic figures in terminal cells; and Ball (1960 *et seq.*) and Soma and Ball (1963), Ball and Joshi (1965), Ball and Soma (1965), in time-lapse studies of marked distal cells, found that these divide, the daughter cells subsequently moving 'down' the flanks of the meristem (*see also* p. 136). Another kind of evidence against the theory was advanced by Gifford and Wetmore (1957). In several gymnosperms they could find no basic structural differences between vegetative and reproductive apices. By observing the incorporation of ^{14}C-labelled adenine with DNA, Clowes (1959) investigated the rate of cell division in the shoot apices of a number of aquatic plants: he concluded that there is no inert distal *resting meristem*.

A point worthy of mention (in a controversial issue which has become much too extensive to be treated in detail here) is that Plantefol's theory brings its own difficulties. So also do the interpretations of the various surgical experiments which have been devised to validate the theory. For full and critical discussion of these investigations, *see* Cutter (1959, 1965). The present writer's views can be stated quite simply:

(1) As an aspect of their organization and physiological activity, shoot apical meristems form regularly spaced, discrete growth centres, which typically grow out as leaf primordia.

(2) Existing primordia exercise regulative effects on new ones.

(3) The shoot apex and its lateral organs grow as a reciprocally regulated, integrated whole, always tending towards a steady state, or dynamic equilibrium.

CHAPTER X

The Root System

THE DIVERSITY OF ROOT PHENOMENA

Viewed collectively, the roots of plants, like their shoots and leaves, are surprisingly diverse in form, structure and function. Some aspects of root morphogenesis which seem to the writer to be of special interest are considered in this chapter. However, only a few can be treated in detail. These include:

1. *Morphological Diversity*. Root systems are very diverse morphologically. They often manifest features of an adaptive character in relation to particular ecological conditions: e.g. the extensive root systems of sand dune and desert species; the rootlessness, or reduced root systems, in aquatic and parasitic species; the prevalence of the mycorrhizic condition; the aerial roots of epiphytes; various special developments in mangrove species; the strut roots of palms; roots as organs of storage and perennation; and so on. In fact, roots afford a rather surprising range of materials for morphogenetic investigation (*see* Figs. 10.20–10.22).

2. *Histological Organization*. The interpretation of the structure and growth of the root meristem raises problems of unique interest. By means of experimental investigations, some of these problems have been partly elucidated. These developments in the primary roots begin in the early embryogeny in some species. Here, also, considerable histological diversity has been noted (Fig. 10.1).

3. *Lateral Roots and Root Buds*. The formation of lateral roots and, in some species, of root buds poses special problems; in particular, the *endogenous* as compared with the *exogenous* inception of new organs.

4. *Differentiation of Tissue Systems*. In species with roots of varying size, the primary stelar tissues may exemplify the size-structure correlation in a remarkable manner. The incidence and development of secondary thickening afford materials that are comparable with those encountered in the stems of herbaceous and woody species.

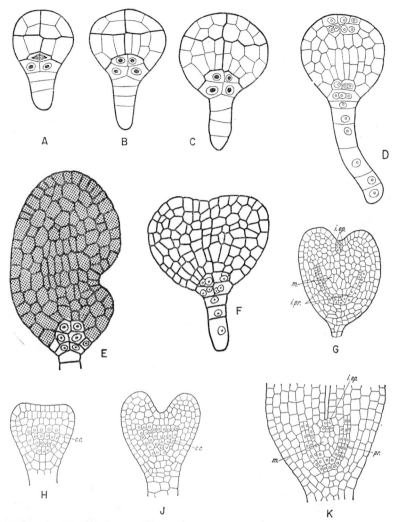

FIG. 10.1. The inception of the primary root in the embryology of various species. The dividing root initials are typically situated above the suspensor and at, or near, the base of the embryo proper. In some species the active development of the root initials can be distinguished at an early stage: in others it is less evident until later. Again, the organization of the root apex may be relatively precocious *vis-à-vis* that of the shoot.

A, B, C, *Ludwigia palustris*. (After E. C. R. Souèges.) D, *Geum urbanum*. (After E. C. R. Souèges.) E, *Luzula forsteri*. (After E. C. R. Souèges.) F, *Spiraea ulmaria*. (After A. Lebègue.) G, *Cassia acutifolia*. H. J, K, *Cardiospermum hirsutum*. (G–K, After O. Pellegrini, 1956.) *i.ep.*, shoot apical (epicotyl) initials; *i.pr.*, procambial initials, closely associated with the root initials; *m*, medulla; *cc*, central cells. Pellegrini has cited *Cassia* and *Cardiospermum* as examples in which root organization is more advanced than shoot organization in embryogenesis.

(Acknowledgements in C. W. Wardlaw, *Encyclopedia of Plant Physiology*, XV/I, 1965.)

5. *Whole Plant Morphogenesis*. The formation and growth relationships of stem, leaf and root take us deeply into the great classical phenomena of correlative developments. These have physiological, genetical and morphological aspects.

6. *Homology of Organization*. As with other organs, roots of particular species have their own distinctive characteristics. Yet, in their main morphological, structural and functional aspects, roots from all the major phyla of vascular plants have much in common: they exemplify a remarkable homology of organization.

7. *The 'Root Category'*. What may perhaps be regarded as the ultimate problem – and like all 'ultimate' problems it is enigmatic and difficult to grasp – relates to the development of some organs as roots and others as shoots. So we may ask: what organizational factors, or system of factors, in embryonic tissue determine(s) which category of organ will be formed? Botanists of the early nineteenth century, and even some great physiologists of a later period, such as Sachs, accepted, and presumably found solace in, the concept of organs of *fundamental categories*; i.e. the *rhizome* or root; the *caulome* or stem; and the *phyllome* or leaf. These fundamental organs were held to be absolute in the sense that there was a limit beyond which scientific investigation could not penetrate. However, as we know, Sachs subsequently moved away from this view. Today, although the great enigma of the 'rootiness' of roots still remains, many cogent observations on factors in their organogenesis have been made.

THE HISTOLOGICAL ORGANIZATION OF ROOT APICES

Since the later decades of the nineteenth century, botanists have been aware that although all roots have many features in common, the histological organization at the apex and the formation of the several major tissues show considerable diversity from species to species. In leptosporangiate ferns, e.g. *Polypodium*, *Marsilea*, etc., the root apex has a conspicuous tetrahedral apical cell from which, by an orderly sequence of divisions, the root cap or calyptra, the epidermis, the cortex and the stele all originate. Sachs figured such an apex (of *Asplenium filix-foemina*) in his celebrated *Lectures on the Physiology of Plants* (1882/87). In the eusporangiate ferns, with their more massive construction, several initial cells are present at the root apex. Considerably more complex histological patterns are encountered in angiosperm apices, such as those of *Pisum sativum* (figured by Janczewski, 1874, and reproduced by De Bary, 1877–84, in his *Comparative Anatomy*); and of *Vicia faba* (Clowes, 1959, 1961), in which it

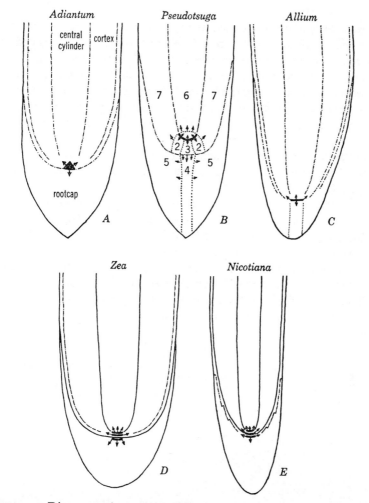

FIG. 10.2. Diagrammatic representation of histological organization of some root apices. (After K. Esau, *Plant Anatomy*, 1953.)

A, a single apical cell (black triangle) is source of all parts of root and rootcap. B, initial zone (black arc) initiates mother-cell zones of the various root parts as follows: 1 (below 6, not marked) of central cylinder (6); 2, of cortex (7); 3, of column of rootcap (4). Longitudinal divisions on periphery of column give cells to peripheral part of rootcap (5). (Adapted from Allen, *Amer. Jour. Bot.* **34**, 1947.)

C, distal region with poorly individualized initials is source of central cylinder, cortex, and column. D, three tiers of initials in the initial zone. First is related to central cylinder; second, to cortex; third, to rootcap. The epidermis differentiates from the outermost layer of the cortex. E, three tiers of initials: first relates to central cylinder; second, to cortex; third, to rootcap. The epidermis originates from the rootcap by periclinal divisions.

is exceedingly difficult to discern the boundary between root-cap and the meristematic tip of the root axis. In *Fagus sylvatica*, as investigated by Clowes (1950, 1959), the boundaries between the meristematic regions, or histogens, can occur 'in different histogens in different roots of a single plant, or even in the same root at different times'. But in species of Gramineae, as illustrated in *Zea Mays* by Janczewski in 1874, the boundary between the root meristem proper and the rootcap is constant. Esau (1953, 1965) illustrated diagrammatically five different types of root-apex pattern: these indicate the structure of the meristems in relation to the derivative tissues; and it is recognized that various intermediate conditions exist. As in shoot apices, extended studies of root apices reveal a very considerable range in histological pattern (Fig. 10.2). (For detailed accounts and refs., *see* Esau, 1953, 1965; and Clowes, 1961.)

In fern roots, with a single apical cell, the apical meristem is not difficult to observe and define. But in other apices, especially those with a *quiescent centre* (p. 251), the term *pro-meristem* is used to denote an actively meristematic group of cells from which all the tissues of the root originate.

Two further significant observations on the cellular organization of the root apex and its meristematic activities may conveniently be noted at this point.

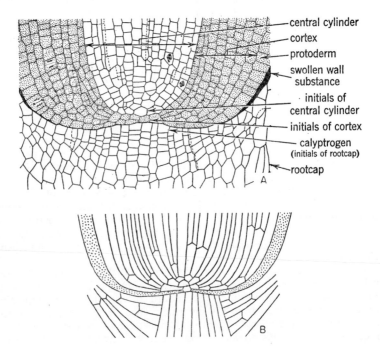

central cylinder
cortex
protoderm
swollen wall substance
· initials of central cylinder
initials of cortex
calyptrogen (initials of rootcap)
rootcap

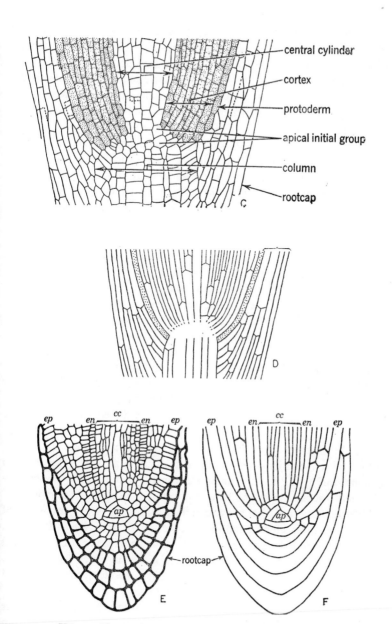

FIG. 10.3. Körper–Kappe (body-cap) concept of Schüepp, 1917, as illustrated by various apices. A, B, *Zea mays*. C. D, *Allium sativum*. (After K. Esau, *Plant Anatomy*, 1965.) E, F, Fern root apex: *Dennstaedtia* sp. (After List, *Amer. Jour. Bot.*, **50**, 1963.)

The Körper–Kappe Theory. The conspicuous apical-cell system in many fern roots, and a general acceptance of Hanstein's histogen theory for both shoots and roots, tended to canalize the interpretation of root apical organization (Clowes, 1961). This impeded more objective observation and assessment of meristematic activities in the roots of different species. In effect, there was a tendency to classify roots in terms of the cell lineages stemming from the histogens. Thus, in some apices the epidermis and cortex are formed from the same histogen; in others there are separate and discrete histogens for the root-cap, the epidermis and cortex; and so on. In 1917 Schüepp proposed his Körper–Kappe (body-cap) theory, or concept, of cellular organization in root apices. The essential feature of this concept lies in the recognition of the position of the histogen boundary between the root-cap and the apex proper. This boundary is constant and determinate in the Gramineae, whereas in species such as *Fagus* the boundary is variable; in fact, it can occur in different histogens. The value of Schüepp's theory in resolving some of the problems of root histogenesis was recognized by Wagner (1939) and Clowes (1961). Figs. 10.3, 10.5 illustrate the application of the concept to a number of roots.

The histological pattern in the root meristem is indicative of the planes of division in the apical cell and its segments. The longitudinal rows of cells, e.g. in a fern, originate near the apical cell. In the formation of these cell rows, a cell divides transversely and then longitudinally, yielding a T-division or junction (Schüepp, 1917; Clowes, 1961). Now Schüepp pointed out that in the centre of the root the top (cross-stroke) of the T is directed acropetally, whereas, in the outer regions, it is directed basipetally: the former region is referred to as the *Körper* and the latter as the *Kappe*. In brief, the Körper–Kappe theory is concerned with differences in the planes of cell division, but it does not attribute a 'destiny' to the two regions during the further differentiation of their tissues. Clowes emphasized that the theory can be usefully applied to all kinds of roots.

The cell pattern in root apices is affected by the presence or absence of autonomous initials for the root-cap. In the aquatic fern, *Azolla filiculoides*, in which cap initial cells are present, a clear boundary can be discerned between the Körper and the Kappe. In *Marsilea*, in which the apical cell initiates all the tissues, no such clear boundary is evident, the Körper and Kappe being, as it were, parts of one system.

Much can, of course, be made of these histological patterns, their similarities and differences, and the root regions which originate from them. But, in the end, as it seems to the writer, we are once again concerned with that important phenomenon, the distribution of growth. In pondering the organization and growth of roots, we must assuredly know the histological facts. But let us not be enslaved by them! On the basis of the segmentation pattern, for example, the root-cap initials in some species are said to be 'autonomous' (Clowes, 1961, p. 118), i.e. independent, or not a mere form or state of some other initials. A further statement is that in roots with tetrahedral apical cells 'the cap is the first tissue to be independent of the other tissues'. Now it cannot be said that these statements are not valid. But, bearing in mind the evident unity of the growing apex, one may ask: how autonomous are the initials? In what way and to what extent are they truly independent? Segmentation patterns notwithstanding, it is an indisputable fact that all the materials of growth, i.e. carbohydrates, amino acids, etc., and also the mineral nutrients and water, are moving acropetally towards the histogenic regions. The 'autonomous', 'independent', root-cap initials participate in utilizing these metabolic materials and perhaps also others which are diffusing into them from contiguous cells. Moreover, as the root apex grows as a whole, apparently in a highly regulated fashion, it seems more reasonable to look for reciprocal and complementary relationships between contiguous histogens and tissues rather than independence (*see* p. 13). The discreteness of particular histogens – the so-called autonomy – is real in the sense that it is the inevitable result of chemical and physical factors which become incident during growth, including the compressive and tensile stresses set up in relation to the characteristic distribution of growth in the apex (*see* pp. 101, 110). Clowes himself wrote (p. 125) that the several regions of the root apex 'grow conformably together'.

THE QUIESCENT CENTRE

From observation of the apical cellular pattern in the *Zea mays* root, Clowes (1954) inferred that the cells at the centre and summit of the epidermis–cortex complex and of the stelar column are not meristematic, i.e. they do not divide to form new cells. This group of cells – a not inconsiderable volume of tissue in the form of a hemisphere or frustum of a spheroid – is now known as the *quiescent centre* (Figs. 10.4 A, B). Such quiescent centres occur in a number of apices, e.g. *Vicia faba, Sinapis alba,* etc. (Clowes, 1959, 1961). This cellular condition is reminiscent of the postulated *méristème d'attente* (the resting meristem) of Buvat in the shoot apex; and, indeed, Buvat *et al.* (1951, 1953) referred to the analogous conditions in shoot and root apices. In attractive demonstrations, using labelled metabolites and autoradiography, Clowes confirmed his anatomical observations: he showed that the synthesis of DNA – a dependable indication of the onset of nuclear division – was absent or negligible in the quiescent centre, whereas DNA was evidently being synthesized in the contiguous tissues. As Clowes (1961, p. 138) stated: 'The shape, size and position of the dark area (in an autoradiograph) fit exactly with the quiescent centre postulated from the analysis of the cell pattern.' This is a satisfactory conclusion, not least because it engenders confidence in the inferences which may be drawn from anatomical observations (*see* below). Clowes (1956) also demonstrated a lower concentration of RNA in the cells of the quiescent centre, this substance being usually high in growing and dividing cells. (For other, confirmatory evidence, and a discussion of the data of mitosis, *see* Clowes, 1961.) On the evidence so far obtained, all roots, except those of pteridophytes with apical cells, appear to have

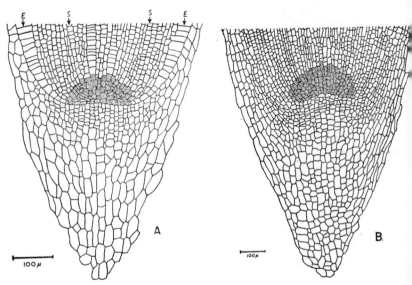

FIG. 10.4. The quiescent centre in root apices. A, *Zea mays*. B, *Vicia faba*. (After F. A. L. Clowes, *Biol. Rev.*, 1959; *Apical Meristems*, 1961.)

quiescent centres. It has been shown by autoradiography, after feeding with precursors of DNA, that the apical cell in the fern root synthesizes DNA just as do the adjacent cells of the meristem.

D'Amato and Avanzi (1965) have advanced evidence to the effect that the single apical cell in the fern root is closely comparable with the quiescent centre in angiosperms; i.e. it may remain undivided for considerable periods, or it may divide only occasionally.

The Significance of the Quiescent Centre. The cells in this region are not incapable of meristematic activity. Clowes (1953, 1954) demonstrated that they can be stimulated to a renewal of growth and division by an incision of the quiescent centre and by irradiation. But, normally, they remain mitotically inert and may so continue during the life of the root; indeed, Jensen (1958) showed that, far from functioning as active apical initials, the cells of the centre have the lowest content of DNA, RNA and protein nitrogen in the whole root tip, their estimated content of DNA being like that of a nucleus after a diploid mitosis. The other apical cells, by contrast, have a DNA content which is intermediate between that of diploid and tetraploid cells. So, on the summation of the evidence, it may be accepted that *all metabolic processes proceed at a diminished rate, if at all, in the cells of the quiescent centre* (see Clowes, 1961, for details and references).

The inception of a quiescent centre, typically present in roots of a certain size and maturity, has an ontogenetic aspect (Clowes, 1961). Some of the relevant observations are in accord with reasoned conjecture, but others are, perhaps, a little unexpected and surprising. In the embryo, in young or very young roots and in lateral roots, all the cells at the apex are meristematic. In primary roots the quiescent centre develops soon after the embryonic phase; in a lateral root its inception coincides approximately with the lateral's emergence from the mother root. By feeding the roots of *Sinapis alba* with adenine-8-C^{14} and preparing autoradiographs, Clowes (1958) found that the quiescent centre appeared in the primary roots after germination. In the newly emerged seedling radicle, there was no DNA synthesis; but when roots were about 5 mm. long DNA synthesis began. At this stage quiescent centres were still absent in some roots, but in others they constituted a group of 4–40 cells. As root development continued, the quiescent centre increased in size until it comprised some 500 cells of the stele and cortex 'initials'.

In the aquatic species *Pistia stratiotes* and *Eichornia crassipes* the lateral roots are formed in or near the apex of the large main roots. These rootlets synthesize DNA while they are still very young and within the maternal cortical tissue; but before they emerge, a quiescent centre begins to be formed. Clowes further ascertained that by the time a lateral rootlet has grown out into the water its quiescent centre has already become fully developed and even quite extensive.

So far, only a small number of root apices have been examined for the phenomenon under consideration. But the observations recorded may well have some generality. A size-structure and functional relationship may be involved in the inception and further development of quiescent centres. Clowes noted that in some roots, e.g. those lacking a columella in the root-cap, quiescent centres are not present, 'or the degree of quiescence may never reach the state found in larger roots' (Clowes, 1961, p. 145).

In an excellent survey of the evidence that bears, directly or indirectly, on the development of the quiescent centre, Clowes (1961) emphasized, among other points, that because the cells of this region are not meristematic, i.e. actively dividing, they are not necessarily metabolically inert or without function. If an apex is damaged by wounding or by irradiation, cells of the quiescent centre become active, the resulting meristematic cells forming a substitute promeristem. Clowes also suggested that they may function as loci of hormone synthesis, 'or even in maintaining the geometry of large meristems' (p. 160). The latter inference, which evidently has its place in a work on morphogenesis, is one to which the writer has been led following other avenues of thought. In diagrams illustrating histogenesis in root apices, i.e. cell lineages, the indicator arrows typically point *away* from the quiescent centre. But a rather different diagram could also be constructed in which the arrows would point *towards* the quiescent centre, suggesting what may happen to metabolic materials as they move, or are drawn, into the distal, apical region from the older tissues. Water and mineral nutrients may be taken up from the soil solution all over the root surface; but all the elaborated organic materials must come from the older region of the root and, more distantly, from the photosynthetic leafy shoot. From our knowledge of root metabolism and general physiology, points of special relevance to the quiescent meristem include the following:

(1) The sugars, amino acids, nucleoprotein precursors, etc., which are moving acropetally towards the active promeristem, by way of the nascent stele and cortex, have to traverse tissues which are in various states of active growth. Now, an actively growing or dividing cell, or a tissue mass, acts as a 'physiological sink', i.e. a locus of active utilization of metabolites. Inevitably, therefore, unless cells are not 'competent to react' to metabolic stimuli, the amounts, or concentrations, of the precursors of DNA, RNA, proteins, carbohydrates, etc., must diminish as the promeristem is approached.

(2) In many metabolic processes the reacting substances must be present in critical concentrations before a particular synthesis can take place. But once this state has been reached, and the reaction 'triggered off' by some appropriate stimulus, the processes of cellular metabolism in meristematic and growing cells, being largely autocatalytic in nature, will take place with increasing rapidity. As a result, the cells or cell masses thus activated will tend to grow at the expense of the contiguous cells. It appears that some such relationship may be established between the active cells of the promeristem and the increasing volume of inert cells in the quiescent centre. In this view, the quiescent centre would be interpreted as a normal resultant effect of the size, geometry, physics and physiology of the apical system; i.e. the active cells, nearer the sources of supply, deprive the more distal cells of the materials of metabolism. Clowes' discussion of the quiescent centre as providing a reserve of diploid cells, as it were serving the interests of the growing root in various circumstances, is

true in a sense. But it perhaps introduces an unnecessary and, indeed, un-intentional, undertone of teleology. (*See* Additional Note, p. 285.)

THE DISCRETENESS OF THE TISSUE INITIALS

In different roots, and in various degrees, the initials of the root-cap, the epidermis, the cortex and the stele may be 'separate', i.e. remain discrete during the entire development of the root. That is to say that cells or tissues systems, which are identical in origin and are closely comparable in many of their metabolic processes, become biochemically differentiated in particular ways and so remain during the life of the organ. However, it seems improbable that contiguous though metabolically differentiated cells or tissues have no exchanges of materials whatever. In root meristems some metabolic complementarity between the active initials and the quiescent centre seems probable; for, as already emphasized, the root apex quite evidently grows and develops as an integrated whole, yielding a mature organ of very considerable constancy in shape and size. This general ob-servation also applies to the roots of a number of species in which, as we now know, a varying polyploidy may occur. (For a review and refs. *see* Clowes, 1961.) Notwithstanding the fact that contiguous cells or tissues in an actively growing root may have nuclei of different ploidy, the root typically develops with a characteristic unity; i.e. the distribution of growth *in the developing region as a whole* transcends, or supervenes upon, the *physiology of particular cells or tissues* of different chromosome complement. Indeed, it may be that, in attempting to interpret the histogenic and morphogenic phenomena of roots, e.g. the seeming and actual discreteness of the apical initials, our primary concern should be with the overall distribution and utilization of metabolic materials. A simple example will illustrate a relationship between these physiological processes and the inception of histogenic pattern. Because of the geometrical relationships of circumfer-ence to radius in a cylindrical body, a root cortex in which there is rapid transverse enlargement, with concomitant tensile stress in the outermost tissues, will tend to be surrounded by a dermal tissue in which all the divisions are anticlinal (unless the materials of growth can move, in some way that we do not yet understand, with great rapidity to the outermost regions). (For more detailed discussions of root apical organization and refs., *see* Clowes, 1961; Torrey, 1965.)

THE UNITY OF THE PROMERISTEM

The 'unity' of the promeristem has been much discussed and is the subject of a considerable literature. Some observers maintain that there is a common promeristem for the whole of the root apex. Thus Guttenberg (1947, *et seq.*), with abundant illustrations (1960), suggested that, in seed plants, all the regions of a promeristem can be traced back to a single central cell (described as the *Verbindungszell* – or connecting cell). Other observers, however, have shown that the developed promeristem can be separated into distinct groups of initials, or histogens, which give rise to the several tissues. These histogens are contiguous with the quiescent centre. In *Fagus sylvatica*, according to Clowes (1950), the promeristem consists of a cup-shaped group of initials; the histogens of the root-cap columella and of the stele form the base of the cup, while those of the cortex and peripheral region of the root-cap form the sides of the cup (Fig. 10.5). Within

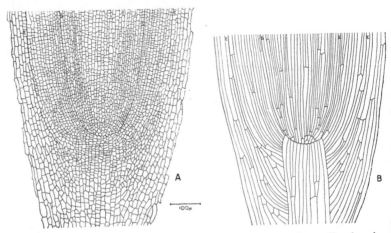

FIG. 10.5. The root apex of *Fagus sylvatica*. A, As seen in median longitudinal section and B, as interpreted in terms of the Körper-Kappa concept. (After F. A. L. Clowes, *New Phytol.*, 1950.)

lies the quiescent centre. Clowes showed that the initials of the stele and the columella, though closely contiguous, are not in full linear continuity. Accordingly, one may recognize that *these complex promeristems comprise several distinct histogenic regions but that they are unified, or in some way mutually regulated, in their collective activities.* More generally, one may accept that a root develops from a single apical meristem, which grows in a state of dynamic equilibrium and is *unified* in its function, but which is chemically and physiologically differentiated into several regions, i.e. the several histogens and the quiescent centre. In ingenious surgical experiments, in which the apical meristem was cut off obliquely, so as to leave the stelar initials intact or to remove them, Clowes (1953, 1954) observed that, in the latter circumstance, regeneration was not obtained, probably because the whole promeristem was removed; but in the former, in which regeneration took place, and from other evidence, he concluded that the promeristem is a large region (Fig. 10.6).

A general concept along the lines outlined above enables us to accept and assimilate the anatomical diversity of differently constructed apices and to

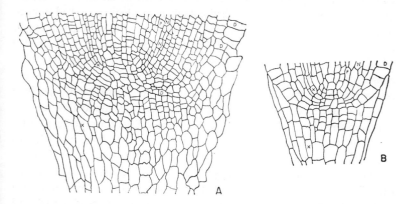

FIG. 10.6. A, *Zea mays*. B, *Triticum* sp. Median longitudinal sections of roots subjected to incisions, illustrating the reactivity of cells of the apical meristem in grass roots (*see also* Figs. 10.3, 10.4).
An oblique segment was removed from the root tip of a seedling by a single cut through the plerome pole, i.e. so as to remove part of the generative centre; and the cut surface was then smeared with lanolin. When the seedlings were then replanted the treated roots continued to grow. Later, on being sectioned, the root apices were seen to have undergone regeneration and growth. X–X, anticlinal row of cells on regenerated side; D, the dermatogen on the undamaged side; P, outer layer of plerome. N, inner layer of periblem. The extent of the modification of the histological organization can be seen by comparing the left- and right-hand sides of the sections ($\times 150$). These experimental results indicate that the cytogenerative centre in these grass roots is a broad promeristem consisting of many cells and not simply of a central initial cell, or small group of central initial cells. But a minimal number of cells is required to maintain the growth of the roots. (After F. A. L. Clowes, *New Phytol.*, **53**, 1954.)

see beyond the demonstrable histological differences to the central fact that all root apices grow in much the same way and yield generally comparable mature organs.

RADIATION EFFECTS ON ROOT APICES

Studies of the effects of ionizing radiations on the organization of root apices have yielded some interesting observations (Gray and Scholes, 1951; Clowes, 1959, 1961). The first and most evident effect of X-rays is a

I

decrease in the growth rate; but, if the dosage is not excessive, recovery usually follows. These effects are due to damage to the apical meristem. When Clowes fed labelled adenine to maize roots after subjecting their apices to 1,200 roentgens he found evidence of disorganization in some, whereas others apparently remained normal. In the latter, however, the number of meristem cells which had not taken up adenine (i.e. had stopped dividing) had increased as compared with the controls. When a longer interval was allowed between irradiation and the application of labelled adenine the absence of DNA synthesis in the meristem cells was still more conspicuous. With an interval of 4 days, the peripheral cells of the quiescent centre began to synthesize DNA; and when the interval before labelling was extended to 6–8 days the quiescent centre was found to have disappeared completely. In fact, in some roots the cells of the quiescent centre were the only ones in the apical region which were synthesizing DNA. In *Vicia*, Clowes also observed that most of the cells of irradiated apices stopped growing and synthesizing DNA. In roots in which growth continued, a new meristem had been formed at the apex, sometimes in a terminal–lateral position, sometimes in the former quiescent centre; and in some instances three new meristems became organized, each eventually forming a new root. However, the most common occurrence recorded by Clowes was that the growth of the root was continued by a single new meristem, with external evidence of the discontinuity, or disruption, within. The collective evidence thus indicates that dividing cells are more sensitive to radiation damage than quiescent ones and that the latter retain their full meristematic potential.

POLYPLOIDY IN DIFFERENTIATING ROOT TISSUES

Contrary to the classical view that the cells of the sporophyte generation of a higher plant have typically diploid nuclei, there is now accumulating evidence that although the cells of the apical meristem in a diploid species are diploid, some of the cells derived from them may soon become polyploids; or, as Clowes (1961, p. 159) stated: 'Most plants are probably polyploid chimeras in which most of the cells are polyploids.' And he added: 'The problem for today is perhaps to look to see how diploidy is maintained in a few important cells rather than to look for the causes of polyploidy.' These are interesting observations and comments, even though, at this early stage, they should, perhaps, be received with some measure of caution and suspension of judgement. Closely associated with polyploidy in cells at varying distances from the promeristem are the questions of the DNA content of their nuclei and the rate of uptake of adenine or other DNA components.

In the matter of polyploidy in root cells, it may be emphasized that, as in the classical periclinal chimeras in the shoot apex of *Datura*, contiguous embryonic cell layers, of different ploidy and of different actual sizes, can grow together compatibly, i.e. without exercising disruptive or damaging tensile or compressive stresses one on the other; and, moreover, they eventually yield an adult plant which, though possessing its own distinctive features, is closely comparable in its major morphological features with the parental stock. In brief, the *general physiology of growth*, characteristic of the species, is more important than, or supervenes upon, the specific growth *effects* of ploidy in individual cells or tissues. The significance and importance of ploidy differences in a community of cells afford scope for much fuller, and preferably more broadly based, inquiries.

POLYPLOIDY, NUCLEIC ACID AND PROTEIN CONTENT IN MORPHO-GENETIC PROCESSES IN ROOTS

In *Hydrocharis* and some other aquatic species the nuclei of the root-hairs undergo endomitosis and become polyploid. In the roots of *Spinacia*, endoploidy occurs in the cortex. In this species, as observed in the root apical meristem, $2n = 12$. At 400 μ below the tip, however, 12 chromosome pairs, or 24 unpaired, were observed; at 50 μ, 24 pairs; at 600 μ, 48 unpaired; and, at 900 μ, there were 48 pairs (Gentcheff and Gustafson, 1939). Now, in endoploidy, the doubling of the number of chromosomes takes place before prophase and is attended by a doubling of the nuclear DNA content. Clowes (1961, p. 177) has given a useful review of the diverse phenomena of polyploidy in roots, both in embryos and adult plants. Some species have apparently no constant or consistent chromosome number in the developing root tissues. In *Hymenocallis calathinum* (Amaryllidaceae) the root cells may contain from 23 to 83 chromosomes, whereas the pollen-mother-cells contain 69–86 (Snoad, 1955). 'So it looks [to quote Clowes, 1961, p. 177] as if the roots tolerate unbalanced numbers better than the anthers. This may well be advantageous to the species but . . . we do not know the mechanism for maintaining relative constancy in chromosome numbers in important tissues.' But do we really know that, in different tissues, chromosome number is consistently important? Fern prothalli, for example, may be functionally effective in the haploid, diploid or triploid conditions.

In this field of study a useful experimental procedure is based on the observation that when IAA is applied to plant tissues or organs it induces non-dividing and seemingly 'mature' cells to become meristematic. Among the differentiated root cells thus induced to divide, many are found to be polyploid. Similarly, cells which have divided in response to wounding have been found to be polyploid. When nuclear DNA is measured in root cells showing this variable polyploid condition the amounts have been found to be, e.g. in *Zea mays* (Swift, 1950), from 2 to 32 times the amount present in the haploid nucleus of a male gamete. In Swift's method of assessment it was found that most of the differentiated root cells in maize have 4 or 8 times the haploid DNA content (or 4C or 8C). The vessel elements may have amounts up to 32C. Moreover, he noted that the farther the cells were from the apex, the greater was the DNA content of their nuclei. Other, generally confirmatory, evidence has been cited by Clowes (1961). It thus appears that when the cells in a developing root cease to divide, the DNA nevertheless continues to accumulate, with or without doubling the chromosome number; i.e. a 4C nucleus is not necessarily tetraploid, since the additional DNA may increase the size of the chromosomes (the phenomenon known as polyteny). There is thus still much to be ascertained and clarified, especially as it affects the phenomena of histogenesis, differentiation and the functional activities of cells and tissues. The general point that has been established is that the quantity of DNA – the 'hereditary substance' – is different in different developing cells and tissues. And, no doubt, as investigations are extended to a wider range of genera and species we shall encounter further variations on the theme. It cannot yet be said that the amount of DNA in a cell which is differentiating in some particular way is the primary cause of that development; but the DNA content is almost certainly a contributory factor. In the cells of the quiescent centre, with nuclei at the 2C content of DNA, both the RNA content and the rate of protein synthesis are lower. On this new and fascinating avenue of inquiry, Clowes (1961, p. 180), has adopted a cautious outlook: 'The fact that it is the hereditary material which is increased in polyploidy may be of little significance in studying what causes differentiation.' In other studies of morphogenesis, it has been found that relatively simple factors, such as the sugar concentration applied to an undifferentiated tissue, may have profound effects, e.g. in the differentiation of vascular tissues (see p. 298). Clowes has called attention to some enigmatic facts regarding polyploidy in tissues. For example, when regeneration takes place in a plant tissue containing diploid and polyploid cells, the new plantlings may be diploid, i.e. they have been formed from persisting diploid cells. In some instances polyploid cells may revert to the diploid state by somatic reduction division. It is also known from the work of D'Amato (1959) that polyploid plantlings can be obtained by wounding a callus tissue, the new shoots originating from pre-existing endopolyploid cells.

Ribonucleic acid (RNA), which is closely associated with the synthesis of proteins, occurs in cells in rather variable amounts, i.e. in comparison with the relative stability of the DNA content. Both in active and quiescent cells the rate of RNA utilization, or participation, in metabolic processes may be quite considerable. Actively dividing cells have more nuclear and cytoplasmic RNA than those which are not dividing. RNA is minimal in the quiescent centre and tends to increase, up to a point, in differentiating cells progressively farther away from it. The amounts in the developing vascular and cortical tissues are quite different, being higher in the former.

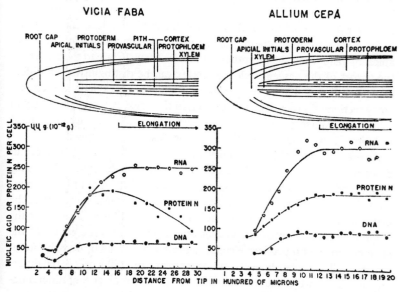

FIG. 10.7. The DNA, RNA and protein nitrogen content of cells in the root apex. (After W. A. Jensen, *Exp. Cell Res.*, 1958.)

There is also some evidence of *qualitative* changes in the RNA present in cells at increasing distances from the meristem. This has suggested to some workers that differentiation may begin with qualitative as well as quantitative changes in RNA, followed by sequential reactions, but always in conjunction with other factors in the metabolic system. Indeed, on the information so far obtained, one begins to see the emergence of a dynamic geometry of metabolic processes (Fig. 10.7).

When protein synthesis is measured by the rate of incorporation of labelled amino acids the promeristem initials have a high rate of synthesis on a per unit volume basis: there is a conspicuous increase, on a per cell basis, in the rapidly enlarging cells of the central stele; and in general the rate of incorporation rises progressively with distance from the meristem, up to the point where cell division ceases (Clowes, 1958, 1961).

On further investigation, it may be expected that these quantitative and qualitative changes in the nucleic acid and protein contents of cells will become more closely related to the characteristic cellular and tissue patterns of differentiation (*see also* pp. 121, 195).

TISSUE DIFFERENTIATION

The root-cap apart, the primary major differential development in roots is between stele and cortex. On the facts of observation, the differentiation of the stelar tissue is acropetal. But, as in shoot and leaf apices, there appears to be a direct causal relationship between the functioning of an active apical meristem and the inception of vascular tissue. Close to the meristem, the tissues of the nascent stele and cortex can be distinguished by differences in cell size. The primary pattern of phloem and xylem, as seen in a cross-section of a root, has its inception in the apex. Although it is easy to follow the course of differentiation within the stele, i.e. by anatomical techniques, the observed developments are less easy to explain.

At the root apex the first embryonic cells affording visual evidence of differentiation, i.e. vacuolation, lie at the centre of the stele. These may become pith parenchyma or xylem elements. Thielke (1966) has demonstrated that, in the roots of *Zea mays*, an enzyme pattern is present in the cell complex in the region of the quiescent centre. This is regarded as the beginning of differentiation. Vacuolation extends from the centre of the stele out to the protoxylem elements. From the sectors of densely protoplasmic cells situated between the xylem rays the phloem is later differentiated. Here we encounter one of the enigmatic problems of differentiation, or, perhaps one should say, of its interpretation. As every student of elementary botany knows, the cells of the protoxylem complete their development, with their characteristic patterns of lignification, etc., before the metaxylem. Yet, on the evidence of vacuolation, it is the inner, metaxylem tracheids, or vessels, in which the first evidence of differentiation is apparent. Furthermore, the maturation and lignification of the xylem elements proceeds centripetally from the already lignified protoxylem groups. However, as in the protoxylem, it is possible that chemical differentiation has already passed through several sequential phases before any visible change becomes manifest; i.e. that protoxylem is truly the first xylem to enter upon differentiation and become mature and functionally effective.

In each of the sectors between the xylem plates a protophloem sieve-tube becomes vacuolated and differentiated near the stelar periphery; and further sieve-tubes are formed centripetally. These sieve-tubes reach maturity soon after they become vacuolated, and mature sieve-tubes can be seen closer to the active meristem than tracheids or vessel segments.

This suggests that they may have an important translocational function in relation to the maintenance of the active meristem. In the root apices of *Hordeum*, Hagemann (1957) demonstrated that the phloem becomes differentiated well in advance of any of the other stelar tissues.

These anatomical developments are still of active interest to contemporary botanists. Their fundamental importance in the economy of the plant cannot be in doubt.

THE SIZE-STRUCTURE CORRELATION IN THE STELE

Roots of species in all the major classes of vascular plants show a remarkable general similarity in their stelar anatomy. Species characterized by large

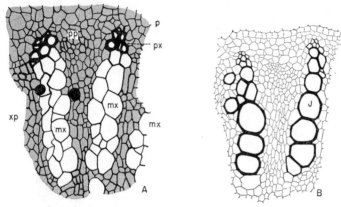

FIG. 10.8. The differentiation of the stelar tissues in A, *Marattia attenuata*. Part of a t.s. of a large root, taken behind the apex. *p*, region of pericycle; *px*, protoxylem, in which the walls have become lignified; *mx*, metaxylem; the tracheids have become enlarged but not yet lignified; *xp*, xylem parenchyma; *pp*, protophloem. (×200.) B, *Gunnera chilensis*. Xylem and phloem differentiation in a large root stele. (After C. W. Wardlaw, *Trans. Roy. Soc. Edin.*, 1928.)

and small roots, without secondary thickening (*see* p. 267), all exemplify the same size-and-structure correlation in their root steles. Thus, whereas the small roots of ferns such as *Marattia* (Fig. 10.8), *Angiopteris* or *Acrostichum* (Fig. 10.9), or flowering plants, such as *Nymphaea* or *Gunnera* (Fig. 10.10) have diarch or triarch structure, the large roots from the same plant may have 15 or more xylem plates (Wardlaw, 1928) (Fig. 10.10). As these characteristic tissue patterns are differentiated just below the apical meristem, it is from cross-sections in that region that comparative measurements should be made in investigations of the inception of the size-structure correlation (Wardlaw, 1965a). These highly regular patterns which, evidently, vary in complexity in relation to the size of the radius, or perimeter, of the stele, lend themselves to interpretation in terms of Turing's diffusion reaction theory of morphogenesis (p. 133); i.e. the number of xylem plates, or of discrete tissue units comprising protoxylem and protophloem, that can be accommodated round the stelar periphery,

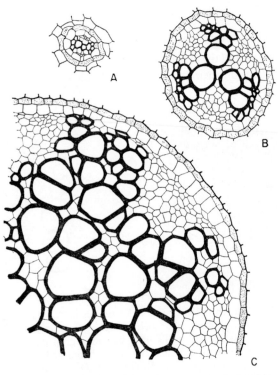

FIG. 10.9. *Acrostichum aureum.* Size and structure relationship, as seen in transverse sections of small and large roots. A, Details of the diarch stele of a small root; endodermis stippled. B, A triarch stele. C, Part of a large polyarch stele (×156). (After C. W. Wardlaw, *Trans. Roy. Soc. Edin.*, 1928.)

is the result of the working of the reaction system in the root apex. On more mature reflection, it may be that, since the protophloem groups are the first tissues to become differentiated, their size and number, in steles of different diameters, should be used as the primary data in interpreting the size–structure correlation. An interpretation of stelar pattern along these lines may be more apt than one based on the pattern of xylem differentiation centrifugally from the centre of the stele (Bünning, 1951,

1952; Reinhard, 1959; Clowes, 1961). In the diarch roots of *Sinapis alba*, for example, Bünning showed that the first evidence of the radial pattern, as seen in cross-section, is the elliptical outline of the central cell of the stele; the major axis of this ellipse is in the plane in which the protoxylem groups and the plate of metaxylem will eventually lie. But this conformation could also be interpreted in terms of a characteristic distribution of growth, the two protophloem groups being the first elements of the pattern to begin to be differentiated. In the end, however, whatever view may seem most appropriate, the essential point is that the root stelar pattern typically

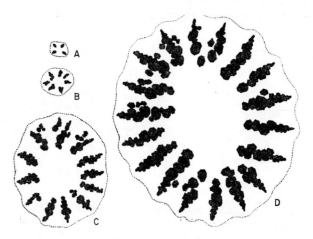

FIG. 10.10. *Gunnera chilensis*. Sections from steles of small and large size (×*c*. 27). (After C. W. Wardlaw, *Trans. Roy. Soc. Edin.*, 1928.)

develops, with a high degree of regularity, as an integrated whole. To abstract, for special consideration, one part of the pattern – usually the most 'showy' part visually, as the writer did in his original drawings of the xylem, e.g. Fig. 10.10 – from the totality of differentiation in the nascent tissue system, has been a common failing among morphologists and anatomists. One may recognize that while the method has its evident uses, i.e. in attempts to interpret difficult and complex developments, it can also obscure the truth.

The stelar anatomy in occasional fasciated roots, such as those of *Caltha palustris* as described by Moss (1924), supports an interpretation along the lines of Turing's theory. Normal roots have typical tetrarch structure. In some fasciated roots a double stele is present, but in others the characteristic xylem/phloem relationship is reproduced not as a radial pattern but as a wave-like conformation (Fig. 10.11).

EXPERIMENTS ON DIFFERENTIATION

The realization that the stelar pattern has its origin in the root apical meristem has led to experimental studies of considerable delicacy and ingenuity; and this primary phenomenon gains in importance when one recalls that the final differentiation of the endodermis and the inception of lateral roots often stand in a direct relationship with the protoxylem groups (*see* below).

It has long been held that the nascent stelar pattern in the meristem is simply an acropetal continuation, or extension, of the pattern already present in the more mature regions below. This concept has now been

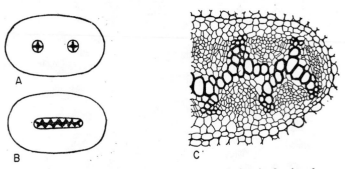

FIG. 10.11. *Caltha palustris*. Size-structure correlation in fasciated roots. A, Bifurcated root, showing normal stelar structure. In the large fasciated roots, B and C, the xylem, as seen in cross-section, is disposed as a sinuous band. (After E. H. Moss, *Annals of Botany*, 1924.)

subjected to experimental tests. By excising the distal 2 mm. of a root and replacing it turned through an angle, Bünning (1952) showed that, on further growth, the newly developed vascular pattern was not continuous with that of the older region. Torrey (1955) (Fig. 10.12) reported experiments in which 500 μ segments were excised from the root apex in *Pisum sativum* (with a nascent triarch stelar pattern) and cultured in sterile liquid media. After growth had taken place, some 20 per cent of the tips were found to have diarch or monarch steles. These patterns, which suggest that a diminution in the size of the root meristem had taken place, later reverted to the normal triarch condition. These experiments demonstrate that the tissue pattern originates in the apical meristem. Torrey further reported that, during the inception of pattern, there is a size-structure correlation between the number of protoxylem groups and the radius of the stele; but this does not obtain in the mature regions of the root. However, as the writer showed, if one selects a species with an extensive range in stelar size, the correlation between number of xylem plates and stelar radius is evident. In further cultural experiments with excised root apices, Torrey (1957) found that, in media containing IAA, originally triarch roots became, and remained, hexarch, provided the IAA concentration was maintained. But, on transfer to lower IAA concentrations, the steles became pentarch or tetrach, the new pattern being referable to the size of the meristem (Fig. 10.13). In intact plants, as Clowes (1961, p. 171) noted, it seems probable that the differentiated tissues in roots and shoots do exercise some effect on differentiation in their respective meristems. It is incontrovertible that the older regions supply the meristem with nutrients, hormones, etc. 'But it appears as if the pattern of supply does not influence the pattern of differentiation' (Clowes). This outlook may, perhaps, need to be reconsidered. For example, in a flowering plant exposed to an appropriate photoperiodic stimulus the vegetative shoot apex is modified by factors proceeding acropetally from below. In these developments the present writer would look for reciprocal relationships between the meristem and the subjacent maturing regions. Thus, when a new lateral root is being formed in the pericycle the pattern of its stele, whether 2-, 5- or n-arch, must be referable to its own apical activities and to the proximal nutritional resources.

Street and his co-workers, as also others, have investigated in considerable detail the nutritional requirements of excised roots growing in aseptic liquid culture. While these studies have little direct morphogenetic content, i.e. for the specific purpose of this chapter, they have evidently an important place in any consideration of 'whole plant morphogenesis' (*see* Chapter XIV). (*See also* p. 203, for information on root formation in tissue cultures.)

SECONDARY THICKENING

As the inception of secondary thickening in roots, and the anatomical changes that occur in the region of transition between root and shoot, are well described in most standard text-books (e.g. Esau, 1965), only a few selected aspects will be considered here.

Secondary thickening begins by divisions in a group of thin-walled cells lying between the phloem and the xylem. A cambium becomes organized and yields new phloem elements on the side contiguous with the metaphloem, and new xylem elements on the inner side. These developments, once again, call our attention to the many unsolved problems of histogenesis. We tend to become familiar with the anatomical details and, all too often, cease to wonder about the underlying causality.

In the roots of some herbaceous species there is no secondary thickening;

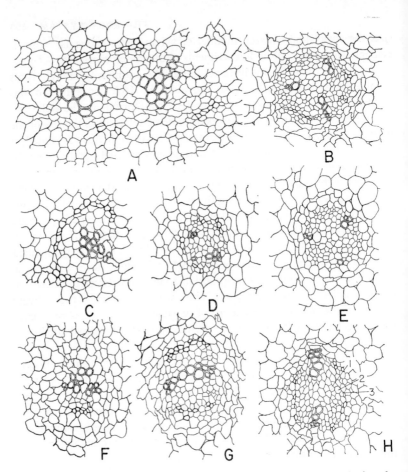

FIG. 10.12. *Pisum sativum:* the determination of vascular patterns during the differentiation of tissues in excised roots. These are tracings from photographs, the mature xylem being recognizable as the thick-walled elements (shaded) and mature sieve-tubes (cells with strong black outlines).

0·5-mm pea-root tips were excised and cultured aseptically in a nutrient medium. Transverse sections of different roots at different levels are illustrated. A, Asymmetrical diarch xylem, at 1200 μ. from base. B, Triarch stelar differentiation in same root 2400 μ further from the base than A. C, Monarch vascular arrangement in another root at 940 μ from base; phloem in arc round xylem. D, Same root as C, but at 1415 μ distal to it, showing diarch and nascent triarch xylem. E, Same root, 4,640 μ distal to D: and 920 μ below the apical meristem: a symmetrical triarch stele is being differentiated. F, Another experimental root with a monarch stele towards the basal region. G, Same root higher up, with symmetrical diarch structure. H, Diarch arrangement in another root at 2900 μ below apical meristem. At this level the transition to the triarch condition is taking place (new xylem elements are stippled and numbered 1, 2, 3 to indicate the centrifugal sequence of their maturation). (All × c. 130.) (After J. G. Torrey, *Amer. Jour. Bot.,* 1955.)

in others a small amount only; and in yet others, as in woody species, it may become extensive. In certain genera, e.g. *Eryngium* (Umbelliferae), some species, e.g. *E. pandanifolium*, *E. serra* and *E. bracteosum*, have roots of variable size: the smaller are tetrarch, while the larger ones have up to ten radiating xylem plates; but there is no secondary thickening (Fig. 10.14). In other species, e.g. *E. giganteum*, the primary diarch xylem soon becomes surrounded by an extensive development of secondary wood; and in *E. sanguisorba* the initial pentarch arrangement also becomes surrounded by a conspicuous secondary development (Fig. 10.14). In such materials,

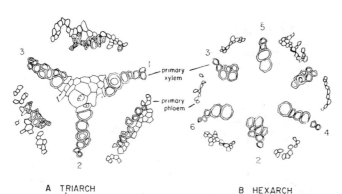

A TRIARCH   B HEXARCH

FIG. 10.13. Stelar pattern, regeneration and treatment with IAA in roots of *Pisum sativum*. A, B, Tracings of photographs of transverse sections of a pea root, taken at two different levels. The root tip had regenerated, in a culture medium containing 10^{-5}M IAA, after the distal o·5 mm. had been excised. A, The original triarch state of the root stele. B, A hexarch stele was differentiated in the regenerated distal region. (A, B, at same magnification.) (After J. G. Torrey, *Cell Organism and Milieu*, 1959.)

in which there is an interesting interplay between genetical factors and those more general physiological factors which are involved in the inception of primary pattern and secondary thickening in roots, there is evidently scope for further investigation (Wardlaw, 1928).

In woody species, such as *Pyrus* (the pear), which has been fully described and illustrated by Esau (1943, 1965a), there are many points of interest regarding the inception and activities of the vascular cambium, the formation and activities of a phellogen of pericyclic origin, the disruption of the endodermis and the eventual breaking-down and sloughing-off of the cortex. As a fact, our understanding of these individual problems of histogenesis is still inadequate. But beyond the specific problems, e.g. the inception and development of any particular cell type or tissue, there is a more general phenomenon, namely, that the system as a whole appears to be regulated, or self-regulated, so that the overall development is one which appears to be harmoniously integrated. One should, perhaps, attempt to investigate the possibility of complementary metabolic relationships between the several developing tissue systems. It is a remarkable fact that the activated pericycle contributes both to the vascular cambium and to the phellogen. How all this is brought about, and whether or not all the components of the resulting integrated tissue system are as highly functional and adaptive as is usually assumed, present themselves as problems to which more thought, leading to new kinds of work, might well be given.

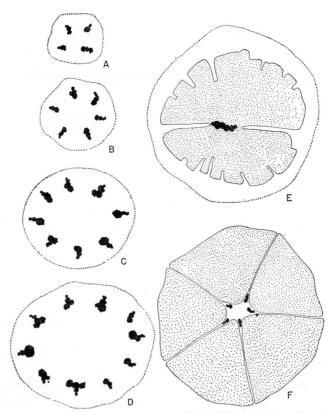

FIG. 10.14. Root steles in *Eryngium*. A, B, C, *Eryngium serra*, transverse section of steles from roots of different sizes (xylem, black; endodermis, surrounding broken line) (×60). D, *E. bracteosum*. Ten xylem groups are present in a stele of large size (×60). E, *E. giganteum*. In this species the roots are diarch and secondary thickening has taken place (×60). F, *E. sanguisorba*. A pentarch stele, with superimposed secondary thickening (×35). (In E, F the secondary xylem is stippled.) (After C. W. Wardlaw, *Trans. Roy. Soc., Edin.*, 1928.)

Both in herbaceous species, e.g. *Chamaenerion angustifolium*, and in woody species, the secondarily thickened root has an almost shoot-like appearance as seen in cross-section. In such organs shoot buds as well as roots may originate endogeneously. Again, in some herbaceous species the main root may undergo a remarkably extensive secondary thickening and function as an organ of storage, e.g. beet, carrot, etc.

LATERAL AND ADVENTITIOUS ROOTS

The formation of lateral roots, which typically originate from localized regions of active, or activated, growth in the pericycle, is illustrated in most standard texts. More extended anatomical and morphogenetic studies of these organs, in different groups of plants, reveal very considerable diversity.

In seed plants lateral roots, or rootlets, are usually, and typically, observed to be: (i) endogenous in origin; (ii) formed from the pericycle in the parent root; and (iii) some considerable distance away from the apical meristem. In pteridophytes lateral roots typically originate from the endodermis, though exceptions are known. The mode of formation of a lateral root may be described in terms of the visible anatomical features, or of growth. A combination of both is desirable. In anatomical studies of lateral root formation, e.g. in a dicotyledon, it can be seen that periclinal divisions begin in a small group of cells of the pericycle, closely followed, in the enlarging locus, by anticlinal divisions. This growing region begins to bulge outwards into the inner cortex and, with disruption of the endodermis and cortical tissues, thrusts its way through the cortex to emerge at the surface of the parent root. At an early stage the distal region of this lateral primordium becomes histologically organized as an apex, complete with a nascent root-cap. In some species cells of the endodermis and inner cortex may participate in the formation of the lateral root. (For details *see* Esau, 1965a.) In terms of growth, these same events may be envisaged as involving the inception of a discrete growth centre (pp. 103, 122) within or on the periphery of the stele, and the polarized growth and development of this centre so that a cylindrical organ is formed which thrusts its way outwards through the cortex. These developments are attended by: (i) a characteristic distribution of growth in the outer or distal region of the nascent primordium so that an apical meristem is organized, and (ii) the inception of a central vascular column below the apex, the differentiating vascular tissues becoming conjoined with those of the parent stele. When stated in these general terms the formation of a lateral root seems not unlike that of a bud, whether it be a normal axillary development, experimentally induced, or adventitious.

Now, let us assume that a lateral root originates as a pericyclic growth centre – the pericycle being itself a potentially meristematic tissue. So, we may inquire, how are endogenous loci of special metabolism determined? As we know, lateral roots often originate in the same radial plane as, and in contiguity with, a protoxylem group, or pole. But they may also originate opposite a protophloem pole, or between a protoxylem and a protophloem pole, as in diarch roots. As a result, the roots in some species occur in rows along the parent root. Moreover, as Esau (1940) reported in *Daucus carota*, additional lateral roots may develop at the base of the original lateral, as it were from an enlarged pericyclic growth centre.

The idea of rootlet growth centres in the pericycle suggests problems of considerable morphogenetic interest, not to say difficulty. In many species, growing under favourable soil conditions, the lateral roots typically emerge at some characteristic distance behind the apex. The growth centres must therefore have had their inception considerably closer to the apex, and lateral root development is probably regulated by the main apex. If the main root apex is cut off, or damaged, an outgrowth of lateral rootlets, often close to the point of excision, soon follows. In some aquatic angiosperms, e.g. *Pistia stratiotes* and *Eichornia crassipes*, the lateral roots actually emerge from the apical meristem (Clowes, 1961, p. 144), indicating that the growth centres must have been formed close to, or perhaps even within, the stelar histogen. In these developments the analogy with the inception of leaf growth centres in the shoot apical meristem suggests itself. In this connection the formation of fern roots – which would come within the definition of *adventitious* (see p. 272) – is of some interest. In this group the root primordia, each with its characteristic apical cell, originate endogenously at the bases of quite young leaf primordia, i.e. in the expanding region of the shoot apex. (*See also* the topic of *phyllorhize*, p. 385.)

The anatomical details of lateral root formation in various species, including those which soon become infected with mycorrhiza, and the contribution, or 'fate', of the pericycle in different instances, have been demonstrated by Berthon (1943), Schade and Guttenberg (1951) and Clowes (1950, 1961). The anatomical details enable a reasonable assessment of the distribution of growth in the developing root to be made.

As in phyllotaxis, it may be provisionally accepted that root-growth centres exist and that there are factors which regulate their location in the pericycle. But we still do not know the nature of these factors. Some observations suggest that hormonal substances are involved, but physical factors cannot be excluded. For example, if a root is bent experimentally the new rootlets typically grow out of the convex side. In some species the main roots show a periodicity in their development in that they have zones of lateral root formation. IAA and related substances are known to promote rootlet formation under experimental conditions. Torrey (1950) found that, in cultured excised roots of *Pisum*, IAA is necessary for the inception of lateral roots. He also noted that decapitated first transfer roots did not form 'laterals' after several days in culture. This observation suggests that a hormonal substance, normally supplied by the root apex, may be involved. In the seedling this substance may be supplied by the cotyledons. Torrey (1952, 1956) reported that, if the cotyledons are removed, lateral roots are not formed and that a substance derived from the cotyledons, and essential for lateral root formation, is destroyed by white light. Moreover, the induction of lateral roots by removing the main root apex can be inhibited by a short exposure to light. Cultural studies of excised roots have shown that cell division, leading to the formation of lateral roots, can be inhibited by the absence of a considerable range of substances, including IAA, nicotinic acid, thiamin and adenine. Decapitation experiments indicate that the root apex metabolizes an inhibitor which is translocated basipetally. Several substances are known which regulate the distance from the main apex at which lateral primordia will be formed. Collectively, these observations are consistent with the view that, in the locus of a lateral root, there is a localized reaction system in which there are the metabolic materials of growth and regulating substances.

ADVENTITIOUS ROOTS

Adventitious Roots. Definition. As a convenient usage, Esau (1965, p. 483) distinguishes the primary root system, established during embryogenesis and comprising the main root and its laterals, from roots which originate adventitiously in other ways, e.g. from the stem or from older roots. As defined by Clowes (1961, p. 164), *adventitious* roots are those formed on organs other than roots or out of their normal sequence.

In its endogenous origin, typically from the pericycle and adjacent tissues, in the relationship of its stele to that of the parent organ, and in its general organization and mode of growth and development, an adventitious root has much in common with a normal lateral root. However, it is especially in the formation of adventitious roots, both in Nature and as induced by various experimental treatments, that we encounter some of the morphological diversity to which reference was made at the beginning of this chapter.

Some of the most spectacular developments of adventitious roots have been obtained when shoots have been decapitated and the cut surface of the stem treated with various natural and synthetic growth substances, e.g. with substituted phenoxy compounds, etc. A remarkable induction of adventitious roots, usually originating in the enlarged pericycle, has often resulted. In treated bean plants, for example, a typical cross-section might show five or six roots in a small sector of the stem internode, growing centrifugally in the usual way, with a smaller number, originating inside the cambium, growing centripetally towards the pith (Fig. 10.15) (*see* Beal, 1946; and Wardlaw, 1952, for review). In experiments with *Phaseolus multiflorus*, Bentley (1950) found that when 2,3,6-trichlorobenzoic acid (TCBA) was applied in various ways local swellings were induced. When the epicotyl was excised and treated with TCBA, one of the cotyledonary

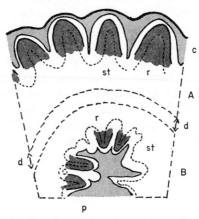

FIG. 10.15. Centrifugal and centripetal root induction in the bean (diagrammatic, combining two levels: tracings from photographs). A, Well-organized root formation in each ray in second internode 17 days after treatment with 2,4,5-trichlorophenoxyacetic acid in carbowax. B, Centripetal root formation in second internode 17 days after treatment with 2,4-dichlorophenoxyactic acid in carbowax. At this level less-well-organized roots had also been induced at the periphery. *d*, discontinuity between sections; *c*, cortex; *st*, stelar tissue; *r*, root; *p*, pith. (After J. M. Beal, *Bot. Gaz.*, 1945.)

buds developed as a knoblike, leafless, swollen structure. When this organ was examined as being of morphogenetic interest the short swollen axis showed a marked distension of the cortex as a result of the formation of a very large number of adventitious roots (Fig. 10.16). These roots were present right up to the apical region (Wardlaw, 1953c).

A rich literature deals with the formation and development of roots in woody and other cuttings. Indeed, a not inconsiderable part of our knowledge of factors in root formation is based on the study of adventitious roots.

Went and Thimann (1937) explored in some detail the process of root formation as distinct from root development. Their studies showed that root formation is a complex process in which many factors are involved, including the action of auxin and other specific substances such as biotin, the utilization of carbohydrates and, not least important, the action of an internal factor of unknown nature, specific to the organism. It has been established that whereas auxin, over a wide range of concentrations, promotes the formation of roots, high concentrations may inhibit their subsequent elongation.

Since the time of Sachs many investigators have ascribed root formation in cuttings to the accumulation of special metabolic substances near the basal cut surface. It is known that rapidly growing buds actively promote root formation, whereas dormant buds do not; and the removal of growing buds stops root formation almost completely. These developments were attributed to the downward movement through the phloem of a hormone or hormones (Van der Lek, 1925). This investigator also distinguished between roots which developed from pre-existent primordia and others which were induced by the experimental treatment. This root-forming substance, which is produced by leaves in the light, and typically moves basipetally, is the *rhizocaline* of Bouillenne and Went (1933) and Bouillenne (1938). In their view, it is also stored in the cotyledons. Němĕc (1934) described these special substances as *rhizogenes*. From extensive experimental observations it is now known that root induction is due to a specific substance formed in the actively growing young leaves, in fact to auxin (IAA). When IAA is applied to cut surfaces of shoots and roots, and to the intact tissues of many plants, there is usually a notable increase in root formation. Natural substances from many different sources – urine, pollen grains, fungi, bacteria, leaves, etc. – are active in root formation. As some of these substances are now known to be identical with auxin, special terms such as rhizocaline have become unnecessary.

In physiological concentrations auxin is typically polar in its movement (but *see* p. 298). By means of ringing experiments Cooper (1936) showed that it descends in the shoot by way of the phloem. According to Went and Thimann (1937, p. 192), 'all substances which act as auxins are, so far as they have been tested, also active in promoting root formation'.[1]

---

[1] 'Thimann showed that indene-3-acetic and coumaryl-1-acetic acids, which are active in promoting growth but appear to be poorly transported, are also active in root formation. Their activity is, however, largely local, and is best exerted when applied at the base of the test cuttings. Phenylacetic acid, found to be active in root formation by Zimmerman and Wilcoxon, was shown to act as an auxin by Haagen-smit and Went. α-Naphthaleneacetic acid is also active for both functions. Indole-3-carboxylic acid, on the other hand, is inactive for both functions, while indole-3-propionic acid has very low activity both for growth promotion and root formation' (Went and Thimann, 1937, where literature is cited).

ROOT BUDS

An intriguing morphogenetic phenomenon is the development of buds from roots. To the practising horticulturist, it is sometimes a menace, some of his most 'noxious weeds' being freely propagated by this means. We rather take for granted the formation of roots from shoots, for indeed it is a commonplace; but the formation of shoots from roots impresses one as being somewhat out of the ordinary. Yet, as noted above, it is not so very uncommon: a considerable but in no sense large number of species are characterized by the formation of buds on roots.

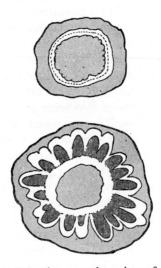

FIG. 10.16. Profuse root induction near the apices of the cotyledonary buds of *Phaseolus multiflorus*, as seen in transverse section, as a result of treatment with 2,3,6-trichlorobenzoic acid. The cotyledonary buds became greatly swollen, knoblike, leafless structures. Profuse root formation had taken place right up into the apical region. Above: normal stem structure; stelar tissue unshaded. (After C. W. Wardlaw, *New Phytol.*, 1953.)

Buds may develop, often endogenously, on roots of different age and anatomical structure (Figs. 10.17–10.19). Murray (1957) showed that root buds in creeping alfalfa originate exogeneously in the callus-like growth formed from the phellogen. Buds may originate endogenously like roots, but they often occur in association with the basal region of lateral root primordia, as in *Linaria vulgaris* (Charlton, 1965), horse-radish, etc. (Fig. 10.18). Esau (1965, p. 515, quoting a Russian worker) stated that: 'If a bud arises in the pericycle, the vascular connection with the initiating root is formed by acropetal differentiation; if the bud is initiated near the surface, vascular differentiation is basipetal.' Not all root buds originate in or near the pericycle; or in association with the bases of lateral roots. In *Ophioglossum vulgatum*, in which most of the new plants originate from root buds, the latter are either derived from segments of the apical meristem, or they originate endogenously in the middle cortex (*see* p. 189 *and* Fig. 10.17). Clowes (1961) specified this tissue as being one in which growth takes place very actively. In the cortex in *O. vulgatum* individual cells, or a small group of them, become densely protoplasmic and meristematic, forming

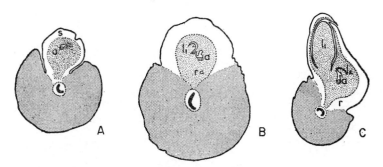

FIG. 10.17. Root buds in *Ophioglossum vulgatum*. A–C, Transverse sections of mature regions of roots, showing experimentally induced buds. The bud apex *a*, its first and second leaves, l_1 and l_2, and its root, *r*, are indicated. The endogenous nature of the induced buds is clearly shown, the bud, with its outer sheath, *s*, having been formed from a sector of the cortical parenchyma An incipient vascular strand traverses the inner cortex between the bud and the root stele. (Figs. A, B ($\times 20$); Fig. C ($\times 12$.) (After C. W. Wardlaw, *Annals of Botany*, 1953.)

spheroidal or ellipsoidal masses of small cells. In these meristematic masses a shoot apex and first leaf are differentiated, soon to be followed by the inception of the first root (Wardlaw, 1953, 1954). The new bud thus formed does not stand in any obligatory positional relationship with the root stele (Fig. 10.17). Sahni (1917) stated that, in *Platycerium* spp. and in *Asplenium esculentum*, the root apex may be transformed directly into a leafy bud.

A further interesting example of the inception of root buds has been reported in *Alliaria officinalis* (Fig. 10.19) by Champagnat *et al.* (1962). The formation and distribution in the soil of roots and root buds – an important aspect of 'whole root morphogenesis' – is illustrated for *Euphorbia esula* in Fig. 10.21.

ROOT MORPHOLOGY IN SWAMP PLANTS

Students who have been introduced to tropical ecology will almost certainly be aware of the curious root developments – the pneumatophores – of mangroves, i.e. of plants of the brackish, or saline, tidal regions of muddy estuaries. These morphological developments, usually referred to as adaptations, include the negatively geotropic roots, which emerge from the mud in great numbers in species such as *Avicennia africana*, the knee-roots of

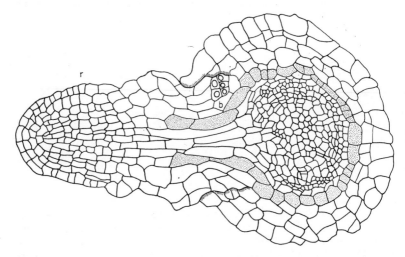

FIG. 10.18. *Linaria vulgaris*: the inception of a root bud (*b*) at the base of a lateral root *r*. The bud begins with active division in a cell, or cells, close to the point of emergence of a lateral root from the pericycle of the parent root stele. The parental root is seen in cross-section, with its endodermis stippled. The boundary of the lateral and parent root is hatched. (Drawing by courtesy of Dr. A. C. Charlton.)

other mangrove species, etc. However, since many tropical forests are fresh-water swamp forests, comprising a great diversity of species, it is perhaps surprising that observations on aerotropic roots are relatively scanty. Species with stilt, or prop, roots are, of course, conspicuous in such forests. A recent paper by Jenik (1967), in which the morphology of aerotropic roots is described, is germane to this chapter. This investigator has shown that some West African tree species growing in swampy soils deficient in oxygen have pneumatophores comparable with those known in mangroves (Fig. 10.20). *Anthocleista nobilis* (Loganiaceae) has negatively geotropic roots of the second order which grow vertically upwards from horizontal main roots and rise some 30 cm. above the level of the water-

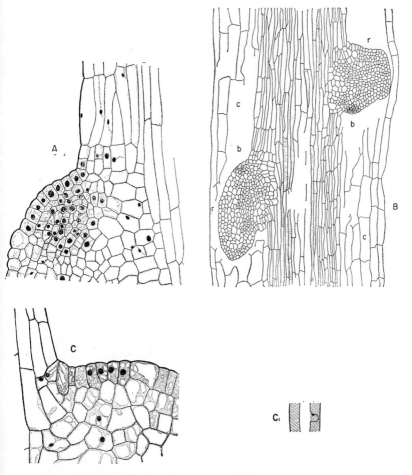

FIG. 10.19. *Alliaria officinalis*: the inception and development of root buds. A, a bud originating superficially on the basal region of a lateral root. B, Two young lateral roots (*r*), still within the cortex (*c*), with buds (*b*) on the upper and lower sides of the two rootlets. C, A very young, superficial, adventive, rootlet bud. C1, Shows the state of development of the rootlet and bud within the parental root cortex. (After M. Champagnat, J. Marichal, and C. Vincent, *Bull. Soc. Bot. France*, 1962.)

logged soil. These pneumatophores resemble those of the mangrove *Avicennia* spp., both in external form and in their internal open, aeration tissue. However, similar developments have not been observed in other *Anthocleista* species. The palm *Raphia hookeri* has branched erect pneumatophores (Fig. 10.20 A–D).

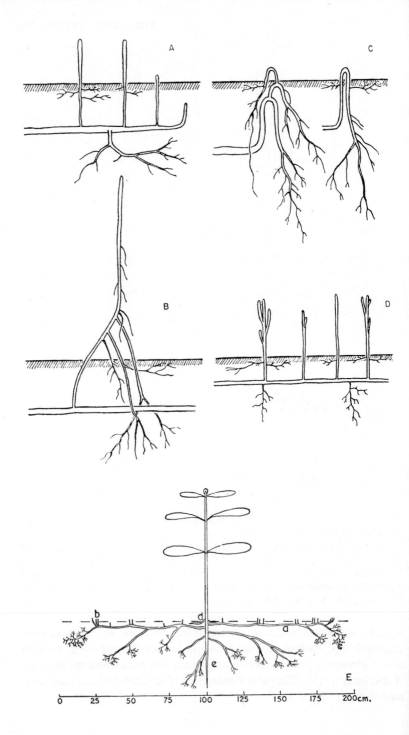

Another arborescent swamp species, *Xylopia staudtii* (Annonaceae), shows some very unusual and, indeed, peculiar root developments. From horizontal roots, deeply set in the mud, slender secondary laterals, without secondary thickening at any stage, grow upwards to a height of two metres above the soil surface. On these erect roots lateral roots grow outwards and downwards, with further branching, so that, eventually, a bushy development of rootlets is present in the soil at and below the parental horizontal root. These 'stilt pneumatophores' present some very peculiar features. For example, the erect root remains very thin and sometimes climbs on to other vegetation. Moreover, the cortex is very thin and devoid of air spaces, and the vascular tissue apparently affords little scope for gaseous movement. The assumed physiological function and adaptive value of these pneumatophores and, indeed, the whole of this unusual sequence of morphogenetic developments call for a full investigation (Fig. 10.20 B).

Richards (1952) and Jenik (1967) have described two fresh-water swamp species, *Mitragyna ciliata* (Rubiaceae) and *Symphonia globulifera* (Guttiferae), in which knee-roots, well known in some mangrove species, are formed. The characteristic morphology of these knee-roots is the result of the negatively geotropic growth of a deeply seated horizontal root, followed by curvature and downward growth. The upper loop-like region may, or may not, be exposed to the air as a result of erosion of the top layer of soil or mud. Usually the loop protrudes only a few centimetres above ground. In some instances new negatively geotropic branches are formed at the top of the loop, so that a multiple knee-root system results. On the face of it, the amount of root exposure to the air, in relation to the considerable amount of growth involved, seems small, and one may well have some suspension of judgement as to the extent to which these curious developments can be regarded as adaptations. A deeper insight into the relevant morphogenetic processes may have an important impact on this aspect of biological thought. However, Jenik concluded that the several root 'adaptations' studied have an important function in the aeration of organs deeply buried in water-logged soils.

FIG. 10.20. Some examples of root morphology in W. African fresh-water swamp species. (A) *Anthocleista nobilis*: simple, negatively geotropic pneumatophores (like those of the mangroves, *Avicennia* spp.). (B) *Xylopia staudtii*: stilt pneumatophore. (C) *Mitragyna ciliata* and *Symphonia ciliata*: simple and compound knee-roots, as in some mangrove species. (D) *Raphia hookeri*: simple and branched erect pneumatophores. (After J. Jenik, *Jour. Linn. Soc. Lond.*, 1967.) (E) *Mitragyna stipulosa*; seedling root system. *a*, lateral horizontal roots; *b*, young vertical pneumatophores; *c*, fibrous absorbing rootlets; *d*, primary adventitious roots; *e*, anchoring roots. (After J. McCarthy, *Phytomorphology*, **12**, 1962.)

SUMMATION AND OUTLOOK

Although root formation can be induced in tissue cultures in which there
are no leafy shoots (*see* p. 203), and although excised roots can be grown
virtually indefinitely in liquid culture, they do not exist as things apart in

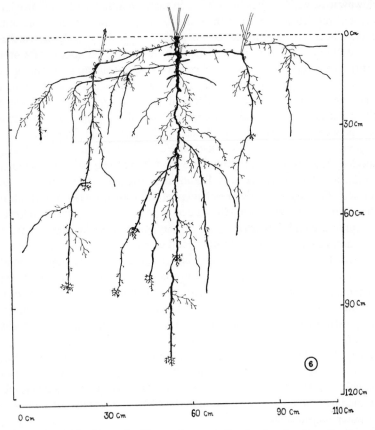

FIG. 10.21. *Euphorbia esula.* Formation and distribution in the soil of roots
and buds. The illustration shows diagrammatically the root system developed
by a seedling. The primary root in the centre shows sympodial growth.
(Roots, in black; buds and shoots, clear outlines.) (After M. V. S. Raju,
T. A. Steeves and R. T. Coupland, *Canad. Jour. Bot.*, 1963.)

Nature: invariably they are part of an integrated unified organism. In
some ferns this integrated development is so close and constant that, as a
typical condition, one root is present at the base of each leaf primordium;
and so also for some aquatic plants such as *Alisma plantago*. Such observations provided the basis of the Phyllorhize Theory of Chauveaud (1921),

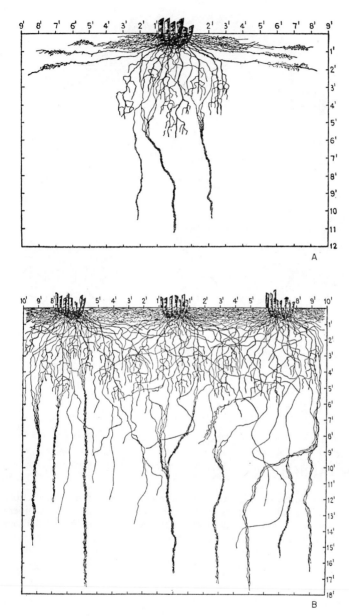

FIG. 10.22. Root distribution in Sugar Cane (*Saccharum* sp.). A, Root system in var. POJ 2727. B, Root system of ordinary Uba cane. (After H. Evans, *Emp. Jour. Exper. Agric.*, 1936.)

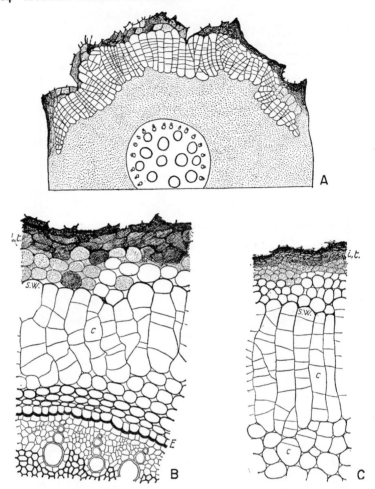

FIG. 10. 23. *Musa* sp. The reactivity of root tissues. Transverse sections of roots in which the outer cortical tissues have reacted by a considerable cambiform formation and suberization to the inroads of fungal pathogens. A, In the Cavendish variety. B, C, In the Gros Michel variety. *i.t.*, decayed invaded tissue; *s.w.*, suberized walls. *c*, cambiform tissue; *E*, endodermis. (B ×210; C ×90.) (After C. W. Wardlaw, *Annals of Botany*, 1930.)

stemming from Gaudichaud (1841), who wrote a paper on 'Recherches générales sur l'organographie' (*see* Wardlaw, 1965a). Roots, however adventitious and erratic their formation may often appear to be, truly pertain to the orderly and harmonious growth of the individual. These matters are more fully considered in Chapter XIV, where root formation, in its several correlative aspects, is seen as an essential part of whole plant morphogenesis. But, after all, what is it that makes roots roots? And shoots shoots? How can we account for such very different organizations, present at the poles of the same axis? Not least, the adaptiveness of roots calls for critical reappraisal.

In this chapter only a few of the manifold problems of root inception and development and, not least, of their distribution in the soil, or other aspects of their environment, have been considered. In agriculture and horticulture the growth and distribution of the root system, as in the sugar cane (Fig. 10.22), are of paramount importance in securing high yields, the economic use of fertilizers and so on. Roots are also subject to the inroads of nematodes, bacteria and fungi, and in some instances, as shown in Fig. 10.23, react in active and characteristic ways to such attacks.

In conclusion, root studies, from which morphogenesis cannot be excluded, may be troublesome – they usually are – but they are worth the effort.

Additional Note on the Quiescent Centre in Maize. F. A. L. Clowes and B. E. Juniper (*Jour. Exper. Bot.*, 15, 622, 1964) compared the fine structure of cells in the quiescent centre with that of contiguous cells of the meristem. The former were characterized by the lowest number of mitochondria and by the smallest nuclei, nucleoli and Golgi bodies.

CHAPTER XI

The Differentiation of Tissues

INTRODUCTION

Biologists have been known to disagree about the meaning, or significance, of the term *differentiation*. Perhaps there is an element of understatement here! Basically, as used in biology, the word *differentiate* simply means *to make or become different* in the process of development (*Oxford English Dictionary*). Specialized functional significance is usually attributed to the products of differential development in tissues, as in the formation of sieve-tubes, tracheids, fibres, endodermis, storage parenchyma, etc. The act or process of *differentiation* is of great interest to the student of development, in that more or less conspicuous differences may appear between cells of the same lineage, i.e. cells derived at first, second or third hand from one embryonic mother cell. It would have indeed been surprising if the process of tissue differentiation had not attracted the attention of anatomists from the outset, not only because it is a normal occurrence in the developing cells of embryos and of shoot, leaf and root apices but also because it typically results in a distinctive and specific tissue pattern. The more highly evolved the organism, the greater is the range of specialized cells differentiated during ontogenesis.

During cellular differentiation, *tissue systems*, which are characteristic of the species, and of great beauty because of the regularity, variety and symmetry of their geometric patterns, are formed. These tissue patterns, e.g. as seen in a cross-section of a stem or root, have been variously interpreted. They are held to be functionally necessary, as they undoubtedly are, though perhaps not always in the manner, or in the high degree, that has been ascribed to them. They have been regarded as the result of an evolutionary division of labour in the interests of the functional economy and perpetuation of the species. But they may, as the writer thinks, be envisaged as the result of complementary physico-chemical processes, i.e. physiological processes during the differential development of contiguous embryonic cells. In this view, so well expressed by D. Thoday (1939), the concept of *functional harmony* during development would replace the older concept of *division of labour*. Long ago, Vöchting stated that any particular cell differentiates as it does because of its position in the plant, e.g. superficial, sub-surface, internal, etc. This idea is still acceptable, but it can probably be taken farther and, indeed, put into a new context (*see* p. 49). Differentiation is normally a process in which order prevails, i.e. differentiating cells typically give rise to a characteristic holistic tissue pattern. So, we may say, a cell differentiates as it does because *it is part of a pattern*. This pattern is the result of the functioning of a unitary reaction system.

Geneticists, supported by cytological skills, have become increasingly interested in the mechanisms of cellular differentiation. As genes are involved in all development, they must participate in the determination of specific differentiation. As already noted (p. 258), it was formerly held that all embryonic cells, e.g. in a shoot or root apical meristem, are cytologically and genetically identical, and that they are totipotent up to the point where some irreversible state of differentiation has been established. In general, this view has been sustained, but evidence has accumulated which is indicative of both cytological and genetical changes during early differentiation. The typical diploid nuclei in some of the cells of a root apex may become variously polyploid as differentiation proceeds (p. 261). Geneticists have elaborated ideas regarding the possible serial, or sequential, action of genes, whereby contiguous embryonic cells, of the same cell lineage, are induced to follow different 'metabolic pathways', with consequential formation of different kinds of cells, e.g. a specialized endodermal cell as compared with a parenchyma cell of the inner cortex. But however we may ascribe the differentiation of embryonic cells to genetical and biochemical factors and to spatial, or positional, relationships in the plant – as indeed we must – we are still confronted with basic processes which are essentially, though specifically, biophysical. At every stage during the growth and development of an embryonic cell, e.g. in the differentiation of a tracheid or root hair, we are concerned with an energy system: forces are acting on matter, moving it round, sometimes seemingly at random, at other times to definite locations, as in the patterned deposition of lignin in tracheids; and the eventual physical reality, at the visual level, i.e. the differentiated cell which we can observe under the microscope, is both a biochemical and a biophysical phenomenon. So also are such important morphogenetic phenomena as polarized development, differential growth, the manner of cell division, the shapes of tissue masses and so on. Some environmental factors which affect growth and differentiation are essentially physical factors, e.g. temperature, light, gravity, etc.; and they are ever-present and pervasive. Accordingly, in his studies of tissue differentiation, the percipient anatomist will constantly bear in mind that what he sees by using ordinary light, phase-contrast or electron microscopy has cytogenetical, biochemical, biophysical, ecological, geometrical and organismal aspects. Thus envisaged, plant anatomy and histology, sometimes derided as old fashioned, outmoded and dull, usually by those whose competence in it is distressingly meagre, are seen to occupy an integrative and essential position in any serious study of developmental botany.

BASIC FEATURES OF CELL DIFFERENTIATION

Some of the basic features of cell differentiation have already been discussed in preceding chapters. If, as a convenient over-simplification, we assume that all the embryonic cells of the shoot apical meristem are essentially alike, or equivalent, then the successive processes leading to the adult, fully differentiated cell include: (1) the establishment of polarity in a meristematic cell; (2) the sequential formation of general and specific enzymes, proteins, etc., some of these processes being associated with particular organelles, which may also be in a state of change; (3) vacuolation and wall extension and growth; (4) differential growth whereby a cell may remain parenchymatous, i.e. approximately equidimensional, or become elongated, or branched, or of semi-irregular outline, interlocking with other cells as in the epidermal cells of leaves of dicotyledons, and so on; (5) the particular development of certain organelles, etc., e.g. of chloroplasts in the more superficial cells; (6) various modifications of the nucleus, including its degeneration; (7) the development of special features in the cell wall, e.g. the formation of sieve-plates, the pattern of lignification in tracheids, tracheae, etc. In relation to differentiation, it used to be said that each species has a 'specific substance': today it seems more appropriate to say that it has a specific system. (For an account of the cytological basis of differentiation, see Buvat, 1965.)

In the *Encyclopedia of Plant Physiology*, Vol. XV, 1965, considerable sections are devoted to cytogenetical, environmental, histological, cytochemical, physiological and physical aspects of differentiation. In scientific investigations it is an evident convenience to separate out these several aspects for individual treatment; but in Nature they are all interrelated in some degree. In this short book, as the reader will appreciate, only a few aspects of tissue differentiation can be considered; but it is hoped that the examples cited will give an idea of how the problems are being envisaged and solved.

GENES AND DIFFERENTIATION

Genic action, being pervasive, is involved in the differentiation of tissue systems and of individual specialized cells. Mather (1965) has stated that genes are the essential agents in the determination and control of development, as distinct from the process itself; and he has emphasized that wherever the causation of permanent differences in development and differentiation can be traced, differences in the nuclear genes have typically, and usually, been found to be involved. Of course, in parenthesis, one should perhaps note that *determination* is also a process, though perhaps of a special kind.

The relative importance of nucleus and cytoplasm in differentiation has been much discussed, and variously emphasized, by different investigators and need not be repeated here (*but see* Wardlaw, 1952, 1965a; Sinnott, 1960; Mather, 1948, 1965). Cells formed by the division of the zygote and in the young embryo, and also in the several meristematic regions, follow different metabolic pathways, and so become differentiated in characteristic ways. According to the circumstances, and in different degrees, either the nucleus or the cytoplasm, or both, are directly involved in these changes. As already noted, differential changes in embryonic cells, whether studied by the physiologist or the cytogeneticist, have been ascribed to regulated serial, or sequential, changes in the system (p. 121). (When viewed with detachment, one can hardly fail to note that each kind of scientist seems to be preoccupied with his own particular mode of interpretation, often to the more or less complete exclusion of other interpretations.) As a working hypothesis, let us accept that differentiation is a progressive process, involving the sequential evocation of genes, which then become the determining and controlling agents; and that these phenomena are quite inseparable from the biochemistry and biophysics of the developing system – i.e. everything that takes place does so in conformity with the laws of chemistry and physics. However, other views, based on histological observations, have also been stated explicitly. Thus Bloch (1965, p. 149) has expressed doubts on the view that differentiation and histological pattern, in normal development, can be ascribed to some precise 'sorting-out' mechanism, i.e. to an orderly evocation of genetical change. To quote: 'Cellular diversity is not truly genetic, at least not nucleo-genetic, in nature, but is, to all appearance, a form of modulation or modification of cytoplasmic potentialities under a variety of conditions.' As it seems to the writer, we have to deepen our comprehension of these phenomena to accommodate: (i) the genetical aspect, which is undeniable, since, as a fact, we do observe specific histological characters; (ii) the organismal aspect, e.g. relating to the position occupied by a cell in the plant; and (iii) the physiochemical aspect, which is fundamental unless we believe that science is really divided, in some absolute way, into biological and physical science.

K

PLANES OF CELL DIVISION AND DIFFERENTIATION

In texts dealing with anatomy and cellular differentiation emphasis is usually placed on cell formation in the meristem, the cell lineages which can be traced to this region, and the rates and planes of cell division (*see*

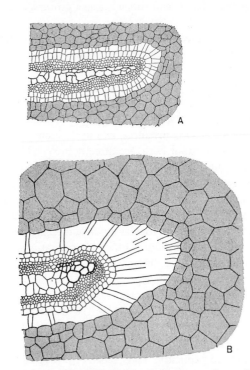

FIG. 11.1. A, B, *Selaginella Wallichii* (×70). Cross-sections of the stem from the apex downwards, showing how localized differential growth can affect the histological pattern. As development proceeds in the subapical region of the shoot (A), cells of the inner cortex grow more rapidly than do those of the stele: hence the stele becomes suspended in a cavity (or lacuna) by drawn-out cells, or trabeculae; the latter, in fact, being modified endodermal cells (B). Section A was taken close to the apex: the cells of the inner cortex, endodermis and pericycle were still of approximately the same size. (After C. W. Wardlaw, *Trans. Roy. Soc. Edin.*, 1925.)

Bloch, 1965, for an up-to-date account of this aspect). What the anatomist portrays in his illustrations are the resultant effects of the action of several factors. In particular, these include: (i) the factors which determine the distribution, localization and utilization of the materials of growth; and (ii) physical factors which become incident in the growing organism, e.g.

the compressive and tensile stresses which develop as a result of normal enlargement and of different rates of growth in contiguous tissues. Such differential developments can be observed in the individual cell, e.g. the particular region of a piliferous layer cell in which a root hair grows out. They can also be observed in whole tissues, e.g. in the characteristic cross-sectional contours of the shoot stele due to the compressive stresses exercised on the incipient vascular tissue by the rapidly enlarging cells of the pith and cortex. The effects of different rates of growth in contiguous tissues are particularly well seen in the trabecular development of the

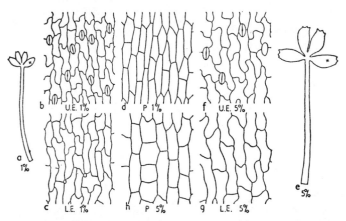

FIG. 11.2. *Marsilea drummondii*. Various aspects of the histological organization of a leaf are determined by nutritional and other physiological factors during growth and development. The effect of transfer of sporeling plants from a medium containing 1 per cent glucose to a medium with 5 per cent is here illustrated. *a, b, c, d*, third leaf before transfer, with upper and lower epidermis of lamina, from part marked X, and epidermis of petiole. *e, f, g, h*, Corresponding figures for the second leaf formed after transfer. (Leaves ×2·5. Epidermis ×157.) (After A. Allsopp, *Annals of Botany*, 1954.)

endodermis in species of *Selaginella*. In the shoot of *Selaginella*, just below the apical meristem, the cells which will later differentiate as the inner cortex, the endodermis and the pericycle are all of approximately equal size. However, slightly lower down in the axis the distribution of growth, and the utilization of metabolic materials, is such that the cells of the inner cortex begin to develop into large parenchymatous cells, whereas the enlargement of the nascent endodermal and stelar cells is relatively slight. As a natural consequence, a considerable cavity develops round the stele and the endodermal cells become radially stretched and tangentially separated into long trabeculae (Fig. 11.1). Somewhat comparable developments are to be seen in the aerenchyma in aquatic species.

All of the foregoing is as much as to say that, in our studies of planes and rates of cell division and of cellular differentiation, we must consider some fundamental but still insufficiently understood aspects of growth. Near the apex of the leaf of a dicotyledon, for example, the nascent epidermal cells are approximately equidimensional. But during their further growth they

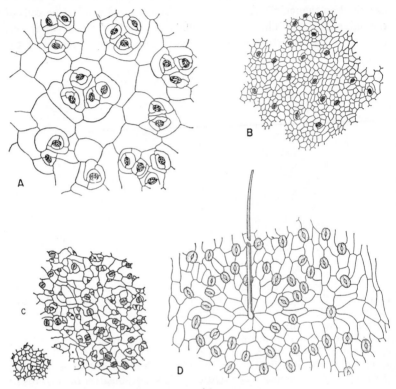

FIG. 11.3. Examples of the differentiation and distribution of stomata and hairs. A, *Begonia semperflorens*. B, *Bougainvillea spectabilis*. C, *Alliaria officinalis*. D, *Pulsatilla*. (From several authors after E. Bünning, *Encyclopedia of Plant Physiology*, XV/I, 1965.)

not only develop as a curiously interlocking system of lobed cells, with a special superficial wall layer, the cuticle, but they also exemplify the inception of a new histological pattern in that some cells of the epidermal layer become specially differentiated as stomata, epidermal hairs, glands, etc. These differential epidermal developments have a taxonomic, i.e. genetical aspect (Stace, 1965); also a nutritional aspect, as demonstrated by Allsopp (Fig. 11.2); and a physico-chemical aspect, as discussed in some detail by Bünning (Fig. 11.3) (1948, 1965). Similar considerations apply to the differentiation of fibres, sclereids, laticiferous cells, etc. Standard works on plant anatomy acquire an enhanced interest when their valuable factual records are re-examined in this comprehensive manner.

THE DIFFERENTIATION OF THE VASCULAR TISSUES

The inception of vascular tissues is typically, though not invariably, associated with the active meristems of shoots, leaves, roots, etc. (*see* p. 118). It is a reasonable assumption that a region of active utilization of metabolic materials and of water, e.g. the apical meristem of a fern-leaf primordium sets up lines of tension in the differentiating tissues below; and it may be that the general contour of the nascent vascular tissue is primarily 'blocked out' in this way. It may also be supposed that such nascent, or incipient, vascular tissue affords a pathway for the downward movement of substances, e.g. auxin, synthesized in apical regions. In brief, although in the normal development of a shoot or leaf the actual differentiation of vascular tissues is typically acropetal, the proximate causation is basipetal. There are some classical instances, e.g. in the development of superficial adventitious buds, in which the differentiation of vascular tissues to the point of conjunction with existing vascular tissues is basipetal (Fig. 7.19, p. 163).

The general idea given above also enables us to resolve the old controversy as to whether the vascular system of the shoot is chiefly cauline, i.e. of shoot origin, or mainly due to the decurrent leaf traces. According to the activity of the meristem, so will the associated vascular tissue, whether cauline or foliar, be strongly or feebly developed.

The differentiation of the vascular tissues, especially xylem and phloem and, of course, the potential or sustained meristematic activities of other stelar tissues such as the cambium and pericycle, have received much attention at the hands of anatomists, experimental morphologists and, more recently, of electron microscopists. Here it will be taken for granted that readers are familiar with the differentiation of the vascular tissues in the major organs of vascular plants. Excellent accounts are available in recent books by Esau (1965a, b).

The Regeneration of Severed Xylem. More than fifty years ago Simon (1908) showed that if an internodal vascular strand in *Coleus hybridus* was severed by making a small notch in an angle of the stem (of square cross-section) a new strand of lignified elements was differentiated basipetally in the pith parenchyma so that the severed ends were once more in continuity. The regeneration strand followed the contour of the incision. An actively dividing cambiform tissue was typically formed round the lignified strand.

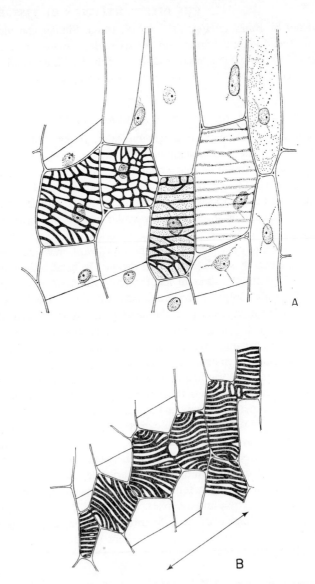

FIG. 11.4. *Coleus hybridus.* The differentiation of regenerative vascular tissue. A, Part of an incipient vascular strand in a wounded stem, showing the division of pith cells, with a reticulate cytoplasmic pattern on the inner walls; this provides the basis for the subsequent lignification. B, Part of a regenerative xylem strand in the pith of a wounded stem, showing the pattern of wall thickening. (*See* text.) (After E. W. Sinnott and R. Bloch, *Proc. Nat. Acad. Sci. Wash.,* 1944; *Amer. Jour. Bot.,* 1945.)

Similarly, in *Achyranthes Verschaffeltii* Simon demonstrated that when the whole vascular system was incised, leaving only an 'isthmus' of central pith, there was again a basipetal differentiation of lignified elements through the plug of pith parenchyma, so that the upper and lower ends of the severed strands were again conjoined. These, and similar researches by other workers, in particular by Kaan Albest (1934), were, in time, to prepare the way for a most fascinating and important sequence of discoveries. For reasons of space, these must here be treated selectively (*but see* Wardlaw, 1965e).

In investigations by Sinnott and Bloch (1944, 1945) the regeneration of severed internodal vascular strands in *Coleus hybridus* was observed in close histological detail. The earlier findings of Simon and others were fully confirmed and, in addition, observations of very considerable significance were made. Thus they showed that the parenchymatous cells lying in the potential pathway of the regenerative strand became more densely cytoplasmic and there was active division in the cells contiguous with this pathway (Fig. 11.4). In agreement with the findings of earlier workers (*see* Bloch, 1965), they noted that cytoplasmic patterns, or configurations, developed on the cell walls in the pathway and afforded the basis for the eventual pattern of lignification in the regeneration tracheids. The major wall pores in the line of tracheidal cells were aligned, the antecedent cytoplasmic bands having formed a continuous system from cell to cell (Fig. 11.4). The various developments are indicative of the incidence of physical and chemical factors.

The phenomena associated with experimentally induced differentiation of vascular tissue are also exemplified by the differentiation of the channels of translocation established between a phanerogamic parasite, such as *Cuscuta* sp., and its host (Fig. 11.5). As illustrated by Thomson (1925), the invasive haustorial filaments make contact with elements of the host's vascular system, and thereafter there is a demonstrable lignification of the filaments backwards from the host tissues to the haustorium.

Induced Vascular Strands. Investigations of the general phenomena of vascular differentiation were taken further by Camus (1943, 1949). He observed that when a bud of chicory (*Cichorium* sp.) was grafted into the phloem region of a piece of root tissue growing in culture the bud stimulated a basipetal induction of a strand of vascular tissue below it, suggesting a downward movement of substance(s) and an upward movement of metabolites. Wetmore (1954) successfully grafted buds of *Syringa vulgaris* into *completely undifferentiated callus tissue*. Though without roots the buds grew into normal plants some 2 cm. in height; i.e. the active apex was evidently drawing metabolic materials from the callus, itself growing in a

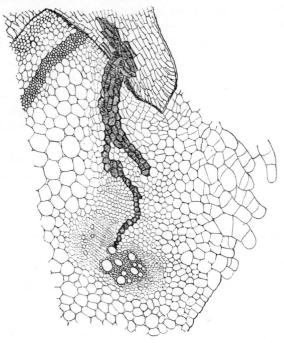

FIG. II.5. Transverse section of a stem of *Cucurbita maxima* invaded by a haustorium of *Cuscuta reflexa* (seen in l.s.). Filaments ('hyphae') from the haustorium have penetrated the interfascicular cambium and have reached the host wood vessels. The cells of the filament have become lignified from the host vessels back to the haustorium. No phloem elements have been differentiated. (×44.) (After J. Thomson, *Trans. Roy. Soc. Edinb.*, 1925.)

culture medium of known composition. But there must also have been a downward movement of a 'histogenic' substance, or substances, since numerous tracheidal vascular strands, constituting a pattern, were induced in the hitherto undifferentiated callus (Fig. 11.6).

Auxin and Xylem Differentiation. Meanwhile, a different but related line of research was being followed by Jacobs (1952, 1954, 1959, 1961) and Jacobs and Morrow (1957). They successfully demonstrated that indoleacetic acid (IAA) is causally involved, in a quantitative manner, in the differentiation of the normal and induced xylem strands in *Coleus*. In regeneration experiments of the kind already described, and in other related investigations, they showed that there is a close relationship between the amount of IAA passing downwards from actively growing young leaves and the amount of xylem, i.e. number of wood vessels, differentiated. A

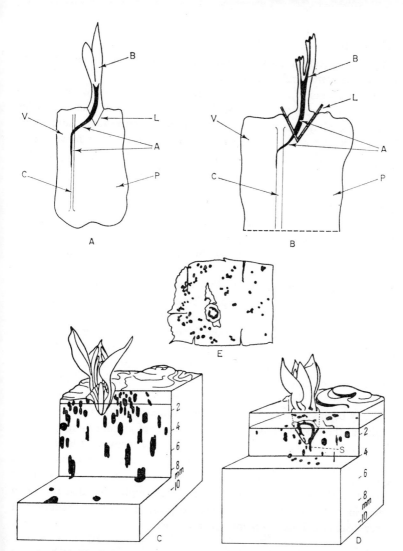

FIG. 11.6. A, B, Chicory (*Cichorium* sp.). A, Effect of a bud (*B*) grafted in to the phloem region (*P*) of a piece of root tissue grown in culture: the bud has stimulated the development of vascular tissue below it, i.e. probably in relation to the basipetal movement of a growth substance and the upward movement of metabolic substances. B, A similar experiment, but here a sheet of cellophane, *L*, was placed between the bud and the tissue below. The same effect was induced, i.e. organic continuity was not essential. *V*, vascular parenchyma; *C*, cambium; *A*, histologically altered tissue; *L*, line of contact between bud and stock, in B with cellophane (double line). (After G. Camus, from E. W. Sinnott, *Plant Morphogenesis*, 1960.)

C, D, E, *Syringa vulgaris*. When a bud was grafted into a quite undifferentiated mass of callus tissue, growing in aseptic culture, a basipetal differentiation of vascular tissue was induced. C and D show (diagrammatically) the relation of the bud to the induced vascular strands as seen in longitudinal section; and E the relationship in transverse section; tracheidal tissue, black. (After R. H. Wetmore and S. Sorokin, *Jour. Arnold Arboretum*, 1955.)

comparable effect on xylem differentiation was observed in experiments in which a synthetic auxin was applied.

Further points of considerable interest emerged from the closely controlled experiments and full anatomical observations of Jacobs and his co-workers. They found, for example, that not all of the auxin from a leaf-base moves downwards in the shoot: about one-third of it moves in an acropetal direction. This is a very intriguing observation. It suggests that young leaves close to the apical meristem, by contributing acropetally moving auxin, may exercise regulative effects on the growth and organogenic activity of the shoot apical meristem in which they themselves originated – an example of a reciprocal relationship in development. The regulative effects of older leaf primordia on younger ones was also demonstrated by Wardlaw (1949) using surgical techniques. Another useful observation by Jacobs et al. was that the auxin production reaches its maximum during the night and that new sites of xylem formation, i.e. where the first xylem of a leaf-trace differentiates, can be observed in plants collected at night. Jacobs' general conclusion was that the amount of auxin supplied by the leaves is the limiting factor in xylem differentiation or regeneration; but the amount that the stem can transport is also a factor in the situation. As a felicitous bonus from a carefully planned experiment with thorough anatomical observations, Jacobs and Morrow (1957) found that contrary to the view that xylem differentiation in procambial tissue typically begins near the base of the leaf primordium, in *Coleus* it always begins at the next node below. The beginning of xylem differentiation in the 'classical locus', i.e. the leaf-base, takes place somewhat later but independently of that in the next node below. In the early differentiation of xylem in a leaf-trace vascular strand the development is both acropetal and basipetal. Not least important, Jacobs (1952) emphasized that the auxin action in xylem differentiation is closely dependent on adequate supplies of sugar. (*See also* Thompson and Jacobs, 1965.)

Xylem and Phloem Differentiation. Once again, we return to Wetmore's experiments on grafting buds of *Syringa* into undifferentiated callus tissue. The induced vascular tissue below the bud was mostly tracheidal. However, Wetmore (1956, 1959) found that it was not essential to have a bud present at all to induce vascular tissue in the callus. By the simple procedure of applying auxin (IAA and NAA) and sugar (sucrose and glucose) to a small notch in the upper surface of callus cultures of a considerable range of species he, and also Wetmore and Rier (1963), showed that low concentrations of sugar, 1·5–2·5 per cent, favoured xylem differentiation; higher concentrations, 3–4 per cent, favoured phloem formation; and intermediate concentrations, 2·5–3·5 per cent induced both xylem and phloem, usually with cambium between. Wetmore and Rier contributed the interesting suggestion that the almost universal association of xylem and phloem in vascular bundles may have its basis in this intermediate range in sugar concentration. These fascinating discoveries also enabled them to comment critically on various long-held views regarding vascular differentiation. On the evidence now available the actual differentiation of vascular tissue does not appear to have any relationship ontogenetically with its function in the mature state: 'Function cannot be a *sine qua non* for the induction of vascular tissues.' They also considered that certain anatomical problems, which hitherto have been regarded as pertaining to the sphere of phylogenetic study, may advantageously be reinvestigated from the causal standpoint.

Mention may here be made of the induction of vascular tissue in the fern prothallus. An example of this interesting and unusual development in the gametophyte has already been noted and illustrated in the prothallus of *Psilotum* (p. 168). In the fern *Todea barbara*, De Maggio, Wetmore and Morel (1963) showed that vascular tissue can be induced in prothalli at will by growing them in a mineral solution to which auxin and sugar have been added in appropriate concentrations. The differentiation of numerous elongated tracheids is in direct relation to the composition of the medium and not to the formation of apogamous sporophytes. (For further recent work readers are referred to Sargent and Wangermann, 1959; Clutter, 1960; Roberts, 1960; Roberts and Fosket, 1962; Esau, 1965a, b.)

Genes and Xylem Differentiation. In some strains of maize a single recessive factor, referred to as *wilted*, delays the differentiation of the two large wood vessels in the vascular strands. As a consequence, the plants become wilted during periods of high transpiration. These metaxylem elements may eventually become differentiated. As seen in a cross-section of the stem, some of the metaxylem vessels are normal but others are compressed by the growth of the adjacent tissues. In relation to these anatomical features, the lower leaves in wilted plants become normal in acropetal sequence. The investigators of these interesting materials (Postlethwait and Nelson, 1957) suggested that it might be worth while to observe the effects of applications of IAA to the upper leaves of plants of 'wilted' maize and also to ascertain the amount of auxin in them.

Further on Phloem Differentiation. Some reference has been made to recent work on sugar as a factor in the differentiation of phloem. However, already in 1934 Kaan-Albest had observed, in experimental studies of phloem regeneration in longitudinally incised stem internodes of *Impatiens*, that sieve-tubes were only regenerated if phloem strands had been severed.

(Wound xylem was only formed if the xylem had been severed.) By removing a certain number of leaves, especially those on the apical side of a transverse incision, the amount of phloem regeneration was diminished. Regeneration of phloem was observed to be basipetal. Stem cuttings made in autumn failed to form roots and did not regenerate phloem, whereas spring cuttings did. LaMotte and Jacobs (1963) suggested that, in these experiments, phloem regeneration had been limited by the supplies of auxin from leaves and buds. They themselves advanced evidence on the action of hormones in the differentiation of phloem, and showed that the effects associated with leaves and buds could be reproduced by applying auxins.

Esau (1954) recorded the thought-provoking observation that, in a shoot of *Linum* with $\frac{3}{8}$ phyllotaxis, the first mature phloem element was observed at the fifteenth leaf, and the first mature xylem element at the twenty-second leaf from the apex. In a shoot with $\frac{5}{13}$ phyllotaxis, the corresponding observations were made at the twenty-fifth and thirty-ninth leaves respectively. In brief, the major morphogenetic developments had taken place before mature vascular tissue was formed.

Spatial Relations of Xylem and Phloem. So far, no adequate interpretation of the commonplace collateral vascular bundle, with phloem towards the exterior and xylem towards the centre of the stem, has yet been advanced. Esau (1965) has reviewed some recent studies and views on this topic, but none seems convincing of itself or capable of being extended to the many other patterns of distribution of xylem and phloem – some of them are usually described as being 'anomalous', but they are, of course, 'natural' or 'normal' to the species – to be encountered in the vascular plants at large.

ULTRASTRUCTURE AND DIFFERENTIATION

In these days, when the electron microscope is rapidly becoming a 'domesticated' piece of apparatus in university botany departments, one may well ask to what extent the new orders of magnification now available are affecting classical views on the differentiation of tissues. As Esau (1963) noted, many of the initial investigations of the ultrastructure of protoplasm were, understandably, made on meristematic and relatively undifferentiated cells. Indeed, we still have a great deal to learn about differentiating cells. Even with the aid of very high magnifications, the manner of inception of vacuoles, usually cited as one of the initial and more evident features of differentiating embryonic cells, is still unresolved; but tannins may be involved (*see also* p. 137). At the moment we are at a stage where much new observation, almost excessively illustrated, is accumulating; but some little time may well elapse before major inferences or hypotheses, based on the visual evidence, reach the level of general acceptance or experimental validation.

The minutely detailed observations that can now be made on differentiating cells are impressive. A few examples may be cited. Buvat (1958) noted that the mitochondrial cristae become more numerous in differentiating photosynthetic cells in the leaf of *Elodea*; and Esau reported that well-developed cristae are present in phloem companion cells and parenchyma in *Cucurbita*, but are absent from the mitochondria of mature sieve-tubes. Similarly, the endoplasmic reticulum has been found to be variable, apparently in some relationship with the state of cellular differentiation: Whaley *et al.* (1960) concluded that there is a progressive breaking down of these organelles during the differentiation of the root cells of maize; but Buvat (1961) did not observe this phenomenon in differentiating root cells in *Triticum*. And so this new work goes on with gathering momentum. In some ways it is reminiscent of the endless opportunities for new investigations that awaited the plant anatomists of 50–100 years ago. The contemporary scientific procedure – critical observation, conjecture, views as to functional importance and attempted validation of hypotheses by such experimental or analytical studies as seem possible – is not, in essence, so very different from that of the great 'anatomical period'.

These new electron-microscope investigations already constitute a great enrichment of botanical knowledge; and there is virtually no limit to what can be achieved. To deal with a single tissue by way of example: during recent decades the phloem has received much attention at the hands of expert adherents of plant anatomy, e.g. Esau (1953; 1965a, b); Esau, Currier and Cheadle (1957); Cheadle (1956), etc. But phloem, collected for examination under different conditions, is now beginning to be studied by means of the electron microscope. In Australia, Wark and Chambers (1965) found that the connecting strands across the sieve-plates of *Pisum* appear to be continuities of the endoplasmic reticulum, each connecting strand being encased in a cylinder of callose. In the still nucleate young sieve-tube the tubules of the endoplasmic reticulum are longitudinally orientated. As maturation proceeds, there is an exudation of nuclear material into the cytoplasm by way of a fibrotubular structure which is described as being distinct from the slime body. The latter disperses in the fully expanded cell. Thereafter, there is a breakdown of the nucleus, the tonoplast and other organelles. These changes apparently leave the endoplasmic reticulum free in the cell lumen (Figs. 11.7, 11.8). According to Wark (1965), the companion cells of the secondary phloem of *Pisum* contain all the organelles characteristic of fully active cells, their cytoplasm changing little during development. However, she observed that these cells are connected to the sieve-tube by complex plasmodesmata (Fig. 11.8).

Esau (1965) reported on an intensive re-investigation (*see* Esau, 1948a, b) of the anatomy and cytology of the phloem in some thirty species of *Vitis* (including *V. vinifera*), using the electron microscope. She found a very considerable uniformity of structure, even in seemingly specific features such as the distribution and types of crystals, the occlusion of certain cells by tylosoids and so on. In *Vitis*, unlike many dicotyledons, the phloem becomes dormant in winter, with occlusion of the sieve-plates by large deposits of callose, and is reactivated with the advent of the growing season. Esau ascertained that the callose encloses very fine protoplasmic strands. At the time of reactivation the callose disappears, almost certainly as the result of enzyme action associated with a proteinaceous slime. In particular, Esau ascertained that, during the differentiation of the sieve-tubes, the pores of the sieve-plates develop in loci occupied by protoplasmic strands, one to each pore site. Callose platelets are deposited at the pore-loci on both sides of the wall *before the locus is penetrated* – an interesting and provocative observation! Esau's studies confirm the general view that a sieve-tube has a 'specialized protoplast'. It has no nucleus and no vascuolar membrane, or tonoplast; but, in *Vitis* spp., the endoplasmic reticulum appears to be dissociated into vesicles, in contrast to the extended cisternae typically found in cells with nuclei. Other minutiae of observation also emerged. For example, in the sieve-elements Esau observed that plastids which elaborate starch grains are structurally considerably less differentiated than are those of the phloem parenchyma. (*See also* Evert and Murmanis (1965) on the ultrastructure of secondary phloem in *Tilia americana*.)

These are no more than sample (and simplified) indications of the new observations that it has now become possible to make. The reader may well ask where all this is getting us in our understanding of morphogenesis. It is still too soon to say. But clearly, at the cellular level of organization, a great deal that is new and interesting is being learnt about detailed aspects of differentiation in different kinds of cells. Here we may recall the De Bary aphorism that organs make cells, not cells organs; but the present writer's view is that we should also look for, and expect to find, reciprocal relationships of many kinds. If we accept that organisms are typically holistic, i.e. fully integrated individuals, then there must be a mechanism, or mechanisms, which bring this about. So if, for example, electron microscopy and ancillary studies enable us to arrive at a closer understanding of the intimate physico-chemical, structural and functional bases of this holism – or whole plant morphogenesis (*see* Chapter XIV) – they will indeed have done much to advance botanical science. But evidently electron microscopy

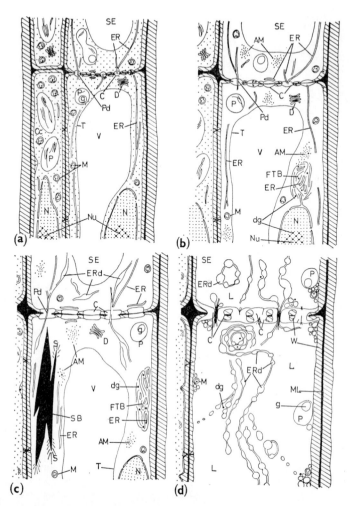

FIG. 11.7. *Pisum sativum.* The fine structure of the phloem. Diagrams illustrating the general structural features of each of the four stages of *Pisum* secondary phloem sieve element ontogeny, as interpreted by electron microscopy. (a), Stage 1 sieve element (and companion cell). (b), Stage 2 sieve element. (c), Stage 3 sieve element. (d), Stage 4 sieve element.

AM, amorphous material; *C*, callose; *Cc*, companion cell; *D*, Golgi dictyosome; *dg*, dense granules; *ER*, endoplasmic reticulum; *ERd*, distended endoplasmic reticulum; *FTB*, fibro-tubular body; *g*, storage granule; *L*, cell lumen; *M*, mitochondrion; *ML*, middle lamella; *N*, nucleus; *Nu*, nucleolus; *P*, plastid; *Pd*, plasmodesma; *S*, slime body; *SE*, sieve element; *T*, tonoplast; *V*, vacuole; *W*, cell wall. (After M. C. Wark and T. C. Chambers, *Australian Jour. Bot.,* 1965.)

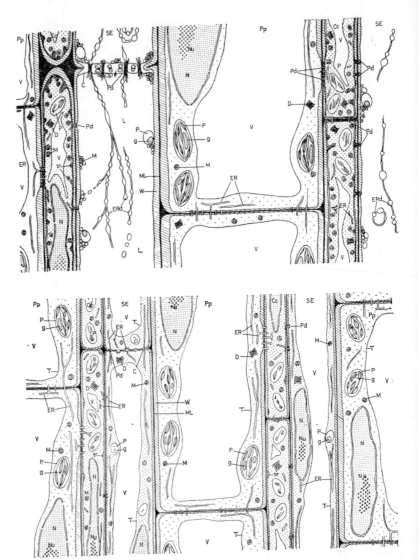

FIG. 11.8. *Pisum sativum*. The fine structure of the phloem. Above: Diagram illustrating the general structural features of anatomically 'young' (stage 1) *Pisum* secondary phloem. Below: Diagram illustrating the general structural features of anatomically 'mature' (stage 4) *Pisum* secondary phloem. *C*, callose; *Cc*, companion cell; *D*, Golgi dictyosome; *ER*, endoplasmic reticulum; *ERd*, distended endoplasmic reticulum; *g*, storage granule; *L*, cell lumen; *M*, mitochondrion; *ML*, middle lamella; *N*, nucleus; *Nu*, Nucleolus; *P*, plastid; *Pd*, plasmodesma; *Pp*, phloem parenchyma cell; *tr*, trabecula; *SE*, sieve element; *T*, tonoplast; *V*, vacuole; *W*, cell wall. (After M. C. Wark, *Australian Jour. Bot.*, 1965.)

may assist advances in many directions, e.g. in enabling us to be more precise about structural, or organizational, bases of the physiological events which lead to the inception of growth centres and their further development into leaves, vegetative buds or flower buds. All this remains to be seen; but what a splendid prospect it affords younger investigators who are the heirs to the sophisticated facilities that are becoming increasingly available. However, let it not be forgotten that *every* living species is of ancient lineage: accordingly, however illuminating the discoveries of the coming decades may be – and the writer thinks that they will be very illuminating – Nature will still remain shrouded in some of her accumulated complex veils.

Esau (1966) has contributed a valuable study of tracheary differentiation in *Cucurbita* (Plate 9).

CAMBIAL ACTIVITY AND THE DIFFERENTIATION OF SECONDARY TISSUES

Unfortunately, space does not admit of more than a passing reference to this most engaging but complex topic. When one reflects on what may be involved in the inception, organization, nutrition and histogenic activities of the cambium in different species at different seasons, in pteridophytes and seed plants, in herbaceous and woody species, and so on, one is conscious of entering into a vast realm, of which, in terms of validated scientific interpretation, only the most preliminary of surveys has yet been undertaken. To take a simple example: in the secondary phloem and xylem of any common woody species, be it lime, oak, elm, sycamore, etc., many different types of cells are differentiated from the cambial segments. But what do we really know about the factors which determine the intermingled pattern of wood vessels, parenchyma, fibres, fibrous tracheids and medullary ray cells. That a pattern is there and that, collectively, each kind of cell constitutes an integrated or continuous system, which is part of a still more complex holistic system, has been ascertained from anatomical studies. But, in terms of causation, have we made anything more than a modest beginning? Again, the pattern in a transverse section of a woody stem, e.g. of *Tilia europaea*, is a specific pattern, differing from that of other species of *Tilia*, *Ulmus*, *Acer*, etc.; i.e. genetical factors are involved. But beyond the many specific differences which become evident in comparative studies, the woody stems of flowering plants have also much in common. These phenomena, in which we can perceive both specificity and general homology of organization, are of a tantalizing difficulty. Fortunately, inventive minds are discovering how to open new doors. Since the pioneering work of Th. Hartig a hundred years ago, it has been realized that the renewal of cambial activity in spring is directly correlated with the reactivation of buds. More recently, this phenomenon has been re-examined in terms of metabolic activities. Thus auxin, synthesized in the growing buds and moving downwards in the stem, is now considered to be one of the effective agents. In *Robinia pseudacacia*, growing under long-day conditions, a cambial stimulus may originate in the mature leaves (Wareing and Roberts, 1956). A feature of cambial activity in spring – the formation of wide wood vessels – is also apparently dependent on high auxin concentrations; and it is known that when the extension growth of the shoot ceases, so also does the formation of spring wood with its conspicuous tracheae. However, the processes involved in the differentiation of the xylem are far from simple: auxin is not the sole regulatory substance. Wareing (1958) found that when gibberellin was applied to young shoots of sycamore and of other trees it stimulated the formation of new tissue from the cambium; but there was no vessel formation or cell lignification. However, when GA and IAA were applied together a conspicuous zone of new wood was differentiated.

The physiology of the cambium and of other secondary meristems in the shoot, with special reference to the action of growth-regulating substances, has been comprehensively reviewed by Reinders-Gouwentak (1965). Readers who are specially interested in this aspect of morphogenesis, especially in the relevant experimental investigations, should consult this well-documented survey.

In conclusion, in the matter of differentiation, may the author make a suggestion to younger workers. Many investigators have been at it, but it hasn't all been done! Adequate interpretations of the inception and maturation of histological patterns, and the specificity and diversity thereof, have still to be proposed and validated!

CHAPTER XII

The Inflorescence and the Flower

INTRODUCTION

The morphological nature of the inflorescence and of the flower, the homologies of the constituent organs, their origin in phylogeny, and their inception and development in the individual plant, have afforded unrivalled scope for the botanical observer, theorist and experimentalist, the more so as the evolution of a quarter of a million living species has provided a range and a diversity that are hard to grasp. Over the decades, botanists have felt that they must not only produce either 'working' or evolutionary classifications of this great assemblage of materials but that they must formulate simplified, or simplifying, general concepts regarding their fundamental nature.

The old, classical, theory of the flower, stemming presumably from Goethe's Theory of Metamorphosis, has had many supporters down through the years to the present time. According to this theory, the constituent parts of the flower are regarded as being formed in normal continuity with the antecedent foliar organs on the vegetative axis, i.e. the flower consists essentially of an axis and lateral organs, which are either of evident foliar nature or are capable of being homologized with foliar organs. The validity of this view is readily apparent in groups such as the Ranales, e.g. in *Ranunculus* or *Magnolia*, in which the perianth members are leaflike in form and structure, as are also the stamens and carpels. In other groups, however, the homology of the stamens and carpels with foliar organs may be considerably less, or indeed not at all, evident; and hence observers like Grégoire (1938) considered that the floral apex was different in origin and in structure from the vegetative apex. A view of this kind brings its own difficulties. Another view, supported by observation, e.g. in the grasses (Sharman, 1947; Barnard, 1955, 1961), in *Allium* (Jones and Emsweller, 1936), is that carpels originate as leaflike primordia, whereas stamen primordia are budlike outgrowths (Fig. 12.1). Again, in the fascicled type of stamen in Malvaceae, Guttiferae, etc., some investigators have envisaged a phylogenetic origin from a branched structure bearing microsporangia, i.e. a telome system. (For a contemporary discussion of the phyllosporous or stachysporous origin of the androecium, and much new information on the androecium in the Malvales, readers are referred to Van Heel, 1966; and see p. 331). These and other observations, especially those in which emphasis is placed on phylogenetic origins, have led to the concept of the *gonophyll*, envisaged as an *ancestral leaflike organ bearing fertile branches* (Melville, 1962, 1963). As a result of evolutionary condensations and losses of parts, the gonophyll has eventually become the contemporary stamen

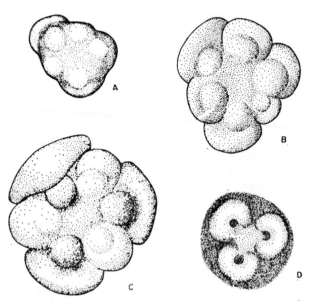

FIG. 12.1. Floral organogenesis in *Allum cepa* (the onion) as seen from above. In A, the three peripheral lobes are the outer tepals, each with an associated axillary stamen primordium. The alternating mounds are the very young primordia of the inner tepals. B and C illustrate later stages in which the primordia of the six tepals and the six stamens can be distinguished. D shows an early stage in the formation of the three syncarpous carpels, with a small region of residual apical meristem in the centre. (After H. A. Jones and S. L. Emsweller, *Hilgardia*, 1936; from K. Esau, *Plant Anatomy*, 1965.)

in its several morphological aspects. According to Melville (1963) and Sterling (1963), the difficulties and inconsistencies of the foliar, or sporophyll, concept of the carpel can be resolved by using the gonophyll concept, i.e. the gynoecium is a foliar organ bearing an epiphyllous fertile branch. According to this system of ideas, as Esau (1965) cogently noted, 'If the floral parts are ultimately derived from branch systems, the flower is a condensed and highly modified inflorescence and the term flower covers reproductive structures in angiosperms in various stages of condensation.' Melville

(1963) argued that, as the term *flower* becomes modified so that it refers to a biological rather than a morphological unit, it becomes applicable both to single flowers and to condensed inflorescences.

Other aspects of floral morphology, much discussed by students of an earlier generation, such as the occurrence of diplostemony, or of obdi-plostemony, in certain families or groups, and the interpretation of these characters, are now being re-examined from the developmental or morpho-genetic standpoint, e.g. Eckert (1966) on Simaroubaceae, Rutaceae, Geraniaceae, Caryophyllaceae, etc. Reviews on various aspects of floral morphology have been contributed by Bancroft (1935), Arber (1937), Wilson and Just (1939), Douglas (1957), and Barnard (1955, 1961).

THE MORPHOGENETIC VIEWPOINT

As in the study of other organs, the morphogenetic approach to floral de-velopment is in no sense new. Already, in 1857, in a beautifully illustrated monograph, *Traité d'Organogénie Comparée de la Fleur*, Payer had shown how much could be learnt by simple observation about the transition from the vegetative to the reproductive state, and the inception and development of the several floral organs. Later, with the help of microtome techniques, many of these primordial developments were studied in greater detail and were admirably illustrated in books such as *Morphology of Angiosperms*, by Coulter and Chamberlain (1912). Much has been achieved since then, but much remains to be done. Indeed, against the background of a quarter of a million species, one may well ask how the basic problems of floral mor-phogenesis are to be defined and tackled. The writer (Wardlaw, 1957, 1961, 1965a) has suggested an approach along the following lines:

(1) There must be adequate information on the initial steady state of the vegetative apex, i.e. its form, cellular constitution, the distribution of growth in it and its organogenic activities, including temporal rela-tionships. The subdistal region of the meristem (p. 132), in which growth centres have their inception, may be regarded as the seat of a complex reaction system in which, among other factors, specific gene products, induced in sequential order, act as components.

(2) The incidence of factors which stimulate or induce changes in the steady state of the apical reaction system, resulting in changes in the distribution of growth and other concomitant developments must be more fully investigated. (Already we have information on the effects of photoperiod and of certain specific substances.)

(3) The serial evocation and specific activities of genes, or groups of genes, suggests itself as an essential hypothesis, but it has still to be validated.

(4) The factors, which are presumably those involved in phenomena of correlation, and which determine the holistic, integrated development of the flower, or inflorescence, have to be defined and understood as components of the unitary reaction system in the floral meristem.

The problems of floral morphogenesis are unavoidably very complex. Nevertheless, the approach outlined above not only opens up new vistas for research but, as work progresses, it seems likely to illuminate, amplify or qualify some of the earlier views on floral morphology.

The Initial Steady State. For a certain period of time during ontogenesis, according to the species and environmental conditions, the vegetative apical meristem continues in a state of active growth and, at regular intervals, gives rise to regularly spaced leaf primordia, often with associated bud rudiments, or potential rudiments. This characteristic and very general property, or function, of the shoot apical meristem, i.e. of forming growth centres by chemical differentiation, persists during the transition to the reproductive phase.

The Stimulus and Transition to Flowering. Under normal conditions at a certain stage in ontogenesis, and usually in relation to an external factor, e.g. temperature or a characteristic photoperiodic exposure, new metabolic substances begin to move acropetally from the leaves and affect the reaction system in the apical meristem. We do not yet know the nature of this substance, or substances; but, in the contemporary view, it is probably a hormone which is common to flowering plants in general (Fig. 12.2 and *see* below). Its initial effects, e.g. in a species in which the terminal apex yields a flower, include a change in the pattern of differential growth in the apex (Figs. 12.2–12.5, 12.14). For example, in a species characterized by an elongating vegetative shoot and long internodes, i.e. in which the vertical component of growth is predominant, an early effect of the floral hormone is to restrict vertical growth and to increase radial growth in the apical meristem. As a result, the conical, rounded or dome-shaped apex develops a broader configuration which morphologists have described as the floral receptacle, thalamus or torus. This change in the distribution of apical growth is particularly well seen in the development of some inflorescences, e.g. the capitulum in the Compositae, and the compact inflorescences in species from Dipsacaceae and Campanulaceae (Philipson, 1946 *et seq.*). Plate 10.

During this phase of transition, notwithstanding various changes in growth and histological organization, the apical meristem continues to form growth centres, some of which undergo a characteristic, though modified, foliar development; i.e. they form bracts which are usually of smaller size and greater simplicity than the foliage leaves. Examples of this aspect of heteroblastic development are familiar to botanists. (*See* Figs. 8.8, 8.11.)

In species characterized by the rosette habit in the vegetative phase, e.g. many Cruciferae, Compositae, etc., in which the vertical component of growth is small, the transition to the flowering phase is usually attended by a rapid elongation of the axis, by heteroblastic development and by the

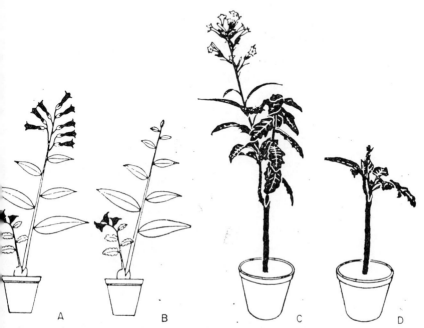

FIG. 12.2. Tobacco (*Nicotiana*) and *Hyoscyamus*. The induction of flowering in grafting experiments. Diagrams illustrating the vernalin hypothesis. A, B, Maryland Mammoth tobacco (flowering and vegetative respectively) grafted on to non-vernalized *Hyoscyamus*. C, D, Vernalized and non-vernalized *Hyoscyamus* grafted on to vegetative Maryland Mammoth tobacco. *See* text. (After A. Lang, *Proc. Biol. Colloq.* Oregon State Univ. Press, Corvallis, 1961; from J. A. D. Zeevaart, *Cell Differentiation and Morphogenesis*, Amsterdam, 1966.)

formation of the flower buds, a capitulum, etc. It has now been demonstrated that the gibberellins, although they may not be the ultimate 'florigenic substance', are closely involved in the stimulus to elongation which closely precedes the inception of the reproductive organs.

The histological changes in the shoot apex associated with the transition from the vegetative to the flowering phase have now been described for a

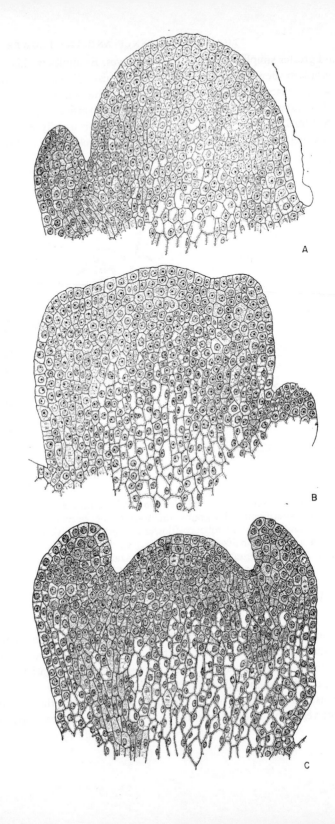

A

B

C

small number of species (Figs. 12.3, 12.5); but there is clearly scope for much further work.

Evidence from Grafting Experiments. Already, in 1937, Melchers had indicated that the annual and biennial forms of *Hyoscyamus niger* are determined by a single pair of genes. He demonstrated that if scion grafts of annual-flowering races are applied to biennial stocks in their first year flower-development is induced in the latter; and if first-year scions from biennial races are grafted on to annual stocks they are induced to enter into the flowering phase. It thus appears that a gene-determined, or controlled, diffusible, 'florigenic' substance (or substances) has passed across the graft-union from the annual to the biennial tissues. These important investigations have been extended by Zeevaart (1958, 1962, 1966), by Zeevaart and Lang (1962), and by others, in grafting experiments in which contemporary knowledge of the induction of flowering by vernalization, photoperiodic exposure, the application of GA, kinetin, etc., has been advantageously incorporated. The inducation of flowering, or its suppression, in grafts within the same species and between different species, in which scion or stock had been vernalized, or given appropriate short-day or long-day treatment and, in some experiments, with the addition of a 'florigen' precursor such as GA or anti-florigenic substances, leave no doubt that some specific substance (or substances), probably of common occurrence, is an essential component of the reaction system in the shot apex, if the reproductive phase is to be induced. The transmission of the floral hormone, or stimulus, across the graft union between species of different genera, invites the conclusion that the hormone is not specific to the particular species. From experiments of the kind indicated above – the details need not concern us here – Lang (1961) suggested that two different floral hormones, *vernalin* and *florigen*, may be involved in different instances. Text Fig. 12.2 illustrates diagrammatically some of the results obtained. The metabolic details which have been long and keenly sought by many different workers are still very incomplete. To date, following Zeevaart (1966, where relevant literature is cited), some of the main, though still tentative, findings are these: the floral hormones are identical in long-day and short-day plants; GA induces flowering in the former but not in the latter, i.e. endogenously occurring GA is not identical with the flower hormone; in the physiological sense, GA may be a precursor of florigen and a limiting factor

FIG. 12.3. *Rubus rosaefolius*, illustrating the transition to flowering, as seen in l.s. of the apex. A, the dome-shaped vegetative shoot apex. B, The young floral apex, which shows a characteristic flattening and widening. C, In relation to the shortening of the plastochrone, the sepals originate almost simultaneously. (After C. J. Engard, *Univ. Hawaii Publ.*, 1944.)

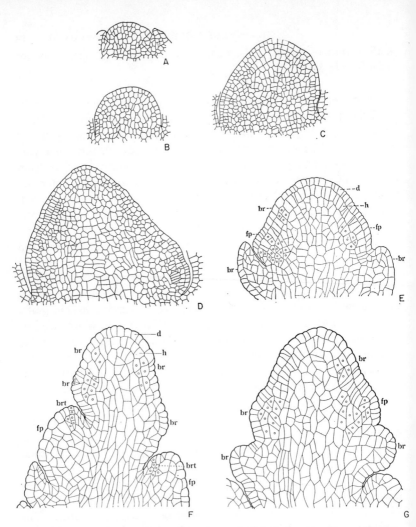

FIG. 12.4. The transition to flowering. A–D, *Arum maculatum. Camera lucida* drawings of longitudinal sections showing apices in transition to the inflorescence state. Throughout these stages of development the two outer tunica layers persist along with the original corpus and come to overlie a central parenchymatous core. A, Vegetative apex. B, Early transition apex. C, Later transition apex. D, Very young inflorescence. July–early August. (×150.) (After A. Walton, *Annals of Botany*, 1964.)

E, *Bulbine bulbosa.* Median section of the apex of the inflorescence axis: *br*, bract; *fp*, flower primordium; *d*, dermatogen; *h*, hypodermis. (After C. Barnard, *Australian Jour. Bot.*, 1958.) (*See* Fig. 12.5 C.)

F, G, *Luzula campestris.* The apices of inflorescence branches in l.s., showing the dermatogen (*d*), hypodermis (*h*), the central corpus tissues, and the inception of bracts (*br*), bracteoles (*brt*) and flower primordium (*fp*). (After C. Barnard, *Australian Jour. Bot.*, 1958.)

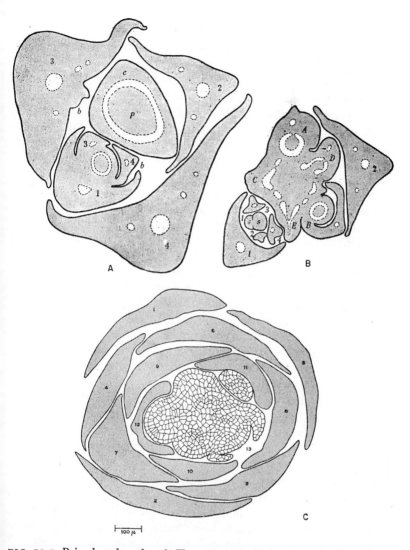

FIG. 12.5. *Primula polyantha*. A, Transverse section of a shoot at the upper extremity of the transition from the vegetative to the floral region. There is an uninterrupted stele (clear) of primary vascular tissue, with a central pith (*p*) and surrounding cortex (*c*). The older leaves, *5, 4*, had no axillary buds; leaf *3* had a small axillary bud (seen in other sections); but the last-formed leaf, *1*, had a large axillary bud. B, Transverse section of the same axis higher up, i.e. in the floral region, showing the much divided stele and the bract and flower-pedicel traces (circular); *A–E*, flower buds and bracts, in the order of their appearance. (×25.) (After C. W. Wardlaw, *Phil. Trans. Roy. Soc.*, 1950.)

C, *Bulbine bulbosa* (Liliaceae). Transverse section through the tip of a raceme, showing the bracts (*1–13*, in the order of decreasing age) and flower primordia in the axils of bracts *11* and *12*. (After C. Barnard, *Australian Jour. Bot.*, 1960.)

in its metabolism; vernalin may be the physiological though not necessarily the biochemical precursor of florigen.

The foregoing is evidently a very interesting and profitable field of experimentation, and it can scarcely be doubted that, in the not distant future, much more will have been discovered about the nature of paths of synthesis of the important hormonal substances involved. But how they contribute to, or participate in, the actual morphogenetic processes has still to be ascertained. What is known is that in vegetative shoot apices, in which the flowering stimulus has been received, new patterns of cell division can be observed and the orderly differentiation of the several floral organs follows as different genes become sequentially activated (*see* p. 318). Eventually, therefore, the chain of events in the onset of flowering leads us to a consideration of nuclear division, DNA synthesis and related phenomena.

Cytohistological Changes During the Transition Phase. These changes have now been studied by a number of workers. Nougarède, Gifford and Rondet (1965) investigated *Amaranthus retroflexus* L. – a quantitative short-day plant. Plants were grown from germination onwards under controlled daylengths of 8, 12 and 16 hours of light, and others under natural summer daylengths. Under all of these light conditions, apices 6 days after the beginning of germination showed a common pattern of zonation, i.e. an axial or central zone, with weak pyroninophilia, surrounded by a flank meristem, with strong pyroninophilia, i.e. affinity of pyronin for ribonucleic acid (RNA). This apical condition was also found in 15-day-old plants when the fourth leaf primordium was appearing. At this stage the apex of a plant on an 8-hour photoperiod, after a brief transitional phase, begins the reproductive phase, the transition being characterized by a general increase in pyroninophilia in the axial zone. This is associated with the presence of a mantle of three or four layers of uniformly staining cells. This period is also characterized by an increase in the volume of the nucleoli, especially in the cells of the axial zone. In plants which had been grown under a 16-hour photoperiod the typical changes indicated above at leaf 4 or 5 did not take place, but the apex changed to what is regarded as an intermediate phase, or condition; e.g. differential responses could be observed in various regions of the axial zone. The tunica cells showed a large increase in nucleolar volume, but their cytoplasm remained weak in pyroninophilia. In the cells of the central corpus there was also an increase in pyroninophilia, but the total nucleolar volume remained less than that in cells of the tunica. In brief, the characteristic features of the axial zone, as seen in a vegetative apex, were not in evidence. However, in this 'intermediate state' apical meristem, vegetative development continued until 14–20 leaves had been formed. With the formation of bracts, denoting the onset of the reproductive phase, pyroninophilia in the central (corpus) and lateral cells increased and a subtunica mantle was formed. Concomitantly, there was a notable increase in the total nucleolar volumes in the cells of the subtunica mantle

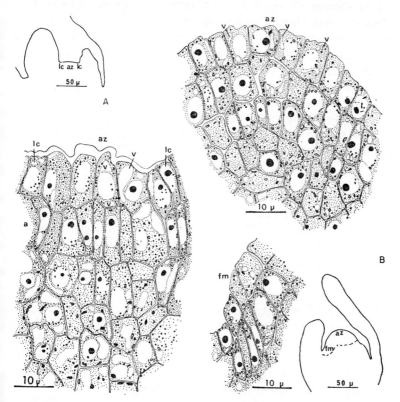

FIG. 12.6. *Amaranthus retroflexus. Camera-lucida* drawings of cytological details of apical meristems fixed and stained according to schedule of Regaud to reveal basophilic image; *az*, axial zone; *fm*, flank meristem; *lc*, lateral cells; *v*, vacuole. A, Apex during minimal-area phase after elevation of first two leaves. The axial zone is reduced in size and its more median cells have smaller vacuoles. B, Apex in passage to transition stage under a photoperiod of 8 hr. Vacuolar system is reduced. Note larger nuclei and nucleoli in cells of axial zone than in those on flanks. (After A. Nougarède, E. M. Gifford Jr. and P. Rondet, *Botan. Gaz.*, 1965.)

in the axial region. These investigators have thus demonstrated that when a meristem of *A. retroflexus* is temporarily prevented from flowering by long photoperiods its structure and cytochemistry are modified. In particular, the activity in the central axial cells is characteristic of reproductive meristems. These precise demonstrations are of special value in that they enable us to understand why there are so many seemingly contradictory views about the changes in the vegetative apex during the transition to flowering (Fig. 12.6).

Lance-Nougarède and Bronchard (1965) have reported on a study in which the metabolism of nucleic acids at different stages in the development of the shoot apex of *Perilla nankinensis* was examined. They measured the density of RNA in the hyaloplasm (assessed as the number of ribosomes per unit surface), and of DNA (using histoautoradiography after the incorporation of tritiated thymidine). Their results lend confirmation to the views of Buvat and others on the regionalization, or zonation, of cellular activity in the vegetative meristem and of the characteristic changes in this zonation which accompany the transition to flowering. Bernier (1966) has also found that the amounts of DNA in different regions of the vegetative apex, and subsequently during the transition to flowering, are in close accord with Buvat's concept. In the vegetative phase, for example, the percentage of labelled nuclei in *Sinapis alba*, which had been grown under closely controlled conditions, was about 2·5 times as great on the flanks as in the distal central cells. The activity of each zone of the apex has been closely related to day length, which markedly affects the plastochrone rhythm. By adjusting the day-length exposures, the apex can be brought into an intermediate stage, as described above by Lance Nougarède *et al.* (*See also* Bernier, 1964.)

Gifford and Stewart (1965) have described the ultrastructure in vegetative and reproductive apices of *Chenopodium album*. Within 3 hours of a single flower-promoting photoinductive cycle, changes in the cytoplasmic structure of the cells of the vegetative apex could be detected. In particular, the distribution of the endoplasmic reticulum was modified and there was evidence of an increase in synthesis of acid phosphatase.

The Serial Evocation of Genes and Floral Development. As already discussed (p. 195), although all the growth centres in the apical meristem share a common basic metabolism, there must also be quantitative or qualitative differences between them, e.g. those leading to the different leaf forms in species showing heteroblastic development. These differences in metabolism may, in some instances, be of considerable magnitude, as, for example, when a vegetative or a flower bud is formed in a leaf site in *Nuphar* (Fig. 7.22). As the transformation apex begins to give rise to the outer groups of floral organs, i.e. the sepals and petals, it is evident that growth centres are still being formed, though now in compact helices or whorls; and, generally, each of the several kinds of floral organs is typically formed in an integrated, distinctive group. In an order like the Ranunculaceae the same considerations also apply to the inception and development of the groups of stamens and carpels: all come from regularly sited growth centres, and each kind of organ constitutes a discrete group. In other words, the formation of a flower usually takes place as a sequence of well-defined phases. Many teratologies have, of course, been recorded in floral morphology; but, in any particular species, the successive formation of the several groups of specific and distinctive organs usually takes place with a high degree of

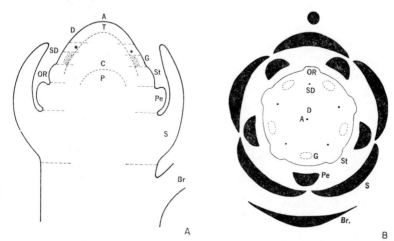

FIG. 12.7. Factors in floral morphogenesis. A and B are diagrammatic illustrations of a theory of floral morphogenesis in a prototypic flower. The longitudinal section here shows, in acropetal sequence, a bract (Br), young sepals (S), young petal primordia (Pe), stamen primordia (St) at their inception, the positions of the next growth centres to become primordia (G), and the beginning of growth centres still closer to the summit of the apex (A); tunica (T), corpus (C) and pith (P). The discontinuous transverse lines are intended to indicate a number of zones into which the organized apex is differentiated: the distal zone (D); the sub-distal zone(s) (SD), in which the reaction system is giving rise to a pattern of growth centres; the organogenic zone (OR), in which the active growth centres have given rise to very young primordia. The transverse lines also indicate the successive phases, or stages, through which the apex passes as floral morphogenesis progresses. (After C. W. Wardlaw, *Growth in Living Systems*, 1961.)

fidelity. One must, accordingly, think in terms of the evocation and sequential activities of genes and their products, the locus of their activities being initially in the growth centres and young primordia (Wardlaw, 1957, 1961, 1965). One may envisage the apical reaction system as passing through a series of states, each state, with its characteristic metabolism, being determined by gene-controlled enzymes and their substrates, preparing the way for the next state (Figs. 12.7, 12.8). At any particular point

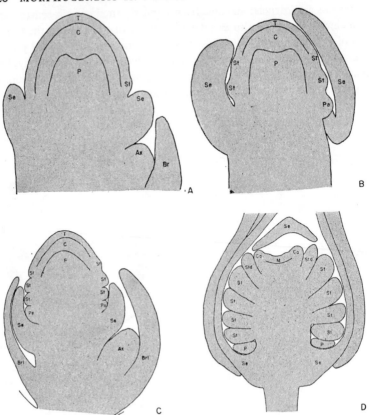

FIG. 12.8. *Aquilegia formosa* var. *truncata*. A, Floral apex, seen in l.s., at the time of initiation of the petals and first stamens. A bract, an axillary bud, two sepals, and the protuberance of the first stamen are visible. (×295.) *Br*, bract; *Ax*, axillary bud; *Se*, sepal; *Pe*, petal; *St*, stamen; *T*, tunica; *C*, corpus; *P*, parenchymatous core. B, A slightly more advanced stage, with petal inception. C, Floral apex forming the later stamen whorls. The axillary bud shown at the right is forming the first bracteole. (×180.) D, Older flower bud. This terminal flower shows young carpel primordia (section is slightly oblique). (×85.) *Brl*, bracteole; *Std*, staminodium; *Ca*, carpel; *M*, merismatic mantle. (After S. S. Tepfer, *Univ. California Publ. Bot.*, 1953.)

in the floral development, e.g. the inception of the 'petal stage', one may suppose that a specific gene-determined substance, probably an enzyme, reaches a critical, or threshold, concentration in the helix of nascent growth centres. It reacts with the substrate, with consequential characteristic effects on the nature of the primordia developed. But the reaction system is also changed in an orderly fashion, and a new set of genes is evoked. At each such critical state, also, physiological correlations and environmental factors are at work. As the morphological differences between the several groups of floral organs, sepals, petals, stamens and carpels are usually sharp and distinct, it may be inferred that so also are the different states of the reaction system; i.e. as in other physiological activities, metabolic substances have no effect until certain threshold values, or appropriate sustaining conditions, for reaction are attained.

A synthesis of the following concepts affords a basis for interpreting floral morphogenesis:

(1) that the vegetative, transition and floral meristem all give rise to growth centres;

(2) that, in relation to an induced restriction in the vertical component of growth, primordia occur in whorls or flattened helices; and

(3) that genic action, essentially biochemical, is serial or sequential.

These are, unavoidably, simplified concepts: in any growing region, or biological development, a great many physico-chemical events are taking place simultaneously. The reaction system is of a complexity that eludes our present comprehension. Under genic control, further characteristic modifications in the distribution of growth take place leading, for example, to the superior type of ovary, on the one hand, and to epigyny, on the other. One begins to realize, in fact, that the diversity in floral morphology may perhaps be referred to a quite small number of main causes.

Tepfer, Karpoff and Greyson (1966) have examined the effects of growth substances on floral buds of *Aquilegia*, excised at various stages, and grown on solid media containing coconut milk, minerals, vitamins, sucrose and varying quantities of GA, IAA and kinetin. Various growth results were obtained, according to the balance of GA, IAA and kinetin in the medium and to the size of the bud. Indications of interaction between IAA and kinetin were obtained. In the culture of very young excised buds, as the kinetin concentration was increased, optimum growth was obtained with increasing concentrations of IAA; but, with older buds, increasing kinetin concentrations required decreasing concentrations of IAA for optimum growth. These investigators have sought evidence which might validate the writer's (Wardlaw, 1957) reaction system theory of floral morphogenesis (*see* p. 318); and of Heslop-Harrison's (1963) further suggestion of a regulator gene-operon hypothesis. Although Tepfer *et al.* were not able to modify the course of morphogenesis by the experimental procedures so far used, they regard their current data as being consistent with the theory. However, as they have pointed out, in order to test the theory, the first essential is to be able to modify the normal sequence of developments experimentally. So far, an important conclusion is that the sequence in which

L

the groups of floral primordia originate is not affected by the presence, absence or actual concentration of the growth substances used.

THE INTERPRETATION OF FLORAL MORPHOLOGY

If the foregoing system of ideas may be provisionally accepted it affords a basis for interpreting some of the main features of floral morphogenesis, i.e. that the several organs are either homologous with leaves or that they originate from growth centres with some of their metabolic activities in common; that the floral organs originate in characteristic groups on the meristem; and that the successive groups of organs are different, distinctive and specific.

The concept of organs originating from growth centres with common metabolites, but also with specific gene-determined substances, enables us to escape, or avoid, some of the difficulties that beset morphologists of an earlier period. For whether a stamen or a carpel in a living species is envisaged as being phylogenetically a modified foliar organ, and homologous with a leaf, or as a modified leaf-branch system, or gonophyll, it has its inception, during the individual development, as a growth centre in the apical meristem; and the whole of its formation is stimulated, regulated and controlled by the several factors, extrinsic and intrinsic, which react and interact as components of the reaction system in the apical meristem, in the individual growth centre, and in the developing primordium.

Organs sui generis. Clowes (1961) has adopted what the writer would describe as a 'liberating' attitude towards the study of floral morphogenesis; i.e. he would like to see it freed from the bonds of older, more static, morphological concepts. He has stated that: 'The student of development may well be advised to treat all organs as organs *sui generis.*' By this, he presumably means that we should think of development as an epigenetic process; and with this one may agree, with qualifications. For the writer, at least, it is very hard to envisage any biological organ as being truly self-generating, or originating as a thing of itself (*sui generis*). Every normal organ originates as part of an organized whole, and every aspect of its inception and development bears witness to order, regulation and the interrelationships of parts during growth; and every organism begins as a generative cell, or tissue mass in which all its potentialities, the result of a long evolutionary process, are embodied in a specific organization.

In a discussion of the relevance of concepts of homology as applied to the floral organs, Clowes noted that the carpel of *Amygdalus communis*, as described by Brooks (1940), appears to be formed from the whole of the distal region of the apex rather than from a region of the meristem. And, again, as Sharman (1947) and Barnard (1955) stated, whereas the carpels in the Gramineae originate as leaf-like primordia, the stamens originate as bud-like primordia. Accordingly Clowes stated: 'It seems to me that there is little to be gained by saying that two organs are homologous because their ontogenetic origin is similar. In most cases it is difficult to see how they could be different.' (And hence his view that each organ should be regarded as being *sui generis*.) However, very young primordia, all having their inception as growth centres, can be, and sometimes demonstrably are, different. As already noted, the flower buds in *Nuphar lutea* (Fig. 7.22) originate in leaf sites in the genetic spiral of primordia. So, some critical metabolic change must take place in a growth centre which develops as a bud and not, as a majority of them do, as a leaf. It is one of the tasks of morphogenesis, firstly to recognize the situation, and then to interpret it. In this particular instance, leaf and bud primordia are homologous; but the homology must not be pushed too far (*see* Wardlaw, 1965a).

The Size of the Floral Meristem. The foregoing considerations lead on to a further important but difficult issue, namely, that in some species with complex zygomorphic flowers the floral apex may be of quite small relative size.[1] In such apices the chemical differentiation of the groups of growth centres, i.e. those of sepals, petals, etc., must take place in a very small superficial area. Moreover, within any one group of organs, e.g. the petals, the potentiality for growth in the several growth centres is different; e.g. in markedly zygomorphic species, such as those of the Leguminoseae or Orchidaceae, some of the petals are small lateral organs, whereas the others are large and sometimes quite elaborate. One has only to study the floret primordia on the capitulum of some Compositae to appreciate how much chemical differentiation must be going on in quite small apical meristems. In these phenomena involving magnitude, there is indeed a wealth of material awaiting adequate physiological–genetical–morphogenetic investigation; for the floral meristem, large or small, is the arena in which obscure but very remarkable biochemical events are taking place. In the concomitant morphological developments one may perceive the effects; (i) of general and specific genic action; (ii) of regulative and correlative factors mediated through the reaction system; (iii) of sequences of orderly biochemical reactions; and (iv) of the biophysical factors which are involved in the translocation of materials and the assumption of form – in short, the visible manifestation of *all* the constituent processes.

[1] The author appreciates that he has raised the critical question: What is 're- latively small'? He has in mind, quite simply, what will seem rather small to the investigator *who is trying to observe*, and *to treat experimentally* a delicate meristematic region in which many reactions and developments are taking place.

FLORAL COMPLEXITY

By training and experience, the comparative morphologist is familiar with a considerable range of species in their vegetative and reproductive diversity. He might, indeed, be accused by some of existing in a kind of bondage to external appearances. For example, on the evidence of fossil and living plant species, some ancient vascular plants seem bulky and complex, and are described as being primitive; whereas other, more modern species, as in the ferns, are less bulky and more precise in their geometrical configuration; these being held to be derivative. The morphological differences between ancient fossil and modern living species are not only impressive in themselves: there is the further interest that some species survived whereas others did not. But, one may perhaps ask, how fundamentally important are morphological differences? From genetical studies of both ferns and flowering plants we now know that quite small hereditary differences, as in mutations, may result in rather conspicuous morphological differences in the adult state. The comparative morphologist has made much of these morphological differences. They are, after all, his basic materials. But, as it now seems, in certain instances at least, too much may have been made of some differences. In the angiosperms, for example, the zygomorphic flower is usually regarded as evidence of a considerable evolutionary advance on related species with actinomorphic flowers. Yet, in some races of the snapdragon (*Antirrhinum*), both peloric (i.e. actinomorphic or radially symmetrical) and zygomorphic flowers are known. When a peloric and a normal zygomorphic type are crossed the F_1 generation has normal zygomorphic flowers. But in the F_2 generation both peloric and zygomorphic flowers are obtained (Fig. 12.9). These and other studies show in a remarkable manner that important and distinctive morphological characters can be determined by a single pair, or by a very small number, of genes. The genes presumably exercise their effects by modifying the distribution or intensity of growth in the petal and other loci, or in the floral receptacle as a whole. This leads on naturally to the further conjecture that, in normal median zygomorphy (i.e. in which the plane of zygomorphy lies in the plane of the axis and bract), growth in the developing flower bud may be regulated by gene-determined factors, possibly hormonal, proceeding from the shoot apex, or from the nascent or developing subtending bract, or perhaps from both. If so, it may be possible to simulate the normal genetical effect by surgical or cultural experiments in which very young flowers buds, or bud sites, are isolated from axis, or bract, or from both. The expectation is that peloric flowers might be obtained. In fact, the writer has attempted such experiments, but without success. The effect of such surgical treatment of the shoot apex of foxglove (*Digitalis purpurea*)

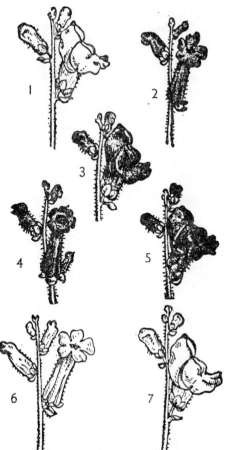

FIG. 12.9. *Antirrhinum* sp. Segregation in a cross between an Ivory, Normal, i.e. zygomorphic, (1) and a Crimson, Peloric (2) snapdragon. The F_1 generation (3) is Pink, Normal. Four of the F_2 phenotypes are illustrated (4, 5, 6, 7), no distinction being made in the diagrams between Pink and Crimson flowers. (After E. Baur, 1930.)

was to cause a return to the vegetative phase, with abundant production of leaves (Fig. 12.16 and *see* p. 336). However, in Nature, plants bearing peloric foxglove flowers are occasionally encountered, especially in certain years. In such plants the notable feature is that a very large, precociously formed actinomorphic flower, with pleiomery of parts, develops in a terminal position, whereas all the lateral buds, in spikate sequence, yield the normal zygomorphic Scrophulariaceous flower (Fig. 12.10).

Peloria, although not very common in Nature, or in horticultural species, can yet be encountered if sought with sufficient diligence. Thus, in species of Labiatae, such as *Galeobdolon luteum* and *Nepeta mussinii*, towards the end of the flowering season, the distal flowers of the inflorescence are actinomorphic, or pseudoactinomorphic, the latter showing evidence of loss of organization (*see* Fig. 10.12 and illustrations in Wardlaw, 1965a).

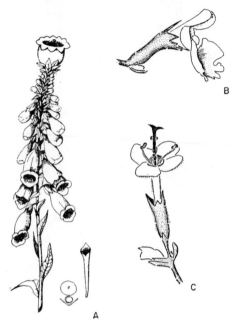

FIG. 12.10. Peloria in A, *Digitalis purpurea* (Foxglove, Scrophulariaceae); and B, C, *Nepeta mussinii* (Catmint, Labiatae). A, The terminal flower is of abnormally large size and is actinomorphic, the lateral flowers being normally zygomorphic (after Velenovsky). B illustrates (diagrammatically) a normal lateral flower of *N. mussinii* and C, a terminal one which has developed with actinomorphic symmetry. (Drawings by courtesy of Dr. E. G. Cutter.)

From observations and experiments on peloria encountered in Nature, or occurring in horticulturists' breeding stocks, it has long been known that, in some instances, the phenomenon is gene-controlled, whereas in others the effect is due to extraneous factors, even although these cannot be specified (Goebel, 1900). These observations suggest considerable scope for a useful combination of further genetical, surgical and chemical experiments. One result might be to confirm or refute the view expressed above that large morphological differences may sometimes be due to relatively simple changes in one or more of the factors in the reaction system in the floral meristem. Critical information of this kind could have a considerable impact on taxonomic, phylogenetic and evolutionary theory.

Some Special Examples of Zygomorphy. Over the wide range of flowering plant species, zygomorphy manifests itself in many different ways. The whole flower may be zygomorphic or the genetically controlled differential growth may be evident in one organ, or in a particular group of organs only. Some of these developments, combined with other features, result in unusual and remarkable floral conformations. As examples, the flowers in various species of Lecythideae may be cited (Fig. 12.11). In the cauliflorous flowers of *Couroupita guianensis* (the cannon-ball tree – *see* p. 355) the androecial component, comprising numerous stamens, has its inception in an initially uniform annulus, or ring, surrounding the style of the inferior ovary. The 'anterior' region of this ring shows considerably greater initial growth than the 'posterior' region and soon forms a ligule-like outgrowth (Fig. 12.11 B). Stamen primordia are formed on the ring. The growth of the ligule is extensive, and at maturity it is a hood-like organ, described as an androphore, with stamens growing out from its inner surface. Related genera, such as *Couratanri* and *Lecythis*, show comparable zygomorphy. In other related genera, such as *Grias* and *Barringtonia* (Fig. 12.11), on the other hand, the development of the androecial ring or cup is uniform. Families showing such developments afford materials of very great interest both for phylogenetic and morphogenetic studies. But, in fact, if one looks around among the flowering plants with imaginative interest there is a virtually unlimited fund of materials for further investigation. In terms of morphogenetic interpretation we have so far done no more than touch the fringes of an extensive and wonderful evolutionary tapestry.

The inception and development of the single legume at, or near, the summit of the floral meristem in the Leguminosae present points of rather special interest for students of morphogenesis, just as they have done in the past for students of comparative morphology. It is not the writer's intention to enter here upon the various conflicting assertions, on the one hand that the legume is lateral to the centre and summit of the floral meristem and can therefore be homologized with a foliar organ; on the other that it originates as a truly terminal organ and must therefore be 'explained' morphologically in some other way, e.g. as an axial structure. For literature and references, *see* Newman, 1933, 1936, and Thompson, 1936. Fig. 12.12 illustrates the inception and further growth of the gynoecium in *Acacia* after the inception of the stamen primordia has been completed. Newman (1936*a*, *b*) interpreted these observations as evidence that the legume or carpel originates on one side of the small apical dome and that it is forced

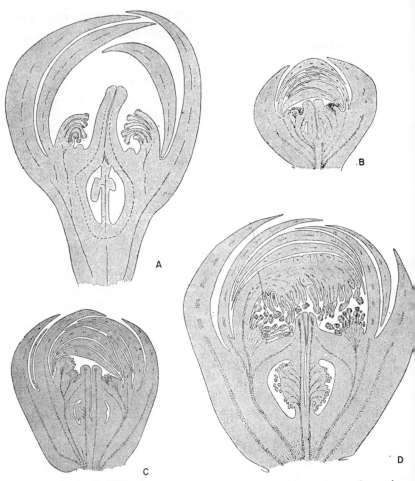

FIG. 12.11. Species of Lecythideae (Myrtales) with profuse stamen formation and, in some species, very elaborate staminal zygomorphy.

A, *Barringtonia samoensis*. Radial longitudinal section of a young flower. In this genus the stamens, which all bear anthers at maturity, originate in a wide ring or cup-like disc which surrounds and surmounts the gynoecium. (×26.)

B, C, D, *Couroupita guianensis* (the cannon-ball tree). B. Radial longitudinal section of a young flower, with stamens being formed on a ring round the nascent style. On the left, i.e. the anterior side, of the staminal disc, a very small outgrowth, described as the ligule, can be seen. (×40.) C, Radial longitudinal section showing the further development of androecial zygomorphy: the ligule, on left, has now formed stamen primordia. (×40.) D. An older bud, showing the fleshy, hood-like ligule or androphore (left), with abundant stamens on its inner face. (×4.)

(After J. McL. Thompson, *Trans. Roy. Soc., Edinb.*, 1921, and *Publ. Hartley Bot. Lab.*, Univ. Liverpool, 1927.)

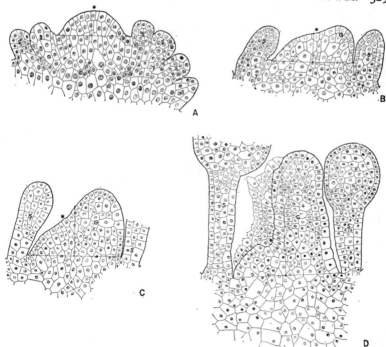

FIG. 12.12. *Acacia suaveolens* Willd. Stages in the formation of the gynoecium – the legume – as seen in median longitudinal sections of the floral meristem. A. A young flower-bud, showing the summit of the dome-shaped apical meristem (asterisk), S, Stamen primordia; T, the 'shoulder' tissue from which the stamen primordia develop; P, pith. B, The inception of the legume, G, the asterisk marking the former position of the summit of the meristem. C, A later stage in legume formation. The dot at the top of the vertical line indicates the centre of the system, as determined by a bisection of the base of the apical cone. The asterisk as before. D. Legume formation is now well advanced. Indications as in A–C. The irregular layer of tissue, to the left of the gynoecium, is a portion of the legume margin. (After J. McL. Thompson, *Publ. Hartley Bot. Lab.*, Univ. Liverpool, 1936, traced from photomicrographs by I. V. Newman, *Jour. Linn. Soc. Bot.*, 1933, and *Proc. Linn. Soc. N.S.W.*, 1936.)

from its lateral position by the pressure of the growing stamens. It thus eventually occupies a terminal position. Meanwhile, the residue of the apical cone or dome is displaced to one side and becomes suppressed or non-functional. Newman, in short, upheld the classical view that carpels are essentially foliar in nature. On the other hand, from an analysis of the same anatomical and morphological data, Thompson concluded that the legume is a terminal organ, and that the facts supported his general view

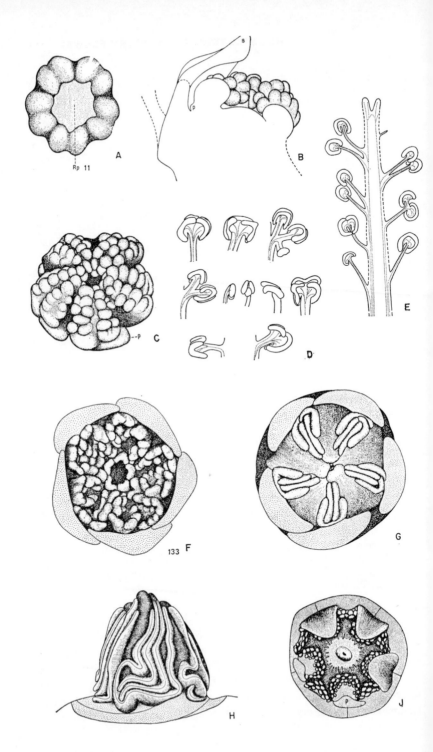

133 F

that the essential feature of the flower is that it is a sporogenous axis, i.e. a strobiloid structure, usually heterosporous and with megaspore formation typically located in the distal region. The writer's theory of floral inception and development, as considered on p. 318, and the knowledge that growth centres may occur high up on the apical dome, whether it be in the vegetative or reproductive phase, lead him to the conclusion that the evidence favours Newman's interpretation. But, as the summit of the apex is also a physiological field and the site of a reaction system, the growth of the most distal region of the floral axis into a terminal gynoccium is in no sense ruled out. These terminal regions of the meristem, however relatively small they may be, may also be envisaged as loci in which gene-determined and correlatively controlled reactions take place. To obtain an adequate understanding of the nature and sequence of the relevant metabolic and biophysical events in the small masses of tissue that are involved, e.g. as in the inception of the legume, is likely to prove a task of very considerable magnitude. But at least the problem in its main outlines is now clearly before us.

ANDROECIAL COMPLEXITY

In a comprehensive memoir, Van Heel (1966) has described and discussed the complex staminal developments in species of Malvales, especially with a view to testing the applicability of telome or classic (foliar) theories of the nature of stamens. In each of the groups examined (Malvaceae, Bomba-

FIG. 12.13. The androecial development in various Malvales. A, B, *Malope trifida* (Malvaceae). A, downward view of dissected flower-bud, showing the staminal buttresses; *Rp*, indicates the petal radius, i.e. the stamen primordia are not quite central and axillary to the petals. B, An older flower as seen in longitudinal view: the staminal buttresses have now formed lobed (antheroid) structures; the petals (*p*), at this stage, consist of small abaxial ridges on the staminal buttresses; *s*, sepals. (A, B, ×*c*. 50.)
    C, *Abutilon darwinii* (Malvaceae). Development of stamen primordia; *p*, petal primordium. (×*c*. 50.)
    D, E, *Hibiscus* spp. (Malvaceae). D, *H. syriacus*, illustrating various stamens. E, *H. rosasinensis* var. *liliiflorus*, showing two antipetalous rows of stamens. F, *Pachira insignis* (Bombacaceae). Downward view of developing flower, showing petals, the very complex staminal development, and (centre) the young carpels.
    G, H, *Ochroma lagopus* (Bombacaceae). G, a stage in the development of the androecium as seen from above. (×16.) H, Side view of staminal development. (×8.)
    J, *Mollia speciosa* (Tiliaceae). Downward view of flower-bud; the androecium consists of ten separate, contiguous, proximally united, diplosteminous groups of stamens. (*p*), petal. (×40.)
(After W. A. van Heel, *Blumea*, 1966.)

caceae, Sterculiaceae, Tiliaceae and Elaeocarpaceae), the nascent androecium is regarded as usually consisting of five primordial units, each of
which may yield a more or less complex group of stamens. Some Tiliaceae
have ten groups, each staminal group having a three-trace vascular system
which is reminiscent of a leaf-trace. A group is deemed to originate from a
single primordium, these primordia collectively being arranged in a
phyllotactic system in antisepalous, antipetalous or in intermediate positions on the floral receptacle according to the species. The carpels alternate
with those regions of the stamen groups which are most advanced at the
time of carpel inception, this suggesting that we are dealing with growth
centres and their fields, the most central of the cells being of high metabolic
and regulative potential. In species of Malvaceae and Bombacaceae the
monothecous, or unitary, stamen primordium becomes deeply divided
into two equal lobes (Fig. 12.13), with facing xylem. In the Malvaceae this
process of lobing may continue for two or three times in succession, all the
new nascent members lying in the same plane. In other species, in which
this division or lobing process goes further, the new parts have a three-
dimensional disposition. Some of the stamen extensions, e.g. the central
one in Sterculiaceae and Tiliaceae may be sterile, i.e. it develops as a
staminode. In some species the primordial staminal lobes are 'distinctly
foliar' in appearance. Van Heel concluded that in the androecium of the
Malvales one can perceive a series of transitions between more branched
(stachysporous) and more foliar (phyllosporous) formations. Reduction in
the number of stamens is considered to be effected during development by
the loss of parts, by congenital fusion, by incorporation and by flattening.
These are, of course, descriptive terms based on the concepts of phylogenetic morphology. The contemporary student of morphogenesis tends
to be critical of this mode of description and comparison. Although the
difficulties are great, for the developmental situations are innately of great
complexity, each event, e.g. the growth of the floral receptacle, the outgrowth and lobing of a stamen primordium, are specifically regulated
dynamic activities, taking place, as it were, here and now in embryonic
tissue. In the development of an embryonic stamen primordium – a simple
object at the outset – one may perceive a progressive elaboration not unlike
the further development of leaf primordia in ferns and some flowering
plants; i.e. one may consider the developments presented by Van Heel in
terms of growth centres as already discussed (pp. 123, 209).

REVERSIBLE AND OTHER CHANGES IN FLORAL DEVELOPMENT

Because of the evident differences between the vegetative leafy shoot and
the compact showy flower of limited growth, some botanists have tended

to regard the two phases as being quite different in kind. And so, of course, they are. With the onset of flowering, the pattern of growth in the apical meristem changes, and an irreversible series of new developments usually ensues, till, eventually, the most distal region of the meristem is used up or remains as an inconsiderable quiescent residue (Fig. 12.14). Yet there are species, such as the pineapple (*Ananas sativus*, Bromeliaceae), in which the shoot apex gives rise to the organs of the floral phase, and then grows on to

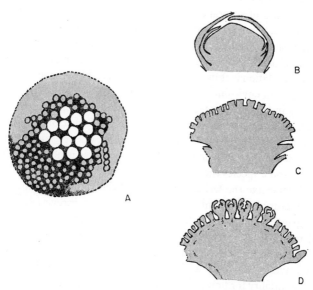

FIG. 12.14. *Tussilago farfara*. A, diagrammatic representation of a young capitulum, with the bracts removed, showing young ray and (centre) the enlarged disc florets at the summit of the floral meristem. (×20.) B, C, D, Stages in capitulum development as seen in median longitudinal section. (These are all tracings from photographs, after C. W. Wardlaw, *Growth in Living Systems*.) (*See also* Plate 10.)

form a leafy axis. In some of the Arales, e.g. *Arum maculatum* (Fig. 12.4), the vegetative apex is transformed into a reproductive one, or spadix, consisting of groups of female, intermediate and male florets, but it finally terminates in a distal, elongated storage organ. There are also records in works on plant teratology of organs intermediate between petals and stamens, or stamens and carpels, or in which regenerative growth takes place in the distal region, with the formation of a new vegetative axis (Worsdell, 1916). These examples of departures from the 'normal' onto-genetic development have been referred in different instances to external factors or to changes in the genetical constitution. Thus, in a study of floral morphology in certain strains of cotton (selfs and reciprocal F_1 hybrids from the 'M8' doubled haploid of *Gossypium hirsutum* and a single plant with the cytoplasm of *G. anomalum*) Mayer (1966, where earlier literature on these materials is cited) reported that both genes and cytoplasm have important effects on the formation of external ovules on the staminal columns, and also on the number of fertile and sterile anthers present. A particular gene (EO) is active in these anomalous ovular developments. However, when all the flowers in individual plants, kept under observation for a period of several months, were examined it was found that, in the same plant, there was nevertheless a highly significant correlation between anomalous floral developments and environmental factors, in particular, the relative humidity and maximum and minimum temperatures. Floral differentiation is thus affected by three variables, namely, cytoplasm, gene dosage and environment.

Instances in which the vegetative apex persists and 'grows through' the inflorescence, and cases of vivipary, in which the flower bud, or some part of it, develops as a vegetative bud, as in various grasses, indicate that the change from the vegetative to the reproductive phase is not invariably irreversible. In some species the reversal can be easily brought about. Thus, in various Compositae the writer found that if the young capitulum was bisected, punctured at the centre or otherwise injured, it reverted completely to the vegetative condition. When *Petasites hybridus* was subjected to such surgical treatments, primordia which would normally have developed as small, simple inflorescence bracts developed as conspicuous, petiolate, laminate leaves. Only fairly well developed capitula retained some residue of their potentiality for flower formation (Fig. 12.15). When young bisected capitula were treated with gibberellic acid, which usually tends to promote the floral phase, a complete reversion to the vegetative phase was still obtained (for fuller details and illustrations *see* Wardlaw, 1965a).

The effects of disbudding plants at the onset of the flowering phase, i.e. to prolong the vegetative phase and form stronger plants for more profuse flowering later, has long been known in horticultural practice. In disbudding experiments using *Xanthium* and *Perilla* (in both of which species the photoperiodic needs for flower induction are now well known), Lam and Leopold (1960, 1961) found that the plants returned to the vegetative phase. If plants of *Xanthium* had not received a sufficient number of the appropriate inductive cycles they returned to the vegetative state without further treatment. In *Perilla crispa*, a short-day species, there was an eventual return to the vegetative state in plants in which appropriate photoperiodic exposures had not been maintained for a sufficient number (about 20) of cycles of short photoperiods. But in plants which had had 35 cycles reversion to the vegetative state was markedly affected by disbudding. The

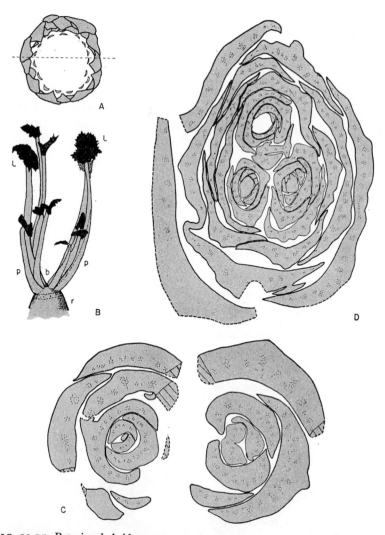

FIG. 12.15. *Petasites hybridus:* return to the vegetative phase after injury to capitula of various ages. A, An older capitulum, with the outer bracts removed, as seen from above. The bracts which will subtend the florets can be seen towards the periphery of the otherwise naked apical capitulum dome. When such apices, and also younger ones, were bisected as shown, punctured at the centre or otherwise injured, they reverted to the vegetative phase, with the formation of large laminate leaves. B, A bisected capitulum, showing evident reversion to the foliose, vegetative phase. C, A bisected capitulum, as seen in transverse section: two well-developed vegetative buds, with large enveloping foliage leaves, have been formed. D, A mid-transition apex which had been bisected. On further growth, the half-meristems have undergone fragmentation and have formed several vegetative apices; three are shown in this half-section. It can be seen that the leaf-bases are fleshy and of large size, partly encircling the axis. The profuse covering of cottony hairs has been omitted. (After C. W. Wardlaw, *Organization and Evolution in Plants,* 1965.)

reverted plants, however, could then be reinduced twice by subjecting the originally induced leaves to appropriate photoperiodic treatment. From their collective experimental observations, Lam and Leopold concluded that, when the inductive treatment was withdrawn, the effectiveness of the stimulus to flowering coming from treated leaves declined with time; and where reversion to the vegetative state was obtained, there was a decline in the stimulus proceeding from the induced leaves. Such observations lend themselves to interpretation in terms of reaction system theory.

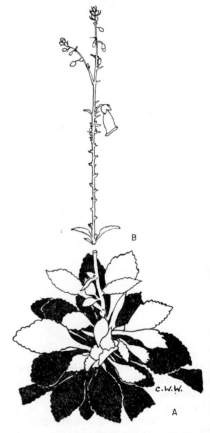

FIG. 12.16. *Digitalis purpurea*. In the foxglove, a characteristic rosette plant with tall, bracteate racemes, injuries to the very young inflorescence apex typically result in an increase in formation of foliage leaves above the rosette and in some instances, as here illustrated, in an axis in which the further development of young flower buds has been mostly suppressed. A, Lower region of a plant with an incised apex, showing part of the original rosette (black) and a considerable increase in the number of vegetative leaves (white) as seen from above. ($\times \frac{1}{2}$.) B, The modified racemose inflorescence, with many small or absent flower buds, which developed. (*See* text, p. 324.) (After C. W. Wardlaw, unpublished, based on tracings from photographs.)

Effects of Surgical Treatments on Digitalis purpurea. In this rosette species even the largest plants, in the writer's experience, have terminal apices which are still in the vegetative state in late autumn and early spring. With the onset of the reproductive phase, in early summer, the apex increases in size and begins to give rise to bracts and flower-buds in an orderly spiral sequence. Using such apices, of plants growing in flat pots to admit of continuous observation under a stereoscopic microscope, the writer attempted to induce young flower-buds, normally zygomorphic, to develop with radial, or actinomorphic, symmetry. The technique used was to make small tangential incisions: (i) above the primordium to preclude basipetal regulative effects from the shoot apical meristem; (ii) between the bract and the nascent axillary bud to preclude regulative effects proceeding acropetally from the foliar organ; and (iii) in both positions. In a considerable number of such treatments, attempted during two growing seasons, the expected result was not realized. However, other effects were of some interest. In particular, even in shoots with still viable and growing terminal apices, many of the lower, normally bracteate leaves underwent further development and had the appearance of small foliage leaves; and there was an outgrowth of basal, leafy shoots. In some instances the floral axis underwent a quite considerable, almost normal, elongation, but, as shown in Fig. 12.16, its lower region was covered with small arrested buds in the axils of small bracts. The upper regions of such axes showed a return to the normal racemose condition, with normal flower-buds in the axils of more foliose bracts. These observations afford further evidence that damage to the inflorescence apex may result in a return to the vegetative phase.

EXTERNAL FACTORS IN FLORAL ORGANIZATION

Some of these factors have been investigated by experimental procedures. J. Heslop-Harrison (1956 *et seq.*) described changes in the structure and function of floral organs which he induced by varying such external factors as temperature and light, and by applying auxin. Y. Heslop-Harrison and Woods (1959) found that when genetically male plants of dioecious *Cannabis sativa* L. are grown under short days and low night temperature, many of the flowers formed are inter-sexual, a considerable amount of meristic variation, fusions and adnations being present in the male flowers. In male flowers the inter-sexuality consisted in a modification of stamens to carpellate and intermediate structures. In some species one or other of the sets of reproductive organs could be more or less completely suppressed in what are normally hermaphrodite flowers (J. Heslop-Harrison 1960); and various correlative changes in other floral members, e.g. the calyx and corolla were noted.

When plants at an early stage in floral morphogenesis were treated with auxin profound changes were induced in the structure and function of the floral members (J. Heslop-Harrison, 1959). In species with hermaphrodite (or monoclinous) flowers the corolla and androecium were suppressed to a more or less marked degree, whereas the calyx and gynoecium become relatively enlarged. In monoecious species, e.g. cucurbits, the formation of the first female flower was advanced in time and the ratio of male to female flowers diminished. In the dioecious hemp plant (*Cannabis sativa*) male plants formed female or intersexual flowers. In these instances Heslop-Harrison considered that the applied auxin had acted as a regulating rather than as a primary determining factor; i.e. it changed the balance of growth between the different kinds of floral organs. This view is in accord with the writer's idea that certain specific properties of the growth centres in any

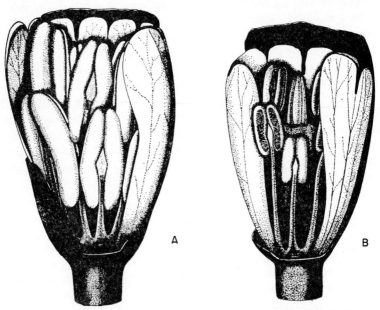

FIG. 12.17. *Melandrium rubrum*. A, Androecium as seen in a partly dissected male flower bud. B, Induced, smaller, smut-infected stamens, as seen in a normally stameless female flower; pistil with its five stigmas in centre. (A and B, both drawn to same scale.) (After C. W. Wardlaw, *Growth in Living Systems*, 1961.)

particular whorl or helix on the floral receptacle, e.g. of calyx, corolla, etc., are determined as the result of serial genic evocation; i.e. once initiated, specific morphogenetic developments can be suppressed; but they cannot readily be fundamentally modified. However, instances of organs of intermediate or dual character are not uncommon; but these, too, can be referred to particular metabolic properties of the growth centres. The results obtained with applied auxin may now be linked with changes known to occur in plants exposed to various environmental conditions. Galun, Jung and Lang (1962) effected sex modification in male cucumber buds (*Cucumis sativus*), growing in aseptic culture, by directly applying IAA to them. The

floral buds had been taken into culture so young that they were morphologically and physiologically still bisexual, or undetermined sexually. IAA
or gibberellic acid (GA_3), or a combination of the two, was applied
directly to the bud surface. On further growth it was found that normally
male flowers had developed a gynoecium, but anther primordia remained
unchanged at an early embryonic stage. Ovaries developed only in media
containing IAA. When GA and IAA were applied simultaneously the
former reduced the effects of the latter. Also, the stamens of buds treated
with GA were more conspicuously developed than those which received
IAA only.

Some fungal infections cause extensive modifications of the normal floral
development, e.g. *Zea mays* infected with *Ustilago maydis*, and *Melandrium
rubrum* attacked by *Ustilago violacea* (Fig. 12.17). In the former, female
flowers appear in the normal male inflorescence, an effect that is now understandable if the monoecism of maize is related to an auxin gradient (J.
Heslop-Harrison, 1959). It is known that the fungus forms IAA in the
presence of tryptophane.

In *Melandrium rubrum* the pathogen induces the formation of stamens in
genetically female plants. (*See* Heslop-Harrison, 1959; and Wardlaw,
1961, for refs.) Many other examples of the effects of external factors on
floral development are known.

THE BIOCHEMISTRY OF FLOWERING

During the vegetative phase the shoot apex forms leaf primordia in a
characteristic pattern. The process impresses one as being essentially of the
same kind throughout, suggesting that the supplies of metabolic substances
to the apical reaction system only change *quantitatively*. However, a stage
in ontogenesis is reached when the vegetative apex undergoes the radical
changes associated with flowering and gives rise to new patterns of organs,
i.e. bracts and the discrete and distinctive groups of sepals, petals, stamens
and carpels. This spectacular transformation is indicative of critical changes
in the supplies of metabolic substances reaching the apex. One may well
suppose that the apical reaction system has changed *qualitatively* and perhaps also quantitatively; i.e. new and important substances have been
introduced into it. The phase of transition to flowering has, accordingly,
been the subject of a considerable amount of experimental work.

Substances are known, e.g. gibberellic acid, which, if not 'florigenic' in a
strict sense, nevertheless promote the onset of flowering: if applied to
many plants which are still in the vegetative phase, GA typically advances
the onset of flowering and may even be a flower-inducing agent. However,
let it be said at once that, as reported in some contemporary studies, GA

has not proved to have either promoting or inducing properties when applied to some species. (For a full account of the gibberellins and flowering, *see* A. Lang in *The Encyclopedia of Plant Physiology*, Vol. 15, Pt 2, 1965.)

Effects on TIBA, etc. 2,3,5-tri-iobodenzoic acid (TIBA) has been shown to induce far-reaching changes in the shoot apices of certain dicotyledons, e.g. the tomato (Gorter, 1949, 1951; for other refs. *see* Wardlaw, 1965a). Other substances, e.g. 2-chloro-3,5-di-iobodenzoic acid, are also active and resemble TIBA in their effects. However, it has not been conclusively demonstrated that any of these substances have truly florigenic properties; but some of them undoubtedly increase the flowering response to an antecedent treatment. The transformation of the vegetative apex is now firmly associated with a low concentration of auxin, though other metabolites are also involved.

When newly germinated tomato seedlings, or even still ungerminated seeds, were treated with TIBA, flower buds were induced prematurely; two or three small leaves were first formed and then the terminal stem appeared. Thereafter, some very curious developments were observed. Instead of continuing to form leaf primordia, the shoot apex became convex, and elevated on a stalk-like structure by the rapid elongation of the stem region immediately below. In the next phase of growth a cluster of crowded, partially formed flower buds appeared on the elevated meristem. Axillary buds also developed into stalked apices, eventually forming flower buds. These would normally have developed as vegetative lateral branches. Some of the elevated apices bore a few small leaves before the inception of the flower buds. Thus, as a result of TIBA applications, there was: (i) a change in the shape of the vegetative apex: (ii) the suppression of leaf formation and growth; (iii) a marked subapical elongation, yielding a stalk-like structure; and (iv) the premature induction of flower buds, though not of normal flowering.

Effects Induced by Gibberellic Acid. A copious and expanding literature deals with the effects of gibberellic acids (GA) on flowering (*see* A. Lang 1957; Lang *et al.*, 1957; Lang and Reinhard, 1961; Michniewicz and A. Lang, 1962, where bibliography is cited; Zeevaart and A. Lang, 1962, etc.: Lang, 1965; Nitsch, 1965; Cutter, 1965).

In some, though not in all, of the species that have been given GA applications the onset of flowering has been more or less conspicuously promoted. In some species, according to Lang and Reinhard (1961), it may even be induced. This claim is still tentative though, as Lang and Reinhard emphasized: 'The gibberellins are the first class of compounds which cause flower formation in numerous plants grown under strictly non-inductive temperature or light regimes, this effect, in any given species, being consistent and reproducible.' These authors also noted that 'the precise function of gibberellin in flower formation is by no means clear and may be indirect in nature'. Evidence and inference of this kind support the view that 'morphogenetic substances', however important they may be in an organizational process, only exercise their effects as components of a compatible reaction system.

Not all of the gibberellins promote or induce flower formation. Michniewicz and Lang (1962) examined the effects of GA_1 to GA_9 on stem elongation and flower formation in five species of flowering plants, namely, *Myosotis alpestris* and a biennial strain of *Centaurium minus* (cold-requiring plants), *Silene armeria* and *Crepis parviflora* (long-day plants), and *Bryophyllum crenatum* (a long-short-day plant). *Myosotis* and *Centaurium* were held at non-inductive temperatures and long days. The other three species were given short-day treatments. Flower formation was only obtained in *Myosotis* with GA_7 and GA_1, the latter being relatively less active. GA_3 was the most effective for *Centaurium*, followed by GA_1, GA_4 and GA_7, and perhaps GA_5 and GA_9. Flower formation in *Silene* was induced only by GA_7, and in *Bryophyllum*, by GA_3, GA_4 and GA_7. In *Crepis* the most effective gibberellins were GA_4 and GA_7. In fact, different gibberellins were different in their florigenic activities. Apart from *Crepis parviflora*, flower inception after GA treatment was always preceded by elongation of the stem or internode, but the correlation between the effects of the several gibberellins on stem elongation and flower induction was not complete in all cases.

Lona (1962) pointed out that in their physiological activities the gibberellins are important in that they link genetical and ecological aspects of plant phenology (defined as the study of the times of recurring natural phenomena). GA or GA-like manifestations may occur at different stages in ontogenesis, e.g. seed germination, hypocotyl elongation, bud sprouting, the grand period of growth, sustained growth in climbing and twining plants, stem and peduncle elongation and the inception of flowering. But there are notable exceptions in which the gibberellins appear to be absent, or almost completely so; e.g. in truly dwarf plants. In general terms, Lona's views on GA-action, which he has elaborated in considerable detail, are to the effect that wherever GA has a significant morphogenetic effect, it acts as a 'congruous' component of the reacting metabolic substances in a growing or formative region.

DNA and RNA in Flower Inception. The onset of flowering is characterized by changes in differential growth and in the organogenic pattern in the shoot apical meristem (or reaction system) and also by a close and usually obligatory sequence of specific genic activities. Accordingly, the synthesis of DNA and RNA is of critical importance during this phase of development. This is now becoming generally appreciated by various investigators, a typical experimental approach being to examine to what extent the induction of flowering, e.g. by appropriate photoperiodic exposures, can be arrested or modified by applications of substances known to interfere with nucleic acid synthesis. Salisbury and Bonner (1958, 1960) found that the photoperiodic induction of *Xanthium pennsylvanicum* was inhibited by applications of 5-fluorouracil (5–FU) (a pyrimidine), this substance being most effective when it was applied directly to the bud at the beginning of the inductive dark period. It appears that 5–FU interferes with the metabolic processes in the apex that lead to flowering. Investigations by Bonner and Zeevaart (1962) showed that the critical process affected by 5–FU is the synthesis of RNA in the apical bud; and also that C^{14}-labelled 5–FU is incorporated into bud RNA, the extent of this process being reduced by simultaneous applications of orotic acid. The synthesis of DNA is also inhibited by 5–FU, but it is the inhibition of RNA synthesis that is of critical importance in offsetting the photoperiodic induction of flowering. These workers also found that 5-fluorodeoxyuridine (5–FDU), a specific inhibitor of DNA multiplication, inhibits the development of floral primordia; but if thymidine is also applied, even at the end of the photoinductive period, the 5–FDU effect can be reversed. Heslop-Harrison (1960), in a study of *Cannabis sativa*, found that 2-thiouracil inhibits flowering, apparently by causing the apices to become unresponsive to the floral stimulus from the leaves; and Moore and Bonde (1962) reported that 2-thiouracil inhibits flowering in *Pisum sativum*.

THE CULTURE OF EXCISED FLOWER BUDS AND FLORAL ORGANS

With the increasing use of the techniques of tissue and organ culture, especially during the late 1940s, it was inevitable that, in time, investigators would apply these valuable techniques to physiological and morphogenetic studies of flower buds and of individual floral organs. In 1942 La Rue cultured flower buds aseptically *in vitro* and described their rooting. Since then a considerable literature has developed on the culture of flowerbuds, stamens, pollen, ovaries, ovules, embryos and endosperm (*see* Maheshwari, 1962, 1963; Maheshwari and Ranga Swamy, 1963; Lang, 1965; Nitsch, 1963, 1965). Only a few examples of the kind of information that is now being obtained can be given here. In general, the principal advances relate to substances which promote the growth of buds, fruits or floral organs when incorporated in media of known composition; but environmental factors also enter into the picture.

As already noted (p. 171), the apices of angiosperms have proved difficult to culture *in vitro*. However, once this difficulty has been overcome, as by the incorporation of GA in the medium (Nitsch, 1963), it is possible to compare the growth and morphogenetic activities of excised apices of photoperiodically induced plants with those which have not been given this flower-inducing treatment. Wetmore, cited by Nitsch (1963), demonstrated that when apices of *Chenopodium album* were excised from plants which had been given the appropriate photoperiodic exposure for flower induction, and grown in aseptic culture, they formed flower primordia, whereas apices from non-induced whole plants remained vegetative. But the inductive effect may also be induced in excised vegetative apices growing *in vitro*. In *Cuscuta reflexa*, a short-day species, Baldev (1959, 1962) induced flowering in excised cultured apices, either in total darkness (sugar was present in the medium) or under photoperiods of less than 10 hours. Again, Chailakhian (1961) and Raghaven and Jacobs (1961), using excised vegetative apices of *Perilla*, were able to induce the formation of flower-buds. In this 'short-day' species the exposure of apices *in vitro* to long-days prevented the full transition from the vegetative to the reproductive phase. A long 'sterile cone' was formed, whereas, after exposure to short-days, inflorescences were induced. Such observations are not only of great technical importance: they also indicate that metabolic changes of a comprehensive character take place in the vegetative apex during its transition to the flowering phase. But they do not yet throw new light on the proximal factors in the actual morphogenetic process.

Lunaria annua, which must have cold treatment for the induction of flowering, has now been made to yield flowers *in vitro* from 3 cm. petiole segments (Pierik, 1965, 1966).

A novel series of observations on the formation of adventitious flower-buds *in vitro* has been reported by Chouard and Aghion (1961). They found that internodal segments of tobacco ('Wisconsin 38') could be grown without auxin or kinetin in the culture medium. Such segments formed a callus and, later, buds. If a segment had been taken from a young plant or from the lower region of an older one it formed *vegetative buds*; but if it had been excised from the upper region of a flowering stem it gave rise to *flower-buds*, with a minimal development of pedicel or bract. Segments taken from intermediate positions first of all formed buds: these formed a few leaves or bracts between the callus and the flower (Fig. 12.18). Moreover, the closer the excised segment was to the inflorescence, the fewer were the leaves and bracts formed before flower-bud formation. These remarkably interesting observations will almost certainly prepare the way for a new attack on the problems of floral morphogenesis. An impressive feature of these experiments is the apparent ability of the 'florigenic factor' (or system of factors) to persist in stem tissue. (*See* Plate 11.)

A further important contribution to this general topic has been made by Paulet (1965): he has shown that adventitious floral buds can be obtained

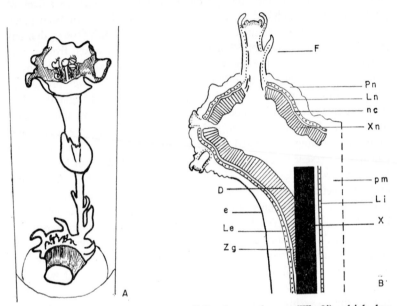

FIG. 12.18. A, A tobacco flower (*Nicotiana tabacum* 'W.38') which has developed from a segment of an inflorescence stalk, growing in sterile culture *in vitro*. (A tracing of a photograph, by courtesy of Danielle Aghion (D. Nicholas), *C.R. Acad. Sci.*, 255, 1962.) (*See also* Plate 11.) B, Longitudinal section of an inflorescence stem segment (proximal pole) which had been grown *in vitro*: a vascularized callus has developed and has given rise to a flower-bud (*F*). *D*, dynamic wedge; *e*, epidermis; *Le*, *Li*, external and internal phloem respectively; *Ln*, phloem of the new callus formation; *Zg*, generative region of vascular tissue; *X*, xylem; *Xn*, neoformed xylem; *nc*, neoformed cambium; *pm*, medullary parenchyma (*see also* Plates 11, 12). (After D. (Aghion) Nicolas, *Physiol. Veg.*, 1965.)

from cultured root segments of *Cichorium intybus*. These buds subsequently expanded into normal mature flowers, comparable in appearance and pigmentation with those of a normally growing plant (*see also* Paulet and Nitsch, 1963, 1964). Only Paulet's main conclusions, based on a long series of cultural experiments, can be indicated here. These include the following: (1) According to its concentration, a particular substance appears to exercise a gradation of morphogenetic effects. (2) To obtain flower-buds, all auxin in the cultural environment must be suppressed. (3) Low concentrations of sugars (1–2 per cent) promote the induction of roots; higher concentrations inhibit this development, but at 5 per cent vegetative bud induction is promoted; at still higher sugar concentrations vegetative bud formation is reduced but flower-bud formation is promoted. (4) The effects of kinins (cytokinins) have to be related to the auxin concentrations present. The kinins appear to be the 'true bud-forming substances', for they alone consistently induce the neoformation of *large* numbers of buds. (5) Other substances, in the categories of purines and pyrimidines, which also augment bud induction, though more feebly in tissue cultures, apparently exercise their effects by counterbalancing the inhibitory action of auxin. (6) Yet other substances, such as various physiologically active phenolic compounds, chiefly amplify the effects of auxins and sugars. (*See* Plate 12.)

Paulet (1965) has summarized contemporary findings in the following table:

Summary of Interactions of Substances Contributing to Organogenesis

(The number of crosses (+) indicates the concentrations)
(After Paulet, 1965)

Organogenesis of	Induction Promoted by			
	Sugars	Auxins	Phenolics	Cytokinins
Flower-buds	+ + +	o	+ +	+
Vegetative buds	+ +	±	?	+ + +
Roots	+	+ + +	+ + +	o

As Paulet pointed out, the results of these investigations enable us to induce vegetative and floral buds in tissues in which these developments had not hitherto been obtained; and the techniques, with modifications, can no doubt be widely extended to other species. Lastly, the information, viewed collectively, supports the present writer's thesis that, in all these morphogenetic developments, we are fundamentally concerned with organismal reaction systems, with different special components in different instances, which reach a state of dynamic equilibrium and yield characteristic organ and tissue patterns. (*See also* Nitsch, 1966 and Plate 12.)

In the culture of anthers of *Allium cepa* and *Rhoeo discolor*, removed from the flower at leptotene–zygotene and diplotene–diakinesis stages, there was 100 per cent survival up to the formation of one-celled microspores when RNA was added to the medium. Additions of DNA gave less successful developments. Kinetin in the medium accelerated the meiotic prophase in cultured anthers of *Tradescantia*. When grown in culture, pollen has yielded callus-like masses, and various hormonal substances have been found to be important in different instances. (For refs. and details *see* Nitsch, 1963.)

The *in vitro* culture of young fruits has a prominent position in this literature (*see* Nitsch, 1963, 1965). As Nitsch and others have shown, ovaries can be excised and grown aseptically in relatively simple media. Tomato ovaries, for example, were grown in this way, the growth curve, developmental pattern, as also the taste and colour of the fruit at maturity, being normal, though, in this instance, the fruits did not attain to large size (Nitsch, 1951). However, Maheshwari and Lal (1958) grew the fruits of *Iberis amara* to larger than natural size *in vitro*. As a further example of what has been achieved using this technique, Nitsch (1951) cultured pollinated flowers of *Cucumis anguria* and obtained viable seeds which, on germination, grew into normal plants. Other species have also been successfully handled in this way (for refs. *see* Nitsch, 1963, 1965). Unpollinated ovaries usually fail to grow in culture. However, if auxins are added to the medium, or applied directly, the ovary is stimulated to grow. These studies have been especially, or perhaps chiefly, important because of the information they have yielded concerning the nutrient requirements of developing fruits of different species. As might be expected, sugars and appropriate nitrogen sources are essential. Of the other substances tested, e.g. coconut milk, plant extracts, kinins, vitamins, etc., variable results, from inhibition to stimulation, have been reported for the small number of species so far examined.

Excised flower buds or ovaries may be induced to develop adventitious roots in culture, especially by the presence of an auxin in the medium. In the tomato Nitsch (1954) found that, once initiated, these roots grew best in the presence of tomato juice or of thiamine or pyridoxine, both known to be essential for the elongation of excised tomato roots growing in culture. Various correlative developments of morphogenetic interest have been noted; for example, the growth of the ovary is slow at first, but is accelerated as the roots become well developed. These results have been variously interpreted, e.g. in terms of competition for main nutrients, the supplying power of developed roots, i.e. by uptake from the medium, or the acropetal movement of stimulatory hormonal substances, synthesized in the roots.

RECENT OBSERVATIONS ON EXPERIMENTAL FLORAL MORPHOGENESIS

During recent years many new observations on experimental floral morphogenesis have been published, especially by French investigators. Some of these are descriptions of teratological materials, sometimes described as 'Nature's experiments', but others record changes induced by the application of growth-regulating substances such as 2,4-D. Considerations of space admit of only a few examples being briefly indicated here.

Vieth (1963, 1964) described and illustrated a number of anomalous inflorescences in the genus *Scabiosa* (Dipsacaceae). It will be recalled that these are very complex inflorescences – they are sometimes referred to as synflorescences – and technical accounts of them, and of various anomalies observed, are also complex. In *Dipsacus*, as studied by various workers, the capitulum, like the leafy shoot, is based on a system of bijugate phyllotaxis. In chemical treatments of plants of *Scabiosa stellata* and *S. prolifera*, Vieth obtained various teratological inflorescences which he distinguished as follows: (i) capitula enclosing at least a multifloral, partial inflorescence; (ii) partly dissociated capitula; and (iii) pauciflorous inflorescences. For example, in the first category Vieth found that, in the axil of one of the lowermost bracts there was not the usual single flower but a partial inflorescence in which the flowers were disposed as a spike or cyme.

Dupuy (1963) has dealt in considerable detail with anomalous vegetative and floral developments in *Ruta graveolens*, *Tropaeolum majus*, *Lonicera periclymenum*, *Physalis alkekengi*, *Bergenia crassifolia*, *Corylus avellana*, *Tilia sylvestris*, *Ulmus campestris*, etc., which were induced by applications of 2,4-D (Fig. 12.19). In a thesis illustrated by some 214 text-figures and 9 plates it is evident that interested readers must have recourse to the original text. Many of the anomalous developments recorded will already be somewhat familiar to students of teratologies and vegetable oddities, e.g. petaloid stamens, fused stamens and other floral parts, virescent floral developments, diplophyllous, hooded and cup-shaped leaves; and so on. Indeed, one is led to reflect that, once the normal organized growth of a species is disturbed, e.g. as in virescent, i.e. green, flowers of *Tropaeolum majus*, an astonishing range of morphological developments may be realized. Some of the curious developments recorded, after applications of 2,4-D, etc., are illustrated in Fig. 12.19. (This paper also contains much interesting information on the natural occurrence and experimental induction of peltate, cup-shaped and other oddities of foliar development.) Dupuy (1964) has also described how plants of *Nicandra physaloides* (Solanaceae), on being treated with 2,4-D, have formed anomalous flowers, with irregular and zygomorphic developments.

In *Galtonia candicans* (Liliaceae), Guyot and Dupuy (1965) recorded the occurrence of small supernumerary flowers on basal enations of the ventral face of the outer tepals (Fig. 12.20). In these curious developments, observed by chance in the upper region of the inflorescence in certain plants, the authors envisaged an acropetal gradient of sexualization in the inflorescence. The observations are compatible with the view that the calyx and gynoecium are homologous in nature; and they demonstrate the possibility

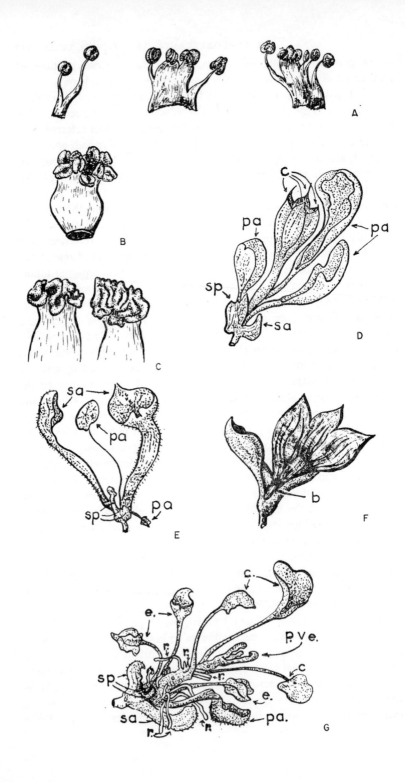

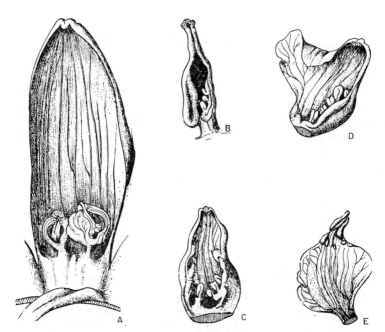

FIG. 12.20. *Galtonia candicans.* The formation of small supernumerary flowers at the base of tepals. A, Small flowers at the base of the ventral, i.e. inner face of one of the outer tepals. A filament of a normal stamen has been pressed down at front. B, An indeterminate organ with pollen-sacs (*on the left*) and ovules (*on the right*). C, D, Tepals which have undergone a 'carpelloid' development. These tepals bear more or less normal ovules in an intramarginal position. E, A staminode which had been formed in one of the supernumerary flowers. (After M. Guyot and P. Dupuy, *C.R. Acad. Sci. Paris*, 1965.)

FIG. 12.19. Anomalous floral developments.

A–C, *Ruta graveolens*. A, Different forms of staminal plates, or layers, as a result of progressive 'fusion' of the filaments. B, The androecium has developed as a tubular structure. C, Tubular fused stamens, which resemble the normal development in *Cucurbita*.

D–G, *Tropaeolum majus*. D, An anomalous virescent flower (induced by 2,4-D), in which the much enlarged gynophore bears four open carpels (*c*). The anterior petals (*pa*) are enlarged and green and not bearded. The claw is also much enlarged, but the posterior region of the flower is atrophied. E, A virescent flower reduced to its perianth, in which the corolla and the posterior region of the calyx are more or less atrophied. *sa*, anterior sepals; *sp*, pollen sacs (greatly inhibited). F, Virescent gynoecium in which the carpels have become open foliar structures. *b*, a small bud, a prolongation of the floral axis. G, A virescent flower, very highly modified, including the formation of roots (*r*) on the floral axis. The anterior and posterior sepals (*sa, sp*) show feeble differentiation and are grouped in verticels; the petals (*pa*) are considerably modified. The floral axis is abnormally elongated; it bears diplophyllous and cup-shaped stamens (*e*) and peltate carpels (*c*); it is terminated by a vegetative proliferation (*P Ve*). (After P. Dupuy, *Thesis. Fac. Sci. Univ. Poitiers*, 1963.)

of obtaining proliferations of axial symmetry from enations in the positions indicated.

Gavaudan and Dupuy (1965) illustrated and discussed the expression of intersexuality as observed in various normal and teratological stamens. They concluded that whether the apical appendage of the staminal connective is developed or reduced, it is homologous with the gynoecial style–stigma complex and that its presence is indicative of a phenomenon of intersexuality in the male sporophyll. Among others, the flowers of *Crataegus oxyacantha* L. *flore pleno* (Rosaceae) were observed to have stamens showing anomalous developments, e.g. foliose developments, the more or less normal pollen-sacs being borne on an enlarged connective; and various carpelloid developments. From a study of spontaneously occurring virescent stamens in *Eschscholzia californica* (Papaveraceae), Dupuy and Guyot (1965) concluded that the staminal structure can be referred to that of vegetative leaves.

Gavaudan and Dupuy (1965) examined the morphogenetic potentialities of *Lilium candidum* by applications of 2,4-D to plants entering the floral phase (Fig. 12.21). They reported the formation of lanceolate and ligulate tepals with hermaphrodite characters, gamopetaly, monadelphy, foliarized stamens, etc., and various morphological features common to the normal development of other Liliaceae and, more generally, to other Monocotyledons, e.g. ventral enations from lanceolate stamens, imperfect flowers and bulbils. A photographic illustration of particular interest shows a hastate tepal in the axil of which multiple buds have been formed, these showing further development into imperfect flowers. An important point made by these workers is that, since the several neo-formations associated with applications of 2,4-D are induced with considerable regularity, experimental work on floral morphogenesis, e.g. of the ligule and paracorolla, becomes possible; and since the anomalous developments occur as normal morphological characters in numerous Liliaceae, and even in other families of Monocotyledons (i.e. they are phenocopies of commonly occurring features), the way lies open for a search for simplifying general truths relating to the large accumulation of morphological and taxonomic data. In other words, many morphological characters, though specific to particular species, are no more than variations upon a central theme. Of course, it is not to be supposed that 2,4-D replaces genes; but it (or more probably, some of the substances to which it gives rise during its metabolic activities), becomes a component of the reaction system in the floral meristem and participates in the formation of floral organs which are anomalous in that species but normal to the genotype of other species, some of which would not usually be regarded as being of close taxonomic affinity.

From a morphological study of numerous plants of cultivated *Pulsatilla*

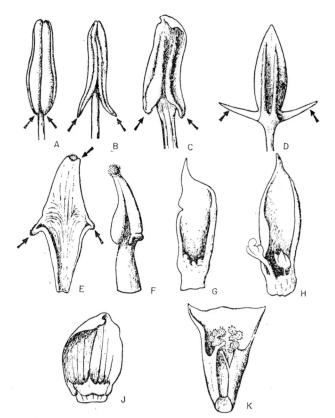

FIG. 12.21. *Lilium candidum*. Abnormal floral developments induced as a result of applications of 2,4-D to the young flowering axis, compared with *normal* morphological developments in other Liliaceous and monocotyledon species.

A, B, C, E, G, H, K, *L. candidum*. A, Normal stamen. B, Abnormal stamen with slight foliar characters. C, A strongly 'foliarized' stamen. The arrows indicate the regions of the anther in which the lanceolate, or rather, hastate (spear-head-like), character has appeared.

D, *Helicodiceros muscivorus* (Araceae). (After Troll.) A young, normal, vegetative leaf.

E, *L. candidum*. An abnormal tepal, with hastate development (arrows), as in D. The distal region (arrow) has undergone a pilose, stigma-like development.

F, *Tofieldia calyculata* (Liliaceae). Gyno-stamen (after Leinfellner).

G, H, *L. candidum*. Bracts from the floral axis in which 2,4-D has induced ventral enations. In H this neoformation is considerably more advanced and multiple buds have developed.

J, *Oceanoros* sp. (Liliaceae). Petal with ventral ligule-like enation – a normal development (after Leinfellner).

K, *Kreysigia multiflora* (Liliaceae). Base of a normal tepal, the lateral enations terminating in arbuscles (tufts), covered with glands (after Leinfellner).

(After P. Gavaudan and P. Dupuy, *C.R. Acad. Sci. Paris*, 1965.)

Mill., Kranich (1958) reported many anomalous developments, both in the vegetative and reproductive regions, these including dorsiventral flowers and branching of the usually single floral axis.

Evidence of Basipetal Regulation within the Developing Flower. So far, the formation of the several groups of floral organs has been considered in terms of an acropetally moving reaction system. However, the point has already been made that the vegetative apex should be regarded as a whole – as a system of interacting regions. A somewhat similar conclusion emerges from experimental studies of floral development. In *Physalis alkekengi* (Solanaceae) the berry-like fruit is eventually completely enclosed within the tubular calyx which enlarges by basal growth and becomes bladderlike. Fujita (1965) has shown that if the pistil is excised the rest of the flower shrivels and an abscission layer is formed at the base of the peduncle. But if the cut surfaces of excised pistils are treated with IAA (0·1, 0·01 and 0·001 per cent) or with GA (0·1, 0·001 and 0·0001 per cent) the calyces become bladder-like inflated organs. GA was considered to be more effective than IAA in that the calyces were more elongated. The removal of young fruits also usually resulted in shrivelling of the calyx and in abscission; and the larger the calyces were at the time of fruit excision, the more they tended to develop to full size, though they were smaller than those in naturally pollinated fruits. From these observations it seems clear that, in *Physalis*, the development of the fruiting flower must be considered as a whole and that basipetal gradients of growth-regulating substances, proceeding from the actively-growing gynoecium, are important in the final characteristic morphogenetic developments.

INFLORESCENCES

Observers of flowering plants soon become aware of the very considerable range of inflorescence types and, in some instances, of the complexity of the numerous yet orderly assemblage of flowers, e.g. as in the banana inflorescence. This aspect has typically been regarded as lying within the province of descriptive botany, providing abundant materials for the taxonomist and morphologist. A comprehensive review of inflorescence classification has been given by Rickett (1944). As an indication of recent and contemporary interest in this topic, readers are referred to Thompson (1933 *et seq.*), Weber (1939), Tucker (1959), Vieth (1963, 1964), Vescovi (1964), Bugnon (1964), Phelouzat (1964), Philipson (1946 *et seq.*).

Whether an inflorescence be racemose or cymose, or a simpler or more complex variant or one or other of these, it is (*a*) characteristic of the species, (*b*) may vary more or less considerably even within the same genus, or in closely related genera, (c) typically shows regulated development and (d) comes into existence as the result of morphogenetic processes in apical regions, external factors such as vernalization or photoperiodic exposure being typically involved in the induction of the initial changes to a new phase of metabolism and growth in a hitherto vegetative apex.

Even in its simplest forms the inflorescence, e.g. the raceme in *Brassica* (Cruciferae) or *Digitalis* (Scrophulariaceae), presents problems in morphogenesis which have been barely touched upon. So, presumably, it is with some such forms that we should begin. Nevertheless, in this book the author hopes to show something of the fullness of the interest and the challenge that await those who would venture into this fascinating, if difficult, field; for, be it noted, in the diversity of the inflorescence, the Plant Kingdom presents a phenomenon of a kind that is unmatched in the Animal Kingdom. And this would still be true, even if we could argue successfully that all inflorescences are ultimately no more than variations upon the themes of the racemose and the cymose patterns of construction.

In the Scitamineae – including such well-known plants as the banana (*Musa* spp.), the traveller's palm (*Ravenala madagascarensis*), the bird-of-paradise flower (*Strelitzia*), the gingers (*Zingiber* spp.), *Heliconia* and other genera familiar to the tropical botanist – we have, admittedly, an order in which the conformation of the inflorescence has reached a very advanced evolutionary state among flowering plants. Yet, in terms of morphogenetic development, it all begins in what seems to be a usual and simple way: a transverse section of a young *Musa* inflorescence discloses the presence of tangentially extended buds in the axils of bracts (Figs. 12.22, 5.2), such buds being formed in acropetal sequence as the floral axis elongates. So the main plan of the inflorescence as a whole is indefinite and racemose. It is the further growth and morphogenetic activities within these small flat buds that are so enigmatic: they give rise to cincinni, i.e. two-layered assemblages of flowers which, later, are recognized as the 'hands' of 'fingers' (i.e. individual fruits) growing out from a common 'cushion'. Thompson (1933), on the basis of developmental studies, interpreted these hands of flowers in terms of a cymose plan. The flower primordia originate as mounds of meristematic tissue, these mounds being arranged in a row, or in two alternating rows, on the meristematic cushion. At an early stage in their development the floral primordia are of approximately equal size, but the cushions on which they are formed may vary considerably in size. While both Thompson and Fahn (1953) noted that the primordia are not formed simultaneously, they are formed in such rapid succession along the cushion as to suggest that the latter is the site or locus of a diffusion reaction system which yields a patternized distribution of growth centres, which become flower primordia (Wardlaw, 1955). The flower assemblages in parts

M

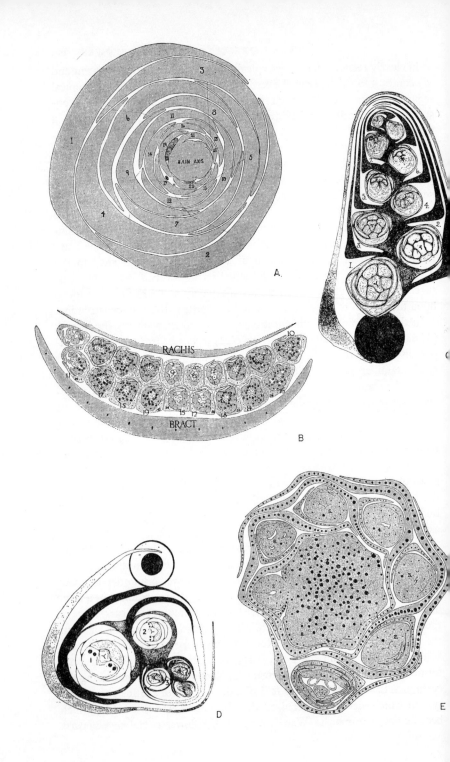

A.

MAIN AXIS

RACHIS

BRACT

B

C

D

E

of the complex inflorescences of *Heliconia, Zingiber* and *Costus* are also illustrated in Fig. 12.22. However, many other major groups are known, e.g. the Gramineae (Weber, 1939), Dipsacaceae (Vieth, 1964), Vitaceae, Asclepiadaceae (Bugnon, 1964), etc., in which the events of floral development result in inflorescences that are not easy to interpret.

Flower-buds of Endogenous Origin. In addition to the very numerous and varied aspects of inflorescence conformation, a special morphogenetic interest attaches to those species in which the flowers are cauliflorous, i.e. originating directly from the surface of the woody stem or trunk. The cauliflorous habit is, indeed, characteristic of certain genera. In some instances, as in *Theobroma cacao*, superficial buds survive on the trunk as it undergoes secondary thickening and eventually become deeply seated. These buds remain meristematic and eventually form groups of flower-buds. In other species, such as the cannon-ball tree (*Couroupita guianensis*), the flowering shoots have their inception as buds deep within the bark and have to penetrate uninterrupted sheets of living tissue before they appear at the surface of the trunk (Thompson, 1952) (*see also* Fig. 12.11). The interest and potential value of such materials for various experimental investigations and for tissue culture studies needs no emphasis.

FIG. 12.22. The complexity of inflorescences as illustrated by the Scitamineae. A, *Musa paradisiaca* L. sub. sp. *sapientum* L. (one of the commercial bananas). Transverse section of the central region at the base of pseudostem, showing leaf-bases and the young floral axis; the axillary buds (dark), close to the main axis, are the primordia of what will later become the hands, or clusters, of bananas. ($\times$30.) B, *Musa chinensis* Sweet. Transverse section of a young inflorescence, showing the main axis (rachis), the subtending bract and a 'hand', or crescentic cluster, of individual flowers, considered by some to be disposed in a cymose 'plan'. ($\times$17·5.) C, *Heliconia bihai* L. Part of an inflorescence: a young flower-bud assemblage, shown partly in section and partly in contour. ($\times$30.) D, *Zingiber zerumbet* Rosc. Transverse section of a young flower-bud assemblage. ($\times$20.) E, *Costus cylindricus* Rosc. Transverse section of a young inflorescence. ($\times$10.) (After J. McL. Thompson, *Hartley Bot. Lab. Publ.*, Univ. Liverpool, 1933.)

CHAPTER XIII

A Brief Excursion into Lower Forms

INTRODUCTION

In some of the larger brown algae, e.g. members of the Fucales, and in archegoniate and seed plants, our thinking about morphogenesis is in terms of embryonic regions, with special cells, apical cell groups or histogenic layers, to which, by way of the cell lineages to which they give rise, we can refer the inception of organs and tissue systems. In some of the 'lower forms', e.g. in green algae such as *Chara* and in many of the filamentous and thalloid brown and red algae, the whole thallus can also be traced back to the growth and orderly division of an apical cell and its segments. Examples are seen in the Sphacelariales and in *Dictyota* among brown algae, and in the Ceramiales among red algae. However, among the algae, the fungi and the lichens there are numerous instances of orderly morphogenetic developments in which *evidently* organized embryonic regions are not present. Nevertheless, the organism, which may consist of associated free cells or of associated filaments, manifests an orderly ontogenesis and is eventually recognizable because of its specific and distinctive morphological characters. Thus, in Ascomycetes and Basidiomycetes, with their elaborate ascocarps, mushrooms, puff-balls, etc., and in the lichens which comprise both algal and fungal components, characteristic morphological forms come into being by the intergrowth of filaments. So, also, in the brown and red algae, there are many organisms in which the morphological form is the result of the regulated growth of variously associated, intermingling filaments. In still more elementary forms, as in the slime mounds, in which the organism grows and spreads over the substratum as an irregular or formless plasmodium, distinctive fruiting bodies are eventually formed. Here, too, it may be duly emphasized that in 'simple' unicellular and filamentous algae the results of morphogenetic processes are evident in the external contour of the cell, the shape and disposition of the chloroplasts, nucleus and so on. Witness the distinctive cellular organization in *Chlamydomonas*, *Spirogyra*, *Oedogonium*, the desmids, etc., and the spatial arrangement of the cells in the water-net, *Hydrodictyon*. These are common and well-known organisms. They afford classical materials for morphogenetic investigation; yet, with some exceptions (*see* D'Arcy Thompson's *Growth and Form* and *Encyclopedia of Plant Physiology*, Vol. 15, 1965), they have received relatively little attention. But morphogenetic investigations of these lower forms will almost certainly lead to a whole new system of ideas and to a desirable broadening of our outlook.

Within the compass of this little book only a few examples can be discussed. But the hope is entertained that what is written here may encourage some young workers, as also dedicated algologists, mycologists and lichenologists, to reconsider the many wonderful and beautiful conformations in lower forms, and the 'stages' in their development, in terms of the morphogenetic factors which may be involved. In some instances, e.g. colonial forms, the single cell is evidently the 'morphogenetic unit'; in others, as in the fungi, the lichens, and in many red and brown algae, the filament is the basic 'unit'.

MORPHOGENETIC MOVEMENTS

In Animals. Zoologists are familiar with the phenomenon of *morphogenetic movement*. In discussing morphogenesis, J. T. Bonner (1952) referred to growth, morphogenetic movements and differentiation as being the most noteworthy constructive processes; and he defined *morphogenetic movement* as being the translocatory movement ('migration') of protoplasm, which leads to changes in form. Unless they are conversant with lower organisms, i.e. algae, fungi, slime moulds and bacteria, botanists have considerably less occasion to be concerned with such movements. In a general sense, of course, protoplasmic movements are also a commonplace in higher plants, e.g. the movement of the protoplasm during the outgrowth of a root hair, or the considerable elongation of some of the products of cambial division. However, this is not quite what zoologists have in mind when discussing the phenomenon. They are concerned with the integrated action of factors which, by controlling the movement of cells in embryonic regions, contribute to the characteristic morphogenetic pattern. The mechanism of this coordination of growth and movement is still obscure; the cause of amoeboid movement, for example, is still not understood (*see* J. T. Bonner, 1952, for a useful exposition). The physical organization of the protoplasm, with its firm outer (cortical) gel layer and its inner liquid layer, is important; and it may be that the forces of diffusion are adequate to determine movement.

In the calcareous sponge, *Grantia*, the zygote divides repeatedly to form an ellipsoidal, hollow blastula which at a certain stage undergoes inversion; i.e. it turns inside out; and thereafter further growth and differentiation result in the formation of the larva. But the physical mechanism is still not known. In echinoderm embryos the hollow, spherical, blastula stage is followed by some remarkable developments involving morphogenetic movement, in particular the invagination of the sphere leading to the gastrula stage. These and other morphogenetic movements have been widely recognized in the Animal Kingdom.

In Plants. As already noted, morphogenetic movements in the zoological sense are not known in the higher plants. Among lower forms, however, some remarkable examples have been investigated.

MORPHOGENESIS IN MYXOBACTERIACEAE

Among the Myxobacteriaceae, e.g. in *Chondromyces crocatus*, the individual organism is a rod-shaped, non-flagellate cell, dividing by transverse

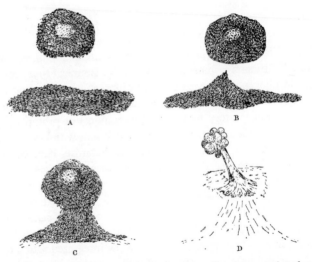

FIG. 13.1. *Chondromyces.* A bacterium in which collective, regulated morphogenetic movements result in the formation of distinctive fruiting bodies. A–D illustrate the movement of the bacteria towards a central locus, with subsequent formation of a fruiting body. (After J. T. Bonner, *Encyclopedia of Plant Physiology,* XV/1, 1965.)

fission. These bacteria, enveloped in the slime which they have secreted, have a gliding or creeping movement which becomes specially important at the onset of the reproductive phase. The individual cells then become aggregated together into masses and subsequently become organized into quite complex branched systems, bearing terminal fruiting bodies – actually multicellular cysts. In this instance, not only is the movement of the individual cells important; there is also a co-ordinated movement which is effective in the whole bacterial mass or aggregate – a very remarkable phenomenon indeed (Fig. 13.1).

MORPHOGENESIS IN THE SLIME MOULDS

Morphogenetic movements in members of this group, especially in organisms such as *Dictyostelium* spp. (Acrasiales), have been the subject of much investigation. The outstanding fact is that whereas, in the vegetative phase, the organism is a creeping naked protoplast, in the reproductive phase it develops into an elaborate and distinctive, stalked, fruiting body. These remarkable developments are brought about by morphogenetic movements (Fig. 13.2). (For a full account, *see* J. T. Bonner, 1952, 1965.)

The individual organism of *Dictyostelium* and other slime moulds in the vegetative state is a single amoeboid cell, or myxamoeba. During growth on an appropriate substratum – *Dictyostelium* lives parasitically on various bacteria and can be grown in culture – this cell undergoes abundant division. After this phase of active growth, and provided environmental conditions are favourable, large numbers of these myxamoebae undergo a streaming movement towards a centre of aggregation. Further, sustained, coordinated movements on the part of the very numerous individual cells result in the formation of branched fruiting bodies, or sorocarps, of specific and distinctive morphology; i.e. these remarkable morphogenetic developments afford evidence of genetic specificity. If the myxamoebae from two species are intermingled in culture, or if experimentally mixed protoplasts are grown, the cells, as a result of morphogenetic movements, become separated so that ultimately distinctive sorocarps, characteristic of the original two species, are obtained. Here, then, we have apparently a biophysical situation; i.e. there is evidence of motive force, derived from, or operating in, a genetically based system. The biophysical mechanism, however, is still obscure.

In some forms of *Dictyostelium discoideum* the aggregating groups of myxamoebae, and consequently the sorocarps, are considerably smaller than in the parent forms. Nevertheless, as Sussman (1955) observed, although the fructification might consist of as few as twelve cells, it still had the conformation and constructional features of larger ones. Now, whether viewed from the biophysical or biological standpoint, this is surely a very arresting observation. Sinnott (1960) referred to it as 'a remarkable example of the inherent formativeness of these cells'. But what is the nature of this 'inherent formativeness'? Have we any adequate ideas or hypotheses about it at all? And, if we have not, where shall we seek them? If the natural sciences, comprising the physical and biological sciences, possess

coherence and unity – as we hope and believe they do – 'inherent formativeness' and specificity must be referable to the physico-chemical properties
of the systems of the inorganic and organic substances of which organisms
are composed. Some day biologists will have to devise a language in which
the relevant interpretations can be communicated in simple terms. In all
this perhaps we can begin to see, at least in a general way, the link between
gene-determined metabolism (in which energy is generated or released),
biophysics and morphogenesis.[1] When we begin to know more about the
energy relations of specific substances, and of the reactions in which they
participate, we shall truly be on our way towards 'scientific explanation'.
Of course, there were percipient biologists who were telling us this – not
quite in the same way, of course – a century ago!

As to energy relations in myxamoebae pseudoplasmodium movements,
the elongation of the corpus takes place in the direction of movement towards the light. Cells at the apical end of the elongating mass, which are
now known to be rich in the substance *acrasin*, are sensitive to the light
stimulus, and collectively function as the directive region for the organism.
This was demonstrated in experiments in which the apical region of the
pseudoplasmodium was removed: the directive movement of the mass
ceased and the organism settled down and entered on the reproductive
phase. It has been shown that while every cell of the pseudoplasmodium is
apparently totipotent – e.g. small isolated groups of cells, if placed in
appropriate media, can grow into new pseudoplasmodia – there is differentiation in cell size and function within the plasmodial mass. The
anterior cells, i.e. near the apex of the mass, are longer than the posterior
ones; the former forming spores. But, irrespective of the actual size of the
pseudoplasmodium, the relative proportion of the two kinds of cells is
maintained; i.e. there is evidence of a regulatory process. A biophysicist
would probably think in terms of a dynamic equilibrium – the resultant of
all the energy relationships in the system, i.e. both within and between the
individual amoeboid cells – in the mass of the pseudoplasmodium as
a whole. In a series of ingenious experiments by K. Raper (1940), the
axis along which the pseudoplasmodium progresses was shown to be
polarized, with distinction of cellular properties and functions at the two
ends. Here, again, there is evidence of individual and collective energy
relationships, even though we are not yet in a position to specify the nature
and magnitude of the forces involved either in variously situated individual

[1] A remarkable example, often quoted, of 'organized' morphogenetic movements
is that of the reconstitution of the component cells of sponges which have been
mechanically disintegrated. The body of a sponge can be broken up into its constituent cells and filtered through cloth of fine mesh. The cells, of several kinds, thus
separated, move about and become associated in various characteristic ways, a
sponge of normal morphology being eventually reconstituted.

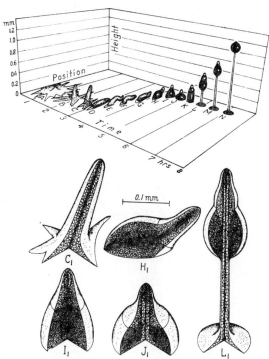

FIG. 13.2. *Dictyostelium discoideum*. A slime mould which, in the vegetative phase, consists of amoeboid cells. With the onset of the reproductive phase, some remarkable morphogenetic movements take place, which, together with differential developments in cell regions, result in the formation of specific and characteristic fruiting bodies. The complete ontogenesis is indicated in the three-dimensional graph. A–C, Phase of aggregation. D–H, Phase of migration. I–N, The final phase of specific and distinctive morphogenetic development. Heavy stippling, prespore cells; black, true spores. The letters in the lower illustrations refer to the corresponding stages above. (After J. T. Bonner, *Amer. Jour. Bot.*, 1944.)

cells or in the organismal system as a whole. (Readers are also referred to a study of differentiation in *Dictyostelium* spp. by Gregg, 1965, in which fluorescent antisera were applied to developing plasmodia.)

MORPHOGENETIC MOVEMENTS IN ALGAE

Only a few of these can be indicated. Perhaps one of the most spectacular examples of the interplay of genetical factors and of forces generated during metabolism and growth is seen in the freshwater green alga, the water-net, *Hydrodictyon reticulatum* (Chlorococcales). In this species the adult plant is a coenobium – defined as an integrated colony of cells, the number of which is determined during early development – and consists of a hollow, cylindrical network, up to 20 cm. long, closed at both ends. The meshes of the net are usually hexagonal, but may be pentagonal, the 'sides' consisting of elongated multinuclear cells. During asexual reproduction this remarkable and beautiful structure is formed in the following manner (Fig. 13.3).

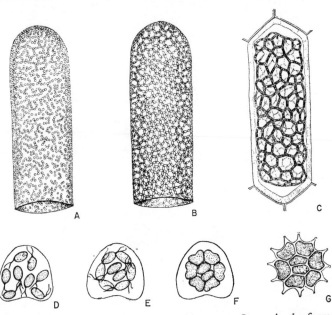

FIG. 13.3. *Hydrodictyon reticulatum* – the Water-net. Stages in the formation of a new net. A, The zoospores initially move about at random, then settle down on the inside of the wall of the mother cell. B, The individual cells begin to elongate and their mutual positional relationships become regularized into a geometric pattern. C, A new net is organized which eventually bursts out from the mother cell. (A, B, after J. T. Bonner, *Encyclopedia of Plant Physiology*, XV/1, 1965; C, after G. Klebs, *Bot. Zeit*, 1891; from F. E. Fritsch, *The Structure and Reproduction of the Algae*, Vol. I, 1935.)

D–G, *Pediastrum* sp. Arrangement of free-swimming zoospores to form a plate-like colonial form of a high order of regularity (after J. T. Bonner (as above)).

Individual cells of the net undergo numerous divisions into smaller and smaller uninucleate pieces, and these become organized as biflagellate zoospores. These zoospores move about, but they are all confined within the now considerably enlarged parental cell wall or membrane. After a time the flagella are withdrawn, or disappear, and a new membrane is secreted round each individual cell. Thereafter the seemingly confused, jostling movements of the cells result in an orderly geometric pattern – a tight net in miniature, lying within and close to the parent cell wall. Protoplasmic connections between cells are apparently not present or involved in this organization. On further development, a complete net can be seen within the parent cell (Fig. 13.3).

In these remarkable developments physical forces, generated during the growth of the reproductive cell and the formation of the zoospores, appear to be of primary importance in producing the eventual geometrical configuration – a figure of symmetry and equilibrium. Initially, the zoospores move about actively in a disorderly fashion, but, as they come to rest, they form more or less regular lines or rows in three directions, close to the wall. At the points of conjunction these rows are separated by angles of about 60°. This geometrical arrangement has been described as that which enables the largest number of units (cells) to be accommodated in the smallest area, yet admitting of a hexagonal meshwork construction (Fritsch, 1935). It is also a conformation that admits of expansion, strength and stability with elasticity. In *Hydrodictyon africanum* the coenobia are saucer shaped. Bonner (1952) discussed the evidence for the view that compressive and tensile stresses are involved in stimulating the elongation of individual cells. Eventually the cells of the nascent net undergo elongation, the parental wall is ruptured and the new net is liberated.

Other organisms among the Chlorococcales, e.g. well-known species like those of *Gonium*, *Pediastrum* (13.3), *Scenedesmus*, etc., and a great many others known to students of cryptogamic botany, all show cell division and morphogenetic movements of the zoospores, or associated free cells, resulting in conformations or patterns of a high order of geometrical regularity; but each has its own specific characters. Somewhat similar patterns, or conformations, based on the cleavage of cells into small zoospores and the association of the zoospores in characteristic ways, are seen in the lower fungi, e.g. members of the Saprolegniales (*see* J. T. Bonner, 1952, for a discussion of these phenomena).

In comparing these remarkable developments in the different forms, J. T. Bonner (1952) stated that it may be argued, or assumed, 'that all forms possess the same mechanism of control of development, just as their metabolic machinery is fundamentally similar, or that there are among organisms many different controlling mechanisms, just as there are many different methods of obtaining energy from the environment'. However, these views are not necessarily mutually exclusive. On the one hand, one may admit – for it is impossible to deny – the diversity of mechanisms and of developments in Nature. On the other, since *all* active systems, however their energy is generated, tend towards a state of equilibrium, the system behaves as a whole, and tends to yield geometrical configurations which are either symmetrical or of balanced asymmetry. Thus, in *Hydrodictyon* the internal and surface energies of the individual zoospores determine their initial haphazard or random movements; but, later, the tendency towards equilibrium in the system, i.e. the mother cell, determines the wholeness and co-ordination of the eventual pattern, i.e. the organization of the new net. Here it may be noted that the resistance to indefinite expansion offered by the wall of the mother cell is a factor in the totality of forces in the growing system.

Inversion in Volvox. Species of the colonial genus *Volvox*, both in asexual reproduction and in the formation of the male gametes, exhibit a very curious morphogenetic movement. It will be recalled that each cell of the coenobium is a zoospore with a pair of flagella. In vegetative reproduction a single large cell (or gonidium) divides by a longitudinal wall, i.e. at right-angles to the surface of the sphere. This is succeeded by a large number of similar divisions, so that a hollow sphere of tightly packed zoospores is formed, all the flagellar ends being directed inwards. A small pore, not occupied by zoospores, is present on the outer side of the sphere. The enlarging daughter colony bulges inwards into the 'cavity' of the mother-sphere. During the process of division little growth takes place in the new organism. However, a stage is reached when rapid growth takes place and the process of inversion begins. The new sphere, in fact, turns outside in, by way of the hole (the phialopore) on its outer side. The result is that the flagellar ends of the individual cells are now facing outwards. New flagella develop, and the colony becomes an independent, free-swimming organism. These morphogenetic movements in *Volvox* have, of course, often been compared with the common phenomenon of gastrulation in animal embryos. In the formation of the motile male gametes in *Volvox*, also involving a large number of longitudinal divisions in single cells, the process of inversion also takes place.

These curious developments in *Volvox*, as Bonner (1952, p. 193) remarked, are evidently highly co-ordinated; yet the control mechanism is still quite unknown. But even if we had some idea of the mechanism, a very enigmatic point would still remain to be explained, or explained away, namely, how the morphogenetic movement, generated by particular forces, happens to be precisely what is needed in the functional economy of the organism, i.e. to bring the flagellar ends of the constituent cells of the coenobium into a position in which they can function. The nature of the forces which cause these morphogenetic movements is still obscure, though some useful ideas have emerged from observations and experiments on gastrulation in animals (*see* J. T. Bonner, 1952). For example, it appears that chemical gradients in the region of the blastopore lip may be important. But various cellular properties and local factors in the immediate environment of the germ or embryo may be involved.

Diatoms, etc. The very characteristic patterns in dendroid diatoms and members of other groups, e.g. *Dinobryon*, suggest that biophysical factors, not unlike those that are at work in *Hydrodictyon* and other Chlorococcales, may also contribute to the visible morphological developments. The study of some of these relatively simple forms may afford a feasible starting-point for biophysical inquiry.

MORPHOGENESIS IN COENOCYTIC ALGAE

The Siphonales, of which very ancient fossil members are known, are characterized by the virtual absence of septation during the vegetative phase. Nevertheless, by the growth and characteristic branching of filaments, typically with a multinucleate protoplast, distinctive and sometimes very elaborate plant bodies are formed. Such are the well-known genera of *Caulerpa*, *Bryopsis*, *Dasycladus*, *Acetabularia*, etc., but simpler forms may consist merely of a spherical cell with a rhizoid, as in *Protosiphon botryoides*, or of an occasionally branched filament as in the well-known *Vaucheria*. In the complex siphonaceous forms, as J. T. Bonner (1952) rightly pointed out, it is the direction in which growth takes place that is important, rather than the laying down of partition walls. Species such as *Bryopsis plumosa*, in which the lateral filaments grow out in an orderly arrangement or symmetrical pattern, are indicative of a localization of particular metabolites in regular positions in the peripheral cytoplasm of the young coenocyte.

Evidence from Acetabularia. Evidence of a unique kind on the relation between the nucleus, the cytoplasm and morphogenesis has been obtained by Hämmerling (1934) in experiments with the coenocytic green alga *Acetabularia mediterranea*. (For recent reviews of his work, *see* Hämmerling, 1946, 1953, 1955, 1957; also Brachet and Lang, 1965; Lang, 1965.) In this organism (Fig. 13.4) the single nucleus occurs near, or in, one of the basal rhizoidal lobes. Hämmerling showed that enucleate fragments can live for a considerable time and can even regenerate missing parts. The umbrella or hat-like distal region is usually regenerated from fragments originating near the distal end, while rhizoids tend to be more easily regenerated from the proximal or basal end. In a number of regeneration and grafting experiments, Hämmerling demonstrated the existence of two gradients of morphogenetic substances, a 'hat substance' concentrated at the distal end and a 'rhizoid substance' at the proximal end, both of which exist independently of the nucleus in enucleate fragments. There is, however, little doubt that the nucleus is ultimately responsible for the production of these seemingly cytoplasmic substances. Thus, when a distal fragment of *A. mediterranea* was grafted on to a decapitated, nucleated rhizoidal fragment of *A. Wettsteinii*, the 'hat' which was eventually regenerated had the characters of *A. Wettsteinii*; the reactions of the cytoplasm were, apparently, determined by the nucleus. A piece of filament isolated from the middle of the stalk contains little of either morphogenetic substance and regeneration rarely occurs. If, however, a nucleated rhizoidal end was left attached to such a middle piece, regeneration commonly took place after an

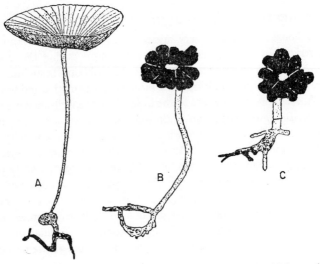

FIG. 13.4. A, *Acetabularia mediterranea*, showing the rhizoidal attachment, the stem and the 'hat'. B, *A. Wettsteinii*. C, 'Hat' regenerated from a piece of *A. mediterranea* stem grafted on to a nucleus-containing rhizoid of *A. Wettsteinii*. (After J. Hämmerling, *Roux Archiv.*, 1934.)

initial latent period. From such evidence Hämmerling concluded that the cytoplasm in this alga does not determine the type of morphological development, but it must be in a suitably reactive state before development can take place, i.e. it must be competent to react to the organizing action of substances proceeding from the nucleus.

In later studies, Hämmerling (1946) indicated that several kinds of morphogenetic substances are probably involved in the developments observed in *Acetabularia*, namely, a non-specific substance which determines the initiation of the cap and a species-specific substance which controls the cap characteristics. Werz (1955) suggested that the latter may be a complex of substances, each responsible for individual cap characters. Hämmerling *et al.* (1959) showed that anucleate plants can not only undergo differentiation; they also continue to synthesize carbohydrates, chlorophyll, protein and other cell constituents. But whereas growth and synthesis take place only in the light in both nucleate and anucleate cells, the synthesis of morphogenetic substances can proceed in the dark in nucleate cells (J. and ch. Hämmerling 1959). Investigations by Beth (1953) pointed to the synthesis of the morphogenetic substances in two stages. In the first stage, in which precursors are formed, light is not required. In the second stage the morphogenetic substances proper are formed. This requires light of sufficient intensity. The formation of the cap may be regarded as a third stage; here again, little or no light is required. Beth (1956a, b) found that cap formation is accelerated by a low-temperature pretreatment and by repeated removal of the growing tip.

Certain special proteins, ribonucleic acids and polysaccharide types of substances are now known to have a polar distribution in the cell; they are concentrated at the tip of the stalk, i.e. in regions of active growth and differentiation, and they apparently precede the actual morphological developments (Werz, 1959, 1960a, b)

MORPHOGENESIS IN MICRASTERIAS

Investigations not unlike those on *Acetabularia* have been made on the desmid *Micrasterias*. This alga consists of two half-cells. These separate at cell division, when each part regenerates a new half-cell, thus restoring the organism to its original symmetry. By various means, e.g. centrifugation during nuclear division, and by cultural techniques, e.g. growth in continuous light, half-cells without a nucleus, with only some of the chromosomes, with supernumerary chromosomes or with two nuclei, have been obtained and their behaviour during regeneration studied (Fig. 13.5) (for review *see* Brachet and Lang, 1965).

The extent of differentiation in the regenerating half-cell was found to be closely dependent on the nuclear content of the adult half-cell. In an anucleate cell, for example, the new development was greatly reduced; but it was increasingly complex in cells containing some of the chromosomes, the normal chromosome complement, supernumerary chromosomes and more than one nucleus. However, even in small anucleate half-cells, the specific pattern of *Micrasterias* was still evident. Such observations have led to the suggestion that the cell form is referable to permanent structures in the cytoplasm. Somewhat similar modifications of the normal differentiation have also been obtained in relation to nutritional and chemical factors. Waris and Kallio (1957) regarded all the morphogenetic effects as being based on changes of equilibria between nuclear action and the cytoplasmic

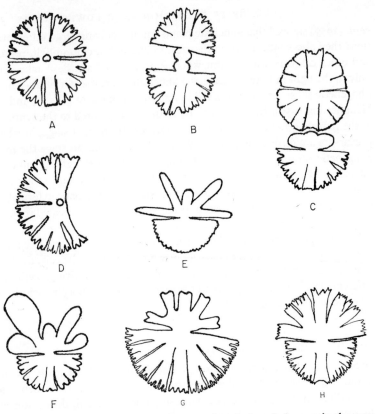

FIG. 13.5. *Micrasterias* spp., illustrating various induced changes in the morphology of the semi-cells (tracings, somewhat diagrammatic, from photomicrographs).

A, *M. rotata*, normal cell, at metaphase. When such dividing cells were centrifuged, one daughter cell was found to contain both nuclei and the other was without its nucleus.

B, C, *M. rotata*, cells which had been centrifuged: B, after 2 hr.; C, after 7½ hr. Various growth and morphological changes have resulted from the denucleation of one cell and the binucleate condition in the other.

D, *M. thomasiana*. A mutational type of cell, in which there has been a unilateral loss of lobes.

E, F, *M. thomasiana* var. *notata*. Examples of centrifuged cells which had also been given particular chemical treatments.

E, Enucleate cell, with 0·1 ml./l. propylene glycol.

F, Enucleate cell, with 1 mg./l. 2, 4-D.

G, *M. thomasiana* var. *notata*, illustrating anomalous lobe formation in a culture medium containing potato extract.

H, *M. rotata* var. *evoluta*. Cell from a diploid clone (the F₃ generation of a centrifuged mother-cell), showing differences in lobing in the two semi-cells. (A–F, H, after H. Waris; G, after H. Waris and P. Kallio; A–F, from *Physiologia Plantarum*, 1950, 1951; G, H, *Ann. Acad. Sci. Fennicae*, 1957; 1958.)

substrate. The diminished morphogenetic activity of anucleate *Micrasterias* cells is probably chiefly due to deficiencies in the materials required for growth, the net synthesis in anucleate cells being very small.

Fig. 13.5 illustrates diagrammatically some of the kinds of morphological changes induced in semi-cells after various treatments, e.g. the enucleation of a semi-cell by centrifugation at metaphase, the application of growth regulating substances, etc. These, as well as many other changes, have been fully described and well illustrated by Waris, Kallio and other investigators (*see* Bibliography).

Effects of Ultra-violet Radiation on Micrasterias *spp.* Results obtained by Kallio (1963, where readers will find up-to-date refs. to his earlier and other relevant studies) on the effects of subjecting desmid cells and semi-cells to ultra-violet rays are not only of interest in themselves but are also of general importance in relation to such major phenomena as the action and interaction of nucleus and cytoplasm in morphogenetic processes. Some of the curious anomalous developments observed are illustrated (semi-diagrammatically) in Fig. 13.6. Kallio pointed out that after cells or semi-cells had been subjected to a standard dose of ultra-violet rays, the new morphogenetic developments were closely comparable with those observed in developing anucleate semi-cells, e.g. as obtained by centrifugation, chemical treatments, etc. He found that the application of RNAase to normal haploid cells also resulted in the formation of characteristic anucleate-shaped (or 'hypohaploid') semi-cells, i.e. smaller semi-cells with lobes. There is evidence that the quantities of RNAs stored in the desmid semi-cell are small. These several observations, taken together, and interpreted in terms of contemporary ideas, have enabled Kallio to reach some important conclusions. In *Micrasterias* growth and differentiation, though modified, can take place even in the absence of a nucleus. The substances which are closely involved in the *specific* differentiation of the species, the RNAs, tend to be concentrated in the region of differentiation in the cytoplasm. Accordingly, any experimental treatment, such as enucleation by centrifugation, with concomitant elimination of the primary source of specific RNAs, or chemical or physical treatments which diminish or eliminate the effective, or critical, amounts of RNAs in the differentiating regions of growing semi-cells, e.g. the destruction of RNA by radiation, by the application of RNAase, etc., will modify the normal course of morphogenesis. Since, according to recent researches, DNA and RNA are among the most sensitive molecular components of the living protoplast, any treatment that affects the DNA in the nucleus will also affect the RNA in the cytoplasm; and the latter may also be directly affected by various experimental treatments. Sometimes, in *Micrasterias*, the nuclear and cytoplasmic

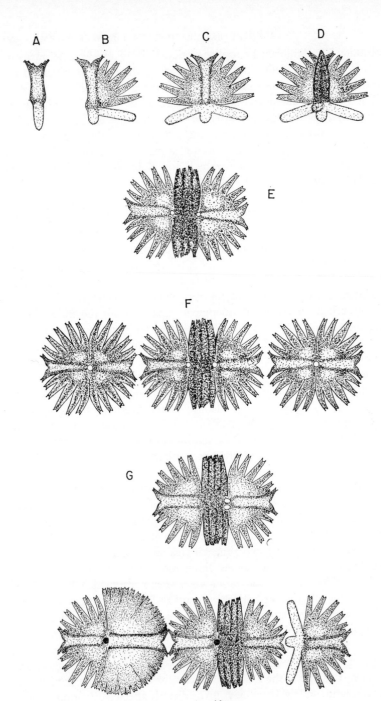

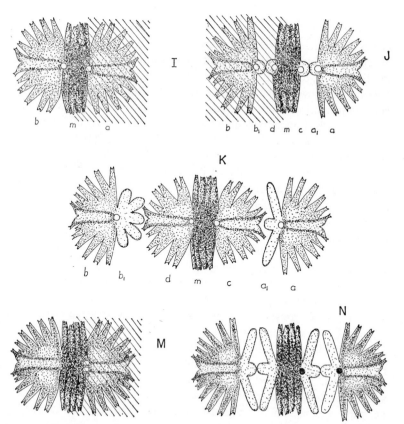

FIG. 13.6. *Micrasterias* spp. Some examples of induced morphogenetic developments following ultra-violet radiation. Haploid nuclei – white; diploid nuclei – black; other cells, or semi-cells, are anucleate. The diagonal shading indicates the cellular expanse subjected to radiation.

A–D, Different types of anucleate cells.

A, *Micrasterias americana*, aradiate.

B, *M. torreyi*, uniradiate.

C, *M. torreyi*, haploid biradiate.

D, *M. torreyi*, diploid triradiate.

E, F, *Micrasterias* sp. (schematic). Double cell of the T1 type (with a haploid nucleus at each isthmus) before and after division respectively.

G, H, *Micrasterias* sp. (schematic). Double cell of the T2 type (with two haploid nuclei in one isthmus) before and after division respectively.

I, J, K, *M. torreyi*. A double cell of the T1 type was irradiated first at the right end (I) and then at the left end (J). The ensuing semi-cell developments are shown in K. Semi-cells a and b are normal haploid; a_1 is anucleate; in b_1, all the nuclear effect has been eliminated in the bulge phase of growth; c and d are hypohaploid semi-cells.

M, N, *M. torreyi*. A double cell of the T2 type was irradiated at the nucleate end (M). As seen in N, four new anucleate semi-cells have been formed. These are characteristic of cells deficient in RNA.

(After P. Kallio, *Ann. Acad. Sci. Fennicae*, 1963.)

effects, as in *Acetabularia*, can readily be distinguished; but, in fact, such effects usually stand in some reciprocal relationship. Kallio has more or less implicitly accepted the RNAs as the morphogenetic substances in differentiation. The view that they are closely involved in specific differentiation is being increasingly supported by new evidence. However, as with other substances which participate in morphogenesis, they can only act as components of a system and, as information accumulates, it is to the understanding of such systems that our attention will be increasingly directed.

In accord with views expressed by Waris (*see* refs.), Kallio concluded that two groups of morphogenetic agents are at work in determining the eventual morphology of the developing semi-cell in desmids. The basic symmetry, or configuration, i.e. the number of lobes, is determined by the cytoplasm, i.e. some kind of 'cytoplasmic skeleton' passes into a developing semi-cell. But, even with the help of electron microscopy, no relevant supporting evidence has yet been obtained. The present writer would incline towards the more basic view that what passes into the initially small but growing semi-cell is a specific cytoplasmic reaction system capable, on further growth, of giving rise to the specific pattern of wings or lobes, chloroplast configuration, etc., but also capable of different morphogenetic developments when the reaction system is modified by the introduction of new factors or components, or by the elimination of some components. The second group of agents, i.e. those which determine the specificity and complexity of developing semi-cells, are gene-based, i.e. they originate in the nucleus and are transmitted to differentiating regions.

SPECIFIC CONFIGURATION BY THE ASSOCIATION OF FILAMENTS

In the brown and red algae, and in Ascomycetes and Basidiomycetes, there are numerous megascopic species of distinctive and specific form in which the whole morphogenetic process depends on the association and intergrowth of filaments or hyphae. Such, for example, are the polystichous Ectocarpales among the brown algae. The somatic development in the Gigartinales and Rhodymeniales among the red algae, the fructifications in the Ascomycetes – apothecia, perithecia, morels, tubers – and bracket forms, mushrooms, puff-balls and earth stars in the Basidiomycetes, are all based on an organized intergrowth of filaments. What is known, or can be said conjecturally, about these developments? (Figs. 13.7, 13.8).

Bonner recognized that such organisms not only raise problems of growth and development but also of the overall and essentially holistic and specific morphogenesis of the fruiting body, e.g. as in a particular species of agaric; but he has offered no clue as to the nature of the factors that are involved. Indeed, it was observation of the orderly growth of the mushroom type of fructification, with its stalk (stipe), cap (pileus), gills or pores (hymenial layer), that led Gurwitsch (1922, 1927, 1947) to propose a 'field theory' of development (*see* p. 152).

An examination of the interweaving of hyphae, or filaments, in fungi and algae, which are best seen in the early stages, e.g. in the formation of an ascomycetous apothecium or perithecium, suggests that chemotactic and tactile, or pressure-contact, stimuli may be involved. Other observations, based on studies of life-histories, point to the importance of nutritional factors, in particular to the accumulation and later mobilization of the materials of active growth. Fungi such as *Rhizoctonia*, when grown in culture, often

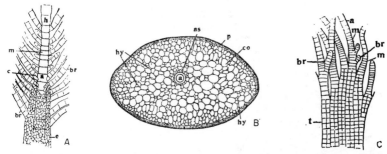

FIG. 13.7. The Brown Algae: more or less complex thalli may be formed by the contiguous growth, branching and differentiation of individual filaments.
A, B, *Desmarestia aculeata*. A, Apex of a growing thallus. B, Cross-section of a mature thallus, the whole construction being essentially of filamentous origin. *h*, hairlike tip of thallus; *m*, meristem; *br*, branch; *c*, primary cells of cortex; *e*, envelope of cortical cells. C, *Zanardinia collaris*, illustrating the formation of a thallus, *t*, by trichothallic growth; *m*, meristem; *a*, assimilatory hair. (From various authors, after F. E. Fritsch, *The Structure and Reproduction of the Algae*, Vol. II, 1945.)

form their sclerotia, consisting of compact masses of interwoven hyphae, in contact with the glass of the culture tube. But in the formation of a mushroom the problem is evidently much deeper, more complex and more comprehensive. At a certain stage the small spherical or cylindrical mushroom, a mass of intermingling hyphae, begins to undergo a kind of differentiation in a particular localized region: in fact, the hymenial layer begins to be formed. A little later, according to the species, further 'differentiation' takes place: the nascent hymenial region can be seen to consist of a hymenial and subhymenial layer, disposed on gills or in pores of characteristic form, distribution and size: and the pileus, stipe and velum (or veil), if present, all show evidence of a distinctive, co-ordinated growth and

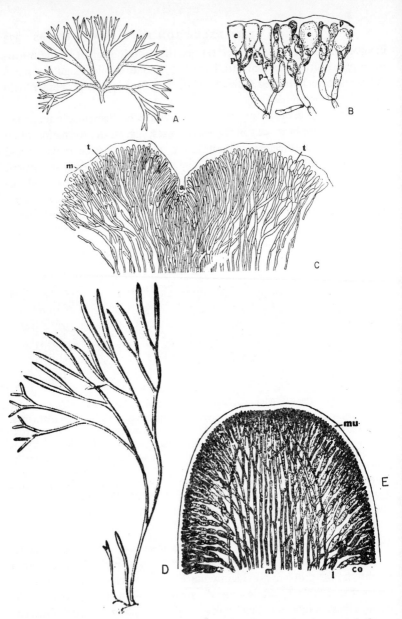

FIG. 13.8. The Red Algae. Tubular and flat thalli, of distinctive morphology, may result from the growing together, branching and differentiation of individual filaments. A, B, C, *Scinaia furcellata*; *A*, the thallus; *B*, the distal filamentous branches; *C*, the apex of a thallus, showing the mass of filaments. *a*, apex; *t*, tips of filaments; *m*, mucilage envelope. D, E, *Furcellaria fastigiata*; D, habit; E, tip of thallus. (From various authors, after F. E. Fritsch, *The Structure and Reproduction of the Algae*, Vol. II, 1945.)

development. In all these developments one cannot fail to recognize the impact of genetical factors; but how they work in producing the regional morphogenetic features in the tangle of hyphae is not at all evident. The possible application of Turing's theory of morphogenesis to the patterns in the fructifications of the Agaricales is suggested by the size and form correlations which these structures exemplify (Ingold, 1946; Bond, 1952).

Development in Fungi. Hawker (1965) has dealt in some detail with the physiology of development in the fungi. The hypha is taken as the structural unit. As several mycelia may eventually contribute to the formation of a fruiting body, Hawker has pointed out that the concept of the individual in the fungi has inherent difficulties. However, any particular fruiting body, consisting as it does of compatible hyphae, may be accepted as a morphogenetic individual.

In the fungi, as in many algae, there are unsolved problems of morphogenesis at the 'simple' level of the individual filament; for example, the factors involved in the formation of septa, the characteristic branching, the fusion of hyphae and the concomitant cytological changes, the association of hyphae in rhizomorph formation and so on. In some of these developments it has been shown that nutritional and regulative factors are at work and that translocation is involved. As every mycologist knows, even 'simple' fungi may exhibit a considerable amount of differentiation in their hyphae, e.g. the formation of rhizoids, appressoria, haustoria and all the specific features of their sporangiophores or conidiophores.

As to the development of the complex fruiting bodies in the larger fungi (Fig. 13.9), Hawker (1965, p. 741) noted that the subject 'is extremely difficult and very little progress has been made'. In his studies of the development of these structures, Corner (1932 *et seq.*) used the method of hyphal analysis. In some of the more complex fructifications, e.g. *Polystictus xanthopus*, he recognized skeletal hyphae, generative hyphae, binding hyphae, etc., all apparently having some special function (Fig. 13.10). That correlative factors are involved in the formation of a complex structure such as a toadstool is indicated by various experimental studies. Thus Borriss (1934) found that morphogenesis in *Coprinus lagopus* is stopped if the pileus is excised at an early stage. He suggested that a hormone, present in the pileus, is essential for the growth of the stipe. Subsequent work by various investigators supports the idea of the hormonal control of morphogenesis in these complex fructifications. In fact, there is now an extensive literature on the effects of various special growth substances on morphogenesis in fungi, especially at the transition from the vegetative to the reproductive phase (*see* Hawker, 1965, for refs.). As work progresses, it will be a matter of considerable interest to observe to what extent there are

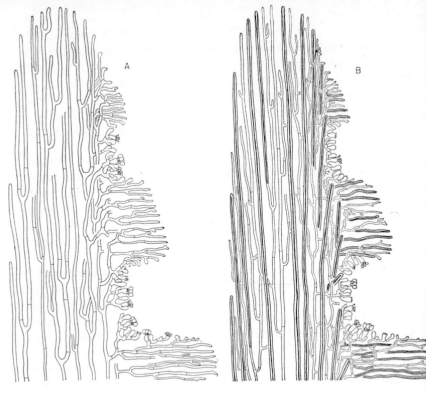

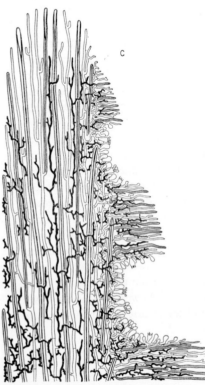

FIG. 13.9. The formation of the fructification in species of Polyporaceae, treated diagrammatically. Structural features in A, a monomitic polypore; B, a dimitic polypore with skeletal hyphae; and C, a trimitic polypore (marginal region), with binding hyphae (black), skeletal hyphae (unbranched, thick-walled) and thin-walled branching hyphae. *See* text. (After E. J. H. Corner, *Phytomorphology*, 1953.)

morphogenetic mechanisms, such as apical dominance, which are common to both higher and lower plants.

Fruiting Bodies of Basidiomycetes. If we consider the fructifications in any of the major groups of the Basidiomycetes from the morphogenetic stand-point, e.g. the Clavariaceae, Polyporaceae, Agaricaceae, Phallaceae, etc., it quickly becomes evident that the manifold phenomena fall into several categories, e.g. the external shape and morphological regions of the fructi-fication, the distribution of the basidia, e.g. on spines, on gills, or in pores, and the more or less considerable differentiation of the hyphae. As a de-scriptive system, based on anatomical studies, Corner (1932a, b; 1950; 1953) analysed the structure of fructifications in terms of monomitic, dimitic and trimitic hyphal differentiation (Figs. 13.9, 13.10). The basic units are the septate, branching, thin-walled growing hyphae, or genera-tive hyphae. These are the longitudinal hyphae of growing regions. A fructification composed of such hyphae is described as *monomitic*. Accord-ing to the species, some of these hyphae, or their lateral branches, remain unbranched and commonly non-septate and they become thick-walled. These are referred to as skeletal hyphae, and a fructification showing this kind of construction, or organization, is described as being *dimitic*. But hy-phal differentiation may be still further diversified. Some of the branches of the generative hyphae become *binding hyphae*, these being typically much branched, narrow, rarely septate, thick-walled and of 'very intricate and limited growth'. Fructifications with the three types of hyphae are referred to as exemplifying the trimitic state. Other kinds of differentiation of the gen-erative hyphae result in the formation of the hymenial layer and the eventual formation of basidia and basidiospores. The dimitic condition may comprise systems either (i) of generative hyphae and skeletal hyphae, or (ii) of genera-tive hyphae and binding hyphae, as in different polypores (Corner, 1953).

Of the Clavariaceae, which Corner (1950) has described and illustrated in great detail, the writer has selected *Clavicorona candelabrum* for illus-tration here. Fig. 13.10 A–D shows dissected-out generative and skeletal hyphae. Some of the more superficial generative hyphae become conspicu-ously enlarged and grow longitudinally, with negative geotropism. These *gloeocystidia* curve outwards into the hymenial layer. The overall result of these several developments during growth is the formation of a fruiting body of characteristic morphology and distinctive, hyphal differentiation as shown in Fig. 13.10 E.

Nutrition, Morphogenesis and Taxonomy. Some fungi, e.g. species of Fungi Imperfecti, are known to taxonomists under several, sometimes many, different names, though eventually, in the light of experience, one

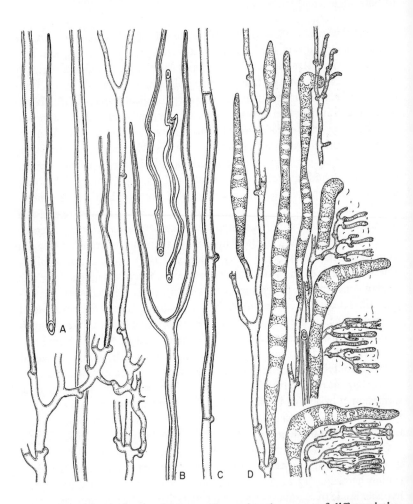

FIG. I3.IO. *Clavicorona candelabrum*, illustrating the extent of differentiation
in one of the higher fungi. A, The tip of a skeletal hypha which has become
secondarily septate. The origin of skeletal hyphae from generative hyphae
is clearly shown. B, An unusual branched tip of a skeletal hypha. C, A
generative hypha with a thick-walled portion. D, E, Longitudinal gloeocyst-

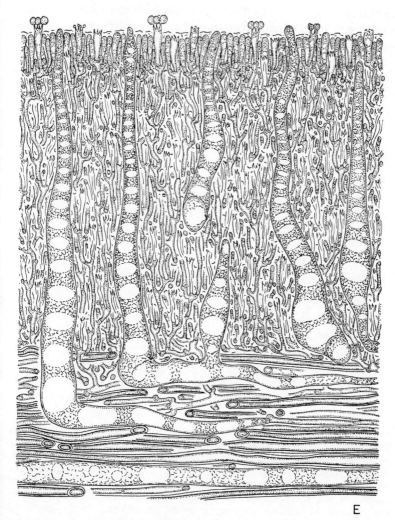

E

idia, assumed to be swollen, sterile hymenial cells – developing from generative hyphae. They grow with negative geotropism and later turn outwards into the hymenial layer. (After E. J. H. Corner, *A Monograph of Clavaria and Allied Genera*. Oxford Univ. Press, 1950.)

particular name is selected. The explanation is simple: on different substrates, e.g. soil, decaying vegetation, etc., or on different hosts, under different conditions, the morphology of the fructifications, used in identification, may be very different indeed. Such is *Botryodiplodia theobromae*, sometimes recognized as a *Diplodia* sp., a tropical fungus which may occur

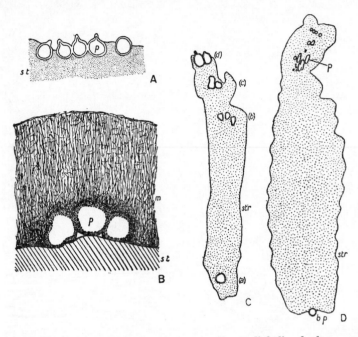

FIG. 13.11. Morphogenesis in the fungus *Botryodiplodia theobromae*; the formation of pycnidia under different conditions. A, Normal sporulating pycnidia (*p*), partly immersed, on surface of banana skin tissue (*st*). B, Immature pycnidia, on surface of banana skin (*st*), under moist conditions: the pycnidia have become overgrown and rendered abortive by a thick weft of mycelium (*m*). C, D, Longitudinal sections of large stromatic fructifications (*str*), grown in culture, showing pycnidia at different levels; *bp*, basal pycnidium. (A ×33; B ×55; C, D, ×8.) (After C. W. Wardlaw, *Annals of Botany*, 1932.)

as a saprophyte or as a facultative parasite. As investigated by Wardlaw (1932) the fruiting bodies may develop as simple, isolated pycnidia, e.g. partly sunken in the superficial tissues of the host plant, or they may occur in groups in large stromatic fructifications. High concentrations of sugar in the medium, and high relative humidity in the environment of the superficial hyphae, favoured the formation of these stromatic fruiting bodies (Fig. 13.11).

Morphogenesis in a Lichen. Both fungal filaments and algal cells contribute to the vegetative thallus and to the eventual development of the considerable and distinctive fructifications (Fig. 13.12).

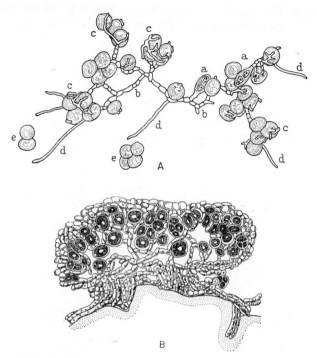

FIG. 13.12. Morphogenesis in a lichen. *Xanthoria parietina*. A, An early stage in the formation of the thallus: fungal hyphae from germinating spores (*a*) become closely associated with algal gonidia (*c*). B, A primary thallus, of characteristic organization, as seen in cross-section. (After M. Steiner, from G. Bonnier and R. G. Werner, in *Encyclopedia of Plant Physiology*, XV/1, 1965.)

MORPHOGENESIS IN BRYOPHYTA

It has long been appreciated that the Bryophyta afford great scope for morphogenetic studies of relatively simple organisms, e.g. von Goebel. In recent years, with the advances in controlled cultural techniques, contemporary investigators have shown that selected bryophytes can be used to advantage in new studies of morphogenesis. Only a few examples can be touched upon in this 'brief excursion'.

By the *in vitro* culture of mosses Allsopp and Mitra (1956) have shown that the classical concept of the *heterotrichous habit* can be made the subject of analytical experiments. Pieces of protonema, on being placed in half-strength Knop's solution with 0·5 per cent agar, and under artificial light (500 ft. candles) or in natural light, grew and yielded plants of characteristic appearance (Fig. 13.13). In several species both erect and procumbent green filaments – the essential feature of the heterotrichous habit – and

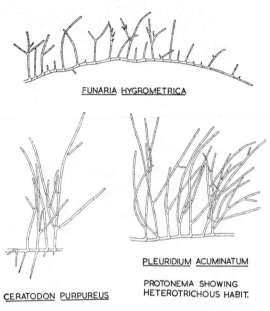

FUNARIA HYGROMETRICA

PLEURIDIUM ACUMINATUM

CERATODON PURPUREUS

PROTONEMA SHOWING HETEROTRICHOUS HABIT.

FIG. 13.13. The *in vitro* culture of mosses. The illustrations are of portions of protonema from cultures of *Funaria hygrometrica* (×c. 15), *Ceratodon purpureus* (×c. 23) and *Pleuridium acuminatum* (×c. 23). The mosses were grown in flasks on half-strength Knop's solution with 0·5 per cent agar. The *Funaria* and *Pleuridium* cultures were grown in artificial light (500 ft. candles) and the *Ceratodon* in natural light. Two of the cultures have manifested the heterotrichous habit, with erect and procumbent green filaments and with a rhizoidal development. (After A. Allsopp and G. C. Mitra, *Nature*, 178, pp. 1063–4, 1956.)

rhizoids were formed. In a study of *Ceratodon purpureus*, Valanne (1966) has demonstrated that, in relation to the conditions provided, the spores may germinate in a number of rather different ways (Fig. 13.14).

The classical species *Marchantia polymorpha* continues to provide new interest, especially when gemmae or thalli are grown under closely controlled conditions. Courtoy (1966), for example, has been able to specify the

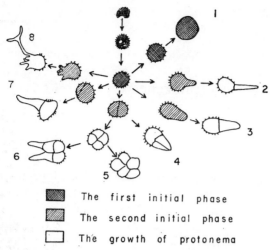

The first initial phase

The second initial phase

The growth of protonema

FIG. 13.14. *Ceratodon purpureus*. According to the conditions provided, the spores of this moss may germinate in different ways: 1, formation of giant globular cells; 2, normal germination – the protonema is beginning to be formed; 3, a 'broad' type of germination; 4–6, various anomalous forms observed when spores were placed in sucrose solution; 7, germination with rhizoid formation; 8, abnormal germination obtained in red light (Semi-diagrammatic). (After N. Valanne, *Ann. Bot. Fennici*, 3, 13, 1966.)

conditions of illumination which result in gemmae developing into thalli bearing gametangiophores. A juvenile phase and a subsequent inductive phase have been recognized, the onset of the latter being promoted by the addition of 1·0 per cent sucrose to the mineral nutrient medium.

CHAPTER XIV

Whole Plant Morphogenesis

INTRODUCTION

The traditional and successful procedure in science is to separate off individual processes, or parts, for special investigation. So also in morphogenesis: some exponents are especially interested in roots; others in leaves or buds; and yet others in the inception of flowering. And, again, some see the relevant problems in terms of physiology, some of genetics and so on. All of these approaches are essential and well defined and can be satisfying to the investigator. But however conclusive any individual biological study may be, it is not in itself enough: it deals with only a part of a greater, integrated system, i.e. the whole individual in relation to its evolutionary history and its present environment.[1] In brief, in so far as it is possible, if specific investigations are to have their full value and impact, they must be considered in the context of *whole plant morphogenesis*. This is not a new idea: rather it is one of those old ideas that is always new. It has been in the minds of biologists and other observers for such a long time that it is as much a philosophical as a biological theme: witness the rich fund of conjecture on this topic in Arber's *Natural Philosophy of Plant Form* (1950). One can perceive the same groping towards an adequate expression of the physical and functional unity of organisms in Driesch's concept of entelechy and Smuts' dissertation on holism. Phyllorhize and telome theories were also basically concerned with whole-plant morphogenesis (Fig. 14.1). The writer's book on *Organization and Evolution in Plants* (1965), and a comprehensive review of shoot morphogenesis by Cutter (1965), have their place within the same general framework of thought. Many roads may lead to one end. Theories of correlative development, relating to the synthesis, translocation and activities of hormonal substances, have reappeared in the caline theory of Went and are still with us – and rightly so – and are basic to investigations in which the aim is to explore the relationships between

---

[1] A student of geography can make a study of the Arctic Region, with all its isolation and individuality, as a specific and distinctive region. But, in a wider context, i.e. the global context, this, and all the other distinctive regions, exist only by virtue of the totality of global astronomical, geological, meteorological and biological phenomena.

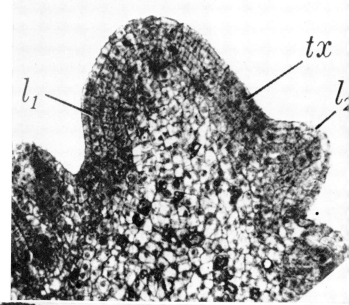

PLATE I. *Parthenocissus inserta.* A, B, Vegetative shoot apices, as seen in longitudinal median sections: metabolism, conformation and organogenic activities at the apex are evidently of a very considerable order of complexity. In this species the lateral organs include leaves, axillary buds and tendrils. $l_{1,2}$, etc., young leaf primordia; $x_{3,4}$, axillary buds; t_2, tendril; tx, site of lower tendril and bud axillary to l_2. (*See also* Text-figs. 8.5, 8.6; after W. F. Millington, *Amer. Jour. Bot.*, 1966.)

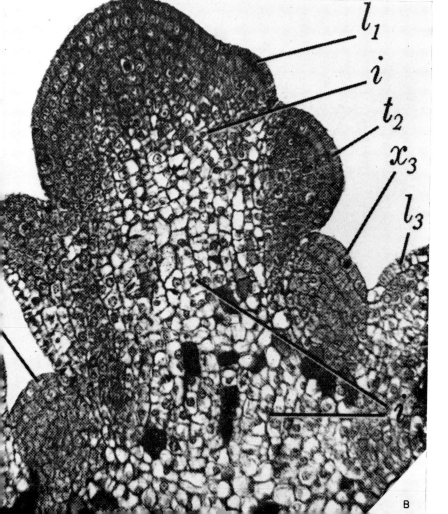

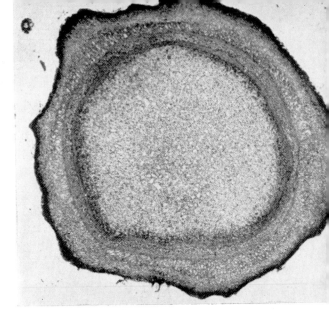

PLATE 2. *Dryopteris dilatata*. Evidence from an experiment in which the result was predicted. *Below:* Transverse section of a normal rhizome, showing the characteristic dictyostelic (meshlike) vascular system. *Above:* Transverse section of the experimental region of the same rhizome from which all the young leaf primordia had been systematically removed: no leaf-gaps were formed and the vascular system is solenostelic. (After C. W. Wardlaw, *Nature,* 1944.) (*See* p. 144.)

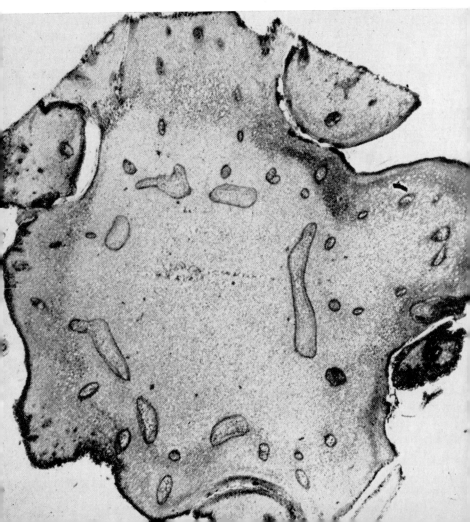

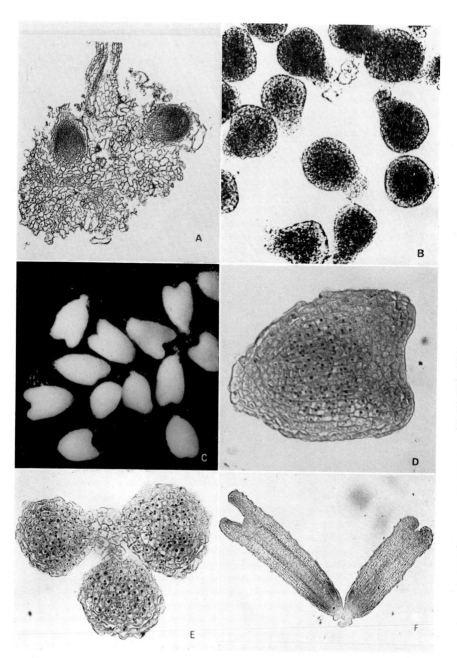

PLATE 3. Root and embryoid formation in wild carrot cell suspensions. A, Rhizogenesis: a cellular mass with two root primordia and an older root (top). B, Globular 'proembryos'. C, Embryos at the 'heart stage', i.e. beginning of cotyledon differentiation. D, Cellular details in young heart-shaped embryo. E, Three globular embryoids with a common 'suspensor'. F, Two mature embryoids with a common 'suspensor'. (*See* p. 79 and Plate 4.) (After W. Halperin, *Amer. Jour. Bot.*, 1966.)

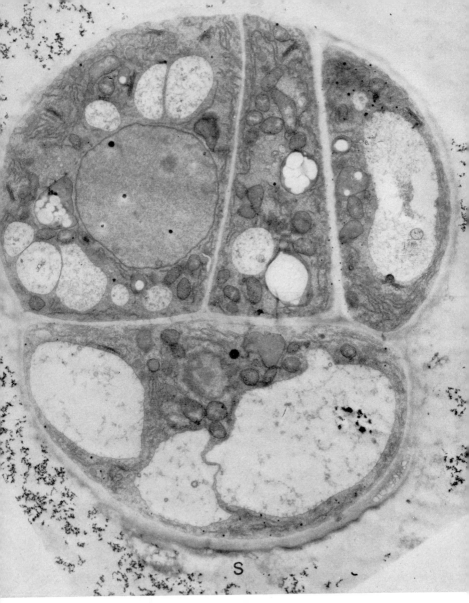

S

PLATE 4. Carrot cell cultures: the ultrastructure in a four-celled 'proembryo', in which polarity has now been established; the distal, or apical, end (*a*) consists of three cells and the proximal, or basal, end of a highly vacuolated suspensor cell. Such 'proembryos' are formed at the periphery of cell clumps or masses, more highly vacuolated cells being present towards the inner region of the mass. These small, polarized embryoids are released from the parental cellular mass; some vesiculated wall remnants can still be observed adhering to the 'suspensor' wall (×10,000). (*See* p. 76 and Plate 3.) (After W. Halperin and W. A. Hensen, *Amer. Jour. Bot.*, 1967.)

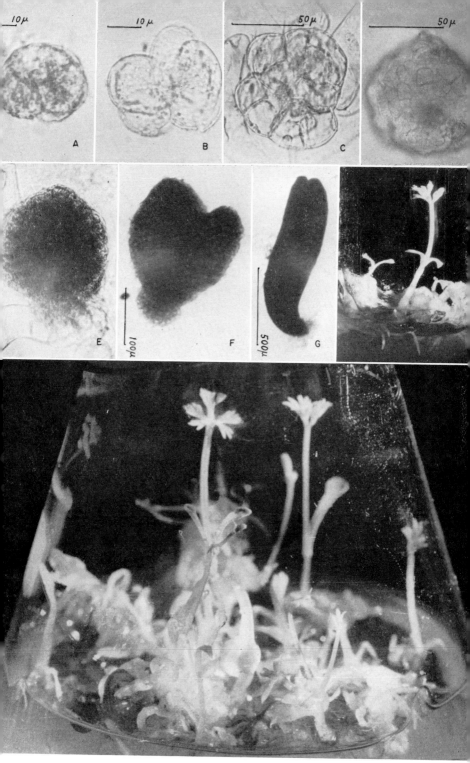

PLATE 5. Morphogenesis *in vitro* from single cells of carrot root. A, B, Four-to-five-celled stage. C, D, E, Globular stage. F, Heart-shaped stage. G, Torpedo stage. H, Plantlets. J, Numerous plantlets in Erlenmeyer flask.(After H. Kato and M. Takeuchi, *Cell and Plant Physiol.*, 1963.) (*See* p. 77.)

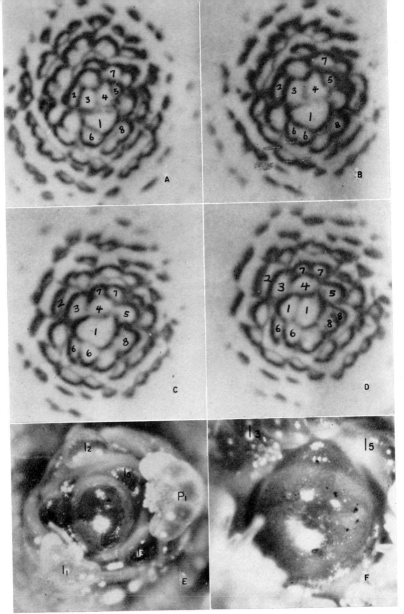

PLATE 6. A–D, Evidence of cell division at the summit of the shoot-apex of *Asparagus officinalis*, using cinematographic technique. A, Initial view of the summit of the shoot apex as seen from above. B, After 27·5 hours: *cell 6*, adjacent to *cell 1*, has now divided; other cells have enlarged. C, After a further 16·5 hours, i.e. 44 hours from the state in A, *cell 7* has divided and *cell 8* appears to be in an early stage of division; *cell 1* is now conspicuous because of its size. D, After a further 6 minutes, i.e. 44·1 hours from A, *cells 1* and 8 have divided ($\times 525$). (After E. Ball, *Phytomorphology*, 1960.) E–F, *Lupinus albus*. Evidence of surface growth at the summit of the shoot apex, as demonstrated by the displacement of centrally placed ink spots. E, After 22 days the ink spot, placed at the exact centre, has been displaced towards the right without dividing ($\times 90$). F, After 22 days the ink spot has become centrifugally dispersed ($\times 140$). (After K. Soma and E. Ball, from *Meristems and Differentiation*, Brookhaven, Symp. 1963.) (*See* p. 136.)

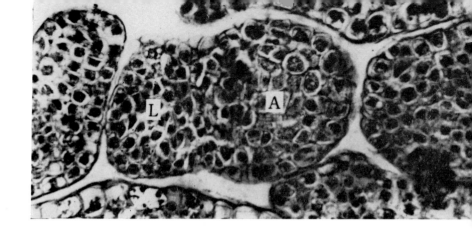

PLATE 7. *Zelkova serrata*. An unusual example of leaf orientation, the plane of the lamina being 90° away from the usual perpendicular relationship with the centre of the shoot apex. *Above:* Transverse section of a young leaf primordium (*L*) showing, at this early stage, a seemingly normal relationship to the parental shoot apex (*A*); however, on the right, it can already be seen that the next older primordium has its upper, flat, laminal face directed away from the shoot apex. *Below:* Transverse section of a shoot apex (*A*) with two leaf primordia (*L*); the anomalous laminal orientation is clearly seen; *s*, stipules. (*See also* Text-figs. 8.17, p. 223; After S. Soma, *Jour. Fac. Sci. Univ. Tokyo*, 1965.)

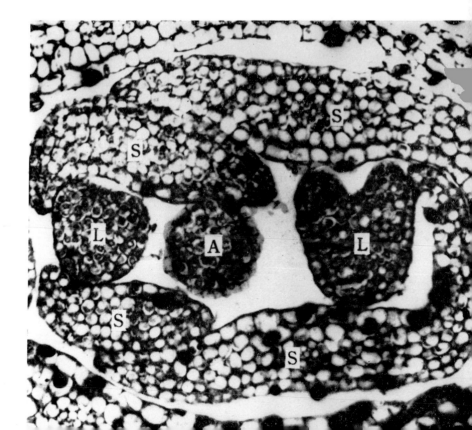

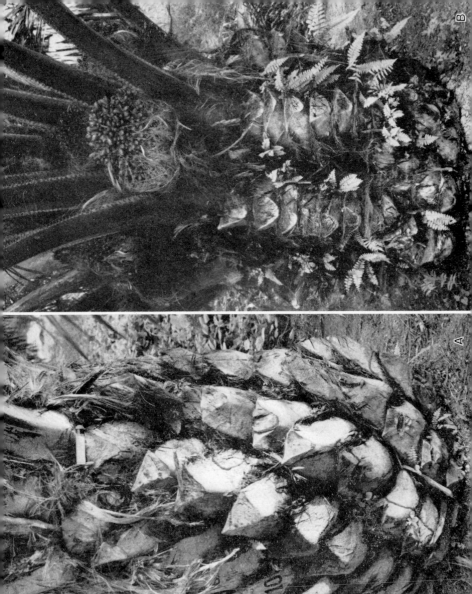

PLATE 8. *Elaeis guineensis.* Phyllotaxis. A, Young *Deli* oil palm, showing the easily observable parastichies, (8 + 13), characteristic of this species. B, A hybrid palm, *Deli* × *Elaeis melanococca*, in which 8 (vertical) orthostichies can readily be distinguished. (*See* p. 228; photographs by courtesy of A. H. Green.)

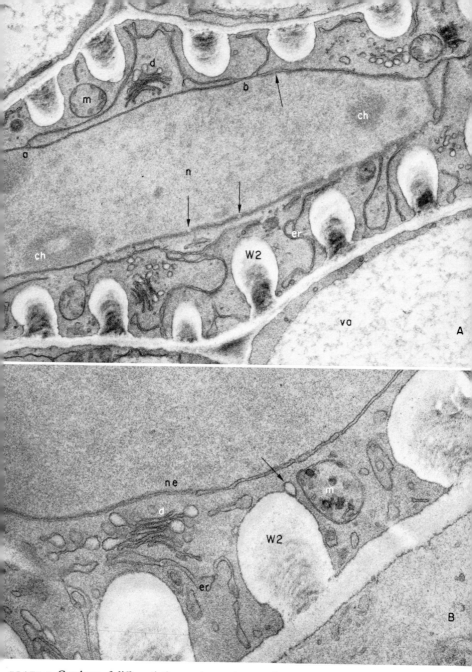

PLATE 9. Cytology of differentiating tracheary elements in *Cucurbita maxima* as revealed by electron-microscopy. A, Part of a tracheary element in which the secondary wall (*W2*) is being formed (the dark regions may indicate lignification); *n*, nucleus: pores in the nuclear envelope are indicated by arrows; this envelope also shows numerous extensions into endoplasmic membranes; one of these shows two connections, at *a* and *b*, with the nuclear envelope. *m*, mitochondrion; *ch*, chromatin unit; *d*, dictyosome or dictyosome vesicles; *er*, endoplasmic reticulum; *va*, vacuole. B, Part of a tracheid wall (*W2*, and associated protoplast. At the arrow, an initial stage of the incorporation of a dictyosome vesicle into the secondary wall can be seen. (*See also* p. 305.) (After K. Esau, *Amer. Jour. Bot.*, 1966.)

PLATE 10. *Tussilago farfara*. A, A dissected bud, showing the late autumn state of development of the capitulum, as seen from above: the disc florets – the last primordia to be formed during the acropetal development of the capitulum – have grown to considerably larger size than the ray florets (×40). B, A longitudinal section of a capitulum as shown above (×50). (After C. W. Wardlaw, *Proc. Linnean Soc.*, Lond., 1961.) (*See* pp. 310, 333.)

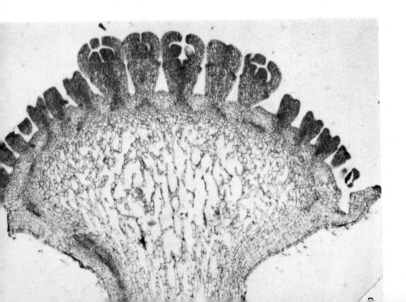

PLATE 11. *Nicotiana tabacum,* cultivar 'Wisconsin 38'. Segments of a floral stem, grown aseptically *in vitro,* formed a callus from which A, flower-buds, and B, fully opened flowers subsequently developed. (*See also* Text-fig. 12.18; after D. (Aghion) Nicolas, *C.R. Acad. Sci.,* 1962; and *Physiol. Veg.,* 1965.) (*See* p. 342.)

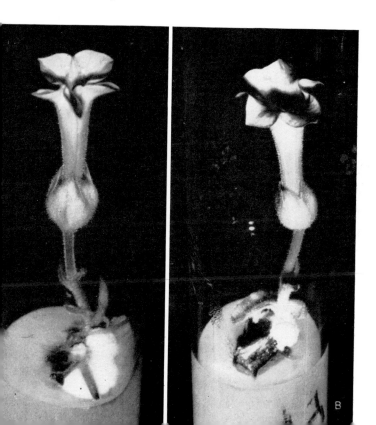

PLATE 12. A, *Cichorium intybus* L., cultivar 'Witloof' (Endive). Neoformation of flowers, induced in inner *root* tissues, i.e. vascular parenchyma, grown *in vitro*: the flower, which was normal and functional, has opened within the culture tube. (*See* Text, p. 344; after P. Paulet and J. P. Nitsch, *C.R. Acad. Sci.* Paris, 1964.) B, *C. intybus*, c. 'Witloof'. Flower obtained from inner root tissue cultured *in vitro*. For such flower induction, the appropriate vernalization of the root was essential: long days are necessary for flower-bud induction in this species and cultivar. (After P. Paulet and J. P. Nitsch, *Ann. Physiol. vég.*, 1964.) C, *Plumbago indica*. Flower induced in a 7 mm. section of internode, excised from a vegetative plant and grown *in vitro*. D, *P. indica*. Flower induction *in vitro*: 5-mm. sections of internode were taken from vegetative plants and grown under long-day (L.D., 16 hr.), short-day (S.D., 10 hr.), and in total darkness (D). (C and D, by courtesy of J. P. Nitsch and C. Nitsch, unpublished, 1967.)

the major plant organs established during growth. These relationships are often, perhaps invariably, reciprocal. Investigations by Torrey (1950, 1952, 1956) on the metabolic requirements of roots and lateral roots illustrate this aspect. The growth relationships between the whole and its parts has been examined, though, so far, only to a limited extent, by the methods of comparative physiology (Lee, 1950).

A recognition of the integrated development of any plant species, and of the need for sustained investigations of the contributory processes throughout ontogenesis, can hardly fail to be deeply implanted in the minds of

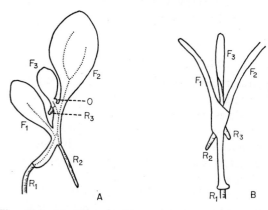

FIG. 14.1. The phyllorhize concept, illustrated by A, *Ceratopteris thalictroides*, and B, *Alisma plantago*, in which the leafy axis can be interpreted as a sequence of morphological units, each consisting of a stem segment, a leaf (F), and a root (R). O, shoot apex. (After G. Chauveaud, 1921.)

those who are conversant with the main facts of embryology; for not only does the whole individual development proceed from a single cell – the fertilized ovum – but the process is characterized by the orderly synthesis, distribution and utilization of the materials of growth, so that at every stage in ontogenesis the individual personifies harmony of development and equilibrium in a strictly physical and mathematical sense.

As a dicotyledon or other embryo elongates, the two major poles, or formative regions, i.e. the shoot and the primary root apices, become progressively separated by differentiated and maturing tissues. In some species the histological organization of the root is more advanced than that of the shoot; in others the organization of the shoot apex is in the lead; and in yet others the developments at the two poles appear to be about equal. We now know that there are important differences in the rates and kinds of biochemical activities at the two poles, these varying from species to species. Nevertheless, the embryo, of whatever taxonomic affinity, typically

N

develops as a whole and behaves like a steady-state system, i.e. a growing system that is always in, or approaching, dynamic equilibrium. For many of us, in contemplating whole-plant morphogenesis, it is difficult to envisage the growing germ as a *continuum* in both space and time. What we tend to retain in our minds are the 'stage'-by-'stage' developments illustrated in morphological works; or various graphical representations of growth, as contributed by physiologists. Each such approach is largely one of convenience, a handy habit that, in due course, will no doubt be replaced by new ways of thinking and recording.

Let us now consider some of the ways in which phenomena of holism in plants have been, and may be, approached.

THE PLANT A COMPLEX CHIMAERA

Recent cytological studies have led to the concept of the plant as a complex chimaera. At an earlier stage in botanical science it was generally accepted – indeed, positively asserted – that all the cells in the normal sporophyte generation of a fern or seed plant are diploid (or of some characteristic ploidy) and actually or potentially genetically equivalent. This view is no longer entirely acceptable, though it cannot be said that the situation has yet been sufficiently explored or clarified.

The view under consideration has emerged from the fact that closer cytological studies of cells at some distance from the apical meristems in shoots and roots have shown that not all of them are diploid: many are demonstrably polyploid (*see* p. 258). In roots, for example, the farther a cell is from the meristem, the higher is the ploidy of its nucleus. Accordingly, plants have been described as 'complex chimaeras' (*see* Clowes, 1961, pp. 176 *et seq.* for résumé of literature). Among the basic facts that must be brought into a proper relationship with other facts of development are: (1) that, in a normally diploid plant, many differentiated cells are polyploid; (2) regenerative processes are mainly based on diploid cells, perhaps suggesting that this cytological state has a stability that is of fundamental importance in the economy of the plant; and (3) whatever the ploidy or cytological state of contiguous cells may be, they differentiate together and constitute a harmonious pattern that is characteristic of the species. Accordingly, one may inquire how important cell or tissue polyploidy is in the functional development of a particular organ or tissue. This is not to suggest or imply that there are no metabolic or other differences in cells of different chromosome number; we know that there are. But it appears that such differences are not of great importance and that the holistic development of an organismal unit, or a specific pattern, transcends the cytological vicissitudes. In the *Datura* periclinal chimaeras, as described by Blakeslee and his co-workers, the vegetative shoot apex comprised histogenic layers of very different ploidy in different instances. These histogenic layers had great stability and gave rise to characteristic parts of the tissue system. Yet, in their ontogenesis and adult morphology, the several chimaeras, though differing in details, were generally comparable, all the characters developed being recognizably those of *Datura*.

To summarize: In contiguous cells or tissues of varied ploidy it appears as if some kind of *complementary physiological mechanism* is at work whereby the mutual relationships of the cells or tissues during differentiation and development are regulated by an over-riding holism and by a pervasive tendency towards equilibrium or steady state.

PHYSIOLOGICAL STUDIES AND WHOLE-PLANT ORGANIZATION

Since the days of Sachs, with his broad conception of chemical morphogenesis and correlation, physiologists have pondered the problems of whole-plant organization. Recently Koursanov (1959) emphasized the importance of physiological studies as the principal means of enabling us to penetrate more deeply into the phenomena of plant life and noted that, as a new metabolic substance with special physiological properties is discovered, it tends to attract an almost unique attention – until the next new substance is revealed! But, he maintained, the major task of the physiologist still remains to be accomplished, namely, to elucidate how growth-regulating substances, and systems of reactions, contribute to the characteristic development of the plant in its entirety. Contemporary physiology has admittedly touched on the topic of whole-plant metabolism – involving as it does a recognition of the special functions of different organs, the different organization of their enzyme systems and elaborated products, and the exchange of metabolic substances between them – but, so far, only fragments of information have been obtained. Yet, this comprehensive problem is probably the one which will best serve to bring together the different branches of botany (Koursanov, 1959).

As a notable aspect of whole-plant physiology, Koursanov dealt in some detail with the metabolic relationships between leaf and root. Thus he showed how sugars, chiefly sucrose, move downwards into the roots and are there utilized in various ways. Various amino and other acids which are synthesized in the roots move upwards into the aerial leafy shoot. These metabolic processes are affected by another functional activity of the root, i.e. its uptake of water and inorganic nutrients from the soil. The availability of nitrogen and phosphorus in the soil (or rooting medium) is of special importance in root metabolism. Even when nutrients are not being taken up from the substratum, the synthesis of substances in roots, essential

N2

to metabolic processes in the leafy shoot, still goes on. In fact, there is a constant movement of important metabolic substances between leaf and root. As a plant enlarges, the two kinds of organs become increasingly separated in space. In this connection, Koursanov cited the example of *Ficus* sp. in which the aerial roots are formed, not at random, but typically in a close relationship with a developing lateral branch (Fig. 14.2). While this kind of information undoubtedly contributes to whole plant physiology, and therefore, in a general way, to whole-plant morphogenesis, it tells us little about the proximal morphogenetic factors. We still have to bring this information on translocation phenomena and the cycles of metabolic changes into a substantial relationship with the visible morphological de-

FIG. 14.2. *Ficus* sp. In this species the aerial roots are formed, not at random, but in a close spatial relationship with a developing lateral branch. (Redrawn from A. L. Koursanov, *Recent Advances in Botany*, 1959.)

velopments. Moreover, as Koursanov showed, these physiological processes are greatly affected by environmental factors, e.g. weather conditions, especially light, heat and relative humidity as affecting transpiration and assimilation in the leaves, and soil conditions as affecting the availability of water and essential inorganic nutrients.

'CONTINUED EMBRYOLOGY': A RE-EVALUATION

As biologists have long recognized, one of the great differences between animals and plants is that, in the development of the former, the growing, differentiating embryo soon reaches a stage in which the *definitive morphological pattern*, characteristic of the adult state, is established. Quite early in ontogenesis, a quadruped is seen to be a quadruped; and, monstrosities apart, the adult state is attained by the elaboration and maturation of the several regions or organs definitively differentiated during embryogenesis. In plants the matter is otherwise. True, the young dicotyledon embryo, with its two cotyledons, plumule and radicle, could, *for a period of time*, i.e. the resting stage in the ungerminated seed, be regarded as a definitive entity – which, in fact, it is. But, under appropriate conditions, the embryonic shoot apex becomes active and grows on; it becomes more highly organized and gives rise to new lateral members to a seemingly, or actually, indefinite extent, according to the species. Similarly, the primary root apex is capable of potentially indefinite growth and extension, with the formation of an unlimited number of new lateral roots. As Bower (1919, 1947) stated: 'The life of the Higher Plants may be described as an *indefinitely continued embryology*, the increase in the number of parts being in a geometric ratio. In this it differs essentially from that of the Higher Animals, in which the parts of the body are laid down once for all in the initial steps of development, and the body is of a circumscribed and limited type.' Bower then proceeded to note that, although the plant body is theoretically unlimited, limitations of various kinds are, in fact, imposed by both physical and biological factors.

That plants exemplify the phenomenon of continued embryology cannot be denied: it is there as an evident fact of observation (the great ascending trunk of a giant Californian redwood may be the result of 3,000 years of apical growth, or continued embryology!). Yet an over-ready acceptance of this observation as an evident truism, i.e. perhaps connoting to some that all development in plants is characterized by *non-finiteness*, may lead us to overlook important facts and to miss opportunities for extending our comprehension. For example, in the early embryogeny of a leptosporangiate fern, a very regular sequence of cell divisions accompanies the growth and enlargement of the germ. The result is a spheroidal or ellipsoidal body, with unalterable polarity and with *specifically differentiated quadrants*, or embryonic regions (Figs. 3.13, 3.14). One quadrant – and it is invariably the same one in its spatial relationships with the gametophyte and with the neck of the archegonium – becomes organized as the first leaf, a contiguous quadrant as the shoot apex, a third quadrant as the first root and the fourth as the foot. Accordingly, the embryo at this particular stage is very reminiscent, in the precision and finiteness of its organ formation, of certain animal embryogenies. Indeed, the basic resemblances are so strong as to suggest that similar physico-chemical factors may be at work in both plant and animal embryos. However, this resemblance is transitory: the fern-shoot apex continues to grow and form new primordia. Nevertheless, in these days, in which there is a strong trend towards a unified Biology, it is salutary to reflect on the fact that, at particular stages in development, there is a regularity in the organogenic pattern in plants that can be compared with the finite development in animals.

Although they do not usually obtrude themselves on our attention, many examples of the finiteness of development in plants become apparent on closer inspection. These include the simultaneous inception of the whorls of leaf primordia, or of floral organs, in different species. What we observe might be described as finite events in a matrix of continuity. If we were to regard the simultaneous inception of 4-6-leaf primordia in a species with whorled phyllotaxis as an individual critical event – the resultant of an integrated system of reactions which becomes manifest at a particular point of time – the continued embryology of that species would appear, not as an inherently indefinite phenomenon, but as a holistic system of regulated, serial events or developments with a temporal aspect, e.g. the plastochrone in phyllotaxis.

While attention may be called to the evident finiteness of development in the flowers of many species, e.g. of an orchid, a saxifrage, etc., there are many species in which the flower, or inflorescence, is a much less definite entity. Thus, in some species of Compositae, Ranunculaceae, Magnoliaceae, etc., the very considerable numbers of bracts of diminishing size gradually merge with the floral members proper, these also being numerous. Of such species, it might perhaps be said that the reaction system in the shoot apex is such that it readily remains in the open state.

Whole Plant Determination. Morphogenetic studies of individual species, growing under relatively constant environmental conditions, have shown that there may be a considerably greater measure of 'whole plant determination' than is sometimes thought. In *Arum maculatum*, Walton (1964) noted that a plant, typically developing from an axillary bud on the rhizome, first forms a cluster of 4–6 adult foliage leaves. Thereafter the shoot apex begins to undergo its transformation into an inflorescence – the spadix. The last-formed foliar organ is the spathe, a pale green, somewhat membranous leaf or bract which envelops the spadix. The point of special interest here is that, although every leaf axil is capable of giving rise to a lateral bud – and simple observation shows that many do – the bud which is destined to become the major vegetative bud of the succeeding 'generation', i.e. the largest and most rapidly growing bud and the one which will duly become transformed into the next inflorescence, invariably originates in the axil of the penultimate foliage leaf. In *Arum maculatum*, then, the correlative developments within the plant are of such an order of precision that the morphological conformation might reasonably be regarded as being more determinate than indeterminate.

It may well be that, in many species, whole plant morphogenesis is susceptible of considerably more precise specification than has sometimes been thought. The general thesis certainly offers scope for further investigation. In *Endymion non-scripta* (the common hyacinth), Turner (1966) observed that although, as in other bulbs of Liliaceae, every scale or leaf has potentially a bud in its axil, the bud which becomes the flowering axis of the next 'generation' is invariably formed in the axil of the last leaf before the inflorescence (Fig. 14.3). It is the writer's conviction that close observation of common species will reveal many other examples of this

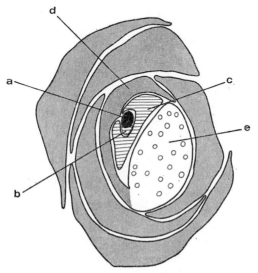

FIG. 14.3. *Endymion non-scripta.* Transverse section of bulb, with the outer leaves removed, below the inflorescence apex. The bud which will become the flowering axis of the succeeding year typically originates in the axil of the last leaf before the current inflorescence. *a*, apex of lateral bud; *b*, leaf primordium of bud; *c*, dorsal prophyll; *d*, youngest leaf; *e*, inflorescence stem. (×23.) (After A. Turner, *Thesis*, Manchester University, 1966.)

kind. In short, although development in vascular plants exemplifies continued embryology, we may also recognize that, in some species, the morphological development is highly regulated and appears to be obligatorily sequential.

The notion of holistic finiteness in plants should obviously not be pushed too far. A plant does not exist alone: it is part of a system comprising organism and environment. A particular species, e.g. a tomato plant, growing in its usual ('normal') environment will typically begin to flower when it has formed a certain (average) number of leaves and reached a certain stature; but the extent of this vegetative development may readily be decreased or

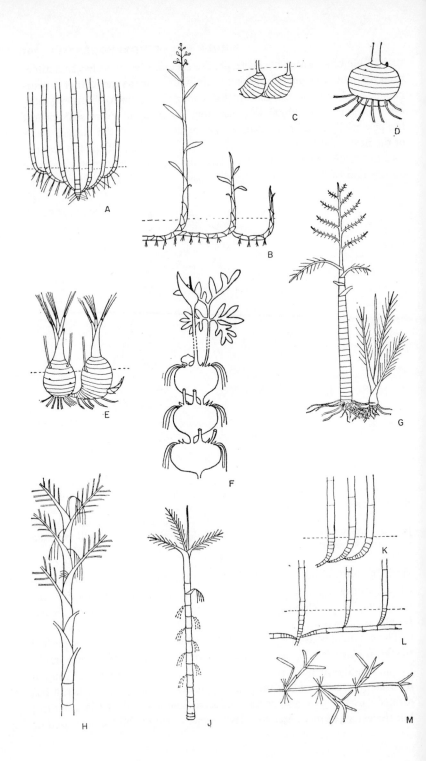

increased by changing one or other of the environmental factors, e.g. the duration and intensity of light, the supply of water and nutrients, and so on. Nevertheless, as one may readily note by consulting any flora, some of the phenotypic characters developed in normal environments can be indicated with a surprising degree of precision.

WHOLE PLANT ORGANIZATION AND MORPHOLOGICAL DIVERSITY

A compelling argument for sustained studies of whole-plant morphogenesis is the sheer morphological diversity of plant species – how to bring simplifying order into the array of materials with which the botanist has to cope. Among the Monocotyledons, for example, there are many seemingly very different forms. Yet, as Holttum (1955) pointed out, a very uniform basic growth pattern is common to a majority, though not to all, of them as observed in Malaya. Thus, bananas, bamboos and other grasses, sedges, pandanus, tufted and single-stemmed palms, epiphytic and terrestrial aroids and orchids, corm-forming and bulb-forming geophytes, etc., can typically be referred, as a matter of whole-plant morphogenesis, to the sympodial habit of branching (Fig. 14.4), described by Holttum as being 'almost universal in the Monocotyledons'. There are, of course, numerous variations of detail within this growth pattern, but, however different the morphological developments may seem to be, all are fundamentally alike. The growth forms among the Dicotyledons are described by Holttum as being more varied in detail but 'much less precisely defined'. Accordingly, they present problems of a different kind for students of morphogenesis.

FIG. 14.4. Growth-habits of Monocotyledons. A, Branching from basal nodes of successive stems, forming a tufted growth. B, Regular rhizomatous growth; rhizome sympodial, each erect stem ending in an inflorescence. C, Fleshy sympodial rhizome, adapted for resting in dry season. D, *Gladiolus* corm (outer sheaths removed), showing old corm at base, and bud (near top) which will form next year's corm. E, Two pseudobulbs of *Spathoglottis*, each bearing leaves and peduncles, with growing bud which will form next pseudobulb. F, Branching pattern of *Amorphophallus* (after Meusel); the inflorescence is terminal on a corm. G, Growth-habit of *Metroxylum sagus*. H, Top of an *Arenga* palm, showing terminal inflorescence, and other inflorescences in leaf-axils in downward succession. J, Habit of an *Areca* palm, an inflorescence in the axil of each leaf (flowers expanding after leaf has fallen); former inflorescences dotted. K, Sympodial branching of *Bambusa*, etc. L, Monopodial runner of *Phyllostachys* type bearing erect stems formed from lateral buds (after Takenouchi). M, Monopodial runner of a panicoid grass (seen from above). (After R. E. Holttum, *Phytomorphology*, 1955.)

THE BASIS OF HOLISTIC FINITENESS

If the views outlined above are valid, the question arises as to the basis of unity and finiteness in the development of plants. The writer has already stated his views on this matter (Wardlaw, 1965a). Briefly, he has ascribed the unified and harmonious development of the rooted, leafy shoot, the morphological developments during the phase of transition to flowering, and the precision and finiteness of the floral development, to correlations and to the existence of a unitary reaction system in the shoot apical meristem. This reaction system (which we can perhaps accept notionally, even though we are not yet in a position to specify it in any detail) is envisaged as an 'open-system' as understood by physical chemists. The rate of the reactions within the system undergoes a steady acceleration during the vegetative phase from the embryo, germ or bud, onwards. This is a direct result of the steady increase in supplies of nutrients diffusing and being drawn into the apical region as the plant undergoes its characteristic increase in size, with amplification of its photosynthetic and root systems. Under certain environmental conditions, and usually at a characteristic stage in ontogenesis, critical changes take place in the metabolic materials reaching the apical reaction system. The pattern of differential growth in the apex is modified, and the genes which determine the specific floral features are evoked in serial sequence. But throughout all these remarkable changes the essentially holistic or unitary character, property or function of the apical reaction system persists. This, admittedly, is a very general kind of statement; but, some day, another generation of botanists will, one may hope, be able to fill in the details with great fullness and precision. *Qui vivra verra*!

In expressing these ideas, let us never overlook the root system. (In some studies of *the plant and the soil* this, alas, does happen!) However, there is an extensive literature which deals with leafy–root, and with main-root–lateral-root, relationships. From tissue-culture investigations it is known that roots may be formed without any associated leaf-shoot development. Holistically speaking, this is extraordinary. In the normal intact plant, however, although the root system has some autonomy in its development, it is closely and reciprocally correlated with activities in the leafy shoot, e.g. supplies of hormones, carbohydrates, etc. So, in the exploration of 'whole-plant morphogenesis', it may be accepted that the development of the root system is closely and reciprocally related to the shoot system throughout ontogenesis.

WHY SHOOTS? WHY ROOTS?

Consideration of 'whole-plant morphogenesis' leads us into very deep and still uncharted waters. The challenge to explore the depths must be accepted. After all, in university classrooms do we ever 'explain' (or, rather, *begin* 'to try to explain') why shoots are shoots, and roots, roots? What are the essential factors which determine 'leafiness', 'shootiness' and 'rootiness'? Elsewhere, an attempt has been made to account for leaf as compared with bud development (p. 201). But the problem of the inherent nature of the shoot and the root, though long considered in both philosophic and realistic terms, is still obscure. Nineteenth-century botanists simplified the problem by assigning roots, leaves and shoots to fundamental categories, *rhizome, phyllome* and *caulome* respectively. Today, we know that shoots and roots can be induced at will in the tissues of some species by the inclusion in the culture medium of a suitable balance of specific ingredients (p. 345). As already noted (p. 345), the kinins are beginning to be accepted as bud-forming substances. This is important information, but it does not of itself help us to understand how the different *physical conformations* of roots and shoots are actually brought about.

Arber (1950) attempted to develop a hypothesis of plant organization which would give an adequate account of the relation of shoot, leaf and root, without using the concept of organs of fundamental categories (*see also* Wardlaw, 1952, for a fuller account). She suggested that a shoot is to some extent analogous to a periclinal chimaera, its central or internal region being of root nature; i.e. like the leaf, the root can be envisaged as a 'partial shoot'. According to this point of view, the vegetative body consists of shoots and partial shoots, 'so that this theory offers an approach to a unified picture of plant construction in the angiosperms' (Arber, 1950, p. 132). As Arber emphasized, shoots and roots have much in common, i.e. radial symmetry, apical growth, the capacity to give rise to lateral members, or units, of the same or of different kinds. Thus, some roots form adventitious shoot buds, and many shoots form adventitious roots. Nevertheless, the differences between the two organs are so great as to make it difficult to state any unified concept which will adequately include both.

The present writer suggests a different approach, namely, that we should begin with a consideration of the reaction systems in shoot and root apices. These systems have many common metabolic components, i.e. the general substances of growth. But they differ quantitatively and qualitatively in respect of particular components. Some substances move acropetally, e.g. thiamin, synthesized in roots; and others, e.g. auxin, formed in growing leaves, move mainly basipetally. In relation to their constitutional differences, the reaction systems of shoot and root will yield different patterns of tissues and organs. The metabolic differences which result in such pattern differences are critical, but not necessarily of great magnitude. As we know, the presence in growing regions of quite small amounts of gene-controlled, or experimentally applied, metabolic substances is often attended by considerable departures from the normal morphological or structural development. In certain tobacco-tissue cultures, high concentrations of IAA in the medium result in root formation, whereas high concentrations of adenine or kinetin *plus* IAA yield buds. In other words, comparable embryonic tissues can yield very different patterns.

Again, as in *Linaria vulgaris*, horse-radish and other species in which roots frequently give rise to shoot buds, the latter are typically formed from, or in close proximity to, nascent root primordia. In these instances quite small differences in the quality or quantity of certain metabolic substances in active loci may determine the inception of the characteristic shoot or root organization (Fig. 10.18).

Polar development in the embryo (whether it be regarded as cause or effect), with its associated organizational features, marks the beginning of chemical differentiation. At the two poles, from the outset, the reaction systems are significantly different in their metabolism. In the shoot apex the reaction system yields both endogenous and exogenous histogenic and organogenic patterns: in roots the patterns are essentially endogenous. If we can advance our thinking and discoveries along these lines we may find a basis for a new approach to the classical problems of whole-plant morphogenesis.

As a dynamic system, and also as a structural–mechanical system, the growing plant will constantly tend towards a state of equilibrium. In relation to the genetical constitution, this state may be attained in different ways according to the species; and environmental factors, which are components of the equilibrium system, may exercise more or less evident effects on both shoot and root development.

THE *sine qua non* OF WHOLE PLANT MORPHOGENESIS

In these days, when the concepts of 'molecular biology' must, to some extent, at least, have entered into the minds of all biologists, and when this new approach has become a virtual, if not an absolute, gospel for some, the author wishes to state quite simply, but with all due emphasis, that he still sees a need for the study of plants as well as of their constituent processes. Hence this chapter. In sharp contrast to those who try to convince us that there is only one contemporary highroad in biology – that of molecular biology – the author would point out the simple and incontrovertible truth that, if you want to understand whole plants, i.e. intact organisms, sooner or later you must study whole-plant morphogenesis and whole-plant physiology. The fruits of molecular biology, which are already remarkable and are growing with increasing acceleration, are of vital importance. But they can never be self-sufficient; for the growing plant has organizational characteristics not only at the molecular level, but also at the several higher levels – cell, tissue, organ – which we see in the harmoniously developed whole organism, as well as in its several specialized organs. For the same reason, there can never be a progressive botanical science based on a single branch of inquiry, be it morphology, physiology, genetics, ecology, etc. Botany – the science of plants – has a heritage from all its branches. Let us cherish this ancient, yet ever new, liberal outlook, not only in our research but in our *scholarship*! If we do not, ours will be the responsibility of having *deprived* a new generation of students of something quite essential.

The organization of any living thing is a very remarkable phenomenon. But there is nothing *mystical* about it, other than that virtually all things are wonderful and mysterious in one way or another. As the writer (Wardlaw, 1965a) attempted to show, organization is a theme on which we *can* work by the methods of analysis and synthesis. Already, at least tentative principles can be stated. The simple fact is that, if our aim is to think in terms of organisms, i.e. whole plants, we must have concepts and principles of organization. After all, what is the alternative? Do we want Botany to be an arbitrary, fashion-based collection of 'bits' of information? This ancient science surely deserves the widest and most comprehensive scholarly effort. To the writer at least, the path to be followed now seems reasonably clear. The morphological conformation, whether perceived by the naked eye macro), or with the help of the electron microscope (ultra-micro), and including *all* that has gone to the making of it – is the visible physical reality.

CHAPTER XV

Outlook

After preliminary studies in mathematics, physics and chemistry – the
stereotyped course of university studies in science in the early decades of
the century – the writer became interested in botany and geology. Plant
morphology was taught in its phylogenetic, or comparative, aspect. The
student was introduced to a very considerable range of organisms, living and
fossil, not in an encyclopaedic fashion, but as the necessary raw materials
for a proper understanding of the splendid, unifying theme of Darwinian
evolution. The great and abiding lesson was that every living species is as
it is because it has behind it a very long ancestry, personifying hereditary
change and natural selection. By the time *Homo sapiens* appeared on the
scene, plants and animals had already undergone a vast amount of evolutionary change and diversification.

One effect of the achievements of the great comparative morphologists
was that they *seemed* to have left singularly little to do for those of us who
were just emerging from studentship. However, in 1917 the first edition of
D'Arcy Thompson's wonderful book *On Growth and Form* was published.
It took a lot of reading to be sure; but since then the writer has never had
any doubts about the importance of mathematics, biochemistry and biophysics in studies of morphogenesis, or 'experimental morphology' as it
was then called. However, some considerable time was to pass before it
began to be clear, whether to morphologists, physiologists or geneticists,
how *new* studies of morphogenesis might be begun.[1] One of the difficulties
was to break away from the old bonds of comparative morphology – essentially an observational science. Another was to discover what specific questions to ask to make an experimental programme feasible: for, notwithstanding the lucidity and charm of D'Arcy Thompson's expositions, it was
not at all evident how a knowledge of physics and chemistry was to be
introduced into an experimental programme on plant morphogenesis. With
the passage of time, however, many new avenues have opened up. The
prospect for the younger biologist is bright, provided his education in biology
and in the physical sciences has been both critical and liberal. Admittedly,

[1] Goebel had already written his *Einleitung in die experimentelle Morphologie der
Pflanzen* (1908).

this is asking rather a lot. Yet the coming decades may well see a considerable influx into botany and zoology of students with talents in mathematics, physics and chemistry. This is to be welcomed and encouraged. The great new discoveries almost certainly lie in the fields of biochemistry and biophysics. But let us hope that there will always remain a substantial number of biologists who appreciate that the essential feature about organisms is that they are organized, whole entities and, as such, transcend, though they also comprise, their constituent physico-chemical processes. An ultimate aim in morphogenesis must be an adequate bio-physico-chemical synthesis, but always bearing in mind that, basically, something must always be accepted *as given,* namely, the specific hereditary constitution of the species, elaborated and selected over vast periods of time.

Many contemporary biologists seem to regard the large numbers of species of animals and plants as an almost intolerable bore. They would almost prefer them not to exist! But they do exist, and their vast number and great morphological diversity are among the inescapable facts, and major phenomena, in biology. Still, one may agree that, professional taxonomists apart, the encyclopaedic approach is not merely out: it is impossible. Nevertheless, one may entertain the hope that, in view of the abundant evidence of homology of organization in Nature, and as our understanding of morphogenesis deepens and widens, it may be possible to arrive at simplified statements of comprehensive concepts, or principles, relating to both the specific and the general morphology of plants (Wardlaw, 1965a).

Of course, it soon becomes evident to the student of morphogenesis that there are some very deep waters which we have not yet either the ideas or the techniques to plumb. Perhaps the most common of the phenomena in this category is that, in the development of any organism, 'the right thing always seems to happen in the right place at the right time!' We can, of course, ascribe this state of affairs to natural selection. This hypothesis may indeed be valid, or valid in some instances; but one never really feels that it enables one to come to grips with the problem, for example, in terms of any close physico-chemical interpretation. Some more profound knowledge of the properties of matter, or of energy and matter, seems to be required. Perhaps there is scope here for biologists to encourage their colleagues in physics and chemistry to venture into some new realm of thought. Meanwhile, let us constantly seek *new facts, liberating ideas, validating experiments and inferences of wide generality.*

Bibliography

(*Note.* Occasional additional references have been included to indicate the full scope of certain researches.)

AGHION, D. (1962) Conditions expérimentales conduisant à l'initiation et au développement de fleurs à partir de la culture stérile de fragments de tige de tabac. *C.R. Acad. Sci.*, **255**, 993–5.

ALBAUM, H. G. (1938) Inhibitions due to growth hormones in fern prothallia and sporophytes. *Amer. Jour. Bot.*, **25**, 124–33.

ALLSOPP, A. (1954) Experimental and analytical studies of pteridophytes. XXIV. Investigations on *Marsilea*. 4. Anatomical effects of changes in sugar concentration. *Ann. Bot. N.S.*, **18**, 449–61.

ALLSOPP, A. (1955) Experimental and analytical studies of pteridophytes. XXVII. Investigations on *Marsilea*. 5. Cultural conditions and morphogenesis, with special reference to the origin of land and water forms. *Ann. Bot. N.S.*, **19**, 247–64.

ALLSOPP, A. (1964) The metabolic status and morphogenesis. *Phytomorphology*, **14**, 1–27.

ALLSOPP, A. (1964) Shoot morphogenesis. *Ann. Rev. Plant Physiol.*, **15**, 225–54.

ALLSOPP, A. (1965a) The significance for development of water supply, osmotic relations and nutrition. *Encyclopedia of Plant Physiology*, XV/1, 504–52, Springer-Verlag, Heidelberg.

ALLSOPP, A. (1965b) Heteroblastic development in cormophytes. *Encyclopedia of Plant Physiology*, XV/1, 1172–221, Springer-Verlag, Heidelberg.

ALLSOPP, A. (1965c) Land and water forms: physiological aspects. *Encyclopedia of Plant Physiology*, XV/1, 1236–55, Springer-Verlag, Heidelberg.

ALLSOPP, A. and MITRA, G. C. (1956) The heterotrichous habit in the protonema of the Bryales. *Nature*, **178**, 1063–4.

AL-TALIB, K. H. and TORREY, J. G. (1959) The aseptic culture of isolated buds of *Pseudotsuga taxifolia*. *Plant Physiol.*, 34, 630–7.

ANANTASWAMY RAU, M. (1951) Development of the embryo in some members of the Papilionaceae. *Phytomorphology*, 1, 80–6.

ANANTASWAMY RAU, M. (1956) Studies in growth *in vitro* of excised ovaries. I. Influence of colchicine on the embryo and endosperm in *Phlox drummondii* Hook. *Phytomorphology*, 6, 90–6.

ARBER, A. (1937) The interpretation of the flower: a study of some aspects of morphological thought. *Biol. Rev.*, **12**, 157–84.

ARBER, A. (1950) *The Natural Philosophy of Plant Form*, Cambridge Univ. Press.

ARNOLD, B. C. (1959) The structure of spines of *Hymenanthera alpina*. *Phytomorph.*, **9**, 367–71.

ARYA, H. C., HILDEBRANDT, A. C. and RIKER, A. J. (1962a) Clonal variation in grape-stem and *Phylloxera*-gall callus growing *in vitro* in different concentrations of sugar. *Amer. Jour. Bot.*, **49**, 368–72.

ARYA, H. C., HILDEBRANDT, A. C. and RIKER, A. J. (1962b) Growth in tissue culture of single-cell clones from grape stem and *Phylloxera* gall. *Plant Physiol.*, **37**, 387–92.

ASHBY, E. (1948) Studies in the morphogenesis of leaves. I. An essay on leaf shape. *New Phytol.*, 47, 153.

AUDUS, L. J. (1953) *Plant Growth Substances*, 1 edn. (2nd edn., 1959), Hill, London.

AUDUS, L. J. (1959) Correlations. *Jour. Linn. Soc. (Bot.)*, **56**, 177–87.

BAILEY, I. W. and SINNOTT, E. W. (1916) The climatic distribution of certain types of angiosperm leaves. *Amer. Jour. Bot.*, **3**, 24–39.

BAIN, H. and DERMEN, H. (1944) Sectorial polyploidy and phyllotaxy in the cranberry (*Vaccinium macrocarpon* Ait). *Amer. Jour. Bot.*, **31**, 581.

BALDEV, B. (1959) *In vitro* responses of growth and development in *Cuscuta reflexa* Roxb. *Phytomorph.*, **9**, 316–19.

BALDEV, B. (1962) *In vitro* studies of floral induction on stem apices of *Cuscuta reflexa* Roxb. – a short day plant. *Ann. Bot. N.S.*, **26**, 173–80.

BALL, E. (1944) Development in sterile culture of stem tips and subjacent regions of *Tropaeolum majus* L. and *Lupinus albus* L. *Amer. Jour. Bot.*, **31**, (suppl.) 1.

BALL, E. (1946) Development in sterile culture of stem tips and subjacent regions of *Tropaeolum majus* L. and of *Lupinus albus* L. *Amer. Jour. Bot.*, **33**, 301–18.

BALL, E. (1948) Differentiation in the primary shoots of *Lupinus albus* L., and of *Tropaeolum majus* L. *Symp. Soc. exp. Biol.*, **2**, 246–62.

BALL, E. (1952a) Morphogenesis of shoots after isolation of the shoot apex of *Lupinus albus*. *Amer. Jour. Bot.*, **39**, 167–91.

BALL, E. (1952b) Experimental division of the shoot apex of *Lupinus albus* L. *Growth*, **16**, 151–74.

BALL, E. (1955) On certain gradients in the shoot tip of *Lupinus albus*. *Amer. Jour. Bot.*, **42**, 509–21.

BALL, E. (1956a) Growth of the embryo of *Ginkgo biloba* under experimental conditions. I. Origin of the first root of the seedling *in vitro*. *Amer. Jour. Bot.*, **43**, 488–95.

BALL, E. (1956b) Growth of the embryo of *Ginkgo biloba* under experimental conditions. II. Effects of a longitudinal split in the tip of the hypocotyl. *Amer. Jour. Bot.*, **43**, 802–10.

BALL, E. (1959) Growth of the embryo of *Ginkgo biloba* under experimental conditions. III. Growth rates of root and shoot upon media absorbed through the cotyledons. *Amer. Jour. Bot.*, **46**, 130–9.

BALL, E. (1960a) Sterile culture of the shoot apex of *Lupinus albus*. *Growth*, **24**, 91–110.

BALL, E. (1960b) Cell divisions in living shoot apices. *Phytomorph.*, **10**, 377–96.

BALL, E. (1962) Studies of living shoot apices. *Plant Tissue Culture and Morphogenesis*, 48–77. (Symp. Amer. Soc. Plant Physiol., Jacksonville, Florida.) Ed. J. C. O'Kelley, Scholar's Library, New York.

BALL E. (1963) *Nature* (London), **197**, 103.

BALL, E. and JOSHI, P. C. (1965) Observations on individual callus cells of *Nicotiana tabacum* in liquid culture. *Botan. Gaz.*, **126**, 233–46.

BALL, E. and JOSHI, P. C. (1965) Division in isolated cells of palisade parenchyma of *Arachis hypogaea*. *Nature*, **207**, 213–14.

BALL, E. and SOMA, K. (1965) Effect of sugar concentration on growth of the shoot apex of *Vicia faba*. *Proc. Internat. Conf. Plant Tissue Culture* (Ed. P. R. White and A. R. Grove), 269–85. McCutchan Publ. Corp., Berkeley.

BANCROFT, H. (1935) A review of researches concerning floral morphology. *Bot. Rev.*, **1**, 77–99.

BARKER, W. G. and STEWARD, F. C. (1962) Growth and development of the banana plant. 1. The growing regions of the vegetative shoot. 2. The transition from the vegetative to the floral shoot in *Musa acuminata* cv. Gros Michel. *Ann. Bot. N.S.*, **26**, 389–411.

BARKER, W. G. and STEWARD, F. C. (1962) Growth and development of the banana plant. 3. The transition from the vegetative to the floral shoot in *Musa acuminata* cv. Gros Michel. *Ann. Bot. N.S.*, **26**, 413–23.

BARNARD, C. (1955) Histogenesis of the inflorescence and flower of *Triticum aestivum* L. *Austral. Jour. Bot.*, **3**, 1–20.

BARNARD, C. (1961) The interpretation of the angiosperm flower. *Australian Jour. Sci.*, **24**, 64–72.

BARTELS, F. (1960a) Zur Entwicklung der Keimpflanze von *Epilobium hirsutum*. II. Die im Vegetationspunkt während eines Plastochrons ablaufenden Zellteilungen. *Flora*, **149**, 206–24.

BARTELS, F. (1960b) Zur Entwicklung der Keimpflanze von *Epilobium hirsutum*. III. Wachstumstendenzen, die zur Entwicklung eines Laubblattprimordiums und Keimblattes führen. *Flora*, **149**, 225–42.

BARTELS, F. (1960c). Zur Entwicklung der Keimpflanze von *Epilobium hirsutum*. IV. Der Nachweis eines Scheitelzellenwachstums. *Flora*, **150**, 552–71.

BASFORD, K. H. (1961) Morphogenetic responses to gibberellic acid of a radiation-induced mutant dwarf in groundsel, *Senecio vulgaris* L. *Ann. Bot. N.S.*, **25**, 279–302.

BEAL, J. M. (1946) Reactions of decapitated bean plants to certain of the substituted phenoxy compounds. *Botan. Gaz.*, **108**, 166.

BELL, P. R. (1959) The experimental investigation of the pteridophyte life cycle. *Jour. Linn. Soc. Lond. (Bot.)*, **56**, 188–203.

BELL, P. R. (1963) The cytochemical and ultrastructural peculiarities of the fern egg. *Jour. Linn. Soc. Lond. (Bot.)*, **58**, 353–9.

BELL, P. R. and MÜHLETHALER, K. (1962) The fine structure of the cells taking part in oogenesis in *Pteridium aquilinum* (L.) Kuhn. *Journ. Ultrastruct. Res.*, **7**, 452–66.

BELL, P. R. and MÜHLETHALER, K. (1964) The degeneration and reappearance of mitochondria in the egg cells of a plant. *Jour. Cell Biology*, **20**, 235–48.

BENTLEY, J. A. (1950) Growth regulating effect of certain organic compounds. *Nature* (Lond.), **165**, 449.

BERGMANN, L. (1959) Über die Kultur von Zellsuspensionen von *Daucus carota*. *Naturwiss.*, **46**, 20–1.

BERGMANN, L. (1959) A new technique for isolating and cloning single cells of higher plants. *Nature* (London), **184**, 648–9.

BERGMANN, L. (1960) Growth and division of single cells of higher plants in vitro. *Jour. Gen. Physiol.*, **43**, 841–51.

BERNIER, G. (1964) Evolution of nucleic acid metabolism during the ontogenetic development of apical meristems. Symposium: *Differentiation of Apical Meristems and Some Problems of Regulation of Development of Plants*, 115–119. (Publ. *Czechoslovak Acad. Sci.*, Praha 1966.)

BERNIER, G. (1964) Étude histophysiologique et histochimique de l'évolution du méristème apical de *Sinapis alba* L., cultivé en milieu conditionné et en diverses durées de jour favorables ou défavorables à la mise à fleurs. *Acad. Roy. Belg., Classe Sci. Mém.* in 4°, Sér. II. 16.

BERNIER, G. (1966) The morphogenetic rôle of the apical meristem in higher plants. pp. 151–211, in *Les Phytohormones et l'Organogenèse* (Ed. R. Bouillenne). Congr. Internat. Univ. Liège, 1965. Publ. Univ. Liège.

BERNIER, G. and BRONCHART, R. (1963) Application de la technique d'histo-autoradiographie à l'étude de l'incorporation de thymidine tritiée dans les méristèmes caulinaires. *Bull. Soc. Roy. Sci. Liège*, **32**.

BERNIER, G., BRONCHART, R. and JACQUARD, A. (1964) Action of gibberellic acid on the mitotic activity of the different zones of the shoot apex of *Rudbeckia bicolor* and *Perilla nankinensis*. *Planta*, **61**, 236–44.

BERNIER, G. and JENSEN, W. A. (1966) Pattern of DNA synthesis in the meristematic cells of *Sinapis*. *Histochemie*, **6**, 85–92.

BERSILLON, G. (1955) Recherches sur les Papaveracées. Contribution à l'étude du développement des dicotylédones herbacées. *Ann. Sci. Nat., Bot.*, XI, **16**, 225–443.

BERTHOLD, G. (1886) *Protoplasma-mechanik.*

BERTHON, R. (1943) Sur l'origine des radicelles chez les angiosperms. *C.R. Acad. Sci.* (Paris), **216**, 308–9.

BETH, K. (1953) Experimentelle Untersuchungen über die Wirkung des Lichtes auf die Formbildung von kernhaltigen und kernlosen *Acetabularia* zellen. *Zeit. Naturforsch.*, **8b**, 334–42.

BETH, K. (1956a) Amputation und Stiellänge bei *Acetabularia*. *Naturwiss.*, **43**, 307–8.

BETH, K. (1956b) Verfrühte Hutbildung bei *Acetabularia* als Folge nächtlicher Kältebehandlung. *Naturwiss.*, **43**, 308–9.

BIENIEK, M. E. and MILLINGTON, W. F. (1967) Differentiation of lateral shoots as thorns in *Ulex europaeus*. *Amer. Jour. Bot.*, **54**, 61–70.

BINDLOSS, E. (1942) A developmental analysis of cell length as related to stem length. *Amer. Jour. Bot.*, **29**, 179–88.

BLAKELY, L. M. (1964) Growth and organized development of cultured cells. VI. The behaviour of individual cells on nutrient agar. *Amer. Jour. Bot.*, **51**, 792–807.

BLAKELY, L. M. and STEWARD, F. C. (1961) Growth induction in cultures of *Haplopappus gracilis*. I. The behaviour of the cultured cells. *Amer. Jour. Bot.*, **48**, 351–8.

BLAKELY, L. M. and STEWARD, F. C. (1962) The growth of free cells. II. Observations on individual cells and their subsequent patterns of growth. (*Abstr.*) *Amer. Jour. Bot.*, **49**, 653.

BLAKELY, L. M. and STEWARD, F. C. (1964) Growth and organized development of cultured cells. V. The growth of colonies from free cells on nutrient agar. *Amer. Jour. Bot.*, **51**, 780–91.

BLAKELY, L. M. and STEWARD, F. C. (1964) Growth and organized development of cultured cells. VII. Cellular variation. *Amer. Jour. Bot.*, **51**, 809–20.

BLOCH, R. (1965) Polarity and gradients in plants: A survey. *Encyclopedia of Plant Physiology*, XV/1, 234–74.

BLOCH, R. (1965) Histological foundations of differentiation and development in plants. *Encyclopedia of Plant Physiology*, XV/I, 146–88.

BOND, T. E. T. (1952) A further note on size and form in Agarics. *Trans. Brit. Myc. Soc.*, **35**, 190–4.

BONNER, J. and HUANG, R. C. (1962) Chromosomal control of enzyme synthesis. *Canad. Jour. Bot.*, **40**, 1487–97.

BONNER, J. and ZEEVAART, J. A. D. (1962) Ribonucleic acid synthesis in the bud an essential component of floral induction in *Xanthium*. *Plant Physiol.*, **37**, 43–9.

BONNER, J. T. (1952) *Morphogenesis, An Essay on Development*, Princeton University Press.

BONNER, J. T. (1965) Morphogenetic movements in plants. *Encyclopedia of Plant Physiology*, XV/I, 492–503.

BONNETT, H. T., Jr. and TORREY, J. G. (1965) Chemical control of organ formation in root segments of *Convolvulus* cultured *in vitro*. *Plant Physiol.*, **40**, 1228–36.

BONNETT, H. T., Jr. and TORREY, J. G. (1966) Comparative anatomy of endogenous bud and lateral root formation in *Convolvulus arvensis* roots cultured *in vitro*. *Amer. Jour. Bot.*, **53**, 496–507.

BORRISS, H. (1934) Über der Einflusz äuserer Faktoren auf Wachstum und Entwicklung der Fruchtkörper von *Coprinus lagopus*. *Planta* (Berl.), **22**, 644–84.

BORTHWICK, H. A. (1931) *Botan. Gaz.*, **92**, 23.

BOUILLENNE, R. and WENT, F. W. (1933) Recherches expérimentales sur la néoformation des racines dans les plantules et les boutures des plantes supérieures. *Ann. Jard. Bot.* (Buitenzorg), **43**, 25.

BOUILLENNE, R. (1938) Contribution à l'étude des facteurs de la néoformation et de la croissance des racines. Rhizocaline, heteroauxine, acides amines, vitamine B_1. *Bull. Soc. Roy. Bot. Belg.*, **7**, 43.

BOUILLENNE, R. (1966) *Les Phytohormones et l'Organogenèse*. Congr. Internat. Univ. Liège, 1965.

BOWER, F. O. (1919, 1947) *Botany of the Living Plant*, Macmillan, London.

BOWER, F. O. (1923) *The Ferns*. Vol. I. Cambridge University Press.

BOWES, B. G. (1963) The structure and development of the vegetative shoot apex in *Glechoma hederacea* L. *Ann. Botany*, **27**, 357–64.

BOWES, B. G. (1965) The ultrastructure of the shoot apex and young shoot of *Glechoma hederacea* L. *La Cellule*, **65**, 351–6.

BOWES, B. G. (1965) The origin and development of vacuoles in *Glechoma hederacea* L. *La Cellule*, **65**, 359–64.

BRACHET, J. and LANG, A. (1965) Genetical aspects of development. I. The role of the nucleus and the nucleocytoplasmic interactions in morphogenesis. *Encyclopedia of Plants Physiology*, XV/I, 1–40.

BRACHET, J. and LANG, A. (1965) The role of the nucleus and the nucleocytoplasmic interactions in morphogenesis. *Encyclopedia of Plant Physiology*, XV/I, 1–40.

BRIAN, P. W. (1959) Effects of gibberellins on plant growth and development. *Biol. Rev.*, **34**, 37–84.

BROOKS, R. M. (1940) Comparative histogenesis of vegetative and floral apices in *Amygdalus communis*, with special reference to the carpel. *Hilgardia*, **13**, 175–306.

BROWN, C. L. and GIFFORD, E. M., Jr. (1958) The relation of the cotyledons to root development of pine embryos grown *in vitro*. *Plant Physiol.*, **33,** 57–64.

BROWN, J. A. M., MIKSCHE, J. P. and SMITH, H. H. (1964) An analysis of H³-thymidine distribution throughout the vegetative meristem of *Arabidopsis thaliana* (L). *Heynh. Rad. Bot.*, **4,** 107–31.

BROWN, R. and ROBINSON, E. (1955) Cellular differentiation and the development of enzyme proteins in plants: in *Biological Specificity and Growth*, ed. E. G. Butler, Princeton Univ. Press, 93–118.

BUGNON, F. (1949a) Sur la phyllotaxie des grappes et des vrilles de la vigne (*Vitis vinifera* L.). *C.R. Acad. Sci.* (Paris), **228,** 770–2.

BUGNON, F. (1949b) Sur la valeur morphologique des grappes et des vrilles de la vigne (*Vitis vinifera* L.). *C.R. Acad. Sci.* (Paris), **228,** 937–9.

BUGNON, F. (1949c) Sur les caractères distinctifs des rameaux végétatifs, des grappes et des vrilles de la vigne (*Vitis vinifera* L.). *C.R. Acad. Sci.* (Paris), **228,** 1967–9.

BUGNON, F. (1953) Recherches sur la ramification des Ampélidacées. *Publications de l'Université de Dijon* II. Presses Universitaires de France, Paris.

BUGNON, F. (1953) 'Recherches sur la ramification de Ampélidacées.' Paris.

BUGNON, F. (1964) Sur les modes de ramification intervenant au cours de la genèse de quelques inflorescences dont la signification morphologique est controversée. *Bull. Soc. Bot.*, *France*, Mém. 101–24.

BÜNNING, E. (1948) *Entwicklungs- und Bewegungs-physiologie der Pflanzen*, Springer, Berlin.

BÜNNING, E. (1951) Über die Differenzierungsvorgänge in der Cruciferenwurzel. *Planta*, **39,** 126–53.

BÜNNING, E. (1952) Morphogenesis in plants. *Surv. Biol. Progr.*, **2,** 105–40.

BÜNNING, E. (1952) Weitere Untersuchungen über die Differenzierungsvorgänge in Wurzeln. *Z. Bot.*, **40,** 385–406.

BÜNNING, E. (1957) Polarität und inäquale Teilung des pflanzlichen Protoplasten. *Protoplasmatologia* (Ed. Heilbrunn, L. V. and Weber, F.), **8, 9a,** 1–86.

BÜNNING, E. (1965) Die Entstehung von Mustern in der Entwicklung von Pflanzen. *Encyclopedia of Plant Physiology*, XV/1, 383–408.

BUTLER, R. D. (1965) Endogenous mitotic rhythm in the shoot apical meristem of *Vicia. Jour. Exp. Bot.*, (In press).

BUTLER, R. D. and LANE, G. R. (1959) The study of apical development in relation to etiolation. *Jour. Linn. Soc.* (*Bot.*), **56,** 170–6.

BUVAT, R. (1952) Structure, évolution et fonctionnement du méristème apical de quelques dicotylédones. *Ann. Sci. Nat. Bot.*, XI, **13,** 199–300.

BUVAT, R. (1953) L'apex de *Triticum vulgare*: modalités de reprise des mitoses lors de la germination et du fonctionnement végétatif. *C.R. Acad. Sci.* (Paris), **236,** 1989–91.

BUVAT, R. (1955) Le méristème apical de la tige. *Année. Biol.*, **31,** 596–656.

BUVAT, R. (1958) Recherches sur les infrastructures du cytoplasme, dans les cellules du méristème apical, des ébauches foliaires et des feuilles développées d'*Elodea canadensis*. *Ann. Sci. Nat.*, *Bot.*, 11, sér. **19,** 121–58.

BUVAT, R. (1961) Le réticulum endoplasmique des cellules végétales. *Ber. Dtsch. Bot. Ges.*, **74,** 261–7.

BUVAT, R. (1965) Les bases cytologiques de la différentiation et la dé-différentiation chez les plantes. *Encyclopedia of Plant Physiology*, XV/1, 100–145.

BUY, H. G. DU and OLSON, R. A. (1937) The presence of growth regulators during the early development of *Fucus. Amer. Jour. Bot.,* **24,** 609.

CAMEFORT, H. (1956a) Étude de la structure du point végétatif et des variations phyllotaxiques chez quelques Gymnospermes. *Ann. Sci. Nat., Bot.,* XI, **17,** 1–185.

CAMEFORT, H. (1956b) Structure de l'apex caulinaire des gymnospermes. *Ann. Biol.,* **60,** 401–16.

CAMUS, G. (1943) Sur le grèffage de bourgeons d'Endive sur des fragments de tissus cultivés *in vitro. Comp. Rend. Soc. Biol.* (Paris), **137,** 184–5.

CAMUS, G. (1949) Recherches sur le rôle des bourgeons dans les phénomènes de morphogenèse. *Rev. Cytol. et Biol. Veget.,* **11,** 1–199.

CASTLE, E. S. (1942) Spiral growth and reversal of spiraling in *Phycomyces,* and their bearing on primary wall structure. *Amer. Jour. Bot.,* **29,** 664–72.

CATHEY, H. M. (1958) Mutual antagonism of growth control of *Chrysanthemum morifolium* by gibberellin and Amo-1618 (Abstr.), *Plant Physiol.,* xliii Suppl., 33.

CAUJOLLE, F. and BERGAL, G. (1949) Influence de l'acide phénylborique sur la germination de quelques Apétales. *C.R. Acad. Sci.* (Paris), **228,** 1249–51.

CAUJOLLE, F. and BERGAL, G. (1950a) Influence de l'acide phénylborique sur la croissance des racines isolées de *Raphanus sativus* en milieu liquide stérile. *C.R. Acad. Sci.* (Paris), **230,** 1101–3.

CAUJOLLE, F. and BERGAL, G. (1950b) Influence des acides boriques et phénylboriques sur la germination et le développement des plantules de quelques dicotylédones. *C.R. Acad. Sci.* (Paris), **231,** 1550–2.

CAVE, M. S., ARNOTT, J. and COOK, S. A. (1961) Embryogeny in the California peonies with reference to their taxonomic position. *Amer. Jour. Bot.,* **48,** 397–404.

CHADEFAUD, M. M. (1949) Sur la morphologie des Vitacées. *C.R. Acad. Sci.* (Paris), **228,** 1660–2.

CHAILAKHIAN, M. K. (1961) Effect of gibberellins and derivatives of nucleic acid metabolism on plant growth and flowering. *Plant Growth Regulation,* Iowa (Ed. R. M. Klein *et al.*), pp. 531–42.

CHAMPAGNAT, M., MARICHAL, J. and CAILLEUX, T. (1962) Origine des bourgeons hypocotylaires chez quelques Euphorbés. *Bull. Soc. Bot., France, Colloque de Morphologie,* Dijon, April 1962, pp. 23–31.

CHAMPAGNAT, M., MARICHAL, J. and VINCENT, C. (1962) Mode d'initiation des bourgeons hypocotylaires ches *Alliaria officinalis* L. *Bull. Soc. Bot. France, Colloque de Morphologie,* Dijon, April 1962. pp. 32–44.

CHARLTON, W. A. (1965) Bud initiation in excised roots of *Linaria vulgaris. Nature,* **207,** 781–2.

CHARLTON, W. A. (1966) The root system of *Linaria vulgaris* Mill. I. Morphology and anatomy. *Canad. Jour. Bot.,* **44,** 1111–16.

CHARLTON, W. A. (1967) The root system of *Linaria vulgaris* Mill. II. Differentiation of root types. *Canad. Jour. Bot.,* **45,** 81–91.

CHAUVEAUD, G. (1921) *La constitution des plantes vasculaires révélée par leur ontogenie,* Paris.

CHEADLE, V. I. (1956) Research on xylem and phloem – progress in fifty years. *Amer. Jour. Bot.,* **43,** 719–31.

CHILD, C. M. (1941) *Patterns and Problems of Development,* Chicago Univ. Press.

CHOPRA, R. N. and SACHAR, R. C. (1963) Endosperm. *Recent Advances in the*

Embryology of Angiosperms (Ed. Maheshwari, P.), pp. 135–70. *Internat. Soc. Plant Morph.*, Delhi.

CHOUARD, P. and AGHION, D. (1961) Modalités de la formation de bourgeons floraux sur des cultures de segments de tige de tabac. *C.R. Acad. Sci.* (Paris), 252, 3864–6.

CLOWES, F. A. L. (1950a) Root apical meristems of *Fagus sylvatica*. *New Phytol.*, 49, 248–68.

CLOWES, F. A. L. (1950b) The promeristem of roots. *Proc. VII Internat. Bot. Congress*, 357–8.

CLOWES, F. A. L. (1951) The structure of mycorrhizal roots in *Fagus sylvatica*. *New Phytol.*, 50, 1–16.

CLOWES, F. A. L. (1953) The cytogenerative centre in roots with broad columellas. *New Phytol.*, 52, 48–57.

CLOWES, F. A. L. (1954a) The promeristem and the minimal constructional centre in grass root apices. *New Phytol.*, 53, 108–16.

CLOWES, F. A. L. (1954b) The root cap of ectotrophic mycorrhizas. *New Phytol.*, 53, 525–9.

CLOWES, F. A. L. (1956a) Nucleic acids in root apical meristems of *Zea*. *New Phytol.*, 55, 29–35.

CLOWES, F. A. L. (1956b) Localization of nucleic acid synthesis in root meristems. *Jour. Exp. Bot.*, 7, 307–12.

CLOWES, F. A. L. (1957) Chimaeras and meristems. *Heredity*, 11, 141–8.

CLOWES, F. A. L. (1958a) Development of quiescent centres in root meristems. *New Phytol.*, 57, 85–8.

CLOWES, F. A. L. (1958b) Protein synthesis in root meristems. *Jour. Exp. Bot.*, 9, 229–38.

CLOWES, F. A. L. (1959a) Reorganization of root apices after irradiation. *Ann. Bot., N.S.*, 23, 205–10.

CLOWES, F. A. L. (1959b) Adenine incorporation and cell division in shoot apices. *New Phytol.*, 58, 16–19.

CLOWES, F. A. L. (1959c) Apical meristems of roots. *Biol. Rev.*, 34, 501–29.

CLOWES, F. A. L. (1959d) The root apical meristem and its cellular organization. *Proc. IX Internat. Bot. Congress*, 2, 76–7.

CLOWES, F. A. L. (1961a) *Apical Meristems*, 217 pp. Blackwell, Oxford.

CLOWES, F. A. L. (1961b) Effects of P-radiation on meristems. *Exp. Cell Res.*, 25, 529–34.

CLUTTER, M. E. (1960) Hormonal induction of vascular tissues in tobacco pith *in vitro*. *Science*, 132, 548–9.

COOPER, W. C. (1936) Transport of root-forming hormone in woody cuttings. *Plant Physiol.*, 11, 779.

CORNER, E. J. H. (1932a) The fruit body of *Polystictus xanthopus*. *Ann. Bot.*, 46, 71–111.

CORNER, E. J. H. (1932b) A *Fomes* with two systems of hyphae. *Trans. Brit. Mycol. Soc.*, 17, 51–81.

CORNER, E. J. H. (1950) *Clavaria and Allied Genera*. Clarendon Press, Oxford.

CORNER, E. J. H. (1953) The construction of polypores – I. Introduction: *Polyporus sulphureus, P. squamosus, P. betulinus* and *Polystictus microcyclus*. *Phytomorph.* 3, 152–67.

CORNER, E. J. H. (1963) A criticism of the gonophyll theory of the flower. *Phytomorph.*, 13, 290–2.

COULTER, J. M. and CHAMBERLAIN, C. J. (1912) *Morphology of Angiosperms*, New York, D. Appleton and Company.

COURTOY, R. (1966) De la sexualisation du gametophyte de *Marchantia polymorpha* L. en milieu conditionné. pp. 223–36 in *Les Phytohormones et l'Organogenèse* (Ed. R. Bouillenne) Congr. Internat. Univ. Liège, 1965. Publ. Univ. Liège.

CRÉTÉ, P. (1938) La polyembryonie chez le *Lobelia syphilitica* L. *Bull. Soc. Bot., Fr.*, **85**, 580–3.

CRÉTÉ, P. (1949) Un cas de polyembryonie chez une Gentianacée, l'*Erythraea centaurium* Pers. *Bull. Soc. Bot., Fr.*, **96**, 113–15.

CROOKS, D. M. (1933–34) Histological and regenerative studies on the flax seedling. *Botan. Gaz.*, **95**, 209.

CROSS, G. L. and JOHNSON, T. J. (1941) Structural features of the shoot apices of diploid and colchicine-induced, tetraploid strains of *Vinca rosea* L. *Bull. Torrey Bot. Club*, **68**, 618–35.

CUSICK, F. (1956) Studies of floral morphogenesis. I. Median bisections of flower primordia in *Primula bulleyana* Forrest. *Trans. Roy. Soc. Edinb.*, **63**, 153–66.

CUSICK, F. (1959) Floral morphogenesis in *Primula bulleyana* Forrest. *Jour. Linn. Soc. (Bot.)*, **56**, 262–8.

CUTTER, E. G. (1954) Experimental induction of buds from fern leaf primordia. *Nature*, **173**, 440–1.

CUTTER, E. G. (1955) Experimental and analytical studies of pteridophytes. XXIX. The effect of progressive starvation on the growth and organization of the shoot apex of *Dryopteris aristata* Druce. *Ann. Bot. N.S.*, **19**, 485–99.

CUTTER, E. G. (1956) Experimental and analytical studies of pteridophytes. XXXIII. The experimental induction of buds from leaf primordia in *Dryopteris aristata* Druce. *Ann. Bot. N.S.*, **20**, 143–65.

CUTTER, E. G. (1957a) Studies of morphogenesis in the Nymphaeaceae. I. Introduction: some aspects of the morphology of *Nuphar lutea* (L.) Sm. and *Nymphaea alba* L. *Phytomorph.*, **7**, 45–56.

CUTTER, E. G. (1957b) Experimental and analytical studies of pteridophytes. XXXVI. Further experiments on the developmental potentialities of leaf primordia in *Dryopteris aristata* Druce. *Ann. Bot. N.S.*, **21**, 343–72.

CUTTER, E. G. (1958) Studies of morphogenesis in the Nymphaeaceae. III. Surgical experiments on leaf and bud formation. *Phytomorph.*, **8**, 74–95.

CUTTER, E. G. (1959) On a theory of phyllotaxis and histogenesis. *Biol. Rev.*, **34**, 243–63.

CUTTER, E. G. (1961) The inception and distribution of flowers in the Nymphaeaceae. *Proc. Linn. Soc.* (London), **172**, 93–100.

CUTTER, E. G. (1963) Experimental modification of the pattern of organogenesis in *Hydrocharis*. *Nature*, **198**, 504–5.

CUTTER, E. G. (1964a) Phyllotaxis and apical growth. *New Phytol.*, **63**, 39–46.

CUTTER, E. G. (1964b) Observations on leaf and bud formation in *Hydrocharis morsus-ranae*. *Amer. Jour. Bot.*, **51**, 318–24.

CUTTER, E. G. (1965) Recent experimental studies of the shoot apex and shoot morphogenesis. *Bot. Rev.*, **31**, 7–113.

CUTTER, E. G. and VOELLER, B. R. (1959) Changes in leaf arrangement in individual fern apices. *Jour. Linn. Soc. (Bot.)*, **56**, 225–36.

CUTTER, E. G. and WARDLAW, C. W. (1963) Induction of buds on older leaf primordia in ferns. *Nature*, **199**, 985–87.

DALE, H. M. (1957) Developmental studies of *Elodea canadensis* Michx. II. Experimental studies on morphological effects of darkness. *Canad. Jour. Bot.*, **35**, 51–64.

D'AMATO, D. (1965) Chimaera formation in mutagen-treated seeds and diplontic selection. *The Use of Induced Mutations in Plant Breeding*, pp. 303–16. Pergamon Press.

D'AMATO, F. (1959) C-mitosis and experimental polyploidy in plants. *Genet. Agr.*, II.

D'AMATO, F. and AVANZI, S. (1965) DNA content, DNA synthesis and mitosis in the root apical cell of *Marsilea strigosa*. *Caryologia*, **18**, 383–94.

DANIELLI, J. F. (1945) Some reflections on the forms of simpler cells. *Essays on Growth and Form*, Oxford Univ. Press.

DASANAYAKE, M. D. (1960) Aspects of morphogenesis in a dorsiventral fern. *Pteridium aquilinum* (L.) Kuhn. *Ann. Bot. N.S.*, **24**, 317–29.

DEMAGGIO, A. E. (1963) Morphogenetic factors influencing the development of fern embryos. *Jour. Linn. Soc. Lond. (Bot.)*, **58**, 361–76.

DEMAGGIO, A. E. and WETMORE, R. H. (1961) Morphogenetic studies of the fern *Todea barbara* (L.) Moore. III. Experimental embryology. *Amer. Jour. Bot.*, **48**, 551–65.

DEMAGGIO, A. E., WETMORE, R. H. and MOREL, G. (1963) Induction de tissue vasculaire dans le prothalle de fougère. *C.R. Acad. Sci.*, **256**, 5196–9.

DENIZCI, R. (1966) Über den Einfluss von Kinetin und Indolylessigsäure auf das austreiben der Knospen von *Pisum sativum*. *Planta* (Berl.), **68**, 141–56.

DE ROPP, R. S. (1955) The growth and behaviour *in vitro* of isolated plant cells. *Proc. Royal Soc. of London, Ser. B-Biol. Sci.*, **144**, 86–93.

DORE, J. (1965) Physiology of regeneration in cormophytes. *Encyclopedia of Plant Physiology*, XV/2, 1–91.

DOSTÁL, R. (1960) Einige Rekapitulationsversuche mit Pflanzen. *Biol. Zbl.* **79**, 343–6.

DOUGLAS, G. E. (1957) The inferior ovary. *Bot. Rev.*, **23**, 1–46.

DUPUY, P. (1963) Contribution a l'étude de quelques problèmes de morphologie et de tératologie expérimentales chez les Angiospermes. *Thesis, Fac. Sci.*, Univ. Poitiers, 1–217.

DUPUY, R. (1964) Formation des fleurs anormales, régulières, irrégulières ou zygomorphes, par l'action de 2,4-D, chez le *Nicandra physaloides* L. *C.R. Acad. Sci. Paris*, **258**, 1307–10.

DUPUY, P. and GUYOT, M. (1965) La structure de l'étamine virescente de l'*Eschscholzia californica*. Cham. *C.R. Acad. Sci. Paris*, **260**, 4811–14.

EARLE, E. D. and TORREY, J. G. (1965) Morphogenesis in cell colonies grown from *Convolvulus* cell suspensions plated on synthetic media. *Amer. Jour. Bot*, **52**, 891–9.

ECKERT, G. (1966) Entwicklungsgeschichtliche und Blütenanatomische Untersuchungen zur Problem der Obdiplostemonie. *Bot. Jahr.*, **85**, 523–604.

ENGARD, C. J. (1944) Organogenesis in *Rubus*. *Res. Publ. Univ. Hawaii.*, **21**, I.

ERRERA, L. (1886) Sur une condition fondamentale d'équilibre des cellules vivantes. *C.R. Acad. Sci.*, **103**, 822. *Bull. Soc. Belge Microscopie*, **13**.

ESAU, K. (1940) Developmental anatomy of the fleshy storage organ of *Daucus carota*. *Hilgardia*, **13**, 175–226.

ESAU, K. (1943) Vascular differentiation in the pear root. *Hilgardia*, **15**, 299–325.

ESAU, K. (1948a) Phloem structure in the grapevine, and its seasonal changes. *Hilgardia*, **18**, 217–96.

ESAU, K. (1948b) Anatomic effects of the viruses of Pierce's disease and phony peach. *Hilgardia*, **18**, 423–82.

ESAU, K. (1954) Primary vascular differentiation in plants. *Biol. Rev.*, **29**, 46–86.

ESAU, K. (1963) Ultrastructure of differentiated cells in higher plants. *Amer. Jour. Bot.*, **50**, 495–506.

ESAU, K. (1965a) *Plant Anatomy* (Second Edition). Wiley, New York.

ESAU, K. (1965b) *Vascular Differentiation in Plants*, Holt, Rinehart and Winston, New York.

ESAU, K. (1965c) Anatomy and cytology of *Vitis* phloem. *Hilgardia*, **37**, 17–72.

ESAU, K. and CHEADLE, V. I. (1962) An evaluation of studies on the ultra-structure of tonoplast in sieve elements. *Proc. Nat. Acad. Sciences*, **48**, 1–8.

ESAU, K., CURRIER, H. B. and CHEADLE, V. I. (1957) Physiology of phloem. *Ann. Rev. Plant Physiol.*, 8, 349–74.

EVERT, R. F. and MURMANIS, L. (1965) Ultrastructure of the secondary phloem of *Tilia Americana*. *Amer. Jour. Bot.*, **52**, 95–106.

FAGERLIND, F. (1946) Hormonale Substanzen als Ursache der Frucht und Embryobildung bei pseudogamen *Hosta* Biotypen. *Sv. Bot. Tidskr.*, **40**, 230–4.

FAHN, A. (1953) The origin of the banana inflorescence. *Kew Bull.*, No. 3, 299.

FAHN, A., STOLER, S. and FIRST, T. (1963) Vegetative shoot apex in banana and zonal changes as it becomes reproductive. *Botan. Gaz.*, **124**, 246–50.

FOSKET, D. E. and MIKSCHE, J. P. (1966) A histochemical study of the seedling shoot apical meristem of *Pinus lambertiana*. *Amer. Jour. Bot.*, **53**, 694–702.

FOSTER, A. S. (1928) Precociously expanding buds and their relation to the problem of bud-scale morphology. *The Naturalist*, **854**, 71–78.

FOSTER, A. S. (1939) Problems of structure, growth and evolution in the shoot apex of seed plants. *Bot. Rev.*, **5**, 454–70.

FOSTER, A. S. (1941) Comparative studies on the structure of the shoot apex in seed plants. *Bull. Torrey Bot. Club*, **68**, 339–50.

FOSTER, A. S. (1951) Heterophylly and venation in *Lacunaria*. *Bull. Torrey Bot. Club.*, **78**, 382–400.

FRITSCH, F. E. (1935) *The Structure and Reproduction of the Algae*, Vol. 1 (1935), Vol. 2 (1945), Cambridge Univ. Press.

FULFORD, R. M. (1965) The morphogenesis of apple buds. I. The activity of the apical meristem. *Ann. Bot.*, *N.S.*, **29**, 167–80.

FULFORD, R. M. (1966) The morphogenesis of apple buds. II. The development of the bud. *Ann. Bot.*, *N.S.*, **30**, 25–38.

FUJITA, T. (1965) Effects of indoleacetic acid and gibberellin on the growth of the calyx in *Physalis alkekengi* var. *francheti* f. *bunyardii*. *Physiol. and Ecol.*, **13**, 53–9.

FUJITA, T. (1965) Shoot apex abortion in the thorn formation of *Lycium chinense*. *Journ. Jap. Bot.*, **40**, 336–41.

GALSTON, A. W. (1948) On the physiology of root initiation in excised *Asparagus* stem tips. *Amer. Jour. Bot.*, **35**, 281–7.

GALSTON, A. W. and PURVES, W. K. (1960) The mechanism of action of auxin. *Ann. Plant Physiol.*, **11**, 239–76.

GALUN, E. (1959) Effects of gibberellic acid and napthaleneacetic acid on sex expression and some morphological characters in the cucumber plant. *Phyton*, **13**, 1–8.

GALUN, E., JUNG, Y. and LANG, A. (1962) Culture and sex modification of male cucumber buds *in vitro. Nature*, **194**, 596–8.

GALUN, E., JUNG, Y. and LANG, A. (1963) Morphogenesis of floral buds of cucumber cultured *in vitro. Devel. Biol.*, **6**, 370–87.

GARCIA, V. (1962) Embryological studies on the Loasaceae with special reference to the endosperm haustoria. *Plant Embryology* (A Symposium: Ed. Maheshwari, P.), pp. 157–61, C.S.I.R., New Delhi.

GARRISON, R. (1949) Origin and development of axillary buds: *Syringa vulgaris* L. *Amer. Jour. Bot.*, **36**, 205–13.

GARRISON, R. and WETMORE, R. H. (1961) Studies in shoot-tip abortion: *Syringa vulgaris. Amer. Jour. Bot.*, **48**, 789–95.

GAUDICHAUD, C. (1841) Recherches générales sur l'organographie, etc., Paris. (In Arber, 1930.)

GAUTHERET, R. J. (1955) Sur la variabilité des propriétés physiologiques des cultures de tissus végétaux. *Ann. Biol.*, **31**, 145–71.

GAUTHERET, R. J. (1966) Phytohormones et culture des tissus. pp. 55–79, in *Les Phytohormones et l'Organogenèse*. (Ed. R. Bouillenne.) Congr. Internat. Univ. Liège, 1965. Publ. Univ. Liège.

GAVAUDAN, P. and DUPUY, P. (1965) Analyse, par l'action de 2,4-D, des potentialités morphologiques latentes du *Lilium candidum* L. *C.R. Acad. Sci. Paris*, **260**, 2297–300.

GAVAUDAN, P. and DUPUY, P. (1965) Sur l'expression de l'intersexualité dans les étaminés tératologiques et normales des Angiospermes. *C.R. Acad. Sci. Paris*, **260**, 4568–71.

GENTCHEFF, G. and GUSTAFSON, A. (1939) The double chromosome reproduction in *Spinacia* and its causes. *Hereditas*, **25**, 349–58, 371–86.

GIBBS, J. L. and DOUGALL, D. K. (1963) Growth of single plant cells. *Science*, **141**, 1059.

GIFFORD, E. M. Jr. (1951) Ontogeny of the vegetative axillary bud in *Drimys Winteri* var. *Chilensis. Amer. Jour. Bot.*, **38**, 234–43.

GIFFORD, E. M. Jr. (1954) The shoot apex in angiosperms. *Bot. Rev.*, **20**, 477–529.

GIFFORD, E. M. Jr. (1960a) Incorporation of tritiated thymidine into nuclei of shoot apical meristems. *Science*, **131**, 360.

GIFFORD, E. M. Jr. (1960b) Incorporation of H^3-thymidine into shoot and root apices of *Ceratopteris thalictroides. Amer. Jour. Bot.*, **47**, 834–7.

GIFFORD, E. M. Jr., KUPILA, S. and YAMAGUCHI, S. (1963) Experiments in the application of H^3-thymidine and adenine -8-C^{14} to shoot tips. *Phytomorphology*, **13**, 14–22.

GIFFORD, E. M., Jr. and STEWART, K. D. (1965) Ultrastructure of vegetative and reproductive apices of *Chenopodium album. Science*, **149**, 75–7.

GIFFORD, E. M., Jr. and TEPPER, H. B. (1961) Ontogeny of the inflorescence in *Chenopodium album. Amer. Jour. Bot.*, **48**, 657–67.

GIFFORD, E. M. Jr. and TEPPER, H. B. (1962a) Histochemical and autoradiographic studies of floral induction in *Chenopodium album. Amer. Jour. Bot.*, **49**, 706–14.

GIFFORD, E. M., Jr. and TEPPER, H. B. (1962b) Ontogenetic and histochemical changes in the vegetative shoot tip of *Chenopodium album*. *Amer. Jour. Bot.*, **49**, 902–11.

GIFFORD, E. M., Jr. and WETMORE, R. H. (1957) Apical meristems of vegetative shoots and strobili in certain gymnosperms. *Proc. Nat. Acad. Sci.* (*Wash.*), **43**, 571–6.

GOEBEL, K. (1900) *Organography of Plants*, Eng. trans. Clarendon Press, Oxford.

GOEBEL, K. (1905) *Organography of Plants*, Part II, Clarendon Press, Oxford.

GOEBEL, K. (1908) *Einleitung in die experimentelle Morphologie der Pflanzen*, Teubner, Leipzig.

GOEBEL, K. (1913) *Organographie der Pflanzen*, Gustav Fischer. Jena, 2nd edn., Pt. I, 181.

GOEBEL, K. (1928a) Morphologische und biologische Studien XIII. Weitere Untersuchungen über die Gruppe der Drynariaceae. *Ann. Jard. Bot. Buitenz.*, **39**, 117–26.

GOEBEL, K. (1928b) *Organographie der Pflanzen*, Pt. I, Allgemeine Organographie, 3rd edn., Gustav Fischer, Jena.

GOEBEL, K. (1930) *Organographie der Pflanzen*, 3rd edn., Gustav Fischer, Jena.

GOETHE, J. W. (1790) *Versuch die Metamorphose der Pflanzen zu erklären*, Gotha.

GOODWIN, R. H. (1937) The rôle of auxin in leaf development in *Solidago* species. *Amer. Jour. Bot.*, **24**, 43–51.

GORTER, C. J. (1949) The influence of 2,3,5-triiodobenzoic acid on the growing points of tomatoes. *Proc. Acad. Sci. Amst.*, **52**, 1185–93.

GORTER, C. J. (1951) The influence of 2,3,5-triiodobenzoic acid on the growing points of tomatoes. II. The initiation of ring-fasciations. *Proc. Acad. Sci. Amst.*, **54C**, 181–7.

GORTER, C. J. (1961) Dwarfism of peas and the action of gibberellic acid. *Physiol. Plant.*, **14**, 332–43.

GORTER, C. J. (1965) Origin of fasciation. *Encyclopedia of Plant Physiology*, XV/2, 330–51.

GRAY, L. H. and SCHOLES, M. E. (1951) The effect of ionizing radiations on the broad bean root. Part 8. Growth rate studies and histological analyses. *Brit. J. Radiol.*, N.S., **24**, 82–92, 176–80, 228–36, 285–91, 348–52.

GREEN, P. B. (1954) The spiral growth pattern of the cell wall in *Nitella axillaris*. *Amer. Jour. Bot.*, **41**, 403–9.

GREGG, J. H. (1965) Regulation in the cellular slime molds. *Developmental Biol.*, **12**, 377–93.

GRÉGOIRE, V. (1938) La morphogenèse et l'autonomie morphologique de l'appareil floral, I: Le carpelle. *Cellule*, **47**, 285.

GREGORY, F. G. (1928) Studies in the energy relations of plants. II. The effect of temperature on increase in area of leaf surface and in dry weight of *Cucumis sativus*. *Ann. Bot.*, **42**, 469.

GREGORY, F. G. and VEALE, J. A. (1957) A reassessment of the problem of apical dominance. *Symp. Soc. Exp. Biol.*, **11**, 1–20.

GUHA, SIPRA and MAHESHWARI, S. C. (1964) *In vitro* production of embryos from anthers of *Datura*. *Nature* (Lond.), **203**, 497.

GUNCKEL, J. E. (1965) Modifications of plant growth and development induced by ionizing radiations. *Encyclopedia of Plant Physiology*, XV/2, 365–87.

GUNCKEL, J. E. and SPARROW, A. H. (1965) Ionizing radiations: biochemical, physiological and morphological aspects. *Encyclopedia of Plant Physiology*, XVI, 551–611.

GUPTA, G. R. P., GUHA, S. and MAHESHWARI, S. C. (1966) Differentiation of buds from leaves of *Nicotiana tabacum* L. in sterile culture. *Phytomorph.*, 16, 175–82.

GURWITSCH, A. (1922) Über den Begriff des embryonalen Feldes. *Arch. Entw. Mech.*, 51, 383.

GURWITSCH, A. (1927) Weiterbildung und Verallgemeinerung des Feldbegriffes. *Arch. Entw. Mech.*, 112, 433.

GURWITSCH, A. (1947) *Acta Biotheoretica*, 7.

GUTTENBERG, H. VON (1947) Studien über die Entwicklung des Wurzelvegetationspunktes der Dikotyledonen. *Planta*, 35, 360–96.

GUTTENBERG, H. VON (1955) Die Entwicklung des Wurzelvegetationspunktes. *Naturw. Rdsch.*, 10, 385–8.

GUTTENBERG, H. VON. (1960) *Grundzüge der Histogenese höherer Pflanzen.* I *Die Angiospermen*, Berlin, Gebrüder Borntraeger.

GUTTENBERG, H. VON, BURMEISTER, J. and BROSELL, H. J. (1955) Studien über die Entwicklung des Wurzelvegetationspunktes der Dikotyledonen, II. *Planta*, 46, 179–222.

GUYOT, M. and DUPUY, P. (1965) Formation des fleurs surnuméraire sur des énations basilaires de la face ventrale des tépales chez le *Galtonia candicans* Decne. *C.R. Acad. Sci. Paris*, 260, 4572–5.

HABERLANDT, G. (1902) Kulturversuche mit isolierten Pflanzenzellen. *S.B. Akad. Wiss. Wien. Math-naturw. Kl.*, 111, 69–92.

HACCIUS, B. (1955a) Experimentally induced twinning in plants. *Nature* (Lond.), 176, 355–6.

HACCIUS, B. (1955b) Versuche zur somatischen Beeinflussung der Organbildung pflanzlicher Embryonen. *Experientia*, 11, 149–52.

HACCIUS, B. (1956) Über die Beeinflussung der Morphgenese pflanzlicher Embryonen durch Lithium-Ionen. *Ber. Dtsch. Bot. Ges.*, 69, 87–93.

HACCIUS, B. (1957a) Über die Regenerationsfähigkeit junger Embryonen von *Eranthis hiemalis* nach Colchicin-Behandlung. *Naturwissenschaften*, 44, 18–19.

HACCIUS, B. (1957b) Regenerationserscheinungen an pflanzlichen Embryonen nach Behandlung mit antimitotisch wirksamen Substanzen. *Beitr. Biol. Pflanz.*, 34, 3–18.

HACCIUS, B. (1959a) Morphoregulatorische Beeinflussung pflanzlicher Embryonen durch Phenylborsaure. *Naturwissenschaften*, 46, 153.

HACCIUS, B. (1959b) Über die unterschiedliche Antimitotica-Empfindlichkeit der Zellen noch undifferenzierter Embryonen von *Eranthis hiemalis*. *Z. Naturforsch*, 14b, 206–9.

HACCIUS, B. (1960) Experimentell induzierte Einkeimblättrigkeit bei *Eranthis hiemalis*. II. Monokotylie durch Phenylborsäure. *Planta.*, 54, 482–97.

HACCIUS, B. (1963) *Phytomorphology*, 13, 107.

HACCIUS, B. (1965a) Further observations on somatogenesis regarding the suspensor cells of *Eranthis hiemalis* embryos. *Planta* (Berl.), 64, 219–24.

HACCIUS, B. (1965b) Haben 'Gewebekultur-Embryonen' einen Suspensor? *Sonderab. Ber. Deutsch. Bot. Ges.*, **78**, 11–21.

HACCIUS, B. and LAKSHMANAN, K. K. (1965) Adventivembryonen aus *Nicotiana* Kallus, der bei hohen Lichtintensitäten kultiviert wurde. *Planta* (Berl.), **65**, 102–4.

HACCIUS, B. and MASSFELLER, D. (1959) Durch Phenylborsäure induzierte Reduktion der Petalen von *Cucumis sativus*. *Naturwissenschaften*, **46**, 585–6.

HACCIUS, B. and REICHERT, H. (1964) *Planta*, **62**, 355.

HACCIUS, B. and REINHOLZ, E. (1953) Somatisch induzierte Veränderung der Keimblattzahl bei *Eranthis hiemalis* durch Röntgenstrahlen. *Naturwissenschaften*, **40**, 533.

HACCIUS, B. and TROMPETER, G. (1960) Experimentell induzierte Einkeimblättrigkeit bei *Eranthis hiemalis*. I. Synkotylie durch 2, 4-Dichlorphenoxyessigsäure. *Planta* (*Berl.*), **54**, 466–81.

HAGEMANN, R. (1957) Anatomische Untersuchungen an Gerstenwurzeln. *Die Kulturpflanze*, **5**, 75–107.

HAGEN, G. L. (1962) Morphogenesis in a tobacco hybrid tumor. *Develop. Biol.*, **4**, 569–79.

HÅKANSSON, A. (1956) Seed development of *Brassica oleracea* and *B. rapa* after certain reciprocal pollinations. *Hereditas* (Lund), **42**, 373–95.

HALBSGUTH, W. (1965) Induktion von Dorsiventralität bei Pflanzen. *Encyclopedia of Plant Physiology*, XV/1, 331–382.

HALL, O. L. (1954) Hybridization of wheat and rye after embryo transplantation. *Hereditas* (Lund), **40**, 453–8.

HALL, O. L. (1956) Further experiments on embryo transplantation. *Hereditas* (Lund), **42**, 261–2.

HALPERIN, W. and WETHERELL, D. F. (1964) Adventive embryony in tissue cultures of the wild carrot, *Daucus carota*. *Amer. Jour. Bot.*, **51**, 274–83.

HALPERIN, W. and WETHERELL, D. F. (1965) *Science*, **147**, 756.

HÄMMERLING, J. (1934) Über Genomwirkungen und Formbildungsfähigkeit bei *Acetabularia*. *Roux Archiv.*, **132**, 424.

HÄMMERLING, J. (1946) Neue Untersuchungen über die physiologischen und genetischen Grundlagen der Formbildung. *Naturwiss.*, **33**, 337–42, 361–5.

HÄMMERLING, J. (1953) Nucleocytoplasmic interactions in the development of *Acetabularia*. *Inter. Rev. Cytol.*, **2**, 475–98.

HÄMMERLING, J. (1955) Neuere Versuche über Polarität und Differenzierung bei *Acetabularia*. *Biol. Zentralbl.*, **74˙** 544–54.

HÄMMERLING, J. (1957) Nucleus and cytoplasm in *Acetabularia*. VIII *Internat. Bot. Congr.* (Paris), Report Sect., **10**, 87–103.

HÄMMERLING, J. and Ch., (1959) Über Bildung und Ausgleich des Polaritätgefalles bei *Acetabularia*. *Planta* (Berl.), **53**, 522–31.

HÄMMERLING, J., CLAUSS, H., KECK, K. and RICHTER, G. (1959) Growth and protein synthesis in nucleated and enucleated cells. *Exper. Cell Res. Suppl.*, **6**, 210–26.

HAMMOND, D. (1941a) The expression of genes for leaf shape in *Gossypium hirsutum* L. and *Gossypium arboreum* L. I. The expression of genes for leaf shape in *Gossypium hirsutum* L. *Amer. Jour. Bot.*, **28**, 124–38.

HAMMOND, D. (1941b) The expression of genes for leaf shape in *Gossypium hirsutum* L. and *Gossypium arboreum* L. II. The expression of genes for leaf shape in *Gossypium arboreum* L. *Amer. Jour. Bot.*, **28**, 138–50.

HANAWA, J. (1953) The embryo sac formation and the embryogeny of *Sesamum indicum* L. in the diploid and tetraploid strains. *Bot. Mag.* (Tokyo) **65**, 777–8.

HANAWA, J. and ISHIZAKI, M. (1953) Malformation in *Sesamum indicum* L. caused by operation on the embryo. *Sci. Rep. Fac. Lib. Arts. and Educ. Gifu Univ., Nat. Sci.*, **1**, 55–61.

HANSTEIN, J. (1868) Die Scheitelzellgruppe im Vegetationspunkt der Phanerogamen. *Festschr. Niederrhein. Ges. Natur. Heilk.*, 109.

HARDER, R. and VON WITSCH, H. (1940) Über den Einfluss der Tageslange auf den Habitus besonders die Blattsucculenz und den Wasseraushalt von *Kalanchoe Blossfeldiana*. *Jahrb. wiss. Bot.*, **89**, 354.

HAWKER, L. E. (1965) The physiology of development in fungi. *Encyclopedia of Plant Physiology*, XV/1, 716–57.

HEEL, W. A. van (1966) Morphology of the androecium in Malvales. *Blumea*, **13**, 177–394.

HENDRICKS, S. B. and BORTHWICK, H. A. (1963) Control of plant growth by light. *In*: Evans, L. T. (ed.) *Environmental Control of Plant Growth*, pp. 233–63, Academic Press, New York and London.

HENRY, A. (1846) Knospengebilder in Beitrag zur Kenntniss der Laubknospen und der Verzweigungsart der Pflanzen.

HESLOP-HARRISON, J. (1956) Auxin and sexuality in *Cannabis sativa*. *Physiol. Plant.*, **9**, 588.

HESLOP-HARRISON, J. (1957) The experimental modification of sex expression in flowering plants. *Biol. Rev.*, **32**, 38.

HESLOP-HARRISON, J. (1959) Growth substances and flower morphogenesis. *Jour. Linn. Soc. Lond. (Bot.)*, **56**, 269.

HESLOP-HARRISON, J. (1960a) Suppressive effects of 2-thiouracil on differentiation and flowering in *Cannabis sativa*. *Science*, **132**, 1943–4.

HESLOP-HARRISON, J. (1960b) The experimental control of sexuality and inflorescence structure in *Zea mais* L. *Jour. Linn. Soc. Lond. (Bot.)*, **172**, 108.

HESLOP-HARRISON, J. (1962) Effect of 2-thiouracil on cell differentiation and leaf morphogenesis in *Cannabis sativa*. *Ann. Bot., N.S.*, **26**, 375–87.

HESLOP-HARRISON, J. (1963a) Plant Growth Substances. In *Vistas in Botany*, Pergamon Press, Vol. III, 104–94.

HESLOP-HARRISON, J. (1963b) Sex expression in flowering plants. In: *Meristems and Differentiation*, Brookhaven Symposia in Biology, **16**, 109–25.

HESLOP-HARRISON, J. and HESLOP-HARRISON, Y. (1957a) Studies on flowering-plant growth and morphogenesis, I: Morphogenetic effects of 2,3,5-triiodobenzoic acid on *Cannabis sativa*. *Proc. Roy. Soc. Edinb.*, B, **66**, 409.

HESLOP-HARRISON, J. and HESLOP-HARRISON, Y. (1957b) Studies on flowering-plant growth and morphogenesis, II: The modification of sex expression in *Cannabis sativa* by carbon monoxide. *Proc. Roy. Soc. Edinb.*, B, **66**, 424.

HESLOP-HARRISON, J. and HESLOP-HARRISON, Y. (1958a) Photoperiod, auxin and sex balance in a long-day plant. *Nature* (Lond.), **181**, 100.

HESLOP-HARRISON, J. and HESLOP-HARRISON, Y. (1958b) Long-day and auxin induced male sterility in *Silene pendula* L. *Portug. Acta Biol.*, **5**, 79.

HESLOP-HARRISON, Y. and WOODS, I. (1959) Temperature-induced meristic and other variation in *Cannabis sativa*. *Jour. Linn. Soc. Lond. (Bot.)*, **56**, 290.

HEYES, J. K. and BROWN, R. (1956) Growth and cellular differentiation. *The Growth of Leaves* (Ed. Milthorpe, F. L.), pp. 31–47, Butterworth, London.

HEYES, J. K. and BROWN, R. (1965) Cytochemical changes in cell growth and differentiation in plants. *Encyclopedia of Plant Physiology*, XV/I, I, 189–212.

HIROE, M. and INOH, S. (1955) Some experiments on the eggs of *Sargassum piluliferum* C. Ag. *Biol. Jour. Okayama Univ.*, **2**, 85–94, Japan.

HOFMEISTER, W. (1862) *Higher Cryptogamia*. Eng. edn. *Ray Soc. Lond.*

HOFMEISTER, W. (1868) *Allegemeine Morphologie der Gewächse*. Hdb. der Physiol. Bot. (Leipzig).

HOHL, H-R, (1960) Über die submikroskopische Struktur normaler und hyperplastischer Gewebe von *Datura stramonium* L. I. Teil: Normalgewebe. *Ber. Schweiz. Bot. Ges.*, **70**, 395–439.

HOLLOWAY, J. E. (1939) The gametophyte, embryo and young rhizome of *Psilotum triquetrum* Swartz. *Ann. Bot.*, N.S., **3**, 324.

HOLSTEN, R. D., SUGII, M. and STEWARD, F. C. (1965) Direct and indirect effects of radiation on plant cells: their relation to growth and growth induction. *Nature*, **208**, 850–6.

HUMPHRIES, E. C. and WHEELER, A. W. (1964) Cell division and growth substances in leaves. *Régulateurs Naturels de la Croissance Végétale*. Colloq. Internat. de Centre de Rech. Sci. Gif-sur-Yvette 1963, No. 123, 505–15.

HUXLEY, J. S. (1932) *Problems of Relative Growth*, London.

INGOLD, C. T. (1946) Size and form in agarics. *Trans. Brit. Mycol. Soc.*, **29**, 108–13.

JABLONSKI, J. R. and SKOOG, F. (1954) Cell enlargement and cell division in excised tobacco pith tissue. *Physiol. Plantarum*, **7**, 17–24.

JACOB, F. and MONOD, J. (1961) On the regulation of gene activity. *Cold Spring Harbor Symp. Quant. Biol.*, **26**, 193–211.

JACOBS, W. P. (1952) The rôle of auxin in differentiation of xylem around a wound. *Amer. Jour. Bot.*, **39**, 301–9.

JACOBS, W. P. (1954) Acropetal auxin transport and xylem regeneration – a quantitative study. *Amer. Nat.*, **88**, 327–37.

JACOBS, W. P. (1959) What substance normally controls a given biological process? I. Formulation of some rules. *Develop. Biol.*, **1**, 527–33.

JACOBS, W. P. (1961) The polar movement of auxin in the shoots of higher plants: its occurrence and physiological significance. In *Plant Growth Regulation*, pp. 397–409, Iowa State Univ. Press.

JACOBS, W. P. (1961) Auxin as a limiting factor in the differentiation of plant tissue. *Recent Advances in Botany*, Univ. of Toronto Press, pp. 786–90.

JACOBS, W. P. and CASE, D. B. (1965) Auxin transport, gibberellin and apical dominance. *Science*, **148**, 1729–31.

JACOBS, W. P., DANIELSON, J., HURST, V. and ADAMS, P. (1959) *Develop. Biol.*, **1**, 534.

JACOBS, W. P. and MORROW, I. B. (1957) A quantitative study of xylem development in the vegetative shoot apex of *Coleus*. *Amer. Jour. Bot.*, **44**, 823–42.

JAYASEKERA, R. D. E. and BELL, P. R. (1959) The effect of various experimental treatments on the development of the embryo of the fern *Thelypteris palustris*. *Planta*, **54**, 1–14.

JENIK, J. (1967) Root adaptations in West African trees. *Jour. Linn. Soc. Lond.*, **60**, 25–9.

JENSEN, W. A. (1958) The nucleic acid and protein content of root tip cells of *Vicia faba* and *Allium cepa*. *Exp. Cell. Res.*, **14**, 575–83.

JOHRI, B. M. and BAJAJ, Y. P. S. (1963) Response of embryos of *Dendrophthoe falcata* (L.f.) Ettings *in vitro*. In *Plant Tissue and Organ Culture – A Symposium* (Eds. Maheshwari, P. & Rangaswamy, N. S.), pp. 292–301.

JOHRI, B. M. and SEHGAL, C. B. (1963) Growth of ovaries of *Anethum graveolens* Linn. In *Plant Tissue and Organ Culture – A Symposium* (Eds. Maheshwari, P. & Rangaswamy, N. S.), pp. 253–64.

JONES, H. A. and EMSWELLER, S. L. (1936) Development of the flower and macrogametophyte of *Allium cepa*. *Hilgardia*, **10**, 415–28.

JONES, L. E., HILDEBRANDT, A. C., RIKER, A. J. and WU, J. H. (1960) Growth of somatic tobacco cells in microculture. *Amer. Jour. Bot.*, **47**, 468–75.

KAAN ALBEST, A. V. (1934) Anatomische und physiologische Untersuchungen über die Entstehung von Siebrohrenverbindungen. *Zeit. Bot.*, **27**, 1–94.

KALLIS, P. (1963) The effects of ultra-violet radiation and some chemicals on morphogenesis in *Micrasterias*. *Ann. Acad. Sci. Fenn.*, Ser. A IV. Biol., **70**, 1–39.

KARSTENS, W. K. H. and DE MEESTER-MANGERCATS, V. (1960) The cultivation of plant tissues *in vitro* with starch as a source of carbon. *Acta. Bot. Neeland.*, **9**, 263–74.

KATO, H. and TAKEUCHI, M. (1963) Morphogenesis *in vitro* starting from single cells of carrot root. *Plant & Cell Physiol.*, **4**, 243–5.

KATO, H. and TAKEUCHI, M. (1966) Embryogenesis from the epidermal cells of carrot hypocotyl. *Sci. Papers Coll. Gen. Educ. Univ. Tokyo*, **16**, 245–54.

KAUFMAN, P. B. (1965) The effects of growth substances on intercalary growth and cellular differentiation in developing internodes of *Avena sativa*. I. The effects of indole-3-acetic acid. *Physiol. Plant.*, **18**, 424–43.

KEY, J. L. (1964) Ribonucleic acid and protein synthesis as essential processes for cell elongation. *Plant Physiol.*, **39**, 365–70.

KNAPP, E. (1931) Entwicklungsphysiologische Untersuchungen an Fucaceen-Eiern. *Planta*, **14**, 731.

KONAR, R. N. (1963) A haploid tissue from the pollen of *Ephedra foliata* Boiss. *Phytomorphology*, **13**, 170–4.

KONAR, R. N. (1966) Single cell culture and morphogenesis. *Portugaliae Acta Biol.*, **10**, 1–32.

KONAR, R. N. and NATARAJA, K. (1964) *In vitro* control of floral morphogenesis in *Ranunculus sceleratus* L. *Phytomorphology*, **14**, 558–63.

KONAR, R. N. and NATARAJA, K. (1965a) Experimental studies in *Ranunculus sceleratus* L. Development of embryos from the stem epidermis. *Phytomorphology*, **15**, 132–7.

KONAR, R. N. and NATARAJA, K. (1965b) Experimental studies in *Ranunculus sceleratus* L. Plantlets from freely suspended cells and cell groups. *Phytomorphology*, **15**, 206–11.

KONAR, R. N. and NATARAJA, K. (1965c) Reproduction of embryoids from the anthers of *Ranunculus sceleratus* L. *Phytomorphology*, **15**, 245–8.

KONAR, R. N. and NATARAJA, K. (1965d) Production of embryos on the stem of *Ranunculus sceleratus* L. *Experientia*, **21**, 395.

KONAR, R. N. and NATARAJA, K. (1965e) The differentiation of embryoids in tissue cultures of floral buds of *Ranunculus sceleratus* L. *Naturwiss.*, **52**, 140–1.

KONAR, R. N. and OBEROI, Y. P. (1965) *In vitro* development of embryoids on the cotyledons of *Biota orientalis*. *Phytomorphology*, **15**, 137–40.

KOURSANOV, A. L. (1959) La physiologie végétale et le probleme de la plante entière. *Recent Advances in Botany*, IX, Internat. Bot. Congr., Montreal (1959), 9–28.

KRANICH, E. -M. (1958) Anomalien der Küchenschelle *Pulsatilla* Mill. *Thesis Inst. Bot. Univ. Tubingen. Flora oder allgem. bot. Zeit.*, **146**, 254–301.

KUEHNERT, C. C. and STEEVES, T. A. (1962) Capacity of fragments of leaf primordia to produce whole leaves. *Nature*, **196**, 187–9.

KUO, J. S. and WANG, F. H. (1963) The effect of IAA and coconut milk on the growth of immature sunflower embryos cultured *in vitro*. *Acta Botanica Sinica*, **11**, 141–50.

KUO, J. S. and WANG, F. H. (1964) The effect of coconut milk, casein hydrolysate and glutamine on the growth of the sunflower young embryos grown *in vitro*. *Acta Botanica Sinica*, **12**, 364–72.

KUO, J. S. and WANG, F. H. (1965) The effect of osmotic value of the medium on the growth of the young sunflower embryos cultured *in vitro*. *Acta Botanica Sinica*, **13**, 127–32.

KURAISHI, S. and MUIR, R. M. (1954a) The relationship of gibberellin and auxin in plant growth. *Plant Cell Physiol.*, **5**, 61–9.

KURAISHI, S. and MUIR, R. M. (1964b) The mechanism of gibberellin action in the dwarf pea. *Plant Cell Physiol.*, **5**, 259–71.

KUSE, G. (1961) Correlative growth of lateral bud in *Ipomoea Batatas* shoot. *Mem. Coll. Sci. Kyoto*, B, **28**, 431–53.

LAM, S. L. and LEOPOLD, A. C. (1961) Reversion from flowering to the vegetative state in *Xanthium*. *Amer. Jour. Bot.*, **47**, 256–9.

LAM, S. L. and LEOPOLD, A. C. (1961) Reversion and reinduction of flowering in *Perilla*. *Amer. Jour. Bot.*, **48**, 306–10.

LAMOTTE, C. E. and JACOBS, W. P. (1963) A rôle of auxin in phloem regeneration in *Coleus* internodes. *Devlpmt. Biol.*, **8**, 80–98.

LANCE, A. (1958) Infrastructure des cellules du méristème apical et des jeunes ébauches foliaires de *Chrysanthemum segetum* L. (Composées). *Ann. Sci. Nat., Bot.*, **11**, sér. 19, 165–202.

LANCE-NOUGARÈDE, A. and LOISEAU, J. E. (1960) Sur la structure et le fonctionnement du méristème végétatif de quelques angiospermes aquatiques ou semi-aquatiques dépourvues de moelle. *C.R. Acad. Sci.* (Paris), **250**, 4438–40.

LANCE-NOUGARÈDE, A. and BRONCHARD, R. (1965) Métabolisme des acides nucléiques dans le méristème apical du *Perilla nankinensis* au cours des diverses phases du développement. *C.R. Acad. Sci.* (Paris), **260**, 3140–43.

LANG, A. (1957) The effect of gibberellin upon flower formation. *Proc. Nat. Acad. Sci.* (Wash.), **43**, 709–17.

LANG, A. (1959) The influence of gibberellin and auxin on photoperiodic induction: in *Photoperiodism and Related Phenomena in Plants and Animals* (Ed. Withrow, R. B.), *Amer. Assoc. Adv. Sci. Publ.*, **55**, Washington, 329–50.

BIBLIOGRAPHY 419

LANG, A. (1960) Gibberellin-like substances in photo-induced and vegetative *Hyoscyamus* plants. *Planta*, **54**, 498–504.

LANG, A. (1961) Entwicklungsphysiologie. *Fortschr. Bot.*, **23**, 312–45.

LANG, A. (1961) Physiology of reproductive development in higher plants. *Proc. Biol. Colloq.*, **22**, 53–78. Oregon State Univ. Press, Corvallis, Oregon.

LANG, A. (1964) Gibberellin and regulation of meristematic activity. Symposium: *Differentiation of Apical Meristems and Some Problems of Ecological Regulation of Development of Plants*, pp. 51–66. (Publ. *Czechoslovak Acad. Sci.*, Praha, 1966.)

LANG, A. (1965). Physiology of growth and development in algae. A Synopsis. *Encyclopedia of Plant Physiology*, XV/1, 680–715.

LANG, A. (1965) Physiology of flower initiation. *Encyclopedia of Plant Physiology*, XV/2, 1380–536.

LANG, A. and REINHARD, E. (1961) Gibberellins and flower formation. *Adv. in Chem.*, **28**, 71–9.

LANG, A., SACHS, R. M. and BRETZ, C. (1959) Effets morphogénétiques de la gibbérelline. *Bull. Soc. Franc. Physiol. Veget.*, **5**, 1–19.

LANG, A., SANDOVAL, J. A. and BEDRI, A. (1957) Induction of bolting and flowering in *Hyoscyamus* and *Samolus* by a gibberellin-like material from a seed plant. *Proc. Nat. Acad. Sci.* (Wash.), **43**, 960–4.

LANG, W. H. (1915) Causal and phyletic morphology *Presidential Address, Rept. Brit. Assoc. Adv. Sci.*, Sect. K., (1915), 701–18.

LA RUE, C. D. (1942) The rooting of flowers in sterile culture. *Bull. Torrey Bot. Club.*, **69**, 332–41.

LEBÈGUE, A. (1949) Embryologie des Saxifragacées: Polyembryonie chez le *Bergenia delavayi* Engl. *Bull. Soc. Bot., Fr.*, **96**, 38–9.

LEE, A. E. (1950a) The growth in culture of intact seedlings and isolated seedling organs. *Amer. Jour. Bot.*, **37**, 312–18.

LEE, A. E. (1950b) The influence of various sugars on the growth in culture of intact seedlings and isolated seedling organs. *Amer. Jour. Bot.*, **37**, 528–33.

LEOPOLD, A. C. and GUERNSEY, F. S. (1953) Auxin polarity in the *Coleus* plant. *Botan. Gaz.*, **115**, 147–54.

LINK, G. K. K. and EGGERS, V. (1946a) Mode, site and time of initiation of hypocotyledonary bud primordia in *Linum usitatissimum* L. *Botan. Gaz.*, **107**, 441–54.

LINK, G. K. K. and EGGERS, V. (1946b) The effect of indoleacetic acid upon initiation and development of hypocotyledonary bud primordia in flax. *Botan. Gaz.*, **108**, 114–29.

LOCKHART, J. A. (1956) Reversal of the light inhibition of pea stem growth by the gibberellins. *Proc. Nat. Acad. Sci., Wash.*, **42**, 841–8.

LOISEAU, J.-E. (1962) Activité mitotique des cellules superficielles du sommet végétatif caulinaire. *Mém. Soc. Bot. France*, 1962, 14–23.

LOISEAU, J.-E. and NOUGARÈDE, A. (1963) Comportement de l'apex des rosettes flottantes et processus de ramification chez *Hydrocharis morsusranae* L. *C.R. Acad. Sci.* (Paris), **256**, 3340–3.

LONA, F. (1962) Ontogenetical sites of gibberellin-like manifestations. From Symposium on *Eigenschaften und Wirkungen der Gibberelline*, pp. 73–93, Springer, Berlin.

LOO, SHIH-WEI. (1945) Cultivation of excised stem tips of asparagus *in vitro*. *Amer. Jour. Bot.*, **32**, 13–17.

LOO, SHIH-WEI. (1946) Further experiments on the culture of excised asparagus stem tips *in vitro*. *Amer. Jour. Bot.*, **33**, 156–9.

LÜCK, H. B. (1962) Sur l'histogénèse et la differenciation cellulaire. *Ann. Sci. Nat. Bot.*, **12**, 3: 1–23.

MACIEJEWSKA-POTAPCZYK, W. (1959) Influence of kinetin, B-indoleacetic and gibberellic acid on nuclease activity of bean (*Phaseolus vulgaris*) hypocotyls. *Nature*, **185**, 557.

MAHESHWARI, P. (1950) *An Introduction to the Embryology of Angiosperms*. New York & London.

MAHESHWARI, P. (1951) Contacts between embryology, physiology and genetics. *Proc. 37th Indian Sci. Cong., Bot. Sect. Pres. Addr.*

MAHESHWARI, P. (1952) Polyembryony in angiosperms. *Palaeobotanist*, **1**, 319–29.

MAHESHWARI, P. (1962) *Plant Embryology – A Symposium*. C.S.I.R., New Delhi.

MAHESHWARI, P. (1962) Contacts between embryology, physiology and genetics. In *Proc. Summer School Bot., Darjeeling* (Eds. Maheshwari, P. *et al.*), pp. 171–92.

MAHESHWARI, P. (1963) *Recent Advances in the Embryology of Angiosperms*, Internat. Soc. Pl. Morph., Delhi.

MAHESHWARI, P. and BALDEV, B. (1962) *In vitro* induction of adventive buds from embryos of *Cuscuta reflexa* Roxb. In *Plant Embryology – A Symposium* (C.S.I.R., New Delhi), pp. 129–38.

MAHESHWARI, P. and CHOPRA, R. N. (1955) The structure and development of the ovule and seed of *Opuntia dillenii* Haw. *Phytomorphology*, **5**, 112–22.

MAHESHWARI, S. C. and GUPTA, S. (1966) Observations on changes in nucleic acids and histones during the photoinduction of shoot apices of *Cuscuta reflexa* Roxb. *Phytomorph.*, **16**, 192–9.

MAHESHWARI, N. and LAL, M. (1958) *In vitro* culture of ovaries of *Iberis amara* L. *Nature* (Lond.), **181**, 631–2.

MAHESHWARI, P. and RANGASWAMY, N. S. (1958) Polyembryony and *in vitro* culture of embryos of *Citrus* and *Mangifera*. *Indian Jour. Hort.*, **15**, 275–82.

MAHESHWARI, P. and RANGASWAMY, N. S. (1963) *Plant Tissue and Organ Culture – A Symposium*, Internat. Soc. Plant Morph., New Delhi.

MAHESHWARI, P. and SACHAR, R. C. (1963) Polyembryony. *Recent Advances in the Embryology of Angiosperms*. (Ed. Maheshwari, P.), pp. 265–96. Internat. Soc. Plant Morph. (New Delhi).

MARCHAL, M. (1965) Le bourgeonnement épiphylle spontané des fougères tropicales. *Adansonia*, **5**, 239–70.

MARINOS, N. G. (1962) Studies on submicroscopic aspects of mineral deficiencies. 1. Calcium deficiency in the shoot apex of barley. *Amer. Journ. Bot.*, **49**, 834–41.

MARINOS, N. G. (1963) Vacuolation in plant cells. *Journ. Ultrastruc. Res.*, **9**, 177–85.

MARTH, P. C. PRESTON, W. H., Jr. and MITCHELL, J. W. (1953) Growth controlling effects of some quaternary ammonium compounds on various species of plants. *Botan. Gaz.*, **115**, 200–4.

MATHER, K. (1948) Nucleus and cytoplasm in differentiation. *Symp. Soc. exp. Biol.*, 2. *Growth*, 196–216.

MATHER, K. (1965) Genetical aspects of development. 2. Genes and cytoplasm in development. *Encyclopedia of Plant Physiology*, XV/1, 41–73.

MAUNEY, J. R. and BALL, E. (1959) The axillary buds of *Gossypium*. *Bull. Torrey Bot. Club*, **86**, 236–44.

MAYER, L. (1956) Wachstum und Organbildung an *in vitro* kultivierten Segmenten von *Pelargonium zonale* und *Cyclamen persicum*. *Planta*, **47**, 401–46.

MCCARTHY, J. (1962) The form and development of knee roots in *Mitragyna stipulosa*. *Phytomorph.*, **12**, 20–30.

MELCHERS, G. (1937) Die Wirkung von Genen, tiefen Temperaturen und blühenden Pfropfpartnern auf die Blühreife von *Hyoscyamus niger* L. *Biol. Zlb.*, **57**, 568.

MELVILLE, R. (1962) A new theory of the angiosperm flower: I. The gynoecium. *Kew Bull.*, **16**, 1–50.

MELVILLE, R. (1963) A new theory of the angiosperm flower: II. The androecium. *Kew Bull.*, **17**, 1–66.

MERICLE, L. W., EUNUS, A. M. and MERICLE, R. P. (1955) Effects of maleic hydrazide on embryologic development. I. *Avena sativa*. *Botan. Gaz.*, **117**, 142–7.

MERICLE, L. W. and MERICLE, R. P. (1957) Irradiation of developing plant embryos. I. Effects of external irradiation (X-rays) on barley embryogeny, germination and subsequent seedling development. *Amer. Jour. Bot.*, **44**, 747–56.

MEYER, V. G. (1966) Environmental effects on the differentiation of abnormal cotton flowers. *Amer. Jour. Bot.*, **53**, 976–80.

MICHAELIS, P. (1965) Cytoplasmic inheritance in *Epilobium* (A Survey). *The Nucleus*, **8**, 83–92.

MICHAELIS, P. (1965) II. The occurrence of plasmon-differences in the genus *Epilobium* and the interaction between cytoplasm and nuclear genes (A historic survey). *The Nucleus*, **8**, 93–108.

MICHAELIS, P. (1966) The proof of cytoplasmic inheritance in *Epilobium*. (A historical survey as example for the necessary proceeding.) *The Nucleus*, **9**, 1–16.

MICHAELIS, P. (1967) Untersuchungen zur Entwicklungsgeschichte des *Epilobium*–Sprosses mit Hilfe genetische markierter Zelldeszendenzen. *Bot. Jb.*, **86**, 50–112.

MICHNIEWICZ, M. and LANG, A. (1962b) Effect of nine different gibberellins on stem elongation and flower formation in cold-requiring and photoperiodic plants grown under non-inductive conditions. *Planta*, **58**, 549–63.

MIETTINEN, J. K. and WARIS, H. (1958) A chemical study of the neomorphosis induced by glycine in *Oenanthe aquatica*. *Physiol. Plant.*, **11**, 193–9.

MILLER, C. O. (1961) Kinetin and related compounds in plant growth. *Ann. Rev. Plant Physiol.*, **12**, 395–408.

MILLER, C. O. and SKOOG, F. (1953) Chemical control of bud formation in tobacco stem segments. *Amer. Jour. Bot.*, **40**, 768–73.

MILLER, H. A. and WETMORE, R. H. (1945) Studies in the developmental anatomy of *Phlox Drummondii* Hook. I. The embryo. *Amer. Jour. Bot.*, **32**, 588–99.

MILLINGTON, W. F. (1963) Shoot tip abortion in *Ulmus americana*. *Amer. Jour. Bot.*, **50**, 371–8.

MILLINGTON, W. F. (1966) The tendril of *Parthenocissus inserta*: determination and development. *Amer. Jour. Bot.*, **53**, 74–81.

MITRA, J., MAPES, M. O. and STEWARD, F. C. (1960) Growth and organized development of cultured cells. IV. The behaviour of the nucleus. *Amer. Jour. Bot.*, **47**, 357–68.

MITRA, J., and STEWARD, F. C. (1961) Growth induction in cultures of *Haplopappus gracilis*. II. The behaviour of the nucleus. *Amer. Jour. Bot.*, **48**, 358–68.

MOENS, P. (1956) Ontogenèse des vrilles et differenciation des ampoules adhesives chez quelques végétaux (*Ampelopsis, Bignonia, Glaziovia*). *La Cellule*, **57**, 369–401.

MOHAN RAM, H. Y. (1958) Post-fertilization studies in the ovules of some Acanthaceae. *Ph.D. Thesis, Univ. Delhi*.

MOHAN RAM, H. Y. (1962) Post-fertilization development of the ovule in *Barleria cristata* Linn. *Jour. Indian Bot. Soc.*, **41**, 288–96.

MOHAN RAM, H. Y., MANASI RAM and STEWARD, F. C. (1962) Growth and development of the banana plant. *Ann. Bot. N.S.*, **26**, 657–73.

MOHAN RAM, H. Y. and STEWARD, F. C. (1964) The induction of growth in explanted tissue of the banana fruit. *Canad. Jour. Bot.*, **42**, 1559–79.

MOHAN RAM, H. Y. and MRIDUL WAHDI. (1965) Culture of excised leaves and leaf explants of *Kalanchoe pinnata* Pers. *Tissue Culture* (Ed. Ramakrishnan, C. V.), pp. 274–82. Publ. W. Junk, The Hague.

MOHAN RAM, H. Y. and MRIDUL WAHDI. (1965) Morphogenesis in tissue cultures: totipotency of cultured cells. *Tissue Culture* (Ed. Ramakrishnan, C. V.), pp. 320–9. Publ. W. Junk, The Hague.

MOHR, H. (1962) Primary effects of light on growth. *Ann. Rev. Plant Physiol.*, **13**, 465–88.

MOLISCH, H. (1929) *Die Lebensdauer der Pflanzen*. Jena: Fischer 1929. English edn. by Fulling, E. H.: *The Longevity of Plants*, 1938, New York.

MOORE, T. C. and BONDE, E. K. (1962) Physiology of flowering in peas. *Plant. Physiol.*, **37**, 149–53.

MOREL, G. (1963) La culture *in vitro* du méristème apical de certaines Orchidées. *C.R. Acad. Sci.* (Paris), **256**, 4955–7.

MOSS, E. H. (1924) Fasciated roots of *Caltha palustris* L. *Ann. Bot.*, **38**, 789.

MOTHES, K. (1960) Über das Alter der Blätter und die Moglichkeit ihrer Wiederverjungung. *Naturwissenschaften*, **15**, 337–51.

MÜHLETHALER, K. (1960) Die Entstehung des Vacuolensystems in Pflanzenzellen. *4th Intern. Conf. Elect. Microscopy*, Berlin, **2**, 491–4.

MUIR, W. H., HILDEBRANDT, A. C. and RIKER, A. J. (1954) Plant tissue cultures produced from single isolated cells. *Science*, **119**, 877–8.

MUIR, W. H., HILDEBRANDT, A. C. and RIKER, A. J. (1958) The preparation isolation, and growth in culture of single cells from higher plants. *Amer. Jour. Bot.*, **45**, 589–97.

MUKKADA, A. J. (1962) Some observations on the embryology of *Dicraea stylosa* Wight. *Plant Embryology* (A Symposium: Ed. Maheshwari, P.), 139–45, C.S.I.R., New Delhi.

MURASHIGE, I. and SKOOG, F. (1962) A revised medium for rapid growth and bio-assays with tobacco tissue cultures. *Physiol. Plantarum* (Kbh.), **15**, 473–97.

MURGAI, PREM (1959) The development of embryo in *Paeonia* – a reinvestigation. *Phytomorphology*, **9**, 275–7.

MURGAI, PREM (1962) Embryology of *Paeonia* together with a discussion on its systematic position. *Plant Embryology* (A Symposium: Ed. Maheshwari, P.), pp. 215–23, C.S.I.R., New Delhi.

NAKAZAWA, S. (1950) Origin of polarity in the eggs of *Sargassum confusum*. *Sci. Repts. Tôhoku Univ.*, 4th Ser. **18**, 424–33.

NAKAZAWA, S. (1951) Invalid stratification to the egg polarity in *Coccophora* and *Sargassum*. *Sci. Repts. Tôhoku Univ.*, 4th Ser. (Biol.), **19**, 73–8, Sendai, Japan.

NAKAZAWA, S. (1953) Differential vital staining of the plasm in the eggs of *Coccophora* and *Sargassum*. *Sci. Repts. Tôhoku Univ.*, 4th Ser. (Biol.), **20**, 89–92, Sendai, Japan.

NAKAZAWA, S. (1955) Abnormal eggs of *Coccophora*, with special interests in the origin of half embryos. *Bot. Mag.* (Tokyo), **68**, 232–4.

NAKAZAWA, S. (1956) Developmental mechanics of Fucaceous algae. I. The pre-existent polarity in *Coccophora* eggs. *Sci. Repts. Tôhoku Univ.*, **22**, 175–9, Sendai, Japan.

NAKAZAWA, S. (1957a) Developmental mechanics of Fucaceous algae. II. Vital staining of the centrifuged *Coccophora* eggs. *Bot. Mag.* (Tokyo), **70**, 1–3.

NAKAZAWA, S. (1957b) Developmental mechanics of Fucaceous algae. III. Differential permeabillty in *Fucus* eggs. *Bot. Mag.* (Tokyo), 70.

NAKAZAWA, S. (1957c) Developmental mechanics of Fucaceous algae. IV. Morphogenetic movement of *Coccophora* eggs. *Bot. Mag.* (Tokyo), **70.**

NAKAZAWA, S. (1957d) Developmental mechanics of Fucaceous algae. V. Differential distribution of lecithine on the surface of the egg protoplasm in *Coccophora* and *Sargassum*. *Sci. Repts. Tôhoku Univ.*, 4th Ser. (Biol.) **23**, 21–5, Sendai, Japan.

NARAYANASWAMI, S. (1954) The structure and development of the caryopsis in some Indian millets. III. *Paspalum scorbiculatum* L. *Bull. Torrey Bot. Club*, **81**, 288–99.

NEEDHAM, J. (1942) *Biochemistry and Morphogenesis*, Cambridge Univ. Press.

NEGBI, M., BALDEV, B. and LANG, A. (1964) Studies on the orientation of the mitotic spindle in the shoot apex of *Hyoscyamus niger* and other rosette plants. *Israel Jour. Bot.*, **13**, 134–53.

NEMĔC, B. (1934) Ernahrung. Organogene und Regeneration. *Vest. Kral. Ces. Spol, Nauk.* Ir., 2, 1.

NEVILLE, P. (1961a) Étude expérimentale de l'influence des ébauches foliaires sur la morphogenèse végétative de *Gleditschia*. *C.R. Acad. Sci.* (Paris), **253**, 1121–3.

NEVILLE, P. (1961b) Influence de la feuille, à ses premiers stades, sur la morphogenèse végétative chez *Gleditschia triacanthos* L. *Bull. Soc. Bot., France*, **108**, 120–7.

NEWMAN, I. V. (1933) Studies in the Australian Acacias. II. *Jour. Linn. Soc. Bot.*, **49**.

NEWMAN, I. V. (1936a) Studies in the Australian Acacias. VI. *Proc. Linn. Soc. N.S.W.*, **61**.

NEWMAN, I. V. (1936b). Ontogeny of the angiospermic carpel. *Nature*, **137**.

NEWMAN, I. V. (1956) Pattern in meristems of vascular plants. I. Cell partition in living apices and in the cambial zone in relation to the concepts of initial cells and apical cells. *Phytomorph.*, **6**, 1–19.

NEWMAN, I. V. (1961) Pattern in the meristems of vascular plants. II. A review of shoot apical meristems of gymnosperms, with comments on apical biology and taxonomy, and a statement of some fundamental concepts. *Proc. Linn. Soc.* (New So. Wales), **86**, 9–59.

NEWMAN, I. V. (1965) Pattern in the meristems of vascular plants. III. Pursuing the patterns in the apical meristem where no cell is a permanent cell. *Jour. Linn. Soc. (Bot.)*, **59**, 185–214.

NICKELL, L. G. (1956) The continuous submerged cultivation of plant tissue as single cells. *Proc. Nat. Acad. Sci.* (Wash.), **42**, 848–50.

NICOLAS, D.: *See also* AGHION-PRAT, D. or AGHION, D.

NITSAN, J. and LANG, A. (1965) Inhibition of cell division and cell elongation in higher plants by inhibitors of DNA synthesis. *Developmental Biology*, **12**, 358–76.

NITSCH, J. P. (1951) Growth and development *in vitro* of excised ovaries. *Amer. Jour. Bot.*, **38**, 566–77.

NITSCH, J. P. (1954) Action du jus de tomate sur le croissance de certains tissus et organes végétaux. *Bull. Soc. Bot., Fr.*, **101**, 433–40.

NITSCH, J. P. (1963) The *in vitro* culture of flowers and fruits. *Plant Tissue and Organ Culture – A Symposium* (Ed. Maheshwari, P. and Rangaswamy, N. S.), Delhi.

NITSCH, J. P. (1965) Physiology of flower and fruit development. *Encyclopedia of Plant Physiology*, XV/2, 1537–647.

NITSCH, J. P. (1966) Phytohormones et genèse des bourgeons végétatifs et floraux. pp. 265–299, in *Les Phytohormones et l'Organogenèse*. (Ed. R. Bouillenne.) Congr. Internat. Univ. Liège, 1965. Publ. Univ. Liège.

NITSCH, J. P. and NITSCH, C. (1964) Néoformation de boutons floraux sur cultures *in vitro* de feuilles et de racines de *Cichorium intybus* L. Existence d'un état vernalisé en l'absence de bourgeons. *Bull. Soc. Bot., France*, **111**, 299–304.

NITSCH, J. P. and NITSCH, C. (1965) The induction of flowering in *Nicotiana*. III. Variations in the level of endogenous growth substances. *Amer. Jour. Bot.*, **52**, 591–8.

NJOKU, E. (1956a) Studies in the morphogenesis of leaves. XI. The effect of light intensity on leaf shape in *Ipomoea caerulea*. *New Phytologist*, **55**, 91–110.

NJOKU, E. (1956b) The effect of defoliation on leaf shape in *Ipomoea caerulea*. *New Phytologist*, **55**, 213–28.

NJOKU, E. (1957) The effect of mineral nutrition and temperature on leaf shape in *Ipomoea caerulea*. *New Phytologist*, **56**, 154–71.

NJOKU, E. (1958) Effect of gibberellic acid on leaf form. *Nature* (Lond.), **182**, 1097–8.

NOODEN, L. D. and THIMANN, K. V. (1963) Evidence for a requirement for protein synthesis for auxin-induced cell enlargement. *Proc. Natl. Acad. Sci. U.S.*, **50**, 194–200.

NOODEN, L. D. and THIMANN, K. V. (1965) Inhibition of protein synthesis and of auxin induced growth by chloramphenicol. *Plant Physiol.*, **40**, 193–201.

NOUGARÈDE, A., GIFFORD, E. M., Jr. and RONDET, P. (1965) Cytohistological studies of the apical meristem of *Amaranthus retroflexus* under various photoperiodic regimes. *Botan. Gaz.*, **126**, 281–98.

OLSON, R. A. and BUY, H. G. DU. (1937) The rôle of growth substance in the polarity and morphogenesis of *Fucus*. *Amer. Jour. Bot.*, **24**, 611.

OSBORNE, D. J. and HOLLAWAY, M. (1960) Auxin control of protein levels in detached autumn leaves. *Nature*, **188**, 240–1.

PAULET, P. (1965) Étude de la néoformation *in vitro* de bourgeons végétatifs et floreaux. *Rev. Gen. Bot.*, **72**, 697–792.

PAULET, P. (1966) Stimulation de la néoformation *in vitro* de bourgeons végétatifs et floraux chez deux *Nicotiana* et leur hybride. pp. 323–40, in *Les Phytohormones et l'Organogenèse*. (Ed. R. Bouillenne.) Congr. Internat. Univ. Liège, 1965. Publ. Univ. Liège.

PAULET, P. and NITSCH, J. P. (1959) Stimulation chimique du bourgeonnement chez *Cardamine pratensis* L. *Bull. Soc. Bot.*, *France*, **106**, 425–41.

PAULET, P. and NITSCH, J. P. (1963) Étude préliminaire du bourgeonnement *in vitro* de *Nicotiana glauca*, N. *suaveolens* et leur hybride. *Bull. Soc. Bot.*, *France*, **110**, 361–6.

PAULET, P. and NITSCH, J. P. (1964a) Néoformation de fleurs *in vitro* sur des cultures de tissus de racine de *Cichorium intybus* L.: étude physiologique. *C.R. Acad. Sci.* (Paris), **258**, 5952–5.

PAULET, P. and NITSCH, J. P. (1964b) La néoformation de fleurs sur cultures *in vitro* de racines de *Cichorium intybus* L.: étude physiologique. *Ann. Physiol. Vég.*, **6**, 333–45.

PAYER, J. B. (1857) *Traité d'organogénie comparée de la fleur*. Texte, 748 pp. Atlas, 154 plates. Paris, Librarie de Victor Masson.

PELLEGRINI, O. (1956) Lo sviluppo embrionale in *Koelreuteria paniculata* Laxm. (*Sapindaceae*). II. differenziamento del procambio e l'organizzazione dell' epicotile nell'embriogenesi di alcune dicotiledoni. *Delpinoa, N.S. Bull. Ist. ed Orto Bot. Univ. Napoli*, **9**, 97–129.

PELLEGRINI, O. (1957) Studio et interpretazione di alcune anomalie cotiledonari in plantule di *Dianthus cariophyllus* L. *Delpinoa, N.S. Bull. Ist. ed. Orto Bot. Univ. Napoli*, **10**, 121–40.

PHELOUZAT, R. (1964) Le système inflorescentiel du *Geum urbanum* L. *Bull. Soc. Bot.*, *France*, Mém., 168–72.

PHILIPSON, W. R. (1946) Studies in the development of the inflorescence. I. The capitulum of *Bellis perennis*. L. *Ann. Bot.*, *N.S.*, **10**, 257.

PHILIPSON, W. R. (1947a) Studies in the development of the inflorescence. II. The capitula of *Succisa pratensis* Moench. and *Dipsacus fullonum* L. *Ann. Bot.*, *N.S.*, **11**, 285.

PHILIPSON, W. R. (1947b) Studies in the development of the inflorescence. III. The thyrse of *Valeriana officinalis* L. *Ann. Bot.*, *N.S.*, **11**, 409.

PHILIPSON, W. R. (1948a) Studies in the development of the inflorescence. IV. The capitula of *Hieracium boreale* Fries and *Dahlia gracilis* Ortg. *Ann. Bot.*, *N.S.*, **12**, 65.

PHILIPSON, W. R. (1948b) Studies in the development of the inflorescence. V. The raceme of *Lobelia Dortmanna* L., and other Campanulaceous inflorescences. *Ann. Bot.*, *N.S.*, **12**, 147–56.

PHILIPSON, W. R. (1949) The ontogeny of the shoot apex in dicotyledons. *Biol. Rev.*, **24**, 21–50.

PIERIK, R. L. M. (1965) Regulation of morphogenesis by growth regulators and temperature treatment in isolated tissues of *Lunaria annua* L. *Proc. Koninkl. Ned. Akad. Wetenschap.* – *Amsterdam*, Ser. C, **68**, 324–32.

PIERIK, R. L. M. (1966) Regulation of morphogenesis by growth regulators and temperature treatment in isolated tissues of *Lunaria annua* L. pp. 81–2, in *Les Phytohormones et l'Organogenèse*. (Ed. R. Bouillenne.) Congr. Internat. Univ. Liège, 1965. Publ. Univ. Liège.

PIERIK, R. L. M. (1966) The induction and initiation of flowerbuds *in vitro* in tissues of *Lunaria annua* L. *Naturwiss*, **2**, 53 Jahrg., 45–6.

PIERIK, R. L. M. (1967) Regeneration, vernalization and flowering in *Lunaria annua* L. *in vivo* and *in vitro, Meded. Landbouwho.*, Wageningen, 67–6, 1–71.

PILKINGTON, M. (1929) The regeneration of the stem apex. *New Phytol.*, **28**, 37–53.

PISSAREV, W. E. and VINOGRADOVA, N. M. (1944) Hybrids between wheat, and *Elymus*. *C.R. Dokl. Acad. Sci. U.S.S.R.*, **45**, 129–32.

PLANTEFOL, L. (1946) Fondements d'une théorie phyllotaxique nouvelle. I. Historique et critique. II. La phyllotaxie des monocotylédones. *Ann. Sci. Nat. Bot.*, XI, **7**, 153–229.

PLANTEFOL, L. (1947a) Fondements d'une théorie phyllotaxique nouvelle. III. La phyllotaxie des dicotylédones. IV. Généralisations et conclusions. *Ann. Sci. Nat. Bot.*, XI, **8**, 1–71.

PLANTEFOL, L. (1947b) Hélices foliaires, point végétatif et stèle chez les dicotylédones. *Rev. Gén. Bot.*, **54**, 49–80.

PLANTEFOL, L. (1949) A new theory of phyllotaxis. *Nature*, **163**, 331–2.

PLANTEFOL, L. (1951) Phyllotaxie et point végétatif. *Scientia*, **86**, 91–8.

PLANTEFOL, L. (1962) Structure et fonctionnement du méristème terminal de la tige. Rapport introductif. *Mém. Soc. Bot.*, France, 1962, 3–14.

PODDUBNAYA-ARNOLDI, V. (1958) Investigation of the process of fertilization in angiosperms *in vivo*. *Bot. Žh.*, **43**, 178–93. (In Russian with English summary.)

PODDUBNAYA-ARNOLDI, V. (1959a) Study of fertilization and embryogenesis in certain angiosperms using living material. *Amer. Nat.*, 93, 161–9.

PODDUBNAYA-ARNOLDI, V. (1959b) Embryologische Untersuchungen an Angiospermen. Embryoentwicklung einiger Orchideen nach lebenden Material. *Trud. Gl. Bot. Sada*, 6, 49–89. (In Russian with English summary.)

PODDUBNAYA-ARNOLDI, V. (1960) Study of fertilization in the living material of some angiosperms. *Phytomorphology*, **10**, 185–98.

POPHAM, R. A. (1951) Principal types of vegetative shoot organization in vascular plants. *Ohio Jour. Sci.*, **51**, 249–70.

POSTLETHWAIT, S. N. and NELSON, O. E., Jr. (1957) A chronically wilted mutant of maize. *Amer. Jour. Bot.*, **44**, 628–33.

POUX, N. (1962) Nouvelles observations sur la nature et l'origine de la membrane vacuolaire des cellules végétales. *Jour. Microscopie*, **1**, 55–66.

PRAT, H. (1945) Les gradients histo-physiologiques et l'organogenèse végétale. *Contr. Inst. Bot. Univ. Montreal*, **58**, 1–151.

PRAT, H. (1948) Histo-physiological gradients and plant organogenesis. *Bot. Rev.*, **14**, 603.

PRAT, H. (1954) Symposium on Gradients. *Rept. Internat. Bot. Congress* (Paris).

PURVES, W. K. and HILLMAN, W. S. (1958) Response of pea stem sections to indoleacetic acid, gibberellic acid and sucrose as affected by length and distance from apex. *Physiol. Plant*, 11–29.

RABIDEAU, G. S. (1954) Morphology of radiation-damaged leaves. *Argonne Nat. Lab.*, No. 5288, 53–5.

RAGHAVAN, V. and JACOBS, W. P. (1961) Studies on the floral histogenesis and physiology of *Perilla*. II. Floral induction in cultured apical buds of *P. frutescens*. *Amer. Jour. Bot.*, **48**, 751–60.

RAGHAVAN, V. and TORREY, J. G. (1963) Growth and morphogenesis of globular and older embryos of *Capsella* in culture. *Amer. Jour. Bot.*, **50**, 540–51.

RAGHAVAN, V. and TORREY, J. G. (1964a) Inorganic nitrogen nutrition of the seedlings of the orchid, *Cattleya*. *Amer. Jour. Bot.*, **51**, 264–74.

RAGHAVAN, V. and TORREY, J. G. (1964b) Effects of certain growth substances on the growth and morphogenesis of immature embryos of *Capsella* in culture. *Plant Physiol.*, **39**, 691–9.

RAJU, M. V. S., STEEVES, T. A. and COUPLAND, R. T. (1963) Developmental studies on *Euphorbia esula* L. Morphology of the root system. *Can. Jour. Bot.*, **41**, 579–89.

RAM, MANASI. (1959) Morphological and embryological studies in the family Santalaceae. II. *Exocarpus*, with a discussion on its systematic position. *Phytomorphology*, **9**, 4–19.

RANDOLPH, L. F., ABBE, E. C. and EINSET, J. (1944) Comparison of shoot apex and leaf development and structure in diploid and tetraploid maize. *Jour. Agr. Res.*, **69**, 47–76.

RANGASWAMY, N. S. (1958) Culture of nucellar tissue of *Citrus in vitro*. *Experientia*, **14**, 111.

RANGASWAMY, N. S. (1959) *In vitro* studies on the ovules of *Citrus microcarpa* Bunge. *Ph.D. Thesis, Univ. Delhi.*

RAPER, K. B. (1940a) The communal nature of the fruiting process in the Acrasieae. *Amer. Jour. Bot.*, **27**, 436–48.

RAPER, K. B. (1940b) Pseudoplasmodium formation and organization in *Dictyostelium discoideum*. *J. Eli Mitchell Sci. Soc.*, **56**, 241–82.

REINDERS-GOUWENTAK, C. A. (1965) Physiology of the cambium and other secondary meristems of the shoot. *Encyclopedia of Plant Physiology*, XV/1, 1077–1105.

REINERT, J. (1959) Über die Kontrolle der Morphogenese und die Induktion von Adventivembryonen an Gewebekulturen aus Karotten. *Planta (Berl.)*, **53**, 318–33.

REINERT, J. (1962) Morphogenesis in plant tissue cultures. *Endeavour*, **21**, 85.

REINERT, J. (1963) Experimental modification of organogenesis in plant tissue cultures. *Plant Tissue and Organ Culture – A Symposium*. Published by the International Society of Plant Morphologists, Delhi. Ed. Maheshwari, P. & Rangaswamy, N. S., pp. 168–77.

REINERT, J. (1965) Growth of single cells from *Haplopappus gracilis* and *Vitis vinifera* on synthetic media. *Proc. Intern. Conf. Plant Tissue Culture Penn. State U., Univ. Park, Pa.* (1963), Ed. White, P. R. and Grove, A. R., McCutchan Pub. Co., Berkeley, Calif. pp. 61–7.

REINERT, J. (1965) Neue Ergebnisse und Probleme mit Gewebekulturen aus höheren Pflanzen. *Ber. deutsch. bot. Gesells.*, **78**, 1–11.

REINERT, J., BACKS, D. and KROSING, M. (1966) Faktoren der Embryogenese in Gewebekulturen aus Kulturformen von Umbelliferen. *Planta (Berl.)*, **68**, 375–8.

REINHARD, E. (1959) Vascular tissue differentiation in roots. *Proc. IX Internat. Bot. Congress*, **2**, 322.

REINHOLZ, E. (1954) Weitere Untersuchungen zur Induktion von Keimblatt-tänderungen durch Röntgenstrahlen. *Experientia* (Basel), 10, 486–8.

RICHARDS, F. J. (1948) The geometry of phyllotaxis and its origin. *Symp. Soc. Exp. Biol.*, 2, 217–45.

RICHARDS, F. J. (1951) Phyllotaxis: its quantitative expression and relation to growth in the apex. *Phil. Trans. Roy. Soc.*, B, 235, 509–64.

RICHARDS, P. W. (1952) *The Tropical Rain Forest*. Cambridge.

RICHTER-LANDMANN, W. (1959) Der Befruchtungsvorgang bei *Impatiens glandulifera* Royle unter Berücksichtigung der plasmatischen Organelle von Spermazelle, Eizelle und Zygote. *Planta*, 53, 162–77.

RICKETT, H. W. (1944) The classification of inflorescences. *Bot. Rev.*, 10, 187–231.

RIETSEMA, J., SATINA, S. and BLAKESLEE, A. F. (1953) The effect of indole-3-acetic acid on *Datura* embryos. *Proc. Nat. Acad. Sci.*, 39, 924–33.

RIETSEMA, J., SATINA, S. and BLAKESLEE, A. F. (1953) The effect of sucrose on the growth of *Datura stramonium* embryos *in vitro. Amer. Jour. Bot.*, 40, 638–46.

RIJVEN, A. H. G. C. (1952) *In vitro* studies on the embryo of *Capsella bursa-pastoris. Acta Bot. Néerl.*, 1, 157–200.

RIVIÈRES, R. (1959) Sur la culture *in vitro* d'embryons isolés de Polypodi-acées. *C.R. Acad. Sci.* (Paris), 248, 1004–7.

ROACH, W. A. (1939) Plant injection as a physiological method. *Ann. Bot.*, N.S., 3, 155–226.

ROBBINS, W. J. (1957a) Physiological aspects of ageing in plants. *Amer. Jour. Bot.*, 44, 289–94.

ROBBINS, W. J. (1957b) Gibberellic acid and the reversal of adult *Hedera* to a juvenile state. *Amer. Jour. Bot.*, 44, 743–6.

ROBBINS, W. J. (1960) Further observations on juvenile and adult *Hedera. Amer. Jour. Bot.*, 47, 485–91.

ROBERTS, L. W. (1960) Experiments on xylem regeneration in stem wound responses in *Coleus. Botan. Gaz.*, 121, 201–8.

ROBERTS, L. W. and FOSKET, D. E. (1962) Further experiments on wound-vessel formation in stem wounds of *Coleus. Botan. Gaz.*, 123, 247–54.

ROHWEDER, O. (1963) Anatomische und histogenetische Untersuchungen an Laubsprossen und Blüten der Commelinacen. *Bot. Jahrb.*, 82, 1–99.

RONDET, M. P. (1962) L'organogenèse au cours de l'embryogenèse chez l'*Alyssum maritimum* Lamk. *C.R. Acad. Sci.*, 225, 2278–80.

ROUFFA, A. S. and GUNCKEL, J. E. (1951) Leaf initiation, origin and pattern of pith development in the Rosaceae. *Amer. Jour. Bot.*, 38, 301–7.

ROWLANDS, D. C. (1954) Control of mitotic activity. *Nature*, 173, 828–9.

RYCZKOWSKI, M. (1964a) Concentration of amino nitrogen in the sap sur-rounding the embryo in developing ovules. *Bull. Acad. Polon. Sci.*, 12, 269–75.

RYCZKOWSKI, M. (1964b) Physico-chemical properties of the central vacuo-lar sap in developing ovules. *Pollen Physiology and Fertilization* (Ed. Liskens, H. F.), pp. 17–25. North Holland Publ. Co., Amsterdam.

RYCZKOWSKI, M. (1964c) Sugars and osmotic value of the sap surrounding the embryo in developing ovules (dicotyledonous perennial plants). *Acta Soc. Bot. Polon.*, 33, 399–406.

RYCZKOWSKI, M. (1965a) Changes in osmotic value of the endosperm sap and differentiation of the egg cell in developing ovules of *Cycas revoluta Bull. Acad. Polon. Sci.*, **13**, 557–9.

RYCZKOWSKI, M. (1965b) The pH of the sap surrounding the embryo in developing ovules. *Bull. Acad. Polon. Sci.*, **13**, 479–83.

SABHARWAL, P. S. (1962) *In vitro* culture of nucelli and embryos of *Citrus aurantifolius* Swingle. *Plant Embryology* (A Symposium: Ed. Maheshwari, P.), pp. 239–43, C.S.I.R., New Delhi.

SACHAR, R. C. and CHOPRA, R. N. (1957) A study of the endosperm and embryo in *Mangifera* L. *Indian Jour. Agric. Sci.*, **27**, 219–28.

SACHAR, R. C. and SIPRA GUHA. (1962) *In vitro* growth of achenes of *Ranunculus sceleratus* L. *Plant Embryology*, (A Symposium: Ed. Maheshwari, P.), pp. 244–53, C.S.I.R., New Delhi.

SACHER, J. A. (1954) Structure and seasonal activity of the shoot apices of *Pinus lambertiana* and *Pinus ponderosa*. *Amer. Jour. Bot.*, **41**, 749–59.

SACHER, J. A. (1967) Dual effect of auxin: inhibition of uptake and stimulation of RNA and protein synthesis: assessment of synthesis. *Zeitschr. f. Pflanzenphysiol.*, **56**, 410–26.

SACHS, R. M., BRETZ, C. F. and LANG, A. (1959) Shoot histogenesis: the early effect of gibberellin upon stem elongation in two rosette plants. *Amer. Jour. Bot.*, **46**, 376–84.

SACHS, R. M. and LANG, A. (1957) Effect of gibberellin upon cell division in *Hyoscyamus. Science*, **125**, 1144–5.

SACHS, R. M. and LANG, A. (1961) Shoot histogenesis and the subapical meristem; the action of gibberellic acid, Amo-1618, and maleic hydrazide: in *Fourth Internat. Conf. on Plant Growth Regulation*, Yonkers, N.Y., Aug. 1959, Ames, Iowa State Univ. Press, 567.

SACHS, R. M., LANG, A., BRETZ, C. F. and ROACH, J. (1960) Shoot histogenesis: subapical meristematic activity in a caulescent plant and the action of gibberellic acid and Amo-1618. *Amer. Jour. Bot.*, **47**, 260–6.

SACKS, T. and THIMANN, K. V. (1967) The role of auxins and cytokinins in the release of buds from dominance. *Amer. Jour. Bot.*, **54**, 136–44.

SAHNI, B. (1917) Observations on the evolution of branching in the Filicales. *New Phytol.*, **16**, 1.

SALISBURY, F. B. and BONNER, J. (1958) Effects of uracil derivatives on flowering in *Xanthium. Plant Physiol.*, Suppl., **33**, 25.

SALISBURY, F. B. and BONNER, J. (1960) Inhibition of photoperiodic induction by 5-fluorouracil. *Plant Physiol.*, **35**, 173–7.

SALISBURY, F. B. (1965). The initiation of flowering. *Endeavour*, **24**, 74–86.

SANDERS, M. E. and BURKHOLDER, P. R. (1948) Effects of amino acids on growth of *Datura* embryos in culture. *Amer. Jour. Bot.*, **35**, 797.

SARGENT, J. A. and WANGERMANN, E. (1959) The effect of some growth regulators on the vascular system of *Lemna minor. New Phytol.*, **58**, 345–63.

SATINA, S. (1944) Periclinal chimeras in *Datura* in relation to development and structure (a) of the style and stigma (b) of calyx and corolla. *Amer. Jour. Bot.*, **31**, 493.

SATINA, S. and BLAKESLEE, A. F. (1941) Periclinal chimeras in *Datura stramonium* in relation to development of leaf and flower. *Amer. Jour. Bot.*, **28**, 862.

SATINA, S., BLAKESLEE, A. F. and AVERY, A. G. (1940) Demonstration of the three germ layers in the shoot apex of *Datura* by means of induced polyploidy in periclinal chimeras. *Amer. Jour. Bot.*, **27**, 895–905.

SCHADE, C. and GUTTENBERG, H. VON. (1951) Über die Entwicklung des Wurzelvegetationspunktes der Monokotyledonen. *Planta*, **40**, 170–98.

SCHAFFALITZKY DE MUCKADELL, M. (1959) Investigations on aging of apical meristems in woody plants and its importance in silviculture. *Forstl. Forsgsvaes* (Danmark), **25**, 310–455.

SCHLEIDEN, M. J. (1842) *Grundzüge der wissenschaftlichen Botanik: Der Botanik als induktive Wissenschaft.*

SCHMIDT, A. (1924) Histologische Studien an phanerogamen Vegetationspunkten. *Bot. Arch.*, **8**, 345.

SCHNARF, K. (1931) *Vergleichende Embryologie der Angiospermen* (Berlin).

SCHNEIDER, R. (1952) Histogenetische Untersuchungen über den Bau der Laubblätter, insbesondere ihres Mesophylls. *Ost. Bot. Z.*, **99**, 252–85.

SCHOUTE, J. C. (1913) Beiträge zur Blattstellungslehre. *Rec. Trav. Bot. Néerl.*, **10**, 153–325.

SCHOUTE, J. C. (1936) Fasciation and dichotomy. *Rec. Trav. Bot. Néerl.*, **33**, 649–69.

SCHROEDER, C. A., KAY, E. and DAVIS, L. H. (1962) Totipotency of cells from fruit pericarp tissue *in vitro*. *Science*, **138**, 595–6.

SCHÜEPP, O. (1917) Untersuchungen über Wachstum und Formwechsel von Vegetationspunkten. *Jb. Wiss. Bot.*, **57**, 17–79.

SCHÜEPP, O. (1963) Mathematisches und Botanisches über Allometrie. *Verhandl. Naturf. Ges. Basel*, **74**, 69–105.

SCHWABE, W. W. (1963) Morphogenetic responses to climate. In *Environmental Control of Plant Growth* (Ed. Evans, L. T.), pp. 311–36, Academic Press, New York and London.

SCOTT, T. K., JACOBS, W. P. and CASE, D. (1965) The rôle of gibberellin in apical dominance in green Alaska pea. *Plant Physiology* (Suppl.), **40**, lxxiii.

SHAH, J. J. (1960a) Morpho-histogenic studies in Vitaceae. I. Origin and development of the axillary buds in *Cayratia carnosa*. *Phytomorphology*, **10**, 157–74.

SHAH, J. J. (1960b) Developmental pattern of the primary vascular system in the stem of *Cissus* sp. *Jour. Indian Bot. Soc.*, **39**, 443–54.

SHAH, J. J. (1960c) Origin, development and morphology of tendrils of Vitaceae. *Proc. Summer School of Botany – Darjeeling*, pp. 430–44. (Ed. Maheshwari, P., Johri, B. M. and Vasil, I. K. Publ. 1962.)

SHARMAN, B. C. (1947) The biology and developmental morphology of the shoot in the Gramineae. *New Phytol.*, **46**, 20–34.

SHIROYA, M., LISTER, G. R., NELSON, C. D. and KROTKOV, G. (1961) Translocation of C^{14} in tobacco at different stages of development following assimilation of $C^{14}O_2$ by a single leaf. *Canad. Jour. Bot.*, **39**, 855–64.

SHULL, G. H. (1905) Stages in the development of *Sium cicutaefolium*. *Carnegie Inst. Wash. Monogr.* No. 30.

SIFTON, H. B. (1944) Developmental morphology of vascular plants. *New Phytol.*, **43**, 87–129.

SIMON, S. (1908) Experimentelle Untersuchungen über die Entstehung von Gefassverbindungen. *Ber. Dtsch. Bot. Ges.*, **26**, 364–96.

SINNOTT, E. W. (1960) *Plant Morphogenesis*, 550 pp., McGraw-Hill, New York.

SINNOTT, E. W. and BLOCH, R. (1944) Visible expression of cytoplasmic patterns in the differentiation of xylem strands. *Proc. Nat. Acad. Sci.* (Wash.), **30**, 388–92.

SINNOTT, E. W. and BLOCH, R. (1945) The cytoplasmic basis of intercellular patterns in vascular differentiation. *Amer. Jour. Bot.* **32**, 151–6.

SITTE, P. (1961) Die Submikroskopische Organisation der Pflanzenzell. *Ber. Dtsch. Bot. Ges.*, **74**, 177–206.

SKOOG, F. (1944) Growth and organ formation in tobacco tissue cultures. *Amer. Jour. Bot.*, **31**, 19.

SKOOG, F. (1950) Chemical control of growth and organ formation in plant tissues. *Ann. Biol.*, **54** (Ser. III 26), 545–62.

SKOOG, F. (1951) *Plant Growth Substances* (a collective work), Univ. Wisconsin Press.

SKOOG, F. (1954a) Substances involved in normal growth and differentiation. *Brookhaven Symp. Biol.*, **6**, 1–21.

SKOOG, F. (1954b) Chemical regulation of growth in plants. In *Dynamics of Growth Processes* (Ed. Boell, E. F.), pp. 148–82, Princeton Univ. Press.

SKOOG, F. (1955) Growth factors, polarity and morphogenesis. *Ann. Biol.*, **59** (Ser. III, 31), 201–13.

SKOOG, F. and MILLER, C. O. (1957) Chemical regulation of growth and organ formation in plant tissues cultured *in vitro*. *Symp. Soc. Exp. Biol.*, **11**, 118–31.

SKOOG, F. and TSUI, C. (1948) Chemical control of growth and bud formation in tobacco stem segments and callus cultured *in vitro*. *Amer. Jour. Bot.*, **35**, 782–7.

SMITH, C. A. (1963) Shoot apices in the family Moraceae with a seasonal study of *Maclura pomifera* (Raf.) Schneid. *Bull. Torrey Bot. Cl.*, **90**, 237–58.

SNOAD, B. (1955) Somatic instability of chromosome number in *Hymenocallis calathinum. Heredity*, **9**, 129–34.

SNOW, M. (1951) Experiments on spirodistichous shoot apices. I. *Phil. Trans. Roy. Soc.*, B, **235**, 131–62.

SNOW, M. (1955) Spirodistichy re-interpreted. *Phil. Trans. Roy. Soc.*, B, **239**, 45–88.

SNOW, M. and SNOW, R. (1931) Experiments on phyllotaxis. I. The effect of isolating a primordium. *Phil. Trans. Roy. Soc.*, B, **221**, 1–43.

SNOW, M. and SNOW, R. (1933) Experiments on phyllotaxis. II. The effect of displacing a primordium. *Phil. Trans. Roy. Soc.*, B, **222**, 353–400.

SNOW, M. and SNOW, R. (1935) Experiments on phyllotaxis. III. Diagonal splits through decussate apices. *Phil. Trans. Roy. Soc.*, B, **225**, 63–94.

SNOW, M. and SNOW, R. (1937) Auxin and leaf formation. *New Phytol.*, **36**, 1–18.

SNOW, M. and SNOW, R. (1942) The determination of axillary buds. *New Phytol.*, **41**, 13–22.

SNOW, M. and SNOW, R. (1947) On the determination of leaves. *New Phytol.*, **46**, 5–19.

SNOW, M. and SNOW, R. (1948) On the determination of leaves. *Symp. Soc. Exp. Biol.*, **2**, 263–75.

SNOW, M. and SNOW, R. (1952) Minimum areas and leaf determination. *Proc. Roy. Soc.*, B, **139**, 545.

SNOW, M. and SNOW, R. (1953) Regeneration of the potato shoot apex. *Nature* (Lond.), **171**, 224.

SNOW, M. and SNOW, R. (1955) Regulation of sizes of leaf primordia by growing-point of stem apex. *Proc. Roy. Soc.*, B, **144**, 222–9.

SNOW, M. and SNOW, R. (1959) Regulation of sizes of leaf primordia by older leaves. *Proc. Roy. Soc.*, B, **151**, 39–47.

SNOW, M. and SNOW, R. (1962) A theory of the regulation of phyllotaxis based on *Lupinus albus*. *Phil. Trans. Roy. Soc.*, B, **244**, 483–514.

SNOW, R. (1948) A new theory of leaf formation. *Nature*, **162**, 798.

SNOW, R. (1951) Experiments on bijugate apices. *Phil. Trans. Roy. Soc.*, B, **235**, 291–310.

SNOW, R. (1952) On the shoot apex and phyllotaxis of *Costus*. *New Phytol.*, **51**, 359–63.

SNOW, R. (1954) Phyllotaxis of flowering teasels. *New Phytol.*, **53**, 99–107.

SNOW, R. (1958) Phyllotaxis of *Kniphofia* and *Lilium candidum*. *New Phytol.*, **57**, 160–7.

SOMA, S. (1965) Developmental studies on the orientation and dorsiventrality of the leaf of *Zelkova serrata* Makino. *Jour. Fac. of Sci., Univ. of Tokyo*, **9**, 1–17.

SOMA, K. and BALL, E. (1963) Studies of the surface growth of the shoot apex of *Lupinus albus*. In *Meristems and Differentiation, Brookhaven Symp. Biol.*, **16**, 13–45.

SOUÈGES, (E. C.) R. (1923) Embryogénie des Joncacées. Développement de l'embryon chez le *Luzula forsteri* DC. *C.R. Acad. Sci.* (Paris). **177**, 705–8.

SOUÈGES, (E. C.) R. (1935) Embryogénie des Oenotheracées. Les principaux termes du développement de l'embryon chez le *Ludwigia palustris* Elliott. *C.R. Acad. Sci.* (Paris), **200**, 1626–8.

STACE, C. A. (1965) Cuticular studies as an aid to plant taxonomy. *Bull. Brit. Museum (Nat. Hist.) Botany*, **4**, 1–78.

STEEVES, T. A. (1957) (Discussion following a paper on 'Histogenesis in plant tissue cultures', by Gautheret, R. J.). *Jour. Nat. Cancer Inst.*, **19**, 583–5.

STEEVES, T. A. (1961a) The development of leaves in sterile nutrient culture. In *Recent Advances in Botany*, **1**, 823–7, Univ. of Toronto Press.

STEEVES, T. A. (1961b) The developmental potentialities of excised leaf primordia in sterile culture. *Phytomorph.*, **11**, 346–59.

STEEVES, T. A. (1962) Morphogenesis in isolated fern leaves. In *Regeneration* (Ed. Rudnick, D.), pp. 117–51, *20th Symp. Soc. Study Dev. & Growth*.

STEEVES, T. A. (1963) Morphogenetic studies of fern leaves. *Jour. Linn. Soc. (Bot.)*, **58**, 401–15.

STEEVES, T. A. and BRIGGS, W. R. (1958) Morphogenetic studies on *Osmunda cinnamomea* L. The origin and early development of vegetative fronds. *Phytomorph.*, **8**, 60–72.

STEEVES, T. A., GABRIEL, H. P. and STEEVES, M. W. (1957) Growth in sterile culture of excised leaves of flowering plants. *Science*, **126**, 350–1.

STEEVES, T. A. and SUSSEX, I. M. (1957) Studies on the development of excised leaves in sterile culture. *Amer. Jour. Bot.*, **44**, 665–73.

STEEVES, T. A. and WETMORE, R. H. (1953) Morphogenetic studies on *Osmunda cinnamomea* L.: some aspects of the general morphology. *Phytomorph.*, **3**, 339–54.

STEIN, D. B. and STEIN, O. L. (1960) The growth of the stem tip of *Kalanchoë* cv. 'Brilliant Star'. *Amer. Jour. Bot.*, **47**, 132–40.

STEFFEN, K. (1963) Fertilization. *Recent Advances in the Embryology of Angiosperms* (Ed. Maheshwari, P.), pp. 105–33, *Internat. Soc. Pl. Morph.* (Delhi).

STERLING, C. (1963) The affinities of *Prinsepia* (Rosaceae). *Amer. Jour. Bot.*, 50, 693–9.

STEWARD, F. C. (1958) Growth and organized development of cultured cells. III. Interpretations of the growth from free cells to carrot plant. *Amer. Jour. Bot.*, 45, 709–13.

STEWARD, F. C. (1963a) Totipotency and variation in cultured cells: some metabolic and morphogenetic manifestations, pp. 1–25. In *Plant Tissue and Organ Culture – A Symposium* (Ed. Maheshwari, P. and Rangaswamy, N. S.), Univ. of Delhi, India.

STEWARD, F. C. (1963b) Carrots and coconuts: some investigations on growth. In *Plant Tissue and Organ Culture – A Symposium* (Ed. Maheshwari, P. and Rangaswamy, N. S.), 178–97.

STEWARD, F. C., BLAKELY, L. M., KENT, A. E. and MAPES, M. O. (1963) Growth and organization in free cell cultures. In *Meristems and Differentiation – Brookhaven Symposia Biol.*, 16, 73–88.

STEWARD, F. C., CAPLIN, S. M. and MILLAR, F. K. (1952) Investigations on growth and metabolism of plant cells. I. New techniques for the investigation of metabolism, nutrition and growth in undifferentiated cells. *Ann. Bot.*, 16, 57–77.

STEWARD, F. C., MAPES, M. O., KENT, A. C. and HOLSTEN, R. D. (1964) Growth and development of cultured plant cells. *Science*, 143, 20–7.

STEWARD, F. C., MAPES, M. O. and MEARS, K. (1958) Growth and organized development of cultured cells. II. Organization in cultures grown from freely suspended cells. *Amer. Jour. Bot.*, 45, 705–8.

STEWARD, F. C., MAPES, M. O. and SMITH, J. (1958) Growth and organized development of cultured cells. I. Growth and division of freely suspended cells. *Amer. Jour. Bot.*, 45, 693–703.

STEWARD, F. C. and MOHAN RAM, H. Y. (1961) Determining factors in cell growth: Some implications for morphogenesis in plants, pp. 189–265. In *Advances in Morphogenesis* (Ed. Brachet, J. and Abercrombie, M.), Vol. I. Academic Press, New York and London.

STEWARD, F. C. and SHANTZ, E. M. (1954) The growth of carrot tissue explants and its relation to the growth factors in coconut milk. II. The growth-promoting properties of coconut milk for plant tissue cultures. *Ann. Biol.*, 30, 399–410.

STEWARD, F. C. and SHANTZ, E. M. (1956) The chemical induction of growth in plant tissue cultures. I. Methods of tissue culture and the analysis of growth, pp. 165–86. In *The Chemistry and Mode of Action of Plant Growth Substances* (Ed. Wain, R. L. and Wightman, F.), Butterworths, London.

STEWARD, F. C., SHANTZ, E. M., POLLARD, J. K., MAPES, M. O. and MITRA, J. (1961) Growth induction in explanted cells and tissues: metabolic and morphogenetic manifestations, pp. 193–246. In *Molecular and Cellular Synthesis* (Ed. Rudnick, D.), Ronald Press Co., New York.

STEWARD, F. C., WETMORE, R. H. and POLLARD, J. K. (1955) Nitrogenous components of the shoot apex of *Adiantum pedatum*. *Amer. Jour. Bot.*, 42, 936–8.

STEWARD, F. C., WETMORE, R. H., THOMPSON, J. F. and NITSCH, J. P. (1954) A quantitative chromatographic study of nitrogenous components of shoot apices. *Amer. Jour. Bot.*, 41, 123–34.

STICHEL, E. (1959) Gleichzeitige Induktion von Sprossen und Wurzeln an *in vitro* kultivierten Gewebestucken von *Cyclamen persicum. Planta,* **53,** 293–317.

STOWE, B. B. and YAMAKI, T. (1957) The history and physiological action of the gibberellins. *Ann. Rev. Plant Physiol.,* **8,** 181–216.

SUNDERLAND, N. and BROWN, R. (1956) Distribution of growth in the apical region of the shoot of *Lupinus albus. Jour. Exp. Bot.,* **7,** 127–45.

SUNDERLAND, N., HEYES, J. K. and BROWN, R. (1956) Growth and metabolism in the shoot apex of *Lupinus albus.* In *The Growth of Leaves* (Ed. Milthorpe, F. L.), pp. 77–90, Butterworths, London.

SUNDERLAND, N., HEYES, J. K. and BROWN, R. (1957) Protein and respiration in the apical region of the shoot of *Lupinus albus. Jour. Exp. Bot.,* **8,** 55–70.

SUSSEX, I. M. (1951) Experiments on the cause of dorsiventrality in leaves. *Nature,* **167,** 651–2.

SUSSEX, I. M. (1952) Regeneration of the potato shoot apex. *Nature,* **170,** 755–7.

SUSSEX, I. M. (1953) Regeneration of the potato shoot apex. *Nature,* **171,** 224–5.

SUSSEX, I. M. (1954) Experiments on the cause of dorsiventrality in leaves. *Nature,* **174,** 351–2.

SUSSEX, I. M. (1955) Morphogenesis in *Solanum tuberosum* L.: experimental investigation of leaf dorsiventrality and orientation in the juvenile shoot. *Phytomorph.,* **5,** 286–300.

SUSSEX, I. M. (1958) A morphological and experimental study of leaf development in *Leptopteris hymenophylloides* (A. Rich.) Presl. *Phytomorph.,* **8,** 96–107.

SUSSEX, I. M. and CLUTTER, M. E. (1960) A study of the effect of externally supplied sucrose on the morphology of excised fern leaves *in vitro. Phytomorph.,* **10,** 87–99.

SUSSEX, I. M. and STEEVES, T. A. (1953) Growth of excised fern leaves in sterile culture. *Nature,* **172,** 624–5.

SUSSEX, I. M. and STEEVES, T. A. (1958) Experiments on the control of fertility of fern leaves in sterile culture. *Botan. Gaz.,* **119,** 203–8.

SUSSMAN, M. (1955) The developmental physiology of the amoeboid slime moulds. *Biochemistry and Physiology of the Protozoa* (Ed. Hutner, S. and Lwoff, A.), Vol. 2, 201–23, Academic Press, New York.

SWIFT, H. (1950) The constancy of desoxyribose nucleic acid in plant nuclei. *Proc. Nat. Acad. Sci.* (Wash.), **36,** 643–54.

TAHARA, M. (1927) Experiments on the eggs of *Sargassum. Bot. Mag.* (Tokyo), **41,** 142–9.

TAILLANDIER, J. (1965) Sur l'incorporation de thymidine tritiée dans l'apex végétatif du *Pinus pinea* L. *C.R. Acad. Sci.* (Paris), **260,** 4043–5.

TEPFER, S. S. (1953) Floral anatomy and ontogeny in *Aquilegia formosa* var. *truncata* and *Ranunculus repens. Univ. Calif. Publ. Bot.,* **25,** 513–648.

TEPFER, S. S. (1960) The shoot apex and early leaf development in *Clematis. Amer. Jour. Bot.,* **47,** 655–64.

TEPFER, S. S., GREYSON, R. I., CRAIG, W. R. and HINDMAN, J. L. (1963) *In vitro* culture of floral buds of *Aquilegia. Amer. Jour. Bot.,* **50,** 1035–45.

TEPFER, S. S., KARPOFF, A. J. and GREYSON, R. I. (1966) Effects of growth substances on excised floral buds of *Aquilegia. Amer. Jour. Bot.,* **53,** 148–57.

THIELKE, C. (1962) Histologische Untersuchungen am Sprosscheitel von

Saccharum. II. Mitteilung. Der Sprosscheitel von *Saccharum sinense*. *Planta*, **58**, 175–92.

THIELKE, C. (1966) Enzyme-pattern in the root-meristem. *Planta* (Berl.), **68**, 371–4.

THIMANN, K. V. (1938) Hormones and the analysis of growth. *Plant Physiol.*, **13**, 437.

THIMANN, K. V. (1949) Plant Growth Hormones. In *The Chemistry and Physiology of Growth* (Ed. Parpart, A. K.), pp. 61–71.

THIMANN, K. V. and LALORAYA, M. M. (1960) Changes in nitrogen in pea stem sections under the action of kinetin. *Physiol. Plantarum*, **13**, 165–78.

THODAY, D. (1933) Some physiological aspects of differentiation. *New Phytol.*, **32**, 274–87.

THODAY, D. (1939) The interpretation of plant structure. *Presidential Address*, Brit. Assoc. Adv. Sci., Sect. K, pp. 1–21.

THOMPSON, D'ARCY, W. (1917, 1942) *On Growth and Form*, Cambridge Univ. Press.

THOMPSON, J. MCL. (1921) Studies in floral zygomorphy. II. The staminal zygomorphy of *Couroupita guianensis* Aubl. *Trans. Roy. Soc.*, Edinb., **53**, 1–15.

THOMPSON, J. MCL. (1927) A study in advancing gigantism with staminal sterility, with special reference to the Lecythideae. *Publ. Hartley Bot. Lab.*, Univ. of Liverpool, **4**, 1–44.

THOMPSON, J. MCL. (1933) Studies in advancing sterility VI. The theory of Scitaminean flowering. *Publ. Hartley Bot. Lab.*, Univ. of Liverpool, **11**, 1–111.

THOMPSON, J. MCL. (1936) On the gynoecial apex and the terminal legume of *Acacia longifolia* Willd. and *Acacia suaveolens* Willd. *Publ. Hartley Bot. Lab.*, Univ. of Liverpool, **16**, 1–33.

THOMPSON, J. MCL. (1952) A further contribution to our knowledge of cauliflorous plants with special reference to the cannon-ball tree (*Couroupita guianensis* Aubl.). *Proc. Linn. Soc.*, Lond., Session 163, 233–50.

THOMSON, J. (1925) Studies in irregular nutrition. I. The parasitism of *Cuscuta reflexa* (Roxb.). *Trans. Roy. Soc.*, Edinb., **54**, 343–56.

THOMPSON, N. P. and JACOBS, W. P. (1965) Vascular regeneration around a stem wound in *Coleus blumei* Benth. *Plant Physiol.*, (Suppl.), **40**, xxxiii–xxxiv.

THOMSON, B. F. and MILLER, P. M. (1962) The rôle of light in histogenesis and differentiation in the shoot of *Pisum sativum*. I. The apical region. *Amer. Jour. Bot.*, **49**, 303–10.

THOMSON, R. B. (1934) Modification of the form of the haustorium in *Marsilea* on development in culture fluid. *Trans. Roy. Can. Inst.*, **20**, 69.

THOMSON, R. B. and HALL, K. L. (1933) Physical laws and the cellular organization of plants. *Bot. Gaz.*, **95**, 511.

TOLBERT, R. J. and JOHNSON, M. A. (1966) A survey of the vegetative shoot apices in the family Malvaceae. *Amer. Jour. Bot.*, **53**, 961–70.

TORREY, J. G. (1950) The induction of lateral roots by indole-acetic acid and root decapitation. *Amer. Jour. Bot.*, **37**, 257–64.

TORREY, J. G. (1952) Effects of light on elongation and branching in pea-roots. *Plant Physiol.*, **27**, 591–602.

TORREY, J. G. (1955) On the determination of vascular patterns during tissue differentiation in excised pea roots. *Amer. Jour. Bot.*, **42**, 183–98.

TORREY, J. G. (1956) Chemical factors limiting lateral root formation in isolated pea roots. *Physiol. Plant.*, 9, 370–88.

TORREY, J. G. (1957a) Cell division in isolated single plant cells *in vitro*. *Proc. Nat. Acad. Sci.* (Wash.), 43, 887–91.

TORREY, J. G. (1957b) Auxin control of vascular pattern formation in regenerating pea root meristems grown *in vitro*. *Amer. Jour. Bot.*, 44, 859–70.

TORREY, J. G. (1965) Physiological bases of organization and development in the root. *Encyclopedia of Plant Physiology*, XV/1, 1256–327.

TORREY, J. G. and REINERT, J. (1961) Suspension cultures of higher plant cells in synthetic media. *Plant Physiol.*, 36, 483–91.

TROLL, W. (1937) *Vergleichende Morphologie der hoheren Pflanzen* (Berlin).

TRUSCOTT, F. H. (1966) Some aspects of morphogenesis in *Cuscuta gronovii*. *Amer. Jour. Bot.*, 53, 739–50.

TUCKER, S. C. (1959) Ontogeny of the inflorescence and the flower in *Drimys winteria* var. *chilensis*. *Univ. California Pub. Bot.*, 30, 257–336.

TUCKER, S. C. (1960) Ontogeny of the floral apex of *Michelia fuscata*. *Amer. Jour. Bot.*, 47, 266–77.

TUCKER, S. C. (1962) Ontogeny and phyllotaxis of the terminal vegetative shoots of *Michelia fuscata*. *Amer. Jour. Bot.*, 49, 722–37.

TUKEY, H. B. (1937) Growth patterns of plants developed from immature embryos in artificial culture. *Botan. Gaz.*, 99, 630.

TULECKE, W. (1957) The pollen of *Ginkgo biloba*. *In vitro* culture and tissue formation. *Amer. Jour. Bot.*, 44, 602–8.

TULECKE, W. (1959) The pollen cultures of C. D. LaRue: A tissue from the pollen of *Taxus*. *Bull. Torrey Bot. Club*, 86, 283–9.

TULECKE, W. and SEHGAL, N. (1963) Cell proliferation from the pollen of *Torreya nucifera*. *Contrib. Boyce Thompson Inst.*, 22, 153–63.

TURING, A. M. (1952) The chemical basis of morphogenesis. *Phil. Trans. Roy. Soc.*, B, 237, 37–72.

TURNER, A. (1966) A morphogenetic study of *Endymion non-scripta*. Thesis, Manchester University.

VAN DER LEK, H. A. (1925) Over de wortelvorming van houtige stekken (with summary: Root development in woody cuttings). *Diss.*, Utrecht.

VAN ITERSON, G. (1907) *Mathematische und mikroskopischanatomische Studien über Blattstellungen*. Jena.

VAN OVERBEEK, J. (1940) Auxin in marine algae. *Plant Physiol.*, 15, 291.

VAN OVERBEEK, J. (1942) Hormonal control of embryo and seedling. *Cold Spring Harbor Symp.*, 10, 126.

VAN OVERBEEK, J., CONKLIN, M. E. and BLAKESLEE, A. F. (1941a) Factors in coconut milk essential for growth and development of very young *Datura* embryos. *Science*, 94, 350.

VAN OVERBEEK, J., CONKLIN, M. E. and BLAKESLEE, A. F. (1941b) Chemical stimulation of ovule development and its possible relation to parthenogenesis. *Amer. Jour. Bot.*, 28, 647.

VAN OVERBEEK, J., CONKLIN, M. E. and BLAKESLEE, A. F. (1942) Cultivation *in vitro* of small *Datura* embryos. *Amer. Jour. Bot.*, 29, 472.

VASIL, I. K. and HILDEBRANDT, A. C. (1966) Variations of morphogenetic behaviour in plant tissue cultures. I. *Cichorium endivia*. *Amer. Jour. Bot.*, 53, 860–9.

VASIL, V. and HILDEBRANDT, A. C. (1965) Growth and tissue formation from single, isolated tobacco cells in microculture. *Science*, 147, 1454–5.

VEEN, H. (1961) The effect of gibberellic acid on the embryo growth of *Capsella bursa-pastoris*. *Proc. Koninkl. Ned. Akad. Wetenschap*, (C) **64**, 79–85.

VEEN, H. (1962) Preliminary report on effects of kinetin on embryonic growth *in vitro* of *Capsella* embryos. *Acta Botan. Neerl.*, **11**, 228–9.

VEEN, H. (1963) The effect of various growth-regulators on embryos of *Capsella bursa-pastoris* growing *in vitro*. *Acta Botan. Neerl.*, **12**, 129–71.

VESCOVI, P. (1964) Étude comparée de l'ontogenèse de la grappe terminale indéfinie sans fleur terminale chez le *Spartina junceum* L. et du functionnement de l'apex du *Lathyrus aphaca* L. dans sa phase réproductrice. *Bull. Bot. Soc., France*, Mém., 173–9.

VIETH, J. (1963) Étude de quelques inflorescences anormales de Scabieuses. *Bull. Soc. Bot., France*, **110**, 36–45.

VIETH, J. (1964) Le capitule de *Dipsacus* représente-t-il un system bijugué? *Bull. Soc. Bot., France*, Mém., 38–47.

VLADESCO, M. A. (1935) Recherches morphologiques et expérimentales sur l'embryogénie et l'organogénie des fougères leptosporangiées. *Rev. Gén. Bot.*, **47**, 422.

WAGNER, N. (1939) Über die Entwicklungsmechanik der Wurzelhaube und des Wurzelrippenmeristems. *Planta*, **30**, 21–66.

WALTON, A. (1964) A morphogenetic study of *Arum maculatum* L. *Ann. Bot., N.S.*, **28**, 271–82.

WANG, F. H. and CHEN, T. K. (1965) Experimental studies of young *Ginkgo* embryos – the effect of coconut milk on the embryos cultured *in vitro*. *Acta Botanica Sinica*, **13**, 224–32.

WANG, F. H., CHEN, T. K. and LEE, S. C. (1963) Experimental studies of young *Ginkgo* embryos. I. The effect of the bee royal jelly on the embryo growth. *Acta Botanica Sinica*, **11**, 217–22.

WANGERMANN, E. (1965) Longevity and ageing in plants and plant organs. *Encyclopedia of Plant Physiology*, XV/2, 1026–57.

WARD, M. and WETMORE, R. H. (1954) Experimental control of development in the embryo of the fern, *Phlebodium aureum*. *Amer. Jour. Bot.*, **41**, 428–34.

WARDLAW, C. W. (1928) Size in relation to internal morphology. 3. The vascular system of roots. *Trans. Roy. Soc. Edinb.*, **56**, 19–55.

WARDLAW, C. W. (1945) Experimental and analytical studies of pteridophytes. VI. Stelar morphology: the occurrence of reduced and discontinuous vascular systems in the rhizome of *Onoclea sensibilis*. *Ann. Bot. N.S.*, **9**, 383–97.

WARDLAW, C. W. (1947) Experimental investigations of the shoot apex of *Dryopteris aristata* Druce. *Phil. Trans. Roy. Soc.*, B, **232**, 343–84.

WARDLAW, C. W. (1949a). Further experimental observations on the shoot apex of *Dryopteris aristata* Druce. *Phil. Trans. Roy. Soc.*, B, **233**, 415–51.

WARDLAW, C. W. (1949b) Experimental and analytical studies of pteridophytes. XIV. Leaf formation and phyllotaxis in *Dryopteris aristata* Druce. *Ann. Bot. N.S.*, **13**, 163–98.

WARDLAW, C. W. (1949c) Experiments on organogenesis in ferns. *Growth* (suppl.), **13**, 93–131.

WARDLAW, C. W. (1950a) The comparative investigation of apices of vascular plants by experimental methods. *Phil. Trans. Roy. Soc.*, B, **234**, 583–604.

WARDLAW, C. W. (1950b) Experimental and analytical studies of pteridophytes. XVI. The induction of leaves and buds in *Dryopteris aristata* Druce. *Ann. Bot. N.S.*, **14**, 435–55.

WARDLAW, C. W. (1951) Comparative morphogenesis in pteridophytes and spermatophytes by experimental methods. *New Phytol.*, **50**, 127–34.

WARDLAW, C. W. (1952a) *Morphogenesis in Plants*, 176 pp., Methuen, London.

WARDLAW, C. W. (1952b) *Phylogeny and Morphogenesis*, 536 pp., Macmillan, London.

WARDLAW, C. W. (1952c) The effect of isolating the apical meristem in *Echinopsis*, *Nuphar*, *Gunnera* and *Phaseolus*. *Phytomorph.*, **2**, 240–2.

WARDLAW, C. W. (1953a). Comparative observations on the shoot apices of vascular plants. *New Phytol.*, **52**, 195–209.

WARDLAW, C. W. (1953b) Experimental and analytical studies of pteridophytes. XXIII. The induction of buds in *Ophioglossum vulgatum* L. *Ann. Bot. N.S.*, **17**, 513–27.

WARDLAW, C. W. (1953c) Action of tri-iodobenzoic and trichlorobenzoic acids in morphogenesis. *New Phytol.*, **52**, 210–17.

WARDLAW, C. W. (1953d) A commentary on Turing's diffusion-reaction theory of morphogenesis. *New Phytol.*, **52**, 40–7.

WARDLAW, C. W. (1954) Experimental and analytical studies of pteridophytes. XXVI. *Ophioglossum vulgatum*: comparative morphogenesis in embryos and induced buds. *Ann. Bot. N.S.*, **18**, 397–406.

WARDLAW, C. W. (1955a) *Embryogenesis in Plants*. 381 pp. Methuen, London.

WARDLAW, C. W. (1955b) Evidence relating to the diffusion-reaction theory of morphogenesis. *New Phytol.*, **54**, 39–48.

WARDLAW, C. W. (1956a) A note on the effect of isolating the fern shoot apex by shallow incisions. *Phytomorph.*, **6**, 55–63.

WARDLAW, C. W. (1956b) Experimental and analytical studies of pteridophytes. XXXIV. On the shoot apex of the Bird's Nest fern, *Asplenium nidus* L. *Ann. Bot.*, *Lond.*, *N.S.*, **20**, 363–73.

WARDLAW, C. W. (1956c) Generalizations on the apical meristem. *Nature* (Lond.), **178**, 1427–9.

WARDLAW, C. W. (1956d) The inception of leaf primordia: in *The Growth of Leaves* (Ed. Milthorpe, F. L.), Butterworth Scient. Publns., London, pp. 53–64.

WARDLAW, C. W. (1957a) On the organization and reactivity of the shoot apex in vascular plants. *Amer. Jour. Bot.*, **44**, 176–85.

WARDLAW, C. W. (1957b) The floral meristem as a reaction system. *Proc. Roy. Soc. Edinb.*, B, **66**, 394–408.

WARDLAW, C. W. (1957c) Experimental and analytical studies of pteridophytes. XXXV. The effects of direct applications of various substances to the shoot apex of *Dryopteris austriaca* (*D. aristata*) *Ann. Bot. N.S.*, **21**, 85–120.

WARDLAW, C. W. (1957d) Experimental and analytical studies of pteridophytes. XXXVII. A note on the inception of microphylls and macrophylls. *Ann. Bot. N.S.*, **21**, 427–37.

WARDLAW, C. W. (1957e) The reactivity of the apical meristem as ascertained by cytological and other techniques. *New Phytol.*, **56**, 221–9.

WARDLAW, C. W. (1960) Some reflections on Errera's Law. In *Commération Léo Errera*, Univ. Libre de Bruxelles, 10–12 Sept. 1958. Imprimerie Gutenberg, Bruxelles, pp. 99–104.

WARDLAW, C. W. (1961) Growth and development of the inflorescence and flower. In *Growth in Living Systems*, (Ed. Zarrow, M. X.), Basic Book Inc., New York, pp. 491–523.

WARDLAW, C. W. (1963a) Experimental investigations of floral morphogenesis in *Petasites hybridus*. *Nature*, **198**, 560–1.

WARDLAW, C. W. (1963b) Apical organization and differential growth in ferns. *Jour. Linn. Soc. (Bot.)*, **58**, 385–400.

WARDLAW, C. W. (1964) Gibberellic acid and flowering in *Petasites hybridus Nature*, **202**, 575–7.

WARDLAW, C. W. (1965a) *Organization and Evolution in Plants*. Longmans, Green, London.

WARDLAW, C. W. (1965b) General physiological problems of embryogenesis in plants. *Encyclopedia of Plant Physiology*, XV/1, 424–42.

WARDLAW, C. W. (1965c) The morphogenetic rôle of apical meristems: fundamental aspects. *Encyclopedia of Plant Physiology*, XV/1, 443–51.

WARDLAW, C. W. (1965d) Physiology of embryonic development in cormophytes. *Encyclopedia of Plant Physiology*, XV/1, 844–965.

WARDLAW, C. W. (1965e) The organization of the shoot apex. *Encyclopedia of Plant Physiology*, XV/1, 966–1076.

WARDLAW, C. W. and CUTTER, E. G. (1954) Effect of deep and shallow incisions on organogenesis at the fern apex. *Nature*, **174**, 734–5.

WARDLAW, C. W. and CUTTER, E. G. (1955) Experimental and analytical studies of pteridophytes. XXX. Further investigations of the formation of buds and leaves in *Dryopteris aristata* Druce. *Ann. Bot. N.S.*, **19**, 515–26.

WARDLAW, C. W. and CUTTER, E. G. (1956) Experimental and analytical studies of pteridophytes. XXXI. The effect of shallow incisions on organogenesis in *Dryopteris aristata* Druce. *Ann. Bot. N.S.*, **20**, 39–56.

WARDLAW, C. W. and MITRA, G. C. (1958) The response of the shoot apex of *Dryopteris aristata* (Vill.) Druce and of 'detached' meristems of *Onoclea sensibilis* L. and *Matteuccia struthiopteris* Tod. to physiologically-active substances. *Bull. Bot. Soc. Beng.*, **12**, 63–84.

WARDLAW, C. W. and SHARMA, D. N. (1963) Experimental and analytical studies of pteridophytes. XL. Factors in the formation and distribution of sori in leptosporangiate ferns. *Ann. Bot. N.S.*, **27**, 101–21.

WAREING, P. F. (1958) Interaction between indole-acetic acid and gibberellic acid in cambial activity. *Nature* (Lond.), **181**, 1744–5.

WAREING, P. F. and ROBERTS, D. L. (1956) Photoperiodic control of cambial activity in *Robinia pseudacacia* L. *New Phytol.*, **55**, 289.

WARIS, H. (1950) Cytophysiological studies on *Micrasterias*. I. Nuclear and cell division. *Physiol. Plant*, **3**, 1–16.

WARIS, H. (1950) Cytophysiological studies on *Micrasterias*. II. The cytoplasmic framework and its mutation. *Physiol. Plant.*, **3**, 236–46.

WARIS, H. (1951) Cytophysiological studies on *Micrasterias*. III. Factors influencing the development of enucleate cells. *Physiol. Plant.*, **4**, 387–409.

WARIS, H. (1956) Cytophysiological studies on *Micrasterias*. IV. Effects of acids upon the nuclear aspect and the resistance of the cell. *Physiol. Plant.*, **9**, 82–101.

WARIS, H. (1957) A striking morphogenetic effect of amino acid in seed plants. *Proc. Soc. Biochemica, Biophysica et Microbiologica Fenniae. Suomen Kemistilehti*, **30**, 121.

WARIS, H. (1958) Splitting of the nucleus by centrifuging in *Micrasterias*. *Ann. Acad. Sci. Fenn.*, Ser. A IV (Biol.), No. 40, 1–20.

WARIS, H. (1959) Neomorphosis induced in seed plants by amino acids. I. *Oenanthe aquatica. Physiol. Plant.*, 12, 753–66.

WARIS, H. (1962) Neomorphosis in seed plants induced by amino acids. II. *Oenanthe lachenalii. Physiol. Plant.*, 15, 736–52.

WARIS, H. (1965) *Soc. Sci. Fennica*, 43: 4, 1–21 (in Finnish).

WARIS, H. (1967) Morphological changes in seed plants induced with amino acids, purines and pyrimidines. *Ann. Acad. Sci. Fenn.* Ser. A, IV. Biol. 106, 1–66.

WARIS, H. and KALLIO, P. (1957) Morphogenetic effects of chemical agents and nucleo-cytoplasmic relations in *Micrasterias. Ann. Acad. Sci. Fenn.*, A 4 (Biol.), No. 37.

WARK, M. C. (1965) Fine structure of the phloem of *Pisum sativum*. II. The companion cell and phloem parenchyma. *Aust. Jour. Bot.*, 13, 185–93.

WARK, M. C. and CHAMBERS, T. C. (1965) Fine structure of the phloem of *Pisum sativum*. I. The sieve element ontogeny. *Aust. Jour. Bot.*, 13, 171–83.

WEBER, H. (1939) Gramineen-Studien. II. Über Entwicklungsgeschichte und Symmetrie einiger Grasinfloreszenzen. *Planta*, 29, 427–29.

WEISS, P. (1939) *Principles of Development*, New York.

WENT, F. W. (1938) Specific factors other than auxin affecting growth and root formation. *Plant Physiol.*, 13, 55–80.

WENT, F. W. and THIMANN, K. V. (1937) *Phytohormones*, Macmillan, New York.

WERZ, G. (1955) Keimphysiologische Untersuchungen an *Acetabularia*. *Planta* (Berl.), 46, 207–79.

WERZ, G. (1959) Über polare Plasmaunterschiede bei *Acetabularia. Planta* (Berl.), 53, 502–21.

WERZ, G. (1960a) Anreicherung von Ribonucleinsäure in der Wuchszone von *Acetabularia mediterranea. Planta* (Berl.), 55, 22–37.

WERZ, G. (1960b) Über Structurierungen der Wuchzonen von *Acetabularia mediterranea. Planta* (Berl.), 55, 38–56.

WETHERELL, D. F. and HALPERIN, W. (1963a) Embryos derived from callus tissue cultures of the wild carrot. *Nature* (Lond.), 200, 1336–7.

WETHERELL, D. F. and HALPERIN, W. (1963b) *Amer. Jour. Bot.*, 50, 619.

WETMORE, R. H. (1943) Leaf–stem relationships in the vascular plants. *Torreya*, 43, 16.

WETMORE, R. H. (1950, 1953a) Tissue and organ culture as a tool for studies in development. *Proc. Seventh Internat. Bot. Congr.* (Stockholm), 369–70.

WETMORE, R. H. (1953b) Carbohydrate supply and leaf development in sporeling ferns. *Science*, 118, 578.

WETMORE, R. H. (1954) The use of *in vitro* cultures in the investigation of growth and differentiation in vascular plants. *Brookhaven Symp. Biol.*, 6, 22–40.

WETMORE, R. H. (1955) Differentiation of xylem in plants. *Science*, 121, 626–7.

WETMORE, R. H. (1956) Growth and development in the shoot system of plants. In *Cellular Mechanisms in Differentiation and Growth* (Ed. Rudnick, D.), pp. 173–90, *14th Symp. Soc. Study Dev. & Growth*, Princeton.

WETMORE, R. H. (1959) Morphogenesis in plants – a new approach. *Amer. Sci.*, 47, 326–40.

WETMORE, R. H., GIFFORD, E. M. Jr. and GREEN, M. C. (1959) Development of vegetative and floral buds. In *Photoperiodism and Related Phenomena in Plants and Animals* (Ed. Withrow, R. B.), pp. 255–73, Washington.

WETMORE, R. H. and MOREL, G. M. (1949) Growth and development of *Adiantum pedatum* L. on nutrient agar (Abs.). *Amer. Jour. Bot.*, **36**, 805–6.

WETMORE, R. H., NITSCH, J. P. and MOREL, G. M. (1954) The contribution of *in vitro* culture techniques to an interpretation of the shoot apical meristem. *Proc. VIII Int. Bot. Congr.* (Paris), Sec. 7 & 8, 270–1.

WETMORE, R. H. and PRATT, C. (1949) The growth and auxin relations of leaves of the maidenhair fern, *Adiantum pedatum* L. (Abs.). *Amer. Jour. Bot.*, **36**, 806.

WETMORE, R. H. and RIER, J. P. (1963) Experimental induction of vascular tissues in callus of angiosperms. *Amer. Jour. Bot.*, **50**, 418–30.

WETMORE, R. H. and SOROKIN, S. (1955) On the differentiation of xylem. *Jour. Arn. Arb.*, **36**, 305–17.

WETTSTEIN, D. V. (1965) Die Induktion und experimentelle Beeinflussung der Polarität bei Pflanzen. *Encyclopedia of Plant Physiology*, XV/1, 275–330.

WHALEY, W. G., MOLLENHAUER, H. H. and LEECH, J. H. (1960b) The ultra-structure of the meristematic cell. *Amer. Jour. Bot.*, **47**, 401–49.

WHITAKER, D. M. (1931) Some observations on the eggs of *Fucus* and upon their mutual influence in the determination of the developmental axis. *Biol. Bull.*, **61**, 294.

WHITAKER, D. M. (1937a) The effect of hydrogen ion concentration on the induction of polarity in *Fucus* eggs. I. Increased hydrogen ion concentration and the intensity of mutual inductions by neighbouring eggs of *Fucus furcatus*. *Jour. Gen. Physiol.*, **20**, 491.

WHITAKER, D. M. (1937b) The effect of hydrogen ion concentration on the induction of polarity in *Fucus* eggs. 2. The effect of diffusion gradients brought about by eggs in capillary tubes. *Jour. Gen. Physiol.*, **21**, 57.

WHITAKER, D. M. (1937c) Determination of polarity by centrifuging eggs of *Fucus furcatus*. *Biol. Bull.*, **73**, 249.

WHITAKER, D. M. (1938) The effect of hydrogen ion concentration on the induction of polarity in *Fucus* eggs. 3. Gradients of hydrogen ion concentration. *Jour. Gen. Physiol.*, **21**, 833.

WHITAKER, D. M. (1940a) Physical factors of growth. *Growth* (Suppl.).

WHITAKER, D. M. (1940b) The effect of shape on the developmental axis of the *Fucus* egg. *Biol. Bull.*, **78**, 111.

WHITAKER, D. M. (1940c) The effects of ultra-centrifuging and of pH on the development of *Fucus* eggs. *J. Cell and Comp. Physiol.*, **15**, 173.

WHITAKER, D. M. (1941) The effect of unilateral ultraviolet light on the development of the *Fucus* egg. *Jour. Gen. Physiol.*, **24**, 263.

WHITAKER, D. M. and CLANCY, C. W. (1937) The effect of salinity upon the growth of eggs of *Fucus furcatus*. *Biol. Bull.*, **73**, 552.

WHITAKER, D. M. and LOWRANCE, E. W. (1936) On the period of susceptibility in the egg of *Fucus furcatus* when polarity is induced by brief exposure to white light. *J. Cell. and Comp. Physiol.*, **7**, 417.

WHITAKER, D. M. and LOWRANCE, E. W. (1940) The effect of alkalinity upon mutual influences determining the developmental axis in *Fucus* eggs. *Biol. Bull.*, **78**, 407.

WHITE, P. R. (1939) Controlled differentiation in a plant tissue culture. *Bull. Torrey Bot. Club*, **66**, 507.

WHITTIER, D. P. and STEEVES, T. A. (1960) The induction of apogamy in the bracken fern. *Can. Jour. Botany*, **38**, 925–30.

WHITTIER, D. P. and STEEVES, T. A. (1962) Further studies on induced apogamy in ferns. *Can. Jour. Bot.*, **40**, 1525–31.

WIBAUT, C. (1965) Ontogenèse des organes végétatifs et reproducteur. *Rev. Cytol. Biol. Veg.*, **28**, 43–132.

WICKSON, M. E. and THIMANN, K. V. (1958) The antagonism of auxin and kinetin in apical dominance. *Physiol. Plant.*, **11**, 62–74.

WILLIAMS, R. F. (1966) Development of the inflorescence in Granineae. In *The Growth of Cereals and Grasses* (Ed. Milthorp, F. L. and Ivins, J. D.), pp. 74–87. Butterworths, London.

WILLIAMS, S. (1937) Correlation phenomena and hormones in *Selaginella*. *Nature*, **139**, 966.

WILSON, C. L. and JUST, T. (1939) The morphology of the flower. *Bot. Rev.*, **5**, 97–131.

WIRWILLE, J. W. and MITCHELL, J. W. (1950) Six new plant growth inhibiting compounds. *Bot. Gaz.*, **111**, 491–4

WORSDELL, W. C. (1916) *The Principles of Plant Teratology* (London).

YABUTA, T. and HAYASHI, T. (1939) Biochemical studies on 'Bakanae' fungus of the Rice. Part III. Studies on physiological action of gibberellin on the plant. *Journ. Agric. Chem. Soc. Japan*, **15**, 403–13.

YAKOVLEV, M. S. and YOFFE, M. D. (1957) On some peculiar features in the embryogeny of *Paeonia* L. *Phytomorph.*, **7**, 74–82.

YAKOVLEV, M. S. and YOFFE, M. D. (1961) Further studies of the new type of embryogenesis in angiosperms. *Bot. Zh. S.S.S.R.*, **46**, 1402–21.

ZEEVAART, J. A. D. (1958) Flower formation as studied by grafting. *Mededel. Landbouwhogeschool Wageningen*, **58**, 1–88.

ZEEVAART, J. A. D. (1962) Physiology of flowering. *Science*, **137**, 723–31.

ZEEVAART, J. A. D. (1966) Hormonal regulation of plant development. *Cell Differentiation and Morphogenesis*, 144–79. Internat. Lecture Course, Wageningen, April 1965.

ZEEVAART, J. A. D. and LANG, A. (1962) The relationship between gibberellin and floral stimulus in *Bryophyllum daigremontianum*. *Planta*, **58**, 531–42.

ZINGER, N. V. and PODDUBNAYA-ARNOLDI, V. A. (1966) Application of histochemical techniques to the study of embryonic processes in certain orchids. *Phytomorph.*, **16**, 111–24.

Index